BK 375.006 M383C
CURRICULUM IMPROVEMENT AND INNOVATION
/MARTIN, WI
1966 .00 FV
3000 091412 30018
St. Louis Community College

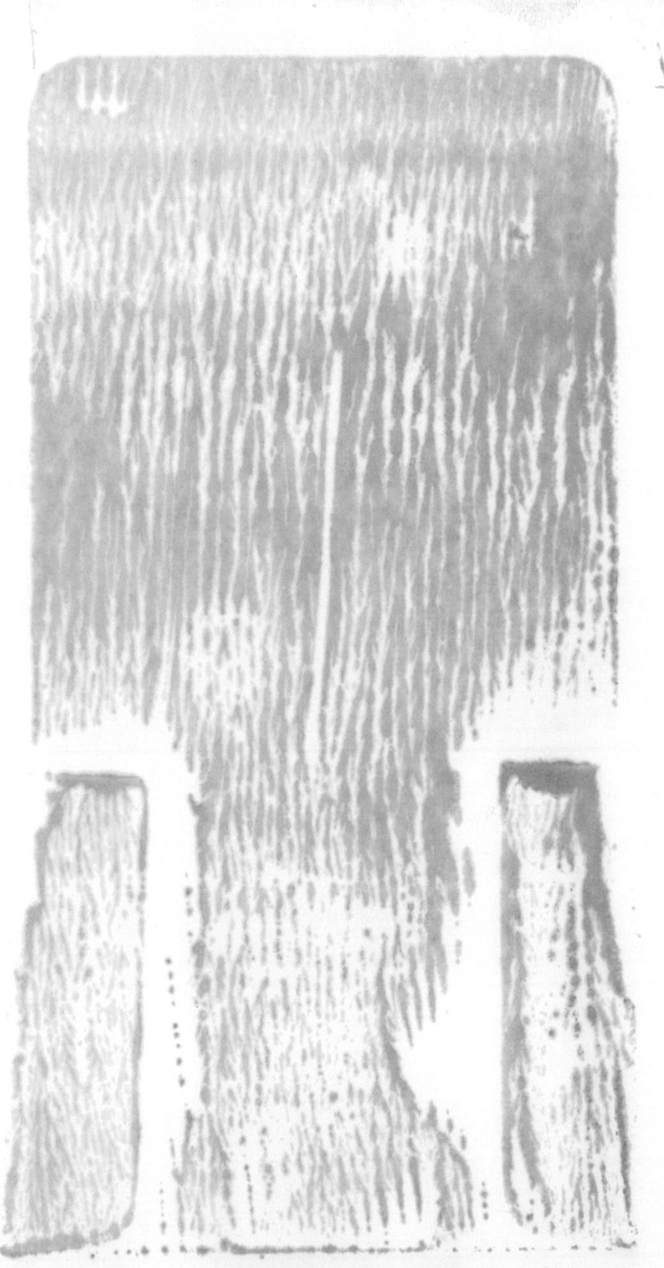

Curriculum Improvement and Innovation: a partnership of students school teachers and research scholars

Curriculum Improvement and Innovation: a partnership of students school teachers and research scholars

Edited by

W. T. Martin
Head, Department of Mathematics
Massachusetts Institute of Technology

Dan C. Pinck
Deputy Director
Educational Services Incorporated

With an introduction by Howard W. Johnson, President, Massachusetts Institute of Technology

1966

Robert Bentley, Inc.
872 Massachusetts Avenue
Cambridge, Massachusetts 02139

Francis Lee Friedman

1918 - 1962

Copyright © Educational Services Incorporated 1966

Library of Congress Catalog Card No.: 66-26783

All rights in this book are reserved. No part of the book may be used or reproduced in any manner whatsoever without permission, except in the case of brief quotations embodied in critical articles or reviews. For information, address Robert Bentley, Inc., 872 Massachusetts Avenue, Cambridge, Massachusetts 02139.

Manufactured in the United States of America

PREFACE

EVER SINCE March 1956, when Professor Jerrold R. Zacharias sent a memorandum to Dr. James R. Killian, Jr., who was then the President of the Massachusetts Institute of Technology, on the subject: *Movie Aids for Teaching Physics in High Schools,* the Institute, through the involvement of its faculty, has been a catalyst in a movement nationally that has been called a revolution in education. From 1956 to 1958, Professor Zacharias and his colleagues on the Physical Science Study Committee, most notably the late Professor Francis L. Friedman, worked to develop a new high school physics course which through its integrity, style, and precision of content created a pattern of educational development subsequently followed by curriculum reform groups throughout the world. One of its essential characteristics is the partnership of university research scholars, teachers, and students—enough of them working for long enough periods of time to attain the precision and style that they wanted.

It was intended that the new course would include an original text, teachers' guides, motion picture films, laboratory experiments with specially designed inexpensive equipment with appropriate guides, tests and examinations, and institutes for high school physics teachers. A set of paperback books for collateral reading was begun as a hedge against success and independent adoption. In 1958, after two years of intensive work by more than fifty professional physicists and more than one hundred high school physics teachers, the PSSC course was ready, in its preliminary form, for trial use and evaluation in the schools. It was not until 1960 that the course was ready for extensive trial use in the schools.

As the work advanced, it became evident that a new organization should be established to handle arrangements for publication and distribution. Consequently a private, non-profit corporation was formed, called Educational Services Incorporated, with a membership drawn partly from M.I.T. but including representatives from other institutions of learning throughout the nation.

As soon as ESI was formed, requests began to come from scholars and teachers for ESI's assistance in attempting to improve curricula in other disciplines, in both schools and universities. ESI now has responsibilities for nine school curriculum projects, in the sciences, mathematics and social sciences; five university curriculum projects, in the physical and life sciences and in several branches of engineering; and two university research and development projects (in India and Afghanistan); and the ESI Film Studio is now making films for ten separate curriculum projects. ESI's course materials are being used in schools and universities throughout the United States and in many nations overseas. About 450 faculty members from 228 colleges and universities and 400 school teachers have worked either full or part-time on ESI's programs in curriculum development and teacher education. They have come from over twenty-five countries. Eighty-four faculty members from M.I.T. have worked on ESI's programs.

A documentary record of ESI's growth exists in the form of the *ESI Quarterly Report* which for several years has described the genesis, philosophy, and content of ESI programs.

During the winter of 1965, a faculty committee at the Massachusetts Institute of Technology, appointed by President Julius A. Stratton, began planning the Fourth M.I.T. Alumni Seminar to be held in September 1966 at the Institute; the subject of the Seminar is to be "The Learning Process and Innovation in Education." The committee decided that it would be helpful to provide alumni participants with a selection of articles from the *ESI Quarterly Report* and with accounts of some curriculum projects outside ESI that are being directed by Institute faculty members. Among the latter articles in this book is one by Professor Richard M. Douglas, Head of the Humanities Department, who directs a social studies program for the high school; and an article on the Science Teaching Center by its director, Professor Robert I. Hulsizer, Jr., and the Center's Executive Officer, Mr. Malcolm K. Smith. An article by Professor A. P. French describes the new introductory physics course at M.I.T. prepared at the Science Teaching Center. We thank Professor

Jerome S. Bruner and the Harvard University Press for permission to reprint a chapter from Professor Bruner's book, *The Process of Education.*

In *Curriculum Improvement and Innovation,* we have also attempted to illustrate the diversity of the programs which are being conducted at ESI and which have had a profound effect on the curriculum reform movement generally. Where the appropriate articles have been available we have included for each of our programs an article on the philosophy and techniques of the course's development and an excerpt from the written materials of the course. Education is an experiment and by its nature an incomplete one; the course materials themselves are for the most part in transition; on the basis of further teaching in the classroom many of them will be modified or changed.

Gladly we make certain acknowledgments. First, to all the members of the 1966 Alumni Seminar Committee who are: Professor Norman C. Dahl, Professor Nathaniel H. Frank, Professor Edwin R. Gilliland, Professor Richard M. Held, Professor Charles P. Kindleberger, Professor Kevin A. Lynch, Professor Donald G. Marquis, Professor Lucian W. Pye, Professor Walter A. Rosenblith, Chairman, Professor Irwin W. Sizer, Mr. Donald P. Severance, Executive Vice-President of the M.I.T. Alumni Association, and Mr. Frederick G. Lehman, Secretary of the Alumni Association. Secondly, the contribution of the private foundations and the government has been large; they have allowed profound changes to become possible on a national front. We recognize the support given to the Institute and to Educational Services Incorporated, particularly by the National Science Foundation, the United States Agency for International Development, the Ford Foundation, the Alfred P. Sloan Foundation, the Esso Education Foundation, the Xerox Corporation, Sanders Associates, Inc., The Shell Companies Foundation, the Charles F. Kettering Foundation, the Victoria Foundation, the Bing Fund, Inc., and the Carnegie Corporation of New York. We would be remiss if we did not mention those persons who have done so much to make the *Quarterly Report* a worthwhile contribution to American education; among them are Miss Ann Venable, the Assistant Editor, and Miss Diane Greene, Mrs. Benjamin Nichols, and Mr. Laurence Hagar. We also thank Mr. John H. Durston, General Editor of the Science Study Series; Professor French; Mr. Ervin H. Hoffart, PSSC Area Meeting Program Director, and Mr. James L. Aldrich, Deputy Director of ESI, for their assistance. We thank Dr. Killian, Professor Zacharias, Professor Philip Morrison of M.I.T., Professor Rosenblith, Professor Held, Professor Frank, and Mr. Gilbert Oakley, Jr., Managing Director of ESI, for their counsel. Most of the excellent photographs were taken by Mr. George D. Cope and Miss Joan Hamblin, both of Educational Services Incorporated.

Many of the recent advances in teaching the sciences, mathematics and the social sciences in our schools reflect—in one degree or another—the perceptiveness of one human being: Richard A. Paulson. Richard Paulson died suddenly on June 11, 1966. As an official of the National Science Foundation, he helped to formulate government policy in education. This policy was strengthened by his ability to involve the right people in assuming responsibility for course content improvement projects and to offer them counsel and friendship. Quality was a watchword for Richard Paulson and pioneering was a way of life. He was a genuinely modest person whose attainments lent his modesty a graciousness that was pleasing to all who knew him.

W. T. Martin
Head, Department of Mathematics
Massachusetts Institute of Technology

D. C. Pinck
Deputy Director
Educational Services Incorporated

INTRODUCTION

Howard W. Johnson
President
Massachusetts Institute of Technology

INTRODUCTION

PERHAPS never before in history have such great expectations been focused on the university. Society looks to the university for solutions to basic social and technical problems—for a rapidly expanding vehicle of education for our youth, for the continuing education of mid-career adults, for a never-ending supply of high and critical talent to manage our expanding economy. As a part of an urban community the university is charged with providing stability for a shifting core city. As part of the international community, it is expected to provide communication links with the members of the scholarly world and to bridge nationalistic gulfs. The university's faculty members are asked to provide a wide range of private and public consulting advice to a still wider range of seekers.

In the face of such enormous and varied demands from society, it is particularly important that the university retain and strengthen the fundamental characteristic of its main purpose: to preserve knowledge and to teach the members of our society; to advance knowledge by discovery; and to find solutions to society's problems by technical and social innovation. If the university ever retreats from these purposes and especially if it fails in its primary task of education, its other contributions to society will soon diminish.

M.I.T.'s objectives, set at its founding by William Barton Rogers more than one hundred years ago, remain a steady guide to our own effort and direction. They are simply stated as follows: "Advancement of knowledge through education and research, both pure and applied, in science, engineering, architecture, management, social sciences, and the humanities. Service to government and industry by consultation and research." This broad definition of objectives raises the question of the relationship between the education and knowledge-advancement function on one hand, and the public service function as such, on the other. Certainly one of the basic challenges confronting the large university today is the achievement of compatibility between the development of its own educational environment, and the contributions it makes to the environment outside the campus. In fact, it can be argued that the contribution of the university to the world must be in dynamic consonance with its first internal requirement of what Alfred North Whitehead called "the imaginative acquisition of knowledge." We know of no better example of such consonance than the curriculum reform movement, long underway at M.I.T., and the concurrent contribution of the Institute and its Faculty to educational improvement throughout the world. The process by which M.I.T. has examined the quality of its own undergraduate education should have had a beneficial effect on the world of secondary and collegiate education in general. It has. Moreover, the research process of improving education has resulted in a dynamic exchange from the outside back to the M.I.T. internal pattern. We at M.I.T. benefit greatly from this relationship.

In sum, educational reform is a major concern of the M.I.T. Faculty and it has resulted in massive experimentation and beneficial results in the development of new methods and approaches to teaching, both within and without the Institute.

Broadly speaking, changes in the M.I.T. undergraduate curriculum in the past ten to fifteen years have followed two concurrent trends: the development of a core curriculum on one hand and the introduction of increased flexibility in the planning of individual students' programs, on the other. Each of these trends represents an imaginative adaptation to changing circumstances which may be briefly identified. First, the intense requirements of the major national mobilization of resources, during the Second World War, led to a surge of new ideas, a wide proliferation of scientific techniques and a vast increase in the scientific and technical literature, with which no ordinary four-year college program was prepared to cope. To this explosive phenomenon of new technology and new fields of knowledge, the Institute responded by placing emphasis on the fundamental scientific principles that underlie the professions. Mathematics, physics and chemistry were basic courses in which all students would have to build a base before choosing a specialization. A basic *core curriculum* was thus developed and it is serving M.I.T. students well.

Now, recent changes in the undergraduate requirements have strengthened the core curriculum and at the same time have permitted more *flexibility* and choice for students in planning their courses. Perhaps the most significant factor responsible for the increase of flexibility in the undergraduate program stems from the new type of entering student that we see here at M.I.T. and in other universities across the country. As a result of remarkable improvements in teaching and learning materials at all grade levels, our students are better prepared when they enter the universities. They have higher competence. They are not only better informed, but they have a broader view. Their higher goals and expectations are expressed in a desire for early responsibility, and they want to make a personal contribution to improving the quality of life. There are those who are concerned with a certain instability in today's campuses which seems to grow out of the resultant ferment of interest and need. I believe this ferment represents readiness for growth with opportunities for us to make dramatic steps forward, and should therefore be welcomed. By allowing the student more flexibility in choosing his courses, and at the same time improving his basic preparation, we hope to encourage him to grow to new levels of achievement and contribution.

Beyond these internal developments in curriculum and student growth, there are many examples of the ways in which the M.I.T. Faculty have served the cause of education beyond the Institute campus. The active participation of the Institute in new educational ventures in India and Africa, the more informal relationships with collegiate institutions in this country and in Latin America, and the individual efforts of members of the faculty in universities all over the world are testimonies to this effort. But the example of the contribution of M.I.T. to the improvement of secondary school programs in the physical sciences, and more recently the humanities, is perhaps the most innovative and most far-reaching of these efforts. In the course of these developments, we have discovered that progress in education requires new kinds of educational institutions and new ways of pooling efforts among schools, colleges and universities. We have found that the process requires involvement of individual faculty members with members of other institutions and with school teachers working cooperatively on improved curricula for the schools and the universities in nearly all the disciplines. M.I.T. has participated in the pioneering that has set up these new kinds of institutions.

A significant difference between educational reform in the past and now is that in the past curriculum development was generally left to an individual faculty member in the context of his own specialty. Today, new confederations and coalitions have become accepted as a more effective way of going about the task. The work of Educational Services Incorporated represents a remarkable example of harmonious collaboration among schools, universities, foundations and private corporations. We at M.I.T. are fortunate to be associated with many ESI programs. We join other universities in acknowledging ESI's contributions and take special pleasure in welcoming the publication of this volume on *Curriculum Improvement and Innovation.*

HOWARD W. JOHNSON
President
Massachusetts Institute of Technology

CONTENTS

PREFACE, W. T. Martin and Dan C. Pinck V

INTRODUCTION, Howard W. Johnson VII

I. EDUCATIONAL SERVICES INCORPORATED: A UNIQUE EDUCATIONAL ORGANIZATION, James R. Killian, Jr. 1

The experience of ESI as a rallying point for innovators in education supports the proposal, under recent Federal legislation, to create regional centers and laboratories for curriculum research. The past decade has witnessed a movement in improvement in education that has been likened to a renascence, but the movement will have failed if it rests on its present achievements or if a rigidly structured national curriculum is the final result. Federal support of curriculum development through the cooperation of university scholars and schoolteachers, working through ESI and similar centers, has encouraged not conformity but bold diversity in the creation of new curricula. The responsibility for continued development and further diversity rests ultimately within the school systems themselves, and it is by encouraging their efforts that the regional curriculum research centers and laboratories will have a major opportunity to improve American education.

II. SCIENCE IN THE ELEMENTARY SCHOOL 7

1. The Curricular Triangle and Its Style, Philip Morrison 9

The schoolroom offers the chance to unite the separate disciplines, at their simplest and clearest. The curriculum, at the elementary level, is not fenced off by frontiers of technique or history. The unity of science is not the topic of the curriculum, but closer to its expected outcome. The child's knowledge of language is evidence that we tend to underestimate his ability to learn. The strong motivation to speak, the student-teacher ratio and the long time devoted to his learning language are signposts for the designers of curricula. Should learning science or history or writing or arithmetic be different from learning language? In the teaching of science to children one mandate is imperative: there must be personal involvement. We must bring a more varied range of science into the child's own hands, where he may be potter and clay at once. The final criterion of the curricular style in the ESI approach to elementary science teaching is this: it takes time. What the textbook can summarize in a page of results — life is cellular, cells have water and carbon, cells divide to multiply — the new methods with the child's own work, with his own hands and microscope and labored arithmetic, may take six weeks of classroom effort. Teachers should not begrudge this time.

2. *Kitchen Physics,* excerpts from the Teacher's Guide 19

"Water is *grabbier.*" Taking advantage of the child's swift insights is the road to success in any teaching. Pages from the Teacher's Guide for a classroom activity in which the children study experimentally the flow of liquids illustrate the ESI Elementary Science Study approach to teaching. The children examine liquid columns falling from bottles, determine whether the hole size or the nature of the liquid has a measurable effect, and represent their findings graphically. Samples of classroom dialogue between pupils and teacher are given.

III. SCIENCE IN THE JUNIOR HIGH SCHOOL 39

1. Objectives and Content of the Introductory Physical Science Course, Uri Haber-Schaim 41

Improvement of the science courses for the last three years of high school has broadened the gap in science education between upper and lower grades and raised the challenge of how to extend the gains to the lower grades. The Introductory Physical Science course is based on the belief that certain values and skills can and should be taught in junior high school science, that a sound foundation can be laid for future courses in science and that sufficient nourishment in the spirit and substance of physical science can be furnished to compose a good terminal course for those who will not continue the study of science. Topics for the course were selected according to the same criteria on which the Physical Science Study Committee physics text was constructed. The introductory study of matter is the central theme. The differences between substances and the idea of quantity are the avenues of approach. The course follows a path through radioactivity to the atom picture because discreteness is very much in the foreground in radioactivity. In the second part of the course the student is shown how his experiences in the first part can be applied to different situations. The orientation, skills and attitude acquired by the pupil in the Introductory Physical Science course should render superfluous much of the earlier material in existing physics and chemistry courses.

2. *Quantity of Matter: Mass,* an excerpt from the Introductory Physical Science text 48

The style of the ESI Introductory Physical Science text is illustrated in this chapter on "Quantity of Matter: Mass." From measurement of stacks of pennies students are led into measurement of volumes and to comparison of different masses. Generalization of the results of simple experiments leads to consideration of the law of conservation of mass.

IV. PHYSICS IN THE HIGH SCHOOL: THE PHYSICAL SCIENCE STUDY COMMITTEE 65

1. The Physical Science Study Committee, Gilbert C. Finlay 67

The Physical Science Study Committee chose to plan a high school physics course dealing with physics as an explanatory system that extends from the domain inside the atom to the distant galaxies. The course tells a unified story, with successive topics developed to lead toward an atomic picture of matter. The student should see physics as an unfinished and continuing activity. He should experience something of the satisfaction and challenge felt by the scientist at the vantage points from which both charted and uncharted vistas can be contemplated. The student is expected to be an active participant, to wrestle with a line of inquiry that leads to basic ideas. Technological applications have not been eliminated, but have been cut back sharply from the prominence they have in many secondary school courses. The laboratory experiments are designed, not simply to confirm earlier assertions, but to supply rooting for the growth of ideas. A great deal of what might ordinarily be called demonstration is provided by films basically built around experiments.

2. *Physics,* excerpts from the PSSC text, Laboratory Guide and Teacher's Resource Book and Guide 79

Failure of the particle model of light to account satisfactorily for all observed behavior of light confronts us with the choice of building a better particle model or looking for a basically different description. Any model must account for the fact that light travels through space. Can anything other than a particle move from one point to another? The wave on a pond gives the answer. We can find all sorts of waves around us. Disturbances that travel through media are waves, but the medium does not go along with the disturbance. To find out whether waves behave like light, we must know how they act. Experiments with a coil spring and a movie camera are a convenient starting point. Travel of wave pulses in the spring is easily demonstrated, and repeated experiments give the same general result, with single pulses or two pulses crossing. Pulses on fixed springs bounce back (reflection). Waves pass through one another undisturbed as do flashlight beams. The crossing of light beams resembles the crossing of waves more than it does the intersection of streams of particles. Pulses passing from one spring to an attached heavier spring are partly reflected and partly transmitted. When light passes from one medium to another, part is reflected and part transmitted. These two wave properties in light lead us to further exploration.

V. CURRICULUM CHANGE IN THE SOCIAL SCIENCES 109

1. Men and Ideas: ESI's Social Studies and Humanities Program, a conversation with Elting E. Morison 111

In an informal conversation Professor Morison gives his ideas, personal and philosophical, of what history is, where it can be useful, and how it should be taught. The author finds a fundamental difference in spirit between the humanities and social sciences. With the development of psychology, the social sciences, in a more systematic way, have taken over some part of the total task that the humanities over the centuries had claimed for their own. However, the contribution of social sciences to an understanding of how people work has been practically nonexistent in secondary schools. Professor Morison thinks there is an area at this level for systematic study of certain social sciences. He sets store by not knowing history but having an historical sense, a feeling for the past, and is inclined to think that with proper selection and proper telling of episodes from the past this sense can be conveyed to students. The constantly changing environment in America, the feeling of living from hand to mouth, calls for the steadying influence of a perspective on things that have gone before. He would look for historical episodes that would reveal the methodology of the processes we live in all the time. A clear feeling of the working of the social-political process is more important than knowledge of General Longstreet's behavior at Gettysburg.

2. From Subject to Citizen, Peter C. Wolff 117

A junior high school course, covering the period roughly from 1600 to 1800, seeks to trace, by concentrating on a few episodes of special significance, the political developments that caused a group of English subjects to become American citizens. The course, designed for the year in which American history traditionally is taught, seeks to avoid the frustrations of "covering" great stretches of history and to study the selected episodes in depth. It assumes that high school students should grapple with the nature of their political culture and become familiar with the crucial events in which a "subject" political culture became a "citizen" or "participant" political culture. Six episodes, three from seventeenth century England, and three from eighteenth century America, are examined as focal points for the six units planned for the course.

3. The Death of the Roman Republic, Arleigh Richardson, III 120

An ESI Social Studies unit on *The Death of the Roman Republic,* in which students working from primary sources will examine the questions and implications of the use of power and the resort to violence in the conduct of human affairs is being readied for trial at approximately the seventh grade level in junior high schools. Conceived as a relatively simple unit on Julius Caesar, *The Death of the Roman Republic* grew in the process of development into a study in which school children, exposed to the literary riches of ancient history, will be asked to consider problems concerning power and political culture that fall in the realm of political science. The writings of Caesar and Cicero, among others, carry the students into the turmoil of the political campaigns of the late period of the Republic with their bribery, corruption and assassination. Student exercises involve questions about the antithesis of law and violence, the tendency of violence to breed violence, the responsibilities of those in government, the consequences of allowing private citizens to take law into their own hands. The unit is designed for a sequence entitled *Inventing the Western World.*

4. The Newton Social Science Sequence, Wayne Altree and Richard M. Douglas 123

A new three-year sequence primarily concerned with the study of historical tradition and drawing upon anthropology, art history, English, political science and sociology, is being offered in the Department of Social Science in the Newton (Mass.) schools. The basic assumption is that history is one of the most humanistic of the liberal arts, that history reduced to methodology can be no less tedious to high school students than history as unending chronology. History is not simply a language of inquiry but a unique kind of perception. In the first unit of the new sequence students read stories and memoirs concerning the confrontation of children and parents, the point being to suggest the variety of ways of experiencing the historical present. The second unit opens with life histories from simple societies to illuminate the cultural concept of custom and tradition. Subsequent units pass from the invention of the city to the formation of the European tradition till the Renaissance and Reformation. Tudor-Stuart England, the Puritan migration to America, Benjamin Franklin, the American and French revolutions considered as historical turning points compose the material of the second year. The American Civil War, interpretation of the English factory system of the nineteenth century, the impact of Europe on the social traditions of Africa and Asia carry the sequence to the present. Textbook assignments are infrequent; the schedule permits many features of the "close-reading" course. A consistent working arrangement between Newton teachers and university consultants in the preparation of materials has been maintained, the teachers having rights of choice and veto.

VI. CURRICULUM CHANGE IN MATHEMATICS 133

1. The Mathematics Curriculum Study, W. T. Martin 135

Goals for School Mathematics (Houghton Mifflin Co., 1963) sets the theme of a long-range plan for curricular revision in mathematics. The small book was the formal report of the Cambridge Conference on School Mathematics, which took place in the summer of 1963, under ESI auspices and at the urging of the mathematical community, to look forward toward more drastic revisions than any attempted in the several reform activities then under way. Publication of *Goals* was followed by a number of conferences and experimental classes concerned with materials proposed in the report. A conference in March, 1965, jointly sponsored by the School Mathematics Study Group and the Cambridge Conference, brought together representatives of various American mathematics projects and one major British reform group to establish better communications regarding the work being carried on and the problems of the future. A Cambridge Conference workshop in the summer of 1965 prepared outlines and exercises in specific topics in line with the program set forth in *Goals.* A Cambridge Conference meeting in the summer of 1966 examines the long-range and huge task of training American teachers to meet the demands of radical curricular revision: "What does the teacher have to know to teach the kindergarten through sixth grade recommended materials as outlined in *Goals for School Mathematics?*"

2. Maneuvers on Lattices, David A. Page 141

Prevent "too much teaching" and "let correct answers to significant questions be your guide" are the watchwords in ESI's program in mathematics for the elementary grades, developed by Professor David A. Page, on leave from the University of Illinois. At schools in Watertown and Concord, Mass., Professor Page has been teaching sixth-grade classes and carrying on a pilot program for the training of elementary mathematics teachers, culminating in a series of films made at the ESI Studio in which his methods of teaching youngsters are shown in action. "Maneuvers on Lattices" begins this topic in first grade with "a sort of code for writing numbers" and follows it to the high school level of mathematical abstraction and elegance in operations on lattices of three dimensions.

VII. NEW CURRICULA FOR THE DISADVANTAGED 155

1. Pooling Education's Resources, Saville R. Davis 157

The deepest moral commitment of Americans is to the work of liberating and developing men and women. A group of Negro colleges and a group of large universities in the United States are banding together and pooling resources for this purpose. The Carnegie Corporation of New York and the Rockefeller Foundation support summer institutes for teachers of predominantly Negro colleges. The plan for the institutes, administered initially under ESI, is to meet the special problems of students who are deprived and segregated, and the participants are confident they can develop and test systems that can be multiplied more than anyone in specialized Negro education had dared to hope.

2. Paper Computing Machines, William L. Barclay, III 164

A classroom approach by which the teacher of elementary mathematics can stimulate inquiry is described. By simple operations on a lattice (a pattern of numbers) pupils can be led to exponents and to the development of paper "machines" that add and multiply. The child proceeds in the spirit of a game to make his own slide rule and learn to compute with it. The aim is not to produce perfect scales but to give students an understanding of the principles on which such scales work. A method of indexing the scale that closely parallels the historical development of logarithms is pursued by answering the question of what number should go midway between 2 and 4 on a scale for multiplication. By participating in development of the material the teacher will get a sense of the possible difficulties students may meet.

VIII. CURRICULUM DEVELOPMENT FOR THE UNIVERSITY AND COLLEGE 177

1. The Cooperative Program in Teacher Education, Nathaniel H. Frank . . . 179

Curriculum improvement emphasizes the critical need for highly competent teachers. One approach to the problem is to re-train teachers in service to handle the new courses, but this process cannot satisfy the over-all need. The crux lies in the education of prospective teachers while they are still in college, introducing them to the new materials and patterns. Not only must courses be updated and improved; the structure of the college curriculum must be recast. Continuing cooperation of college faculties and groups engaged in curriculum revision is essential. Development of first-rate courses geared to the background of the college students involved is the major goal of the cooperative program to improve the undergraduate preparation of prospective teachers. In the first phase collaborative programs were undertaken with state colleges of Massachusetts. It is the intent of the project to move as rapidly as possible from the beginning effort to the broader arena of national needs.

2. Educational Films in Fluid Mechanics, Ascher H. Shapiro 182

Although the subjects of the usual courses on applied science and engineering rest on experimental foundations, the experimental phenomena generally have been absent from the lecture hall. Emphasis has been on the conceptual side of the subject and the perceptual side relegated to the background. Dramatic phenomena could never be conveyed with equal force by words alone, any more than could a piece of exciting music. Students became proficient in analysis without understanding what the analysis was about. The National Committee for Fluid Mechanics Films has labored to see whether the pedagogical dilemma could be solved by putting demonstration experiments on films. The outlook is hopeful not only in fluid mechanics but in most branches of applied science. As a good lecture differs in style from a good book, so a good film differs from both. In the film the visual takes precedence over the aural. Practice has been required to achieve a written script in correct relation to the visual action. To explain the physical phenomena in simple language is no mean feat of composition. Experiments and apparatus have to be developed from scratch. While the technology of books is relatively simple, the technology of film use is relatively complicated, comparatively expensive and by no means perfected. But new developments are sure to come. As educational films become available in quantity, the technology of projection equipment will make possible library facilities for film. The lecturer will be able to assign not only readings in texts and problems for exercise, but also films to be seen.

3. The Semiconductor Electronics Education Committee, Campbell L. Searle . . 200

Before 1960 few colleges offered adequate undergraduate courses in semiconductor electronics. The inadequacy stemmed from the rapid growth of the transistor. A group at M.I.T. concluded that the problem was national in scope and that broad technical support was needed. In February 1961 the Semiconductor Electronics Education Committee was formed and began working under ESI. A philosophy for creation of a course in transistor physics at the third year of college was developed along specific lines. Text material, to be published in paperback format, was written at summer workshops in 1961, 1962 and 1963. "Feedback meetings" were held twice a year. In 1962 a major breakthrough in preparation of undergraduate laboratory materials was made. Films have been prepared.

IX. THE SCIENCE TEACHING CENTER AT THE MASSACHUSETTS INSTITUTE OF TECHNOLOGY 205

1. The Science Teaching Center, Robert I. Hulsizer, Jr. and Malcolm K. Smith . 207

The increasing complexity of science and the increasing integration of science in our culture require basic changes and better methods in the presentation of science in the universities. The universities must take account of the needs not only of students gifted in science but of students not so gifted. At the M.I.T. Science Teaching Center a serious attempt is being made to bring the insights of leading scientists to bear on the creation of materials for introductory courses. Good scientists often have simple ways of thinking about their fields of knowledge and can find simple, clean points of view to make difficult points clear. The Center is experimenting also in the development of learning aids—filmed demonstrations and lectures, corridor exhibits, laboratory experiments (some in kit form for students to use on their own). Integrating the traditional disciplines, at least in introductory courses, is another interest. The Center is giving thought to understanding of the learning process and to the psychological factors students bring to school. It is hoped that such study may indicate steps by which the college environment can be made more conducive to learning and to the development of effective citizens as well as productive scientists. The impact of current pressures of society on the educational system is a further concern of the Center. The roles of education, testing and selection need to be identified and separated, and protected from overwhelming one another.

2. A New Introductory Physics Course at the Massachusetts Institute of Technology, A. P. French 210

A chief aim at the Science Teaching Center at M.I.T. has been to take a fresh look at introductory college physics. A key feature of the approach has been "the particulate view," starting from the assumption that a workable description of the physical world can be made in terms of particles and their behavior. The dynamics of a star in a galaxy or of a planet in the solar system is as much the dynamics of a particle as is the motion of an electron in a cathode ray tube. One advantage of this approach is a breaking down, at least in part, of the customary barriers and compartments into which physics is conventionally divided. Physics as it is presented on the pages of textbooks often bears surprisingly little resemblance to physics as it is actually practiced. The material is sterilized, abbreviated and codified so that one loses all sense of the actual process of discovery—the real experiments, the false starts, the inspired guesses and all that goes into a living science. In developing the material the Science Teaching Center has tried hard to instill this approach. The student should read from many sources, and not just one textbook; he should do relevant experiments, and his acquaintance with real phenomena should be developed with the help of demonstrations and films.

X. EDUCATIONAL ASSISTANCE OVERSEAS 217

1. Scientific and Engineering Education in Newly Developing Countries, Jerrold R. Zacharias 219

Professor Zacharias recreates the inspiration and milieu that inaugurated the African Education Program and presents the remarks of the late Reverend Solomon B. Caulker of Sierra Leone, at the 1960 International Conference on Science in the Advancement of New States, at the Weizmann Institute in Rehovoth, Israel. The author describes him as the man who "stood out above all others" at the meeting. Dr. Caulker in his recorded remarks warns his fellow Africans, having thrown off foreign political domination, not to be dominated intellectually. Nuclear fission, he says, is interesting but at the moment "a bit too far removed" for Africans. The primary problem in science education for Africans is to persuade them that a relationship exists physically between cause and effect, whether typhoid is caused by drinking dirty water or by magic spells, whether babies die of improper feeding or from having a sickness "put on" them.

2. The Use of PSSC in Other Countries, Uri Haber-Schaim 225

A suggestion of the favorable response abroad to the PSSC approach to teaching physics is given by the prefaces, reprinted here, from the Japanese and Swedish editions of the text, along with excerpts from "PSSC Newsletter" communications from New Zealand and Brazil. Even before the preliminary edition of the PSSC course was complete, inquiries about the new materials began coming in from abroad, and foreign interest in the program has remained keen. Full-fledged PSSC courses lasting four to six weeks were given abroad, staffed by American physicists. The Physical Science Study Committee received invitations to present its ideas at conferences. Since those early days the course has been used in Sweden, Norway, Italy, Israel, Brazil, Uruguay, Chile, Canada and New Zealand.

3. The African Education Program, W. T. Martin and J. L. Aldrich 237

A cooperative program among scientists, mathematicians, school teachers and educators to bring new and improved school curricula in mathematics and science to Africa resulted from a 1961 meeting at Endicott House, Dedham, Mass., organized by ESI. The African Education Program, inspired by the late Reverend Solomon B. Caulker of Sierra Leone, has brought together people from Africa, the United Kingdom and the United States to work out with African scholars and teachers the means of developing new course materials indigenous to African needs and relevant to African inspirations. The African Mathematics Program, the first part of the effort, has accomplished much in subsequent years. The materials, produced at workshops at Entebbe, Uganda, have been used in schools or teachers' colleges in ten African nations. Fourteen teacher education institutes have been held, over 500 Africans attending. Transcending regional and national boundaries, the Program has brought men of good will together to work on major problems of common concern.

4. The Indian Institute of Technology at Kanpur, Norman C. Dahl 243

The pattern evolving at the Indian Institute of Technology, Kanpur, is strongly reflective of the lines along which American engineering and scientific institutions are developing, but it is not identical since it must reflect India's cultural traditions and educational needs. The need is for problem-recognizing and problem-solving men who will have the confidence, inclination and training to do something about India's problems. There is strong emphasis on experimental investigation and on the technical arts necessary to carry out such work, but there is much to learn about how to make this part of the program vital. The quality of the students and Indian faculty is such that courses are taught at levels comparable to those in the Consortium institutions. Many of the ideas of academic and faculty organization being worked into the Kanpur scheme are new to Indian education, and their introduction gives heart to many of the younger generation of scholars eager to participate in needed reforms. The Program has found it possible to make a significant contribution in a complex cross-cultural situation where progress is often difficult and sometimes impossible.

XI. LEARNING BY TEACHING 249

1. Learning by Teaching, Jerrold R. Zacharias 251

The author presses for increased involvement of students in the education of other students and proposes some experiments. Scientific papers and texts record "only the happy hours," but teachers learn the other things. Fear is a contagious disease, and if the young teacher or mother is fearful of intellectuality the fear can be transmitted to the child. The author describes a course in sunlight and shadow by which students could introduce younger children to science. Such involvement, besides improving the education of both ten-year-olds and eighteen-year-olds, should lead to recruiting of a new group of enthusiastic teachers. A bold plan to enlist children to help each other in the arts of speaking or writing is needed. Recent development of new materials in self-contained units for study over periods of four to six weeks provides material for the venture in learning by teaching. The units are built around phenomena children can investigate in their own ways. Comparable efforts in fields other than science are possible, and the author proposes that universities, colleges, high schools and elementary schools join in experimenting with programs of learning by teaching. New federal legislation on education makes it possible now to test innovations on scales large enough to show statistical validity.

2. A Pilot Program, Stefan Machlup 255

A casual luncheon chat leads to an exciting experiment. Pursuing a suggestion from Jerrold Zacharias, the author organizes a volunteer program in which Ohio high school physics students teach third- and fourth-graders, using the Elementary Science Study unit called "Batteries and Bulbs." One teacher, expecting a dozen volunteers at most, gets forty-three. Letters from teachers reflect the success of the experiment. Third-graders embrace "Batteries and Bulbs" with joy; fourth-graders display imagination in developing switching circuits. The high school pupils prove themselves as teachers—"gentle and understanding." The importance of having the right materials to work with is thoroughly established. The climax of the experiment is reached when one initiated class of third-graders undertakes to teach the unit to another class of their contemporaries.

3. More about Learning by Teaching, Ervin H. Hoffart 259

PSSC teachers, concerned about the quality of science instruction at all levels, conduct workshops using science materials prepared for elementary grades. The great success of a 1965 program in which college freshmen taught science to sixth-graders leads to experiments with PSSC students as teachers in Illinois and Massachusetts, as well as Ohio. Reports indicate favorable reactions among the elementary pupils and a generally rewarding experience for all concerned. The volunteer PSSC student-teachers prove themselves able to find their own solutions to problems of the classroom, to reorganize teaching procedures to meet specific situations and to criticize constructively their own performances. One Ohio teacher remarks on the respect the younger children show for their volunteer teachers from the Senior High School. The experiment turns the thoughts of the high school students toward teaching as a career and brings requests from elementary school principals for extension of the program.

XII. PERSPECTIVES ON CURRICULUM REFORM 263

1. Intuitive and Analytic Thinking, Jerome S. Bruner 265

Development of effective intuitive thinking is an objective of many teachers in mathematics and science, but little systematic knowledge of the nature of intuitive thinking, or of the variables that influence it, is available. In a time of curriculum improvement an attempt to outline the kinds of research that would begin to provide information is appropriate. In contrast to analytic thinking, intuitive thinking advances by maneuvers seemingly based on implicit perception of total problems. The thinker arrives at his answer with little awareness of the steps he took and sometimes solves problems he could not solve through analytic thinking. Though formalism has devalued intuition, in recent years designers of curricula have become convinced that work is needed to learn how to develop intuitive gifts. Procedures to characterize and measure intuitive thinking are needed. What variables seem to affect intuitive thinking? Will emphasis on the structure or connectedness of knowledge increase facility of intuitive thinking? What is the place of heuristic procedures? Is guessing to be encouraged or penalized? The objective of education is not production of self-confident fools, but it seems likely that development of confidence and courage in students does foster effective intuitive thinking. Psychologists and teachers should not allow practical difficulties to discourage attack on the problems of intuitive thinking.

2. Research Scholars and Curriculum Development, Jerrold R. Zacharias . . . 270

Why are scientists willing to spend large parts of their short lives outside their lovely towers trying to help the schools to help themselves? The question inspires the author to examine the scientist's outlook on the world and to conclude that social conscience has moved scientists from their laboratories into school work. Scientists seek evidence before they try to create order and they do not expect, or hope for, complete proof. Incomplete their theories may be, but they all enjoy the benefits of due process of law. Dogmatism cannot enter and unsupported demagoguery has a tough time with scientists. Children are captured by the kind of problems that interest scientists. It is never the teacher who answers the questions but Nature, when properly asked.

3. The New Curricula and the Educational Climate, B. Alden Thresher 274

To appreciate the ideas from which the new curricula are emerging requires a century or so of perspective. In our discouragement at how little has been done compared with what needs to be done, it is easy to forget how much better schools are now than they used to be. An advance is now evident in public appreciation of the key importance of education. Perhaps the most important idea of the last decade is the discovery that we have a great deal more of potential talent than we ever suspected. Ideas have been evolving about how to salvage human ability. We now know that even in the most unpromising environments a substantial proportion of children can be salvaged and urged on to solid achievement. Our philosophy of educational selection is changing. Today we stress the development of every child to his full potential. Our mistake has lain not in exercising selection but in carrying it out by negative and destructive means. Today's new educational projects speak so directly to the child's innate urge to learn that they provide in themselves a powerful influence to salvage and develop talent. In back of a number of advances lies one central intuition: education is a seamless web, all of a piece from cradle to grave.

4. Evaluating New Science Materials: Thoughts on Methods and Goals, G. C. Quarton, M.D. 280

Evaluation of education is controversial, some arguing that no action should be continued unless proven effective, others believing that evaluation is both destructive of the effort and ineffective because of the complex interactions of the factors. The trick is to keep simple feedback from getting lost in methodological complexities or in political manipulation. Evaluation can provide a factual base for arguments that something believed to be worth doing is in fact doing what it is supposed to do. A real beginning can be made by a clear separation of the goals of evaluation from those of curriculum development and by recognizing that evaluation is a means to an end. We need to develop evaluation methods concerned with finding out whether students have developed new skills of problem-solving and whether they can carry these skills from one task to another. An evaluation process may provide useful information but interfere with realization of broad teaching objectives—for instance, by antagonizing teachers. Evaluation of a teaching method can be considered a scientific experiment requiring the most sophisticated techniques of design and statistics, highly trained investigators and a receptive social setting. If these requirements are not met, the result may be at best meaningless and at worst destructive. The evaluating tail should not wag the teaching dog.

XIII. DISTRIBUTORS AND APPROXIMATE PRICES OF ESI CURRICULUM MATERIALS 283

I

EDUCATIONAL SERVICES INCORPORATED: A UNIQUE EDUCATIONAL ORGANIZATION

James R. Killian, Jr.

Chairman of the Corporation
Massachusetts Institute of Technology
Chairman of the Board
Educational Services Incorporated

ESI: A UNIQUE EDUCATIONAL ORGANIZATION

by James R. Killian, Jr.

Recently in testifying before a Senate Committee in favor of the Education Bill S. 370, Dr. James R. Killian, Jr., presented the following statement about Educational Services Incorporated as the prototype of the "educational laboratories" proposed in the Bill.

I INVITE your attention to an organization which in many respects is the prototype of the educational laboratories proposed in the Education Bill S. 370. Its experience and accomplishments provide an instructive background for visualizing the potential benefits of the proposed laboratory centers. I speak of Educational Services Incorporated, a new kind of nonprofit educational organization which was founded in 1958 to handle the new high school physics course developed by the Physical Science Study Committee (PSSC). Educational Services Incorporated is now engaged in a score of course content improvement projects in the sciences, mathematics, social sciences and engineering sciences, from the primary grades through college.

ESI was established to engage in a number of activities that existing colleges and universities find difficult to undertake themselves. For example, when the new high school physics curriculum began to be used in the high schools across the nation, it became necessary to enter into contracts with publishers, laboratory equipment manufacturers, and moving picture distributors. ESI was designed to relieve the universities of the burden of such arrangements. With great care it has developed pioneer policies and procedures for commercial publication and distribution of new teaching materials financed by public funds and for introducing new courses into the schools. It has also arranged to facilitate the curriculum development activities of the scholars and teachers who become associated with it. But, most importantly, from its inception ESI has served as a vehicle for confederating scholars and teachers from a number of institutions, university, precollege, and industrial, making it easier for them to work cooperatively, in an interdisciplinary, interinstitutional pooling of talents.

Scientists from approximately fifty different universities and forty industrial organizations, and more than one hundred teachers worked on the initial development of the PSSC course, which, during this academic year—only four years after its widespread introduction in the schools — is being taught to approximately 200,000 students, or fifty per cent of those studying high school physics in the United States.

Since its inception approximately 350 faculty members from over 200 colleges and universities and several hundred school teachers have worked either full- or part-time on ESI's curriculum development and teacher education programs.

ESI has been a rallying point for innovators in education, from the universities, schools, and industrial research laboratories. It has sought by its method of operation to recruit innovative men and women and to give them the utmost freedom in conducting their research and to provide these educators of differing backgrounds and levels of education with the maximum opportunity to work together and to test their ideas and materials in the classroom. With its own core staff of scholars, scientists, teachers, and specialists in various teaching media, ESI provides the organization and support to make this partnership of educators effective. ESI's film studio, which has produced more than 200 films and film loops, has established a unique reputation for lucid presentation and for implicit respect for the advice of the scholars who cooperate with the technicians in the production of educational films. The studio's policy has served as a model during the development of the other teaching aids.

The majority of those working on curriculum development at ESI are on leave from their home institutions or are sponsored by them to work on specific projects, generally throughout the entire period of initial course development; accordingly, the talents of many persons can be mobilized without uprooting them from their careers. Since ESI is a cooperative effort in which the spirit of commitment and involvement prevails, it is important to note, too, that the atmosphere in which the work is done is free from the competitive pressure that is sometimes found, and quite properly so, in many universities.

ESI is also a means for bringing together funds from a multiplicity of sources: five government agencies, eleven private foundations, and a number of industries have made funds available to it for innovative development, aimed at creating new curricula on a national scale. A total of $20,203,940 has been received from government agencies from the beginning of December, 1958, through December, 1964; the largest amount, $11,912,290, from the National Science Foundation for work in the sciences at all grade levels and in the university, and for the development of mathematics curricula. During this same period, a total of $3,715,456 has been received from private foundations.

While new curriculum materials developed by ESI are being extensively used nationally and internationally, ESI operates close to the local and regional scene. Its closest working relationships, especially during the period of initial course development and testing, are with urban, suburban, and state educational institutions, both public and private, in Massachusetts. It is ESI's conviction that effective curriculum development occurs only when it is conducted in the "real world," in which the materials are tested in the classroom and revision can take place quickly as a normal process of curriculum research and development. ESI's influence in the Greater Boston area has been considerable; and, with an ever-increasing number of school systems and institutions of higher learning, a symbiotic partnership is being effected. ESI is actively engaged in a cooperative program with a number of the State Colleges of Massachusetts to devise new curricula and learning aids for prospective teachers. Approximately seventy-five per cent of the graduates of the State Colleges teach in the Commonwealth's public schools following graduation.

The style of the work of the PSSC and the success of its methods—the numbers of men and women of high professional skill working to present a unified and coherent pattern in physics instruction with a variety of learning aids; the careful provision for the education of teachers by in-service and summer institutes; and the insistence upon constant liaison with PSSC teachers to provide criticism and suggestions for course improvement—were very early seen to apply to massive and sustained reforms in other disciplines. ESI, therefore, has not limited itself to science or to high school courses. As its policies were stated by the Board of Trustees, ESI was chartered to accept the responsibility "to promote the public welfare and the advancement of learning by the study of means and methods of teaching science, mathematics, history, law, literature, economics, the arts and other educational subjects and by the design, preparation, production and distribution of learning materials and teaching materials," and further, "to cooperate with schools, colleges, universities and educational institutions and foundations in the preparation of learning materials and teaching materials . . . ."

From the beginning it was obvious that ESI was fulfilling a national need and many additional projects were suggested—many more than it could accept or would want to undertake. With the PSSC the organization had demonstrated that science, presented rigorously and with elegance, simplicity and a spirit of inquiry, could excite both the student and the teacher; that the professional physicist, confronting the most profound concepts of his field and deepening his own understanding in the process of working out a high school presentation, could share his involvement with science with the high school student and teacher; and that the fundamental insight into some of the fundamental principles of the physical world could, with a full complement of teaching and learning aids, be transmitted not passively but with its full impact to the teacher and his student.

The scientist, working at the forefront of his discipline, would not be likely to effect an improvement in curricula in the schools unless he had the high school teacher to work with him in designing and developing inexpensive but exact laboratory apparatus; in creating original tests and examinations that might actually be—as good tests should be—a learning as well as a teaching aid for both student and teacher; and in composing laboratory experiments which give the student evidence for believing what he is taught, an insight into the ways of making inquiries into nature as the scientist does and techniques for handling components of science along the way.

The new curricula can neither be learned by rote nor taught by rote because they demand that teacher and student alike achieve real understanding; they are generally designed to involve both in the learning process. Because of the diversity and interrelations of the teaching aids developed by ESI, teachers need to become familiar with the entire course, its philosophies, techniques and methods, as they are intricately bound together in the presentation; teachers may have to be taught the subject itself in order to teach the course effectively. The teacher remains a partner in the further development of the course and in the refinement of the materials; through area meetings, which are held in fifty sections of the nation biennially, he remains in contact with the professional staff in Watertown, Massachusetts, and with professional physicists in his area. The education of teachers—and of curriculum planners and developers—does not, and should not, stop at any time during their careers. The PSSC and other projects have demonstrated the necessity of having the scholar and the teacher work together intensively for the duration of the initial course development; ESI facilitates this association and offers the means to continue it after the course has been introduced widely in the schools.

ESI seeks to engage, and is in turn sought out by, many outstanding scholars; and once they have worked on one project at ESI, they often return to work on others. Many of the scientists associated with the initial phases of the PSSC are now working on the development of science materials for the elementary school, and others are working on introductory college physics materials. Thus, ESI has established what might be called a network of outstanding scholars who have continued their interest in improving education—at many grade levels.

ESI has also been called upon to help other nations seeking to establish or improve their own work in education; to develop in concert with African educators basic mathematical and scientific materials for the schools (ten nations in tropical Africa are now using twenty-three texts prepared by ESI's African Education Program); and to provide technical assistance with the support of the United States Agency for International Development to assist the Governments of India and Afghanistan in bringing to bear their capabilities for research and education in engineering and science. In the latter programs, ESI assisted in forming two consortia of American universities whose faculty members are serving overseas to aid in the development of the Indian Institute of Technology/Kanpur and the Faculty of Engineering at Kabul University in Afghanistan.

The cooperation of a consortium of institutions was introduced because the resources of any one American institution would be severely overtaxed if it were by itself to offer a representative staff to carry on a sustained program overseas; a consortium can draw upon a broader spectrum of ideas and resources than can a single institution.

The course content improvement projects developed by ESI are not limited in their use by national boundaries. The PSSC, and other projects, are being employed in the pursuit of excellence in education throughout the world.

I would like to note briefly some of the other course content improvement projects which ESI is working on now:

Elementary Science Study: In this interdisciplinary program thirty-eight physicists, chemists, biologists, mathematicians and scientists from other disciplines are participating in the preparation of science materials for the elementary grades. Materials are being developed to involve elementary school children in activities in the classroom and at home that would lead them to the delight and excitement that are found in scientific exploration. Preliminary materials are being taught on a pilot basis in 245 schools in 30 states. Fourteen colleges and universities are jointly working with ESI in introducing ESI materials into the curriculum of prospective teachers.

Introductory Physical Science Program: This is a one-year course in physical science mainly for use in the junior high schools, concerned with a systematic study of matter and paying little attention to the traditional divisions between chemistry and physics. The materials are being taught in their preliminary version in approximately sixty schools this academic year.

Social Studies Curriculum Program: Professors Elting E. Morison, Jerome S. Bruner and Franklin Patterson are co-directors of this Program and are working full-time, on leave from their respective universities, on the preparation of materials for the elementary school (social anthropology); junior high school (comparative case studies in English and American history at the time of the American Revolution); and high school (impact of science and technology on the nineteenth and twentieth centuries' cultural and social organization). Preliminary materials are being taught this year in selected school systems in several parts of the United States, including Colorado, New Jersey, New York, Massachusetts, Connecticut and Florida.

University of Illinois Arithmetic Project: Professor David A. Page, director of the Illinois Arithmetic Project, has been on leave at ESI from the School of Education at the University of Illinois since 1963. He is developing teacher education methods at ESI, working with both text and film. His course is aimed primarily at teachers in the field, though some work with undergraduates in teachers colleges is underway. Rather than immediately publishing his mathematical innovations and techniques, many of which are quite significant in themselves, he is concentrating on developing courses to teach elementary school teachers the content and methods of mathematics in which few of them are adequately grounded.

College Physics Committee: An introductory college physics course for physics and engineering students is being developed by a group based at the University of California at Berkeley. Its membership includes Dr. Edward M. Purcell, of Harvard University. The course comprises five original textbooks—the first of which was published in January, 1965—laboratory apparatus and manuals.

Semiconductor Electronics Education Committee: A group of forty-seven scientists and engineers from universities and industrial firms are preparing a series of seven textbooks and three films to teach and to demonstrate introductory semiconductor physics and the principles of transistor circuits. It was taught experimentally last year at fourteen universities, in the junior or senior year. The first three texts are now available commercially and the course is now being taught at many universities.

National Committee for Fluid Mechanics Films: The films produced by this Committee at ESI's film studio are being used at more than eighty universities and government research stations in improved teaching of aeronautical engineering, and in chemical, civil, mechanical and marine engineering. They are also being used to improve the instruction in meteorology, applied mathematics, and in medicine. These films are being used by twenty-one countries overseas. Excerpts from the film "Surface Tension" have been incorporated into a film loop "The Beading of a Column of Water" for the Elementary Science Study.

Pre-College Centers: Based on ESI's course materials in English and mathematics, six centers in the South, at Nashville, Atlanta, Houston, New Orleans, St. Louis, and Washington, D. C., have been formed around universities which have a predominantly Negro enrollment, to give prospective college students special courses in these subjects with the aim of improving their chances of succeeding in college.

Summer Institutes for Faculties of Predominantly Negro Colleges: Last summer ESI accepted the responsibility of organizing and administering institutes to improve the skills of the faculty at predominantly Negro colleges. These institutes were held at the following schools: Princeton University (physics); University of North Carolina at Greensboro (biology); University of Wisconsin (mathematics); Carnegie Institute of Technology (history); Indiana University (English). Additional institutes are planned for this coming summer.

Cooperative Teacher Education Program: To better prepare the prospective teachers in Massachusetts for their tasks in the schools (approximately seventy-five percent of the graduates of the eleven State Colleges of Massachusetts teach in the public schools in the Commonwealth), to educate and train them to be able to use the new curricula effectively in the classroom, a program was initiated in 1964 to introduce jointly with the faculty of the State Colleges a modern curriculum based on the knowledge of subjects that they will be expected to teach after graduation. ESI's curriculum projects in the sciences and mathematics are now engaged in the joint adaptation and development of course materials for the Colleges. It is intended also that courses developed by other curriculum groups will be introduced in the Colleges. If these new curricula prove successful in Massachusetts, they could then be applicable to colleges throughout the nation engaged primarily in educating prospective teachers.

This statement has mentioned briefly some of the activities of Educational Services Incorporated in this country and overseas; since its founding, the organization has clearly demonstrated its capacity for making new departures in curriculum research and development. Its projects are noted for their integrity, their scholarship, and their taste.

Educational Services Incorporated is not a member of any particular educational establishment: its province and master are the schools and the teachers throughout the land.

Educational Services Incorporated is not concerned with shaping educational policy: it is committed to the task of improving the substance of education in the classroom and of making available a greater variety of choices to our teachers.

Educational Services Incorporated is not bewailing the mis-education of American teachers: it is concerned with helping in every school, every university and school of education, when they seek to improve the teaching process.

Educational Services Incorporated is not beholden to any one, or group, of universities, schools, school systems, educational associations of any sort: it is the servant of all.

Educational Services Incorporated is not concerned with perpetuating itself or creating others in its own image: it does encourage the formation of other curriculum development groups, each of which may differ in form.

Educational Services Incorporated discourages uniformity and rote acceptance in the school curricula: it can do this by encouraging and assisting others to set out on important new departures and by making alternative, diverse innovations in education.

During the past decade, in summary, we have witnessed a movement in improving education that many observers and critics—for we would not wish to have an absence of critics or to be uncritical ourselves—liken to a revolution and others to a renascence in learning. It is a movement that can best be characterized by the consistent cooperation of those most concerned professionally with education, from the primary school teacher to the Nobel Laureate in a university, from the school administrator to the industrial research scientist, from the commercial textbook publisher to the manufacturer of scientific equipment for the schools.

But we shall fail in our task if we consider our efforts to be a stopgap that can be ended at a certain predetermined date. We shall fail at our task if we consider that the ultimate, grand design is a national curriculum, structured and rigid. We shall fail at our task unless we manage to create in our educational system the desire and the means, as well as the competence, to work on the diverse problems of education, and, in particular, the development of improved curricula. The responsibility for curriculum improvement must ultimately rest within the schools—and I mean all school systems, if not every school within those systems—and upon university scholars working with the school teachers in their communities; for it is only when this base of curriculum development is assured, that is, one in which the desire and the competency for self-examination and self-renewal are built into each school system, that we can feel confident of combatting obsolescence by steadily enhancing quality.

The result of Federal support of curriculum development has been to encourage diversity and non-conformity in our educational system. There are approximately 36,000 separate school systems in the United States, each autonomous and free to select that curriculum it believes most suited to its student and community needs. However, the lack of diversity in the curriculum, of having alternatives among which to select the most appropriate, can be illustrated by the fact that although there were many textbooks on mathematics twenty years ago, each text, by and large, was teaching the same math with little dissimilarity. During the past five years, new and bolder and diverse ways of teaching mathematics have been developed by many groups of scholars and teachers, largely supported by the National Science Foundation; these new mathematics courses are likely to stimulate diversity in educational practice. Whereas about twenty years ago many considered that there was a national curriculum in mathematics, with different books teaching the same thing, now with the support of the Federal Government our schools have a wider and wiser choice. This analogy holds true, I believe, for the other disciplines. To encourage and support curriculum development is to create more diversity in our school systems, not less; more opportunities of choosing improved ways of teaching many disciplines to students, not fewer.

Let me offer my full support of the proposed regional curriculum research centers and laboratories. Based upon the experience I have described, they have a major opportunity to improve American education.

March 1965

II

SCIENCE IN THE ELEMENTARY SCHOOL

THE CURRICULAR TRIANGLE AND ITS STYLE

by Philip Morrison

"The potter who shapes the clay has long been the image of a godlike power, but this is not the perception of the potter himself. He must be sensitive to the properties of the mix, and to its responses to firing in shape and color and texture. The potter is as much transformed by his art as the clay is."

David Hawkins, *The Language of Nature,*
W. Freeman, San Francisco, 1964.

THE earth and the stars, fire and air, light and dark — categories like these span the inanimate world. The tree and the flower, wheat and the dog, measles virus and mold — these sample the living world. We, perforce, stand and move, see and breathe and reckon according to subtle but rigorous statutes of the physical world. Our very beings display in every act and gesture our unmistakable kinship with the rest of living things. Yet we are human beings, tool-makers, speakers, the proud legatees of a million painful and glorious years of human culture. What we see, what we describe, and what we create are all matters of human art. Science is not itself the world; it is one reaction to the world. It is on this view of science, and on the view of man which underlies it, that we choose to rest the structure of our growing curriculum.

Any study of a part of science need not necessarily connect with the rest of the fabric. Neither life nor the inanimate lies, for our curriculum, at the center; there is no center, though man, even as a child, carries with him an apparently shifting center in the experience of daily life. Here we view the elementary approach as distinct from that of the usual professional. Around each of the vertices of the triangle, the physical, the biological, the human, there cluster knots of disciplines and whole worlds of specialization. The detail and the demanding technique at the frontiers of science often occupy the professionals so completely that there is relatively little to say across their social boundaries. The divisions of the academies, the pigeonholes of our university departments, the jargons of the mismatched specialists, do not belong in the elementary school, but problems and puzzles of science, real, concrete, and varied, certainly do.

We expect to bring varied techniques and varied materials into the schoolroom. But all of the techniques must remain inexpensive, small-scale, and relatively unspecialized. In the schoolroom we have a chance to unite the disciplines, at their simplest and clearest. In the schoolroom we have a chance to bring the whole range of the world from butterflies or bones to lenses and millimeters into the same hands. The particular key which opens a new door for a particular child is not predictable. Therefore our curriculum is not at all to be cut into separate disciplines, fenced off by frontiers of technique and history. At the same time, we would not admit that this is merely a consequence of the simple and introductory character of the work we propose. The curriculum does not merely precede discipline; it is in part post-disciplinary as well; for we believe that the physicist can be interested in the motion of animals, and that the logic of circuits is not foreign or irrelevant to the sociologist. The unity of science is not the topic of our curriculum; it is closer to its expected outcome.

As the child grows, economy of time, symbolic skills, sheer tradition will demand of him a more and more subdivided and disciplinary approach to his work. This

---

Copyright 1964 Educational Services Incorporated

Professor Morrison, a member of the Elementary Science Study Steering Committee and an initial contributor to the PSSC, is a professor of physics at M. I. T. This article is a chapter from his forthcoming book, "Experimenters in the Schoolroom: A Science Program for the Grades."

trend may not be wholly intrinsic to the nature of learning, but we do not now propose to set ourselves against it. Rather we shall continue to mix and to connect, to provide the tissue of science as a whole, and to let the divisions grow sharper as the child moves closer to specialization. It is not entirely accidental that in so doing we recapitulate the growth of science itself. Galileo, the astronomer, wrote of animal motions; Maxwell, the mathematical physicist, studied color vision; in the twentieth century, perhaps for the first time, technique has divided the realm of science. We can hope, at least, that the ecumenical trend we advocate echoes a little, too, the growth of mergers between physics and astronomy, between chemistry and biology, between mathematics and literary criticism, which are so marked in science today.

The physicist can look clearly, if distantly, at life. What he sees may be expressed in his relatively colorless palette as a complex, open thermodynamical system. It consists of numerous interacting populations, feeding upon the energy set free from the nuclear engine of a near-by star and exploiting for their intricate architecture all the molecular aggregates possible on the planet. Within the rain of free energy, the living species flourish and change. In his study of the nature of life, the biologist often tends to look apart from all that; he invents an analytical apparatus of cells and genes, or organisms and species, with their wonderfully subtle interactions, their responses to the patterns of the environment, their in-built history of generations long gone. There is a way of looking at this expressed in classical style in the remarkable, slightly dated but rich work, *On Growth and Form* by D'Arcy Wentworth Thompson, which immediately places the whole in its physical, indeed in its mathematical, substratum. It is perhaps in this spirit that our physical and biological science merge at the one margin.

The biologist is not only the master of the analysis of life into cells and polymers; he is the revealer of the whole tangled interaction of beings, of ecology. Within this matrix, the elementary classroom has always depended heavily upon the natural history, the description of life cycle of many an organism. The ant and the bee are Biblical models for human behavior. Fabre, Seton and others bring this style somewhat more up to date. If the physical world is our house in the sense of floor and roof, the world of biology is our home. For we are all one family, marked by carbon and by optical kinship as much as by our grandfather's nose. In the study of living things, not as parts but as reacting and sentient wholes, the modern biologist inherits this style. He studies knowingly and unsentimentally the very crises and preoccupations of our own lives: birth, survival, reproduction, death. The chance to see these matters whole and clear has in it the quality of the fable; the life of the carrot butterfly can grip most imaginations. The egg hatches; the hungry larval instars come forth in their struggles to grow; the chrysalis is formed; and the image is resurrected, to mate, lay new eggs and die. All this can be presented in an elementary school classroom in six weeks. As each of these crises can be watched, not merely in a single animal, but in dozens, the class comes, not entirely by a play of words, to know life. This story, close enough to the fables and the metaphors of the oldest and greatest of classical literatures, plainly marks the other margin of biology, the human world. The chance, for once, to see life with some detachment, to modify it, to analyze it, to see its cruelties and its beauties seems to belong not merely to developmental entomology but also to the curriculum of human growth. There is not much new in this; what is new is the completeness, the detail, the sense of control, which is made possible only by hard work of the skilled biologist as he finds out how to bring many organisms alive into the classroom in *all* of their stages.

Less pointed, but even grander, is the microecology of decay, molds and fungi. The role of this pattern in the cycle of life, so clearly required by the need for a materials balance coldly imposed by chemistry, is also worth long pursuit. One needs here the logic of the indirect, the technique of the negative experiment and the control. One needs the twofold way of looking: looking either at whole colonies with unaided eye (but with the subtle technique of enrichment), or at single microscopic beings under the powerful new eye of the microscope. (The microscope itself illustrates a junction of disciplines. A microscope is all engineering and physics, but its user is most often a biologist.) In our elementary school science units, living cells, and inanimate but growing crystals both form objects for the student's microscope — which we hope each student will have the opportunity to use. Behind all of this lies the genetics of the molds, pathway to the molecular biology of today. The topography of our elementary school science is not that of a great museum, with distinct ranks of exhibit halls; rather, it is like a tree with branches great and small, dividing and reuniting— if sometimes with a small jump at the end.

Content has been the theme of this argument, but there is also a form, a style, a context of determining effect. The style is not single, for it must reflect the diversity of authors and topics. But it has a single tendency which it derives perhaps most strongly from the relationships we see between science and the many other activities of children in and out of school.

First and chief of all the learned activities of man is language. The reader may perhaps recall that charming little boy who pouts a challenge to you out of the Berlitz ads. The advertisement boasts that the child can speak Ewe—difficult grammar, tonal constructions and all—at a highly practical level. "By the age of four to six," one linguist writes, "the child is a linguistic adult. He controls . . . the phonetic system of his language; he handles the grammatical core; he knows and uses the basic vocabulary of the language." Of course he has a lot to learn; but that remains true through life. It is the nearly invariable success in learning this complex and subtle tool of thought that convinces us that we tend to underestimate the abilities of children. The strong motivation a child has to learn to speak, the excellent student-teacher ratio and the long time spent at the task are certainly signposts for those who would design curricula.

But there is much more. Of course language learning requires much practice in memorization, even drill. But the standard of learning is not at all set by the results of analysis of language. The Ewe boy, like your own children or you yourself at age five, could not pass any schoolbook sort of test, listing the paradigms of Ewe verbs. His is a superior sort of knowledge which can be recognized by a much more reasonable test. Linguists speak of *productivity* as a characteristic of all language. It is the speaker's ability to say something that he has never heard or said before and to find himself perfectly well understood. It is this ability which makes that boy an Ewe-speaker. Language, the supreme tool of the mind, must be productive to be real; but the other subjects, especially science, cannot be genuine without a strong measure of that same ability. It is here that the scientist parts company sharply from those who would test by memory, even by the retention of well understood facts; productivity, the mastery of how to make new structures meaningful even at the most introductory level, is his touchstone.

We are not expert at language development. Still, some observations force themselves upon us and have meant much for the style in which we seek to work. The children who learn to speak make mistakes, many of them. They try again, learning from error. They talk in all sorts of contexts, formal recitations, games, jokes, even insults and fights. They make slow progress, and they make rapid progress. They store and learn all sorts of words and forms whose utility is not clear and not soon displayed. They sing and dance; they try little plays; they listen to the Bible and to the TV com-

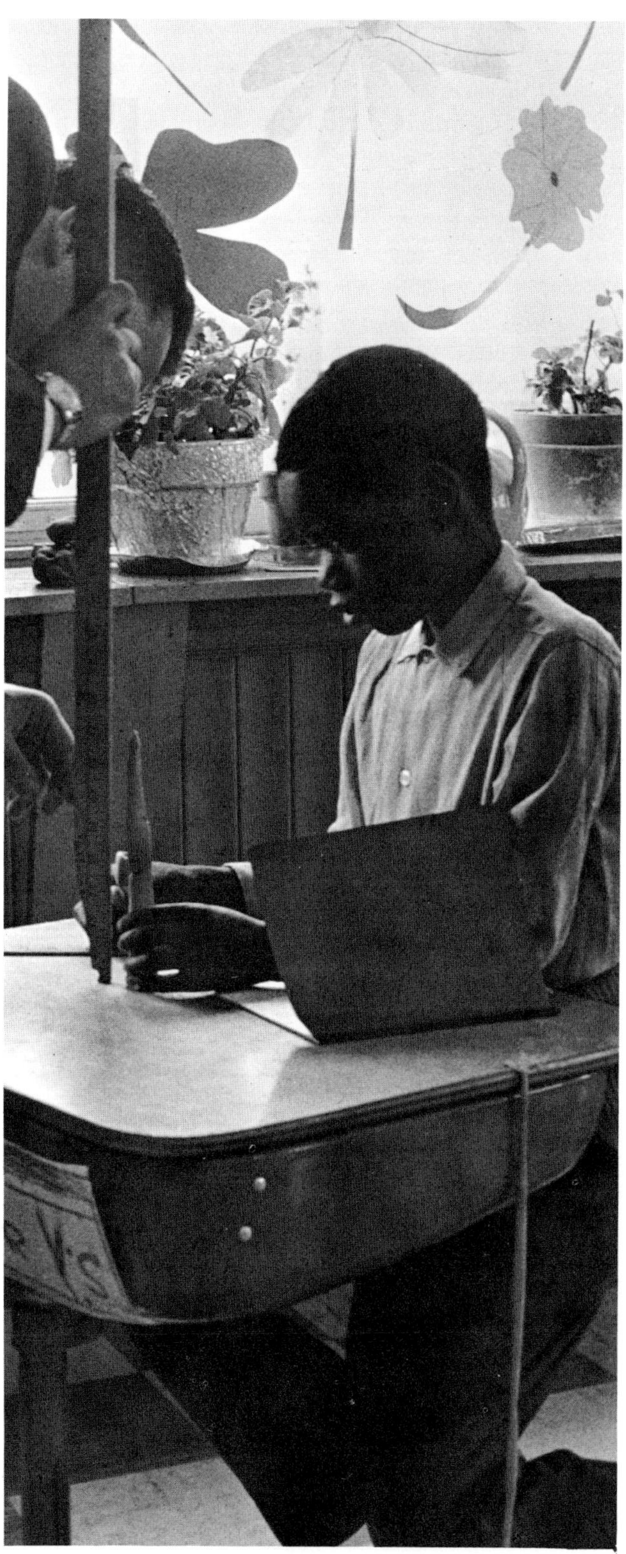

The structures unit is conceived as a study of the properties of structures and of the materials from which they are built. Each child is given a half-pound of plasticene to make various shapes. Who can build the tallest tower? Who can build the longest bridge?

mercials; they speak for themselves and they listen to others, both adults and children. The street experience molds their speech more often than the school.

Learning a formal subject, say Arithmetic, English, or Science, does not normally proceed along such lines. Learning is not all to be managed, it seems, by a wholly logical route. The effect is no less important. A rich context, a cheerful one, sometimes playful, sometimes earnest, sometimes austere, sometimes baroque — that is the condition for imparting not mere recall but productive use of language. Should learning about science be different? Or learning history or arithmetic or writing, for that matter? The scientists of the Renaissance who gave us science as a vigorous sapling in the seventeenth century were men of their times. They did not disdain to decorate the microscope with handsome engravings. The wholly utilitarian style of instruments and laboratories, the austere and humorless style of texts, is no intrinsic part of science. It is a consequence of the economic pressures of time and money, a part of Whiggish utilitarian or perhaps even Puritan views of human values. The books and journals of the scientists are more serious, more ponderous, than are the living men in their real laboratories. Few are the productive labs in which the humanity of the scientist is not marked by the obvious, the coffee cups, the newspapers, the joking remarks on the blackboard. It is inexcusable to make the style of science more remote for young children than it is in the reality of an adult scientist.

This is not an effort to destroy the purity of argument and experiment, the elegance of unornamented design, which surely has attracted many minds to mathematics and to science. "Euclid alone has looked on Beauty bare. . . . " That will remain, in many points. All we speak against is an *unvarying* humorless, austere, undecorated style. It can be argued that many of those persons — and I here include a very large number of young girls — who are led by cultural and psychological traits to cut themselves off from all mathematically related knowledge would find new interest if the simple style variations here proposed were more widely used.

Language learning has served as a model for a style of teaching in science. But it is not less important to point out that school science can very much aid the maturing of the little "linguistic adults" of the first grades. Much of science is improving and sharpening of concepts once first efforts at description have been made. The materials for narration and argument are plainly rich. The kindergarten has a far too conventional "show and tell" period; the scientist is acting the same role with earnestness all of his working life. The incentive which science provides for reading and questioning is strong. Questions can find answers, and the pursuit of answers becomes a skill worth mastering. There are plenty of stories like that of the boy who was far below his grade level in reading and who made his first real progress in a tough book about a circuit he wanted to understand. While everything we say goes against unproductive verbalism or mere parrot-work or list-grubbing, science remains largely a process of writing and talking. It is the task of science to explain, to express, to communicate. The impulse to make such communication better and clearer is a valuable aid to language learning beyond the earliest levels. Understanding without language, its symbolic expression, is still incomplete; and expression without understanding is empty. Their fusion is frequent in the successful laboratory. Here, too, our strictures on style bite in; if the style of expression is too limited by economy and convention, the channel of ideas narrows. It is a good deal more enjoyable to read Darwin or Galileo or even Einstein than the *Physical Review* of 1964, or more than one high school textbook.

We turn from man's speech to a still earlier function, vision. The school child probably looks more at black-and-white type and at the flickering grays of the TV screen than he does at the colorful face of the real world. The eyes become instruments for learning the content of a highly-restricted visual field, marked with stereotypes — codes — standing for the reality beyond. Sport and play, out of school, employ vision more naturally than does the schoolroom. The world has become simplified for the senses into a code, admittedly a most subtle and complex one—but still a code—in which more or less repetitive patterns are to be discriminated only with respect to certain combinations. Two great activities of men deny the primacy of the symbol or the representation: science and art. They do not seek wholly to represent, but also to present. Art cultivates novelty, challenges eye and ear with ever-new patterns, avoids the stereotype, the code, demands close attention by the individual mind to all that is in fact given, not merely to some portion held relevant. Thus the artist shares the most basic problems with the scientist. He must present a wide range of the real world to his audience. It is not enough to make marks on the blackboard or to talk a bit. There needs to be paper and pigment, or catgut and horsehair, or clay and chisel.

To work in art is always to solve some problem of handling a portion of the real world, not merely to mark its meaning in the abstract. Here is a fundamental kinship of science and art. The potter is a ceramic en-

Studying the structure and development of molds in the ESS "Microgardening" unit.

Examining a sample of pond water, as a part of the ESS unit, "Small Things," an introduction to the microscopic world.

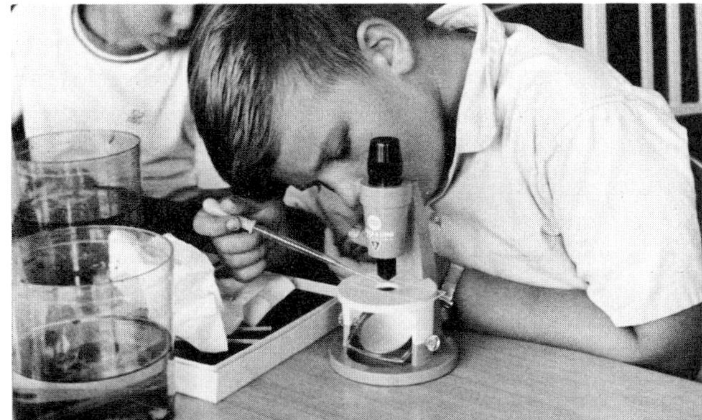

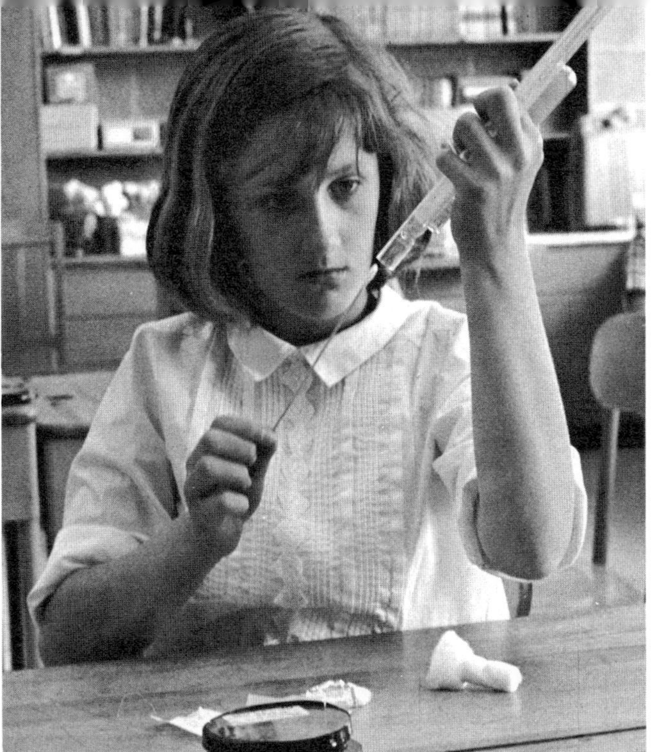

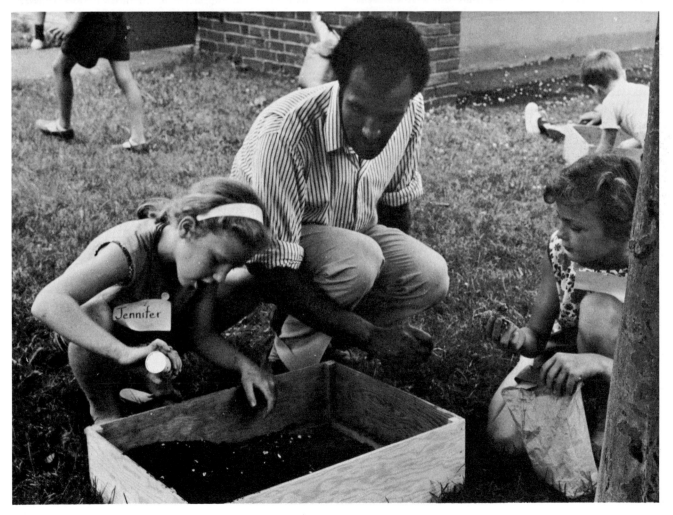

Mr. Miguel B. R. Savage, ESS staff member, teaching a class on the ESS unit, "Growing Seeds." This August Mr. Savage began work on a program for teaching science in the elementary grades in Africa.

gineer; the painter, a student of anatomy and of color; the sculptor, a master of the foundryman's art or of the stonemason's cutting edges. In art we cannot expect productive teaching without materials; nor can we expect it in science. The scientist must analyze and describe, while the craftsman need never do so. If the craftsman analyzes, he turns part-scientist. The artist, too, need not analyze (though he may become critic). In both cases, the difference is real, but we would stress here the kinship between art and science. The experience is indispensable to art; in the style we hope to build for science, it is no less essential. There is an aesthetic of pushing a lever or turning a crank or seeing a yeast cell bud or hearing the Doppler-shifted train whistle or tasting the diluted quinine or smelling the green mold colony or balancing on the swing or waiting for the precipitate to form jet black, which cannot be replaced by words or pictures. We believe we deeply share this aesthetic with the artist; and we feel that it ought to be strongest in the earliest experiences in science.

We can make out a hierarchy of experiences. The minimum for some understanding is linguistic, either oral or written. Then come representations in chalk, or drawings, or paintings and photographs; then models, samples, preserved materials. The film comes next with its dimension of motion and change. Finally the material itself is presented or, best of all, is discovered by the child himself as he detects the phenomenon or elicits it from the context he has been given. We are convinced that this aesthetic approach is of the highest value.

Only the full range of experience can make science real. This is not merely the instinctive consensus of scientists; we have the strongest of arguments for the point. The essential act of the scientist is abstraction; he abstracts some part of the world's complicated and indivisible whole. That act is his boldest and most difficult one. In it lie his errors, as well as his victories. But it is exactly that action which the book, the lecture, the programmed text, never allow the student to share. For, restricted to a representation on paper or in words, the teacher has necessarily already done the key job of abstracting. Only the material, without its man-made labels to suggest relevance, can instruct in this process, and only the errors so made can lead to a real and a productive understanding. Experiments *always* "work," though usually they don't work the way the planner anticipates. Here is the lesson that only the laboratory, and only the free laboratory, can impart. To be sure, all sorts of approximations and compromises and mixtures of approach are possible, even necessary; once again, our style insists not upon a rigid prescription, but upon a widened range of approach.

The appeal to the maximum range of what the child can do or sense is justified then on grounds of scientific content. Without claiming psychiatric insight, we would claim it has an equal justification in the emotional feeling toward the work. Touch is one of the earliest of the senses to play a role in the development of the individual; the chemical senses, too, lie close to the root of emotions. The use of the large muscles, the sense of strain, the fast pulse, the joy in dexterity or even in a clumsy effort, accompany both game and work. They are by no means foreign to the laboratory. We try hard to bring them there. In Chinese tradition a fine piece of jade must please by its look and lustre, by its silken and polished feel, by the cold hardness of its touch, and by its rich click as it strikes another ornament. It is this diversity of impression which we must emphasize in an introduction to scientific work. And the range of laboratory experience can be wider than the world of books can ever be. This again it shares with the arts and the work of the craftsman.

An example from another area is striking. The great mime, Marcel Marceau, performs one remarkable and simple piece. On the flat bare floor of the stage, he presents to us the commonplace crisis of a man climbing seven long flights of stairs to his garret apartment somewhere in the *Quartier Latin.* At first he strides cheerfully, two steps at a time, around the long ellipse of the stair well. Gradually he slows. Soon he is making heavy going of each step. Before long, the railing, until now disdained and hardly noticed, has become conspicuous. Now the man all but clings to it. Finally, winded, panting, he stands with a great sigh before his own door. All this, recall, on a bare and unmarked flat stage. Before your eyes he has created a staircase seventy feet high and mounted it. From the observation of experience, his own and that of others, he has reconstructed the interaction between the body of man and the earth's gravitational pull, in a specific mechanical context. This lies close to the work of the theoretical physicist. The mime has been forced to an analysis of the action of muscle and bone in order to display that action in a context where it is not really present. Whether he has written a scenario, in which he has formulated his understanding in words, I do not know. In any case, his aim is to convey that understanding, just as the physicist hopes to do, but in a different way. Marcel Marceau communicates his understanding without words, in action and stance. The large muscles and the small, the whole complex of tired body and impatient mind, he recreates from an earlier understanding.

Here is a peculiar art, an art close indeed to the scientific, at a highly stylized level. In such a performance we could see that expression of understanding can be more than verbal. This comes close to the situation in the laboratory, when a child builds some working device whose function implies a kind of understanding, even if the child has not yet the ability to express his understanding in conventional symbols. Can we doubt that Marceau knows more about stair-climbing than all but the most advanced of the specialists in the mechanics of the human body? They may have a more quantitative control of what happens but Marceau has done more than they: he has expressed his knowledge with absolute clarity. It is this sort of behavior we seek to cultivate in the children: Marceau's mime is the synthetic counterpart to that analytic effort we see so much in science.

The union of analysis and synthesis, best demonstrated in what we call design, from the design of a pantomime to that of a jet aircraft or a mural decoration, is not easy to bring in to the schoolroom. It can be seen, however, that symbolic systems other than words can provide a rich range of communication. Graphs, diagrams, charts, maps, and models are plainly in this area; their importance is clear. Gesture and dance are presumably less expected and less suited, but ought not to be excluded.

The greatest of non-linguistic symbol systems is mathematics. Low in ambiguity, international, traditional in schools because of its applicability to the economics of everyday life, close to science in origins and logical structure, it is plainly of major concern in any scheme of elementary science. The amount of work which has gone into recent elementary school mathematics cannot be justly appraised, let alone presented, in an aside like this. But we can point to the traditional use of the real world to supply models and examples for the concepts of mathematics, for the ideas of *number* and *set* themselves to *function,* and, especially in the simpler sciences, to relations like *proportionality, scaling* and *similarity, reciprocity,* and the like. There is no end to such relevance, but it is far from easy to make real. The necessity for approximation and model-building in passing from almost any empirical system to the precise structures of modern mathematics makes that passage very far from trivial. It is indeed here that the act of abstraction takes clearest form. The use of number, measurement, graph and map are evidently real problems for the teaching of both mathematics and science. We are confident that mutual aid, symbiosis, is possible. In the examples which follow in this book, much appeal to mathematics will be visible, but it has not yet been merged with the newer approaches. There is real danger for this working relationship. Mathematical structures are logically free of any need for exemplification, since exemplification is normally approximate. The mathematician's joy is precision. Generality has tended to lead school mathematics away from emphasis on the intuitive and experiential beginnings of number, geometry, calculus, even algebra. It seems to us that the significance and excitement of many such mathematical structures is muted unless a pre-mathematical basis in experience has preceded or accompanied the more formal elaborations.

There is more. Even in biology, where the more formal mathematical language has been slow to find application, the traditional mathematical virtue of logical connectedness and discipline is present. Yet we want the children to look away from the butterfly and the balance board at some point. They need to argue what must happen from already-established statements. The *experiment in thought* ought to be as vivid and familiar—and as much open to skepticism—as the *experiment in fact.* This relation of theory to experiment is close to the spirit if not always to the form of mathematics. We count heavily upon it. The more conventional side of computation, graphing, geometrical relations and simple algebra, are tools for science hardly less important than the word or the hand.

There is not much need to elaborate upon the relations between science in this style and the other school subjects aside from mathematics, language and art. We have already mentioned and we will say more about the relevance of history, geography, and the other studies of man. Here we speak of delicate and unproved matters, those which touch not upon the content or the results of work but upon the tone in which it is carried out, upon the affect and the emotions. We have seen in science a source of motivation for children. We have noticed its power to bring forward the child who has been non-verbal. Science has an important objectifying effect; many children are too intensely preoccupied with interpersonal relations, with approval or disapproval from peers, parents or teachers. An insect or a lens does not respond to temper tantrums or to the high social status of parents or to notes of written excuse or to smiles and tears. By the same token, it never penalizes nor takes offense at the color of one's skin, one's name, one's accent, one's frayed clothing or a scar on the face. There is in the relationship with the apparatus—again not at all in the relation with the textbook—a tempered optimism. It *will* work right if I do the right things. There is no easy authority; the right answer comes not from the quickest kid in the class but from the apparatus itself. There is a kind of reasoned skepticism as the complex chains of cause become known, and a growth of self-reliance. But this self-reliance is not arrogant; the indispensability of cooperation can be easily felt. The chain of obligation which stretches to the pioneer in India or Italy, or to the glassmaker in Corning, New York, without all of whom one's own best work is naught, bears witness to human interdependence and to tolerance of differences. In school the cooperation *between classmates* becomes a necessity for certain kinds of exploration. The cooperation is spontaneous. The need for tentative conclusions, for acting *as if*, for guessing and estimation, for the whole arsenal of the heuristic, comes clear. Novelty and change become part of the real world; they are to be expected.

The nature of play and playfulness can be seen in a laboratory. Play is notoriously hard to define, but part of its nature is surely that it consists of activities which, though clearly structured, have no obvious goal. Role-playing approaches this; games are not far away; and experiment based on curiosity is surprisingly close. One of the differences between science and technology has been the essentially playful activities of the scientist. He has tried to see how bodies fall not only in order to design rockets or cannons, but, simply, to see. The suspicion that cannons would be improved thereby has often proved true. Still, the ability to suspend a goal for the sake of clarity and human delight is part and parcel of science. Play makes no pots, but playing with clay makes potters. The potter is his own clay, as the epigram tells us; and the scientist, or the child studying science, is also his own experiment. We would not forget this, nor would we forget that the tone of playfulness is not the tone of prescribed and demanding ends. The child who does something off the track is usually not wasting time and effort; what he changes is himself, if not the apparatus. School is an institution for changing children, and perhaps teachers, too. Our experimental directions ought not always to be efficient, clear, earnest and single-minded. Sometimes they have to be easy-going, ambiguous, laughable and rambling. No single attitude can properly span all of what we mean by science.

One mandate is imperative for our style of work: there must be personal involvement. The child must work with his own hands, mind and heart. It is not enough for him to watch the teacher demonstrate or stand in line to take a hurried glimpse of the reflection of his own eyelashes in the microscope eyepiece. It is not enough for him to watch the skillful classmate at work, not enough to follow the TV screen. He needs his own apparatus, simple, workable. This is not a peremptory command. Many matters are handled by film or in a group or, sometimes, by the teacher. But we must work hard to bring a more varied range of science into the child's own hands, where he may be potter and clay at once.

Possibly, the very assumption of communicability to which we here commit ourselves distinguishes science from magic. The rain-making magician assembles the medicine bundle and mutters the spell as carefully and precisely as the bacteriologist flames his loop and inoculates the slant. The magician may even have empirical statistics on his side: those who drum the dragon moon away from the sun-swallowing eclipse have, so far, never failed. It is free communication and the capacity for it that marks science. We believe we can see what to do, and we believe anyone else can do it. One need not have had the mystic vision of the shaman or the laying on of hands or the proud name of a priestly caste. Granted, there is a sort of magic in the mind of an Einstein, but it is the magic of our humanity. We who follow at a distance can grasp it. Unless that belief is brought honestly into the classroom, the science of our times may become the magic of a later generation, a magic residing with those who are clever, have gone to M.I.T., own the computer or talk from the moon. We pay a great deal in effort and in money to bring real participation to each child insofar as we are able, but we would not begrudge at even higher price. For nothing we have done would withstand the shock of having all of science demonstrated nicely by an expert standing in front of the class.

The final criterion of our curricular style is this: it takes time. What the textbook can summarize in a page of results—life is cellular, cells have water and carbon, cells divide to multiply—our methods with the child's own work, with his own hands, with his own microscope and his own labored arithmetic may take six weeks of classroom effort. We do not begrudge this time. We are not disturbed by slowness, for what goes slow can run deep. And school hours are not all of life. To stroll into reality, the detail of it and the context, to unravel and to uncover it is a better thing than to sprint past, reading the billboards of science.

2

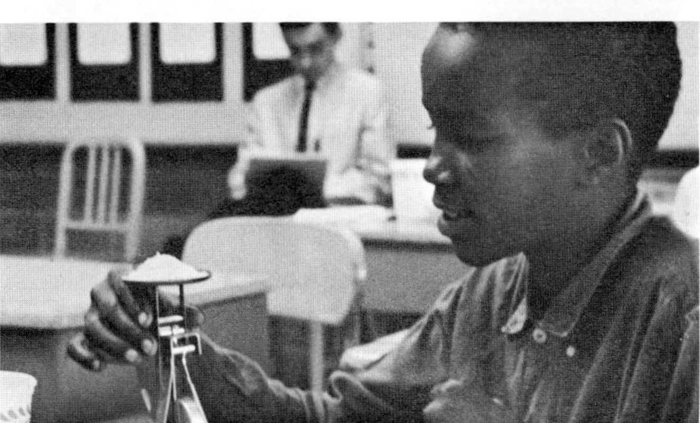

3

4

1. Children conducting a "Gases and Air" experiment.

2. Investigating certain properties of liquids in ESS Unit on "Kitchen Physics."

3. Weighing rice: An assay in sampling techniques in the "Peas and Particles" unit.

4. Third-grade students growing molds in petri dish.

5(a)

5(b)

5. Children in the kindergarten and fourth grade at the ESS Summer School investigating shadows in a unit being developed by Mrs. Phylis Singer, ESS staff member, and Miss Mary Lou Hartley, of the Fulton Elementary School, Minneapolis, Minnesota (ESS summer staff). Miss Hartley is in the picture, at left.

6. Conducting an experiment in "Kitchen Physics."

7. Mr. William Hull, ESS staff member, and a class in "Structures."

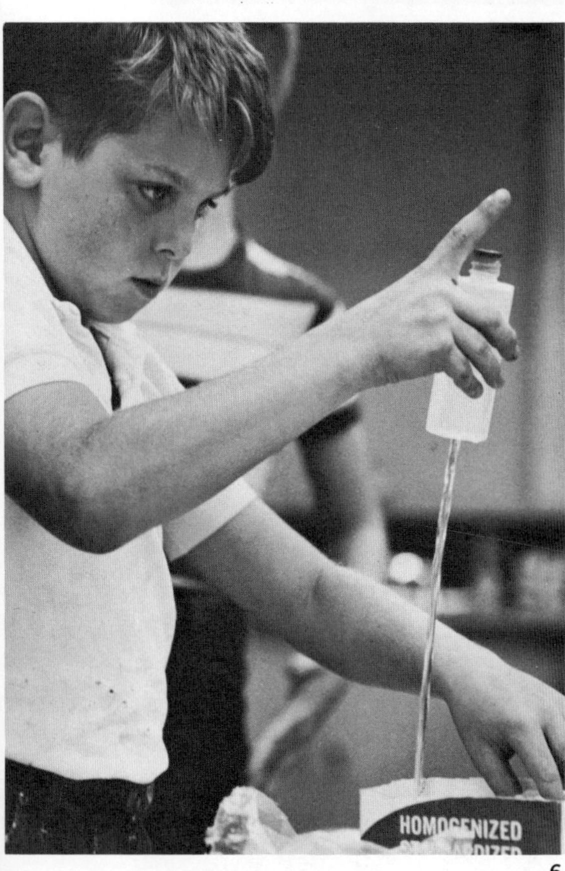

6

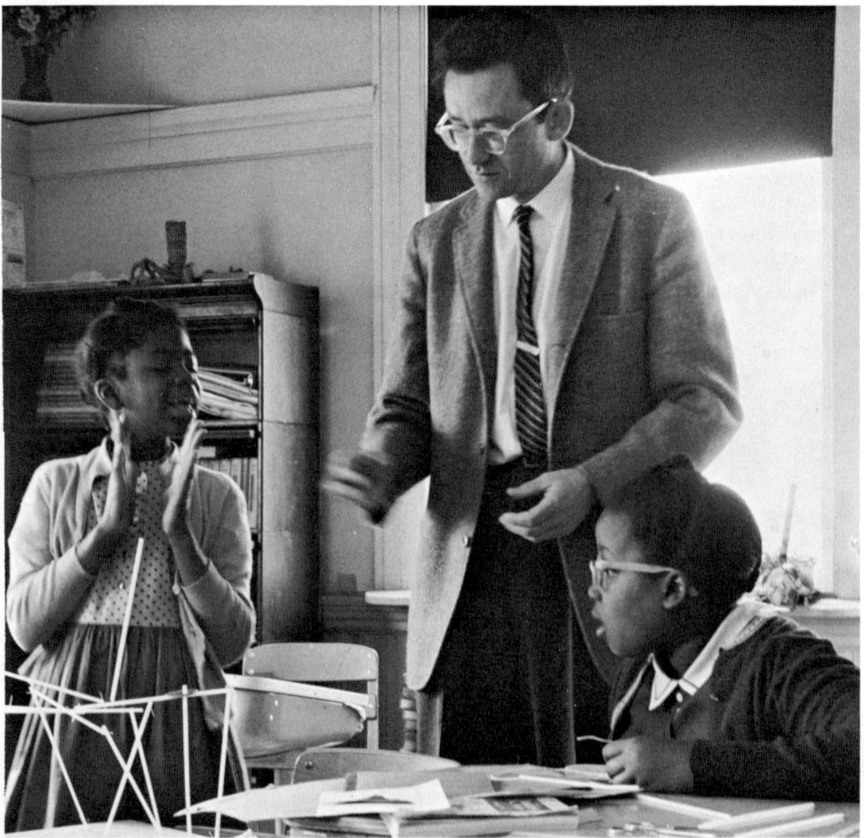

7

Two chapters from *Kitchen Physics* — a guide for teachers — are reprinted in the following pages. These chapters are *Beading of Water Columns* and *Absorption and Evaporation.*

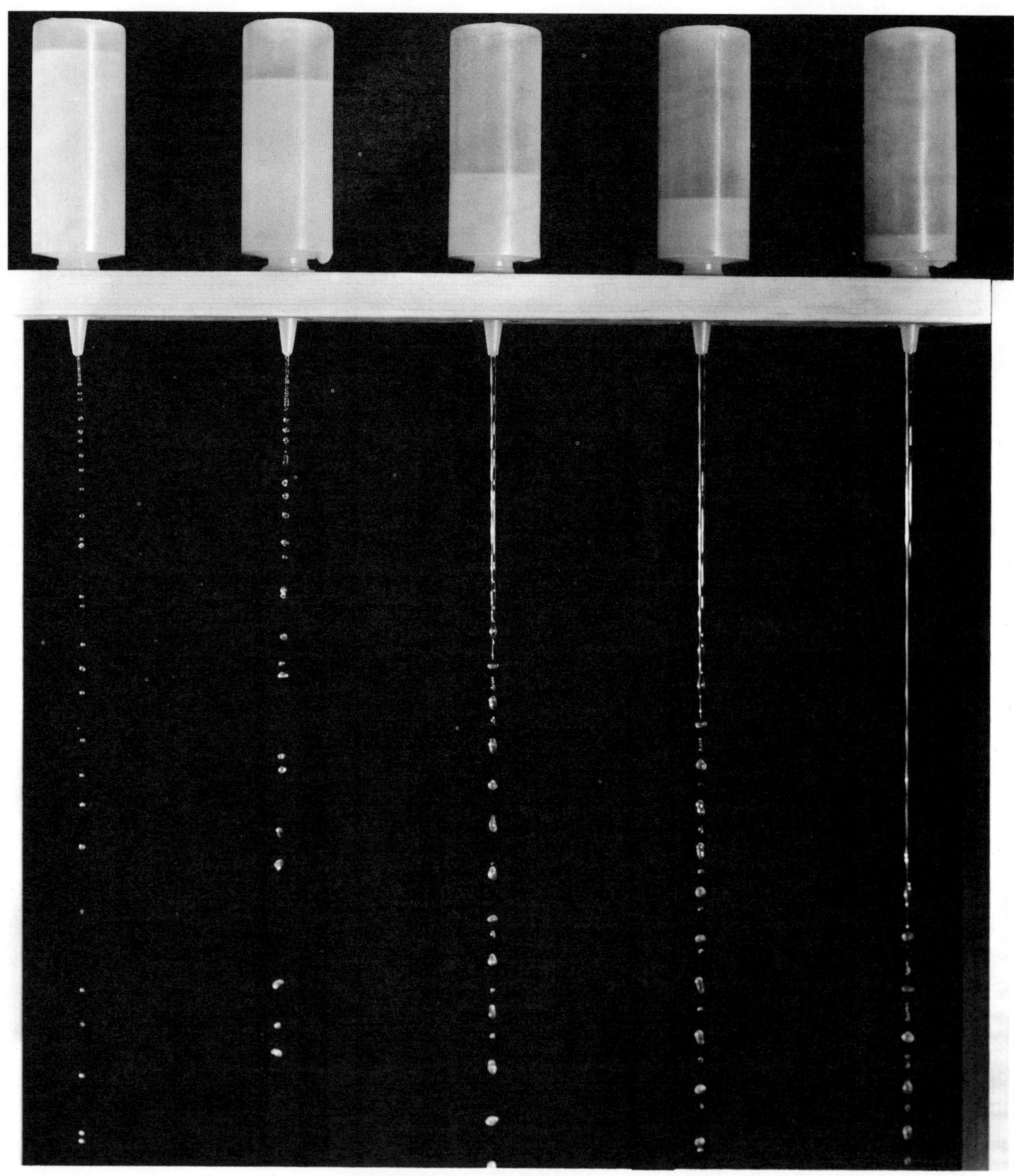

FIGURE 4 · The Beading Effect.

The cap opening in each bottle is different, increasing from left to right. Notice the points at which beading occurs in each column.

A special kit to perform the experiments in this section is available from Robert Bentley, Inc. For full particulars, see page 285 in Section XIII, DISTRIBUTORS AND APPROXIMATE PRICES OF ESI CURRICULUM MATERIALS.

2 Beading of Water Columns

(4 to 5 Lessons)

SUMMARY OF ACTIVITIES The children continue to examine the flow of liquids, this time by taking a closer look at the liquid column as it falls from a bottle and breaks up. Once again they find out that varying either the hole size or choice of liquid or both has a measurable effect. (See Figure 4.) They learn to represent their data graphically and begin to appreciate the usefulness of logically ordered arrangements.

MATERIALS

For each team of two students you will need

1 bottle with 5 fitting caps
1 container for water

You will also need

water
soapy water (1% solution or about 50 cc liquid soap or detergent per gallon of water)*
construction paper (1 sheet for each child plus about 3 extra sheets to be cut into strips approximately ½″ x 30″)
transparent mending tape or paste
paper towels
newspapers (to cover desks)
soap and hot water (for cleaning up)

Suggested Procedure

If during the previous set of experiments your students observed and commented on the nature of the column of liquid as it flowed from the bottle, they will be quite ready for this new activity. If not, the following demonstrations will help direct their attention to the liquid column.

If your classroom has a sink and a water tap, ask the children to look closely at the shape of the water column coming out of the tap. Keep turning the faucet handle to change the rate of flow. (This is like changing the size of the hole.) Children

* In our trial classes, we have used a 1% solution of Lux. You might like to try other liquid soaps or detergents. We have found that Lux gives the most noticeable difference when compared with water.

comment on "breaking up," "making drops," and so forth. The place in the column where this "breaking up" or "making drops" occurs varies as the rate of flow varies — the faster the rate, the longer the unbroken column of water.

Once the children are thinking about water columns, perform the following demonstration in addition to or in place of the one described above.

Fill up one of the bottles with tap water and insert a cap with a medium-sized hole. Turn the bottle upside down and ask the children to observe the falling water column carefully. It may be necessary to repeat the procedure, but eventually someone will notice "the beading effect" which occurs just as the column of water starts to break up. (See Figure 4 on page 12 and Figure 5 at the right.)

Tell the children to close their eyes and listen. When you raise the bottle high enough for the droplets to form in the air, they should hear the sound of water splashing as it hits the container below; when you lower the bottle so that the water hits the container before the column of water has started to bead, they will no longer be able to hear it splash. This listening and watching experience will help them find the beading points of liquid columns when they begin to work by themselves.

Now ask one of the children to come up and measure the length of the unbroken column of water by tearing a strip of paper at the beading point as shown in Figure 6 below.

Ask the children whether they think the strip will be the same length for every cap size. Ask them if they can find out how the hole size might affect the length of the unbeaded column.

FIGURE 5 · The Beading Effect.

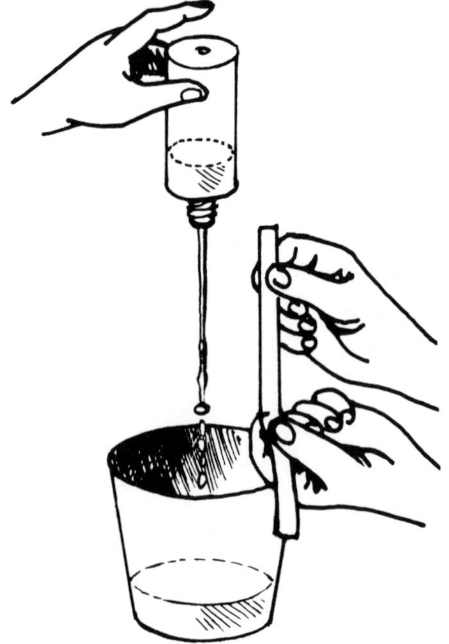

FIGURE 6

Measuring the Unbroken Column.

With the strip of paper, measure the unbroken column. Tear at beading point.

After observation and discussion of the beading effect, the children will be ready to test their ideas.

Pass out the paper strips and ask them to measure the beading points of water columns for each of the five different caps.

By looking at their strips, what can they tell you about beading? Were there any differences in the length of the five unbroken columns?

After discussing what the strips tell, ask each child to paste his collection of strips on a large piece of construction paper. (This could be done as a homework assignment.) Resist the temptation to tell the children how to do it. The more their paste-ups vary, the more useful they will be as a basis for the discussions that follow.

Select a variety of the children's paste-ups for display — some ordered and some quite random as shown in Figure 7. These can be taped to the chalkboard or to the wall.

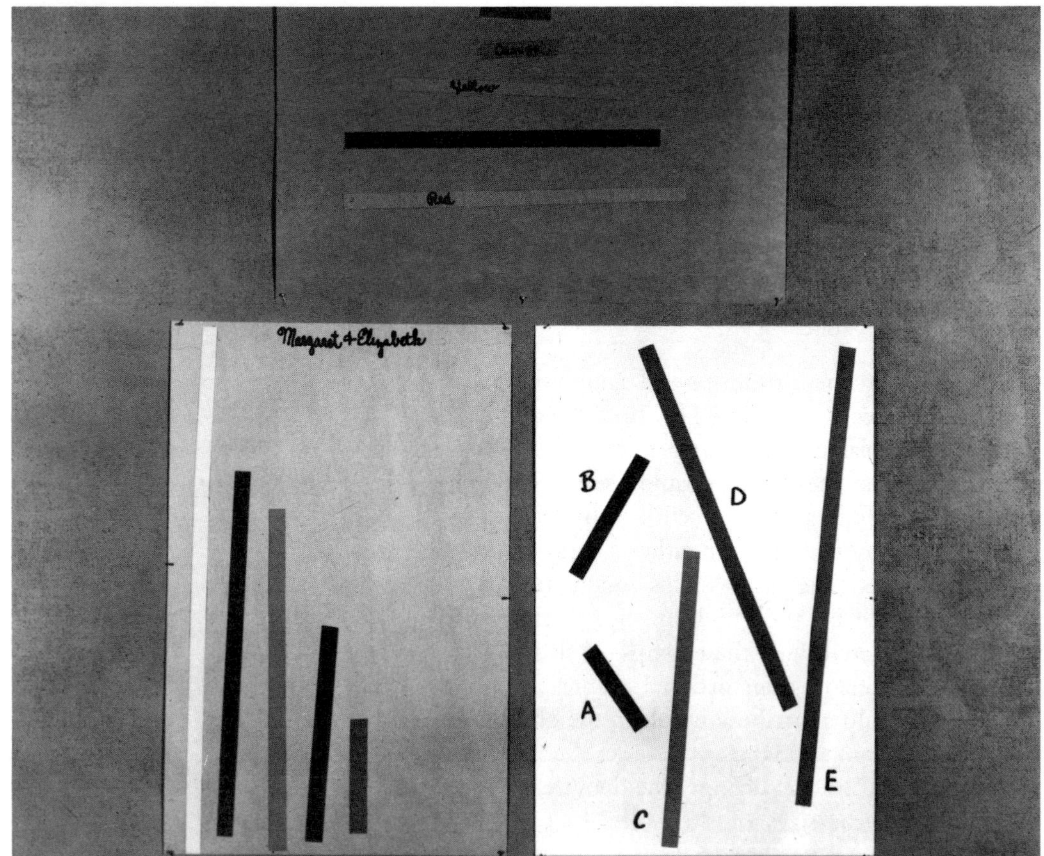

FIGURE 7 · Typical Paste-ups — Ordered and Random.

Cut a strip of construction paper somewhere in between the longest and shortest of the children's strips on display. Hold it up and tell the class that your strip came from an experiment similar to theirs. Ask if the children can tell you what the strip represents.

"It's the same as the column."
"It's as long as the solid column."
"It's the distance from the bottle to the drops."
"From the bottle to the pan."

From their answers you should be able to ascertain whether or not they really associate the length of the strip with the length of the solid (unbroken) column of water. Answers like the last one will certainly indicate that someone didn't get the idea. This kind of question-and-answer period will do much to remove any confusion.

Children often just measure the whole distance from the bottle to the catching pan including both solid and beaded portions of the column.

Now ask if by looking at the strip they can tell you which hole the solid column of water flowed through. If your strip is relatively long, they might say, "It's one of the big holes." In that case, ask the class:

"How big?"
"Is it as large as the largest hole?"
"Smaller than that?"
"How can you tell?"
"Can you tell me where on this chart I could place my strip?"
(Point to one of the unordered paste-ups on display.)

Their answer will probably be like one of the following:

"It goes anywhere."
"It doesn't go anywhere in particular."
"Put it next to the long one."

Turn to an ordered arrangement of strips and again ask where on the chart you should place your strip. This time the children should have no difficulty placing your strip between the next larger and next smaller strips. Also, they should have no trouble seeing that the size of the hole associated with your strip is in between those represented by the strips on either side of it.

Play the game again, this time using strips much longer or shorter than the strips made by the children. See if they can infer the size of hole associated with these strips. Ask them to try placing your strips on one of their ordered graphs.

This type of activity should contribute much to the children's appreciation of logically arranged data.

Next, ask your class: "Can we change the lengths of the columns without changing the sizes of the holes?"

Here are some of the answers you may get:

"Squeeze the bottle."
"Hold it higher."
"Use a different liquid."
"Add something to the water."

Each of these answers can, of course, be tested. The last two could be used to encourage the children to try soapy water, which is, in fact, the liquid used in the following activity. Ask the children whether they think soapy water columns will break up differently than plain water columns do. After they've all had their say, ask them to check their answers experimentally. They should also make a set of strips for the soapy water columns and paste them up for comparison with their strips for plain water. Hopefully, this time more of the children will arrange their strips in some order that more nearly approximates a graph.

Start a discussion about the beading points of plain and soapy water columns. Try to word your questions in a way that makes the children look at their strips for the answers.

When the children have completed experimenting with beading of liquid columns, wind up the subject with an overall discussion of their experiences and results. In our test classes we got very lively response to questions that started out with: "What do you think happened?" whereas "What happened . . . ?" drew little or no response.

In trying to explain their ideas, the children should be urged to base their statements on their own experimental experiences — to justify as well as suggest reasons. Some of the words and phrases that children use in explaining, though occasionally contradictory, are nicely descriptive.

> "Water is *grabbier*."
> "Soap *holds together* better, so there is less left over to hold to the bottle."
> "Soap is *thinner*."
> "It is more of a solid; there's more stuff in soap."
> "Soapy water is *heavier*, so it *sticks together* better."
> "Air pushes the column apart."
> "Some drops fall faster than others and so break away from the slower ones."
> "If the hole is big, the force of air breaks it immediately."
> "Water has more togetherness."

During the discussion period, the arguments presented and defended make some children think more critically about what they have done. They may wish to return to the materials and do the experiments over. Whether to prove a point or test a new idea, by all means let them try the experiments again. If you are reluctant because of the time, remember that sometimes *slower is faster*. What we mean is that it might be more important to explore in depth and encourage self-improvement in one area than to finish every chapter in the entire unit.

If you plan to use the film loop, *Beading of a Water Column*, we recommend that you show it at this point after the children have had several days of observing and talking about what they've seen and done.

If time and fortitude hold out, experiments could also be performed with both alcohol and cooking oil. These can be done by the children or by you as a demonstration. Some students may want to try other liquids at home. Welcome this, by all means. It would be particularly useful for those who did not keep records or for those who were confused during the classroom activities.

We recommend that you not provide the children with thick dense liquids such as molasses until after completing Chapter 4. (See experiment 8 on page 39.)

Some of your more knowledgeable students (especially those with knowledgeable parents) may come up with words like "surface tension," "molecules," and similar technical terms. Since, at this age, these probably represent glibness rather than comprehension, we recommend avoiding the definitive scientific word. Too often it is the clincher in a child's mind; that is, the "right" answer given in the "right" words often blocks off the process of observing, thinking, and predicting. The natural vocabulary leads to better expression and far greater understanding.

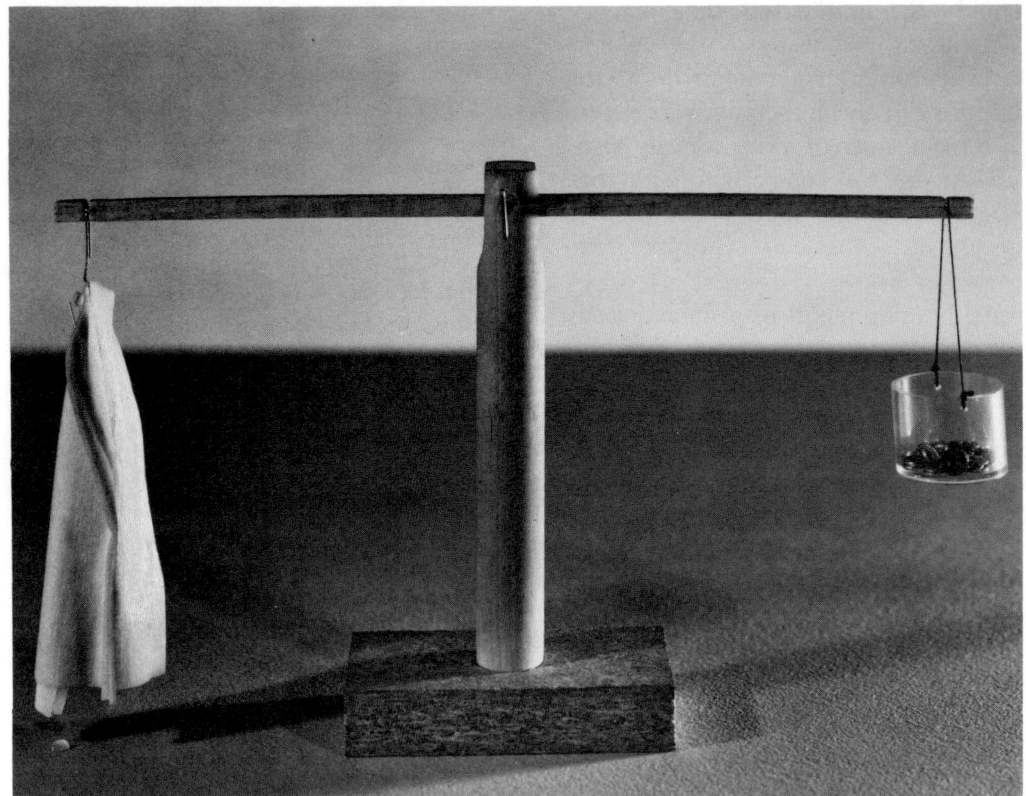

1. Wet towel on balance.

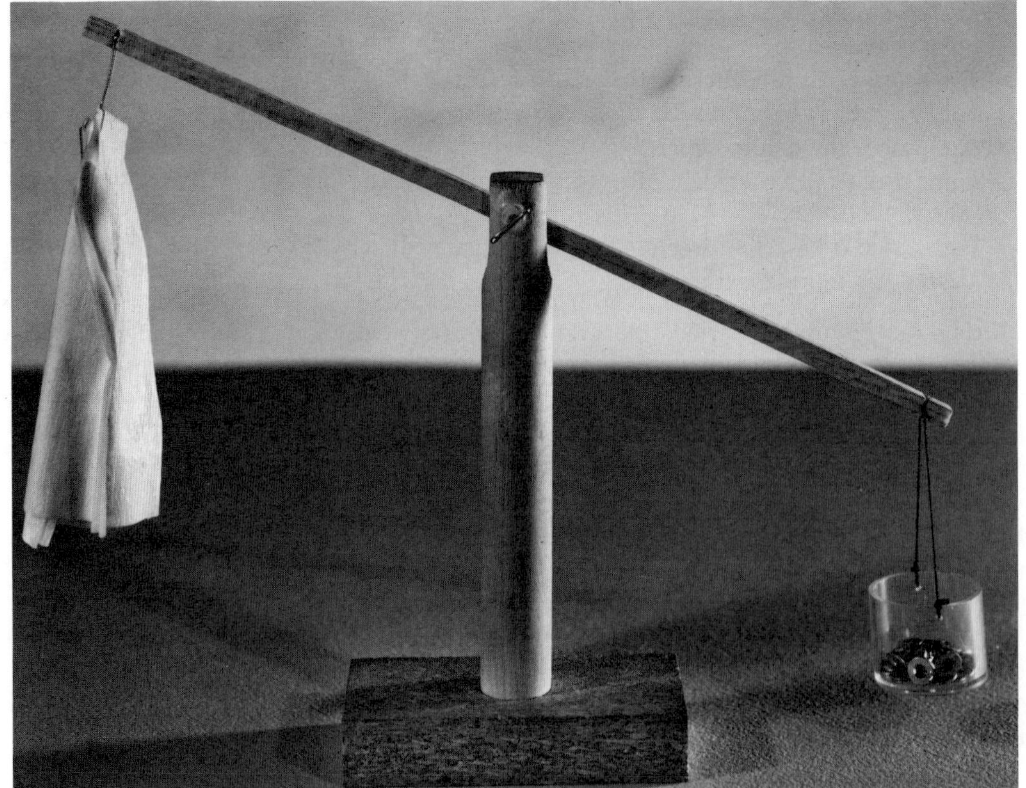

2. Why did the towel get lighter?

FIGURE 25 · Weighing a Wet Towel.

A special kit to perform the experiments in this section is available from Robert Bentley, Inc. For full particulars, see page 285 in Section XIII, DISTRIBUTORS AND APPROXIMATE PRICES OF ESI CURRICULUM MATERIALS.

Absorption and Evaporation

(6 to 12 Lessons)

SUMMARY OF ACTIVITIES The children perform several experiments involving absorption and evaporation of different liquids in different materials to reveal still another aspect of *grabbiness* — cohesive and adhesive forces at work. In the process, they become aware of the need to design experiments with only one variable (changing factor), and, by observing that opposite forces acting simultaneously tend to nullify each other, they begin to develop an understanding of the *state of equilibrium*. The list of materials below contains all the materials you will need to do all the experiments in this chapter. How many of these will be needed and when you will need them will depend on the sequence developed in your class.

MATERIALS

For each team of two students you will need

- a balance
- washers
- blotter paper (cut in strips about 2 cm wide)
- blotter paper (cut in strips ranging in size from ¼ cm to 4 or 5 cm; we recommend you cut the narrower strips yourself since children find it difficult to cut strips of less than one centimeter)
- polyethylene tubing (waxed paper, plastic wrap, or some such transparent material could be substituted)
- drilled plastic capillary block

You will also need

- paper towels (preferably light in color)
- paper clips
- cloth (various types; could be brought in by the children)
- plastic bags or glass jars
- milk containers (cut the long way, or long plastic dishes; the milk containers may be lined with plastic bags or wrap for holding soapy water and oil)
- glass plates (optional)
- water
- soapy water
- rubber bands
- cooking oil
- food coloring
- alcohol
- microscopes (hand lenses or a microprojector may be used instead)
- thin piece of wood

(list continued on next page)

thin wire
rulers
paper cutter or shears
transparent mending tape
a fan (optional)

Suggested Procedure

1. *How much water can a paper towel absorb?* Throughout this unit (as many times in their daily lives), the children have used paper towels to soak up water they spilled. Leading into this experiment, therefore, can be a very natural process of asking, "How do you think a paper towel works?"

The usual response is, "It absorbs water." If you ask them, "What do you mean by *absorb*?" they will probably substitute synonyms such as "takes up," "soaks up," and "picks up." That is, they can tell you *what* it does, but not *how* it does it. However, they *can* think of a way to find out *how much* a paper towel absorbs, and usually do: "Weigh a dry towel; soak it in water; weigh it again."

To prepare the balance for weighing, bend a paper clip into a hook and hang it from the notch at one end of the balance beam. Then, hang a folded paper towel from the hook as shown in Worksheet 4. To determine its weight, add washers to the opposite balance pan until the beam balances. Once this technique is learned, the children will have no trouble weighing dry and wet towels and comparing the two results.

Another activity which children frequently become engaged in is the use of paper towels as siphons. They may find that if they leave a paper towel hanging over the edge of a container of water, the water will move out of the container through the paper towel. Children enjoy transferring water from one container to another by means of their paper towel siphons.

2. *Why do wet towels get lighter?* If in the last experiment the wet towels were left hanging from the balance, the children might have noticed that after a while the towels got lighter. In case this doesn't happen, you could bring the effect to the attention of the class by setting up the demonstration in advance as shown in Figure 25 on page 48.

When the children observe this "getting lighter" effect, they will probably say, "It's because the water evaporates." Ask them, "What do you mean, *evaporates*?" A common response is, "It goes off into the air."

Ask them if they can think of ways to keep the water from evaporating or of ways to make it evaporate faster. To prevent evaporation, they often suggest, "Put the wet towel in a glass jar," or "Put it in a plastic bag." To speed evaporation, they might think of opening up the folded towel, thereby exposing more surface area to the air. (If they do, be sure the towel remains spread out during the weighing experiment; a thin wire could be threaded along one edge before hanging the towel on the balance.) Other common suggestions are: "Use a fan" and

A Way to Find Out How Much Water a Paper Towel Can Absorb

KITCHEN PHYSICS · WORKSHEET 4

NAME

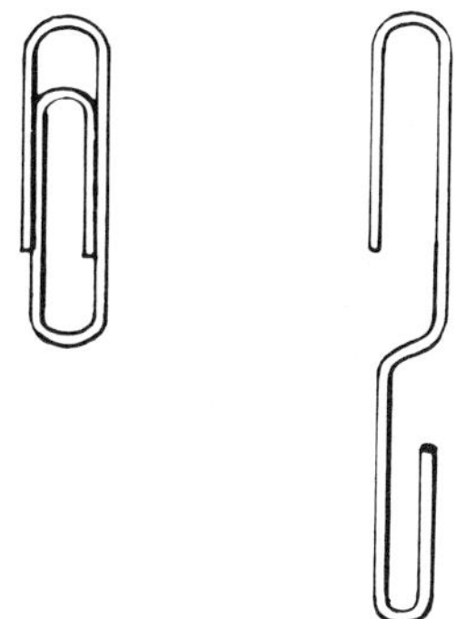

1. Straighten out paper clip.

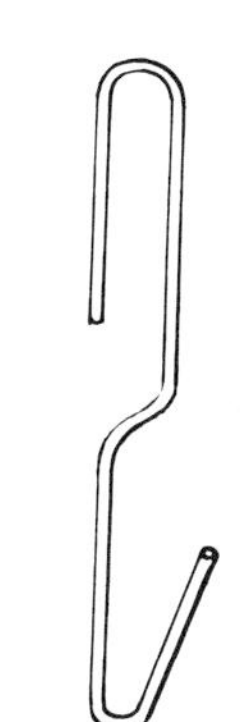

2. Twist narrower loop out to form hook.

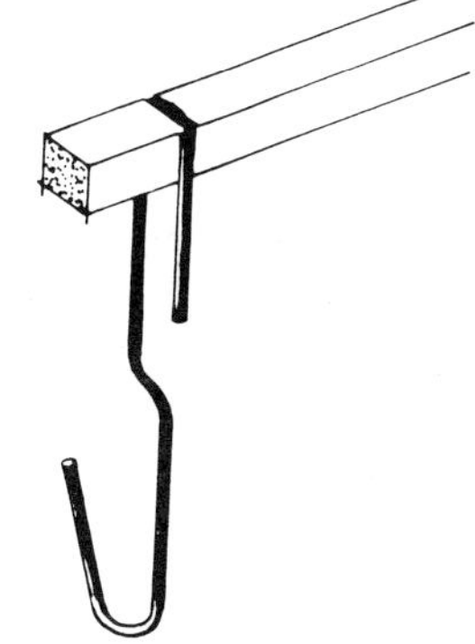

3. Hang the hook you have made on one end of the balance.

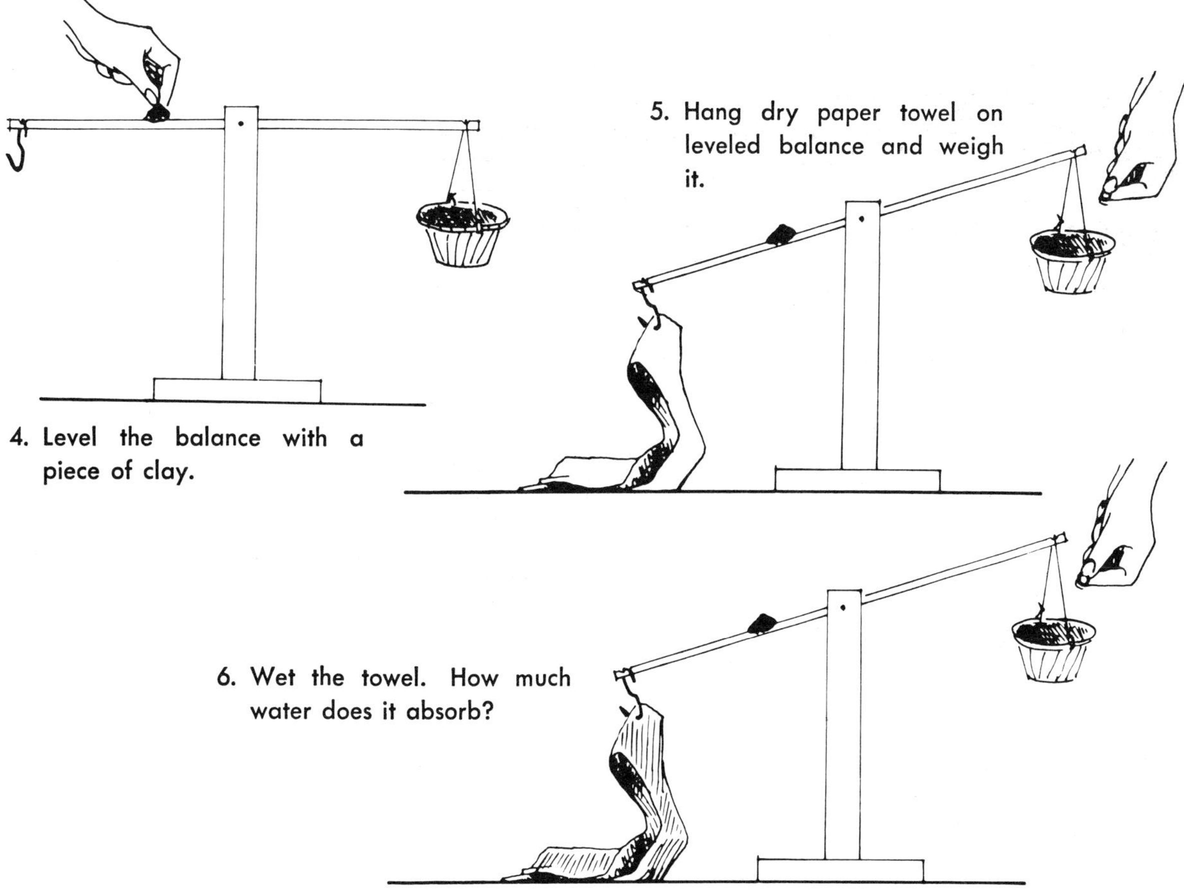

4. Level the balance with a piece of clay.

5. Hang dry paper towel on leveled balance and weigh it.

6. Wet the towel. How much water does it absorb?

"Place it near a radiator or some other place where there is warm air."

Before they test their various methods, some standard time interval should be established. Some which the children might suggest are:

"Find out how much weight each of the towels loses in 20 minutes."
"Find out how long it takes for each towel to return to its dry weight."
"Find out how long before each of the towels feels dry."

This last suggestion, although not quantitative, usually has more meaning to the children than the others.

When they have completed their activities and collected the data, discuss the results of each method tried and encourage the children to explain why their techniques either increased or decreased the rate of evaporation.

Did their methods make wet towels evaporate faster or slower than the folded wet towel evaporated?

With older children who wish to investigate the rate of evaporation, you might ask them to make a graph of their data.

3. *How fast is water absorbed?* You can find out how fast water is absorbed by suspending a dry towel from the balance, dipping the lower end into a container of water, and noting the number of washers that have to be added each minute to keep the balance beam level. (See Figure 26.)

When the children try this experiment they should find out that the amount of water absorbed per minute decreases with time.

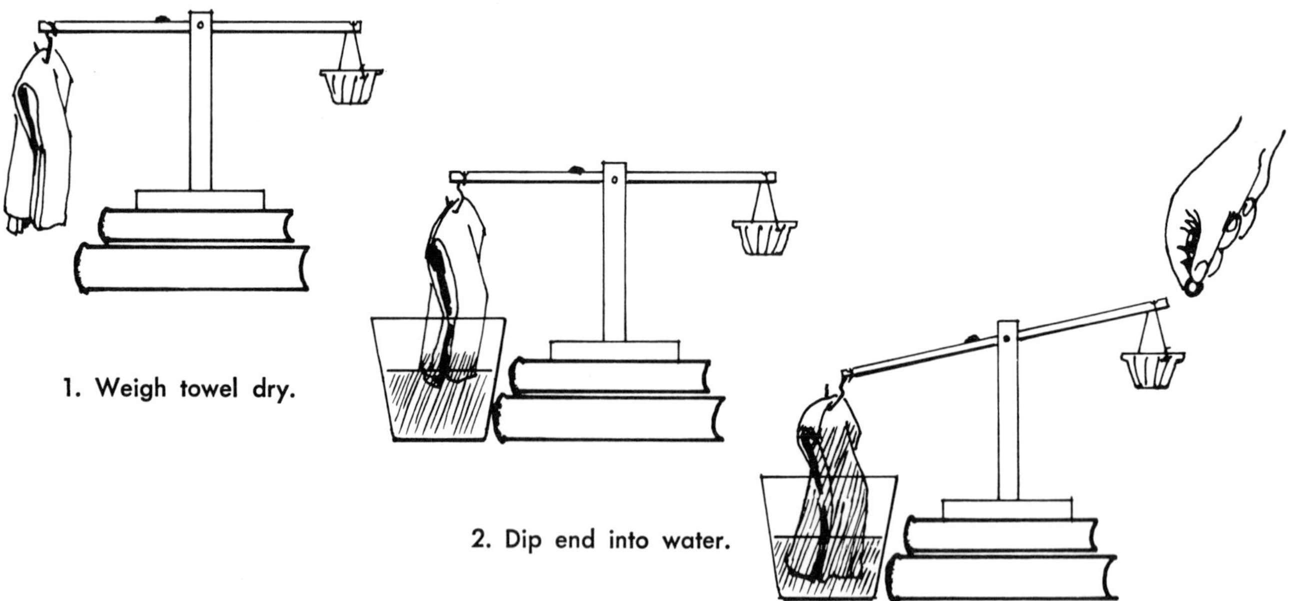

1. Weigh towel dry.

2. Dip end into water.

3. Add washers periodically to keep beam level.

FIGURE 26

How Fast Is Water Absorbed by a Towel?

Students might be encouraged to make a graph of their results, plotting weight against time as shown in Figure 27. From such graphs, they should be able to answer questions of this type:

"When does it absorb water fastest?"
"When does water seem to stop going in?"

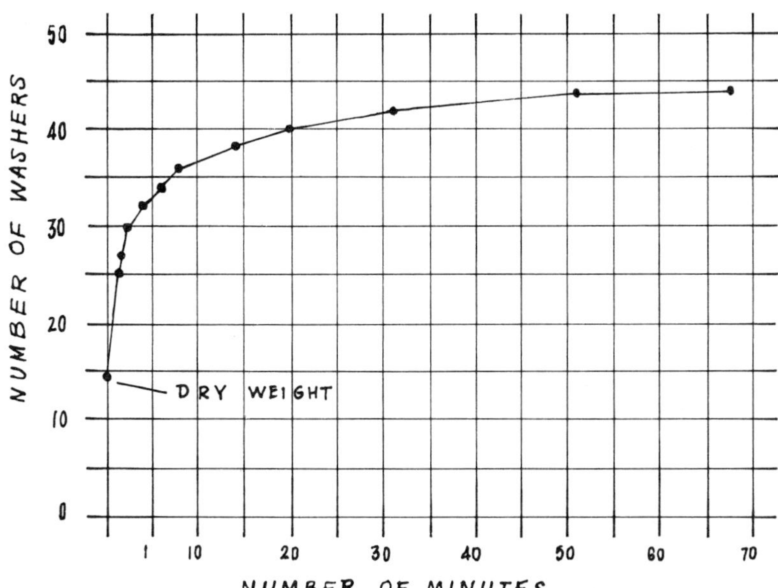

FIGURE 27

Graph of Weight of Water Absorbed by Paper Towel vs. Time.

4. Do other materials absorb water? The children could be asked to bring from home a variety of materials — cloth, sponges, fiber glass, blotters, and so forth — to help them find out which are good absorbers.

Some children may already have noticed how the wetness moved up in the paper towels dipped in a pan of water. Ask the children whether they think water will rise to the same height in the strips of different materials. After they have offered and discussed their predictions, let them test their ideas experimentally.

The strips of material can be prepared by the students. The tops of the strips can be taped to a wall (or to the side of a chair, table, desk, or anything like that) and suspended side by side. The bottom ends should rest in a container of colored water. (This will help the children see the effect much better.)

When they complete this activity, encourage them to discuss their results and to talk about any difficulties they encountered in performing the experiment or in interpreting the results.

If in the course of discussion someone raises the question of what difference the width of a strip makes in how much water is absorbed, you could suggest postponing the discussion until the class has tried the experiment on the rise of water in blotter

This discussion should lead to the realization that it is almost impossible to find out the relative amount of water absorbed by the different materials because of the many variables involved — the density of the materials, the size, the different degrees of attraction between the materials and the water, and so on.

strips, presented later in the chapter, or you might skip parts 5 and 6 and move to part 7 where this experiment is done. You can return to parts 5 and 6 later or omit them.

5. Do other liquids rise up in the same way as water? Borrowing from their earlier experiences in this unit, some students may suggest trying different liquids to see if they all are absorbed in the same way.

Before they attempt this activity, they should be reminded of the difficulties they encountered doing the previous experiment (4). They should realize (or be helped to realize) that if they use different materials as well as different liquids, they will not be able to tell whether their results are due to the liquid or to the material.

When they understand this problem clearly, they will probably suggest that only one kind of absorbing material be used in testing the effect of different liquids. If they don't, make the recommendation yourself.

Bring out as many blotter paper strips (about 2 cm wide) as you have liquids to test. Pour the different liquids into separate containers and put a blotter strip in each as shown in Figure 28.

To improve visibility, food coloring may be added to all the liquids except cooking oil.

FIGURE 28

Four Blotter Strips in Different Liquids.

The results should surprise them. Because oil does not evaporate appreciably, it will rise higher than expected, while the reverse is true of alcohol. Also, some students should infer that the grabbiness of the liquids is a factor in absorption because, to some extent, the results of this experiment correlate with the results obtained in the earlier activities, namely beading, heaping, and tensiometer measurements.

Some students might suggest that thick (viscous) liquids, like oil,will take longer to rise up the strips, just as they took longer to flow out the bottles. Let them watch for this if they are interested.

6. Fibers and narrow tubes. If either microscopes or hand lenses or a microprojector are available, the children could examine the structure of torn edges of cloth, paper, and blotters very closely. But even with the naked eye, it should be evident to them that all these materials are made up of tiny, closely packed fibers. Could this explain why all these materials absorb liquids? The children might like to use the microscope to watch the colored water rise between the fibers.

Give each team of two students a drilled plastic capillary block and some colored water in a shallow pan. Using this equipment, let them explore their materials in their own way until they have made some pertinent observations.

Usually the children will associate the rise of water in the tubes of the capillary block with the rise of liquid in the closely packed fibers of the absorbing material. Among the things they might notice is that the narrower the tube, the higher the water rises. (See Figure 29.)

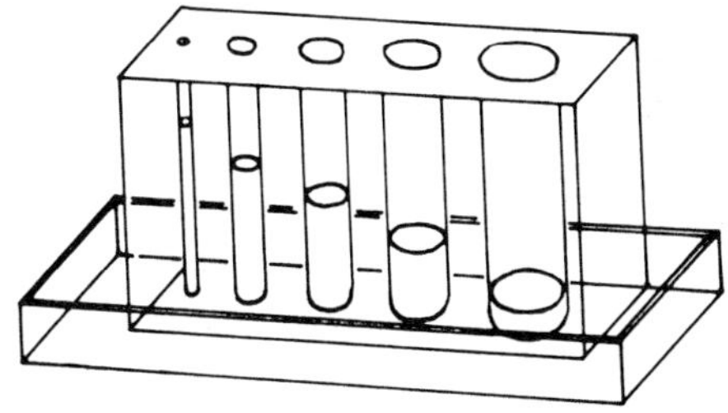

FIGURE 29

Drilled Plastic Capillary Block in Colored Water.

For an explanation of the relationship of height of water rise to width of tube, see page 60.

Some children think that the volume of water which rises up each tube is the same. You may want to investigate this question with them. See Background Information, pages 59–61, for a treatment of this subject.

Someone will undoubtedly ask, "Why does water rise up into narrow spaces?" In discussing this question, someone might come up with a reasonable explanation somewhat like this one presented in one of our trial classes:

"The water is attracted to the tube and so it climbs up the tube; but the water holds together, so the climbing water hangs onto the other water (not in contact with the tube) and pulls it along up the tube."

If the children are not able to suggest an explanation at this time, you might try again after they have placed the tubes in different liquids.

> *Again, it is essential that the tubes be clean. The tubes can be rinsed under a faucet, and the water that clings to the tubes can be blown out by moving your mouth along the capillary block "harmonica fashion." Because of the difficulty in cleaning, it is probably best not to use these blocks in cooking oil.*

Some children may want to try different liquids with their capillary blocks. Perhaps they can already predict that water will rise higher than other liquids. In any case, the experiment should help them explain the rise of liquids in small tubes, since they will observe that the liquids that hold together best are the ones that rise the highest.

An eighth grade student and Akindele O. Osiyale, from the Ijebu-Ode Grammar School, Ijebu-Ode, Nigeria, investigating shadows.

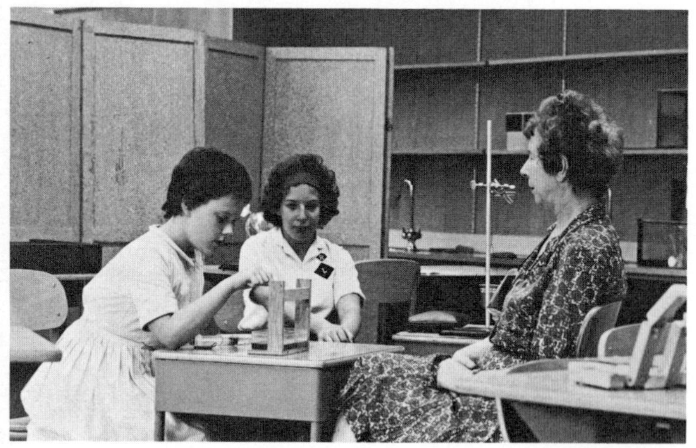

Children making airs visible in the Young Explorers Center with Dr. Alma Wittlin of the Radcliffe Institute for Independent Study, Cambridge, Massachusetts, and formerly an E.S.S. staff member.

Miss Kumiko Ishida, a kindergarten teacher at Lawrence School, San Mateo, California, and a visitor to the conference, watching kindergarten children using structural mathematics materials.

A lizard (dipsosaurus by name).

Miss Emily Richard , Elementary Science Study staff member, working with children in preparation of the butterfly unit.

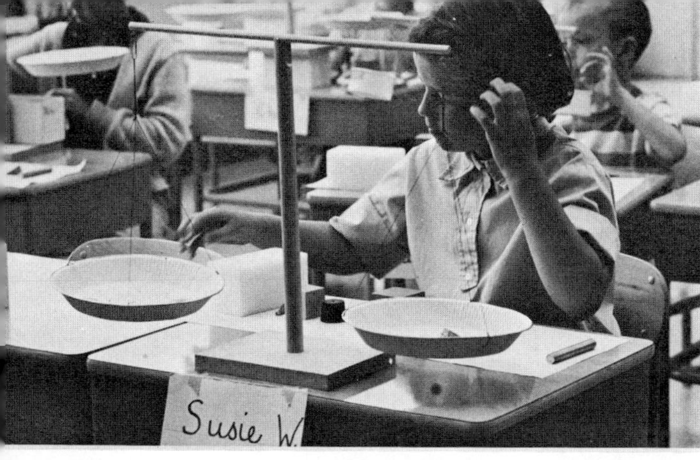

Which is heavier? Second graders using pan balances in Playground Physics.

The fourth grade discussing molds with Professor William Weston, Professor of Biology, Emeritus, at Harvard University. Professor Weston is an Elementary Science Study staff member.

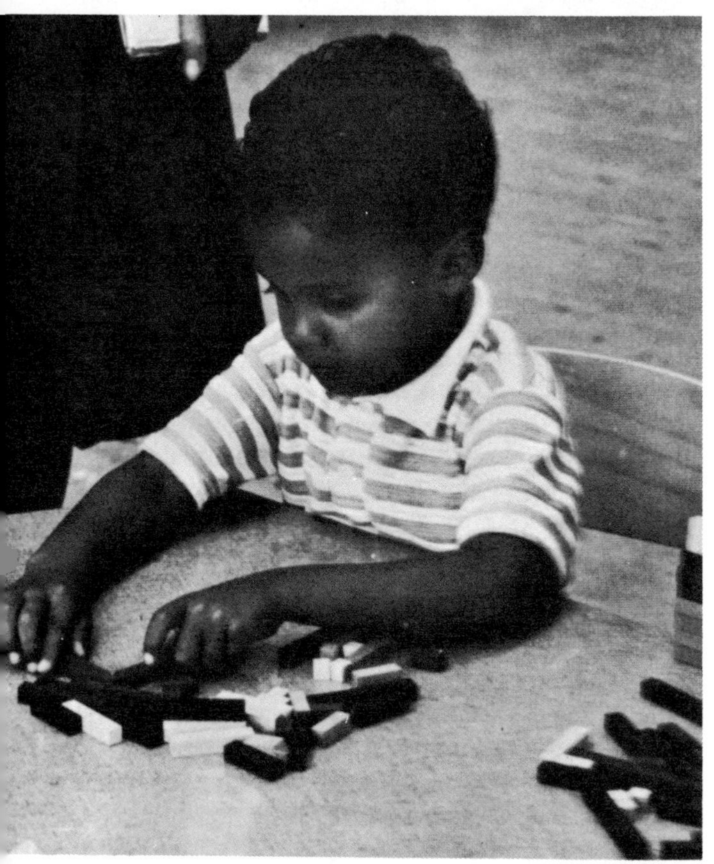

Kindergarten child using structural mathematics materials.

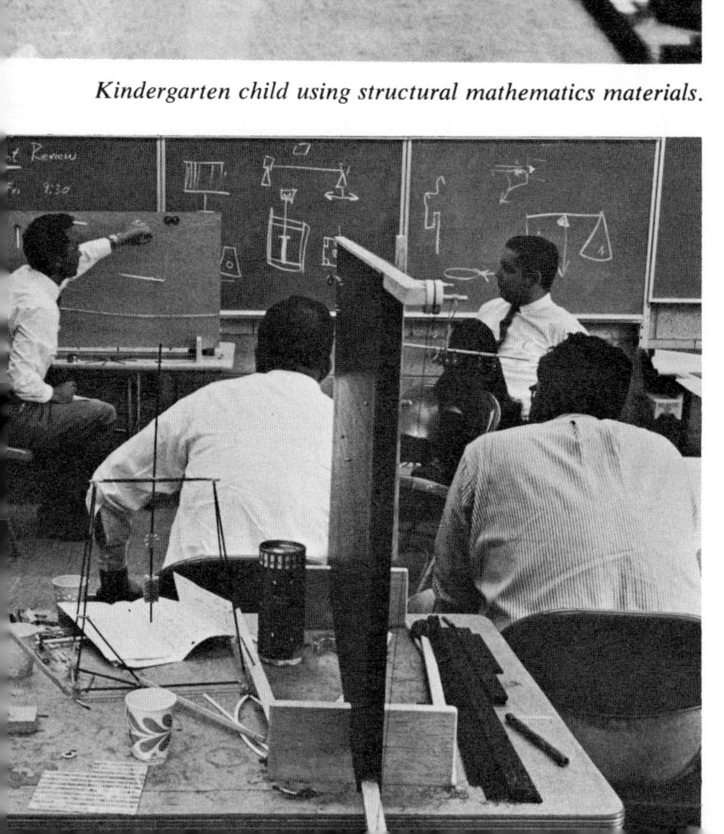

Structures group engaged in development work with (left) William Hull, Elementary Science Study staff member, and (right) Neil Mitchell, Professor of Architecture at Harvard University, Cambridge, Massachusetts.

III

SCIENCE IN THE JUNIOR HIGH SCHOOL

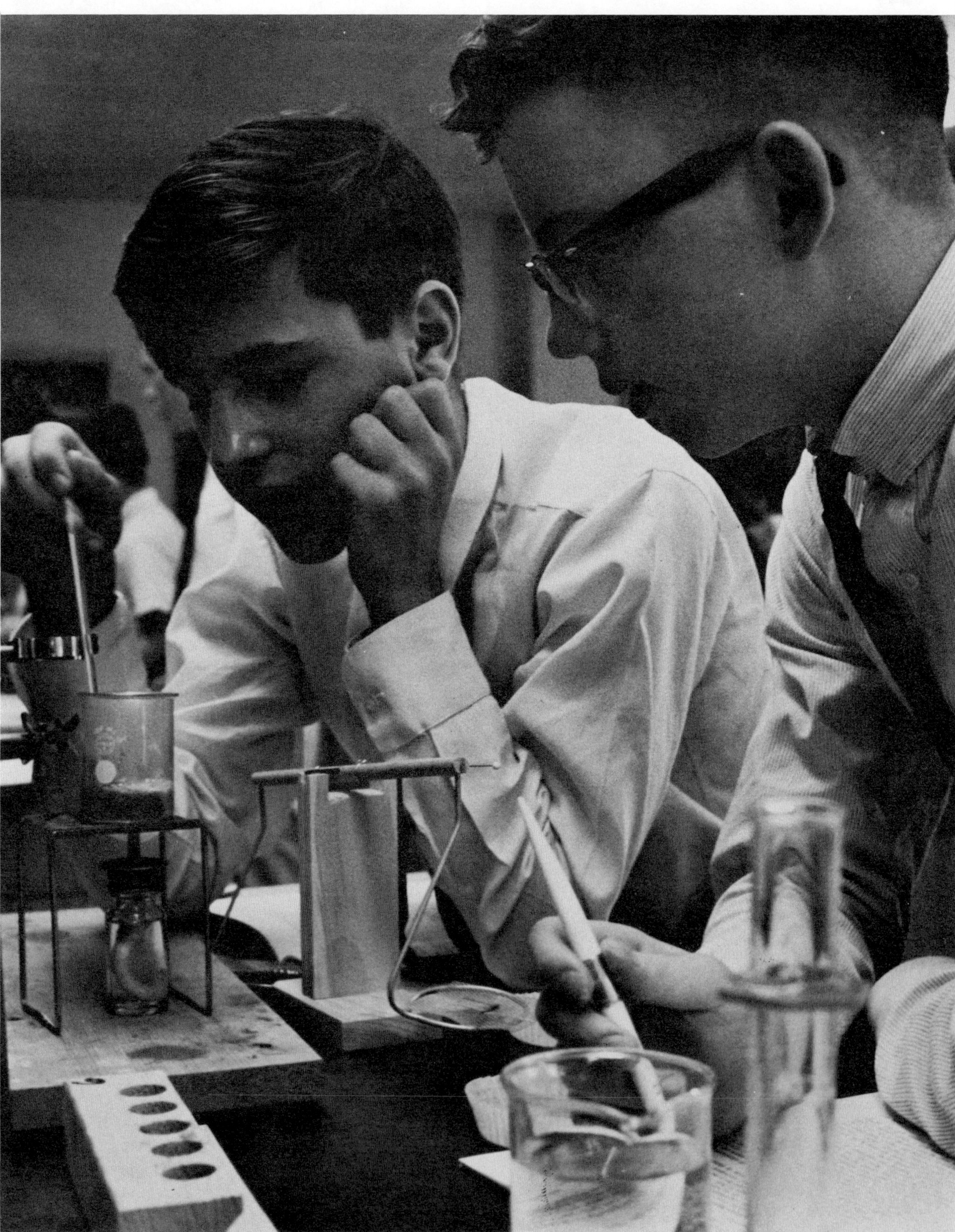

OBJECTIVES AND CONTENT OF THE INTRODUCTORY PHYSICAL SCIENCE COURSE

by Uri Haber-Schaim

There has been considerable progress in recent years in the teaching of physics, chemistry, and biology in the secondary schools. The Physical Science Study Committee course in physics, the Chemical Bond Approach and Chemical Education Material Study in chemistry, and the Biological Sciences Curriculum Study in biology are well known. But these courses do not exhaust the field of science instruction at the pre-university level. Some science is usually taught in grades 7, 8, and 9 in the junior high school, often in all three grades. By providing new course material for the last three years of high school, we increased the contrast between those years and grades 7, 8, and 9.

The question is: What can one do, or what should one do, to extend the gains achieved in the upper grades to the lower ones? What should be the content, what should be the emphasis, and what, primarily, should be the purpose of science instruction in those years? There are certainly more than one answer to these questions. Here we have confined our attention to a one-year course in physical science, aimed primarily at the ninth grade.

It is worth while to recall briefly the main questions which we asked at the very beginning of the PSSC physics course development. We asked: What is the objective of the course? What do we want to achieve? What is the purpose? What are the values we want to get across? From the answers to these questions we constructed an outline of what the content should be and how it should be taught. The chemists and biologists did likewise in planning their programs. In planning the present course for junior high school we had before us the work of PSSC in physics, of BSCS in biology, and of CBA and CHEMS in chemistry, so the matter of aims was not an entirely independent question any more.

The greatest handicap faced by science teachers in the new curricula is that most students in senior high school have no experience in observations, no basic laboratory skills, no knowledge of how to apply elementary mathematics to experimental results; they also lack the ability to correlate an abstract idea with a concrete situation. Often they have no idea of orders of magnitude, no feeling for approximation, no ability to judge what is important and what is not.

Often their earlier training has given students the idea that science is remote from real life and from anything they can do. The standard phrase in many textbooks is that "scientists have found such and such," and "scientists do so and so," and the student is requested just to memorize it. Science in many books means primarily vocabulary. All too often, important words are printed in heavy type and the student is asked to remember them. In science, however, words can have meaning only as they are associated with an action or an operation.

Students need time to digest knowledge. From the very first, PSSC physics teachers kept saying that if only we could get into the earlier grades some of the basic ideas and skills which are needed so badly in PSSC, it would make the

Dr. Haber-Schaim is the Director of the Introductory Physical Science Program as well as of the Physical Science Study Committee.
This article is adapted from a lecture given at Florida State University, Tallahassee, Florida.

course much easier to teach and give the students much more time to digest the materials. And so, out of requests from teachers in the field came the call to start something to serve as a common foundation for the later courses in the senior high schools. This means not only a foundation of subject matter, but also an attitude of inquiry coupled with experimental and mathematical skills.

Physics and chemistry are elective subjects, and a fair fraction of the school population takes tenth grade biology as its last course in science; some students have no science at all in senior high school. Unfortunately, many can even get through college with no additional science, and will be ill equipped to understand a world dominated by the terminology and implications of science and technology. Therefore, our new course must also serve as a terminal course in physical science for many students, as well as provide a foundation for further work.

Thus we must have a program to serve two purposes: on the one hand to be a sound foundation for future physics, chemistry, and perhaps biology courses; and on the other hand to furnish sufficient nourishment in the essence, the spirit, and the substance of physical science to be a good terminal course for those who will not study physical science later on.

We believe that there are certain values and skills that can and should be taught in junior high school science. First, we want to give a feeling for the kind of human effort that is involved in the development of science. We want to put across the point that the root of all science is phenomena and that the names come later. We should like the student to get his information from the original source, from nature itself. This calls for real investigation in the laboratory. But science is not all laboratory work. We have to correlate and generalize our observations. We have to construct models or theories which can be manipulated logically and which will raise new questions. Later we do other experiments to seek the answers to these questions.

This poses many technical problems in constructing such a course. It is hard to design an experiment which, when handled by ten young fingers, will come out the way you think it should. Following a schematic drawing in a textbook is not enough.

Time is always an important limiting factor in the laboratory, and this may make it hard to draw valid conclusions from the limited data available. This difficulty can often be relieved by combining the data of all the students and putting it on the board. Here is a good opportunity to teach the handling of errors. When students compare their measurements, they see the errors and learn how to decide which results are significantly different and which are within the experimental errors. We can save time by not asking all students to do exactly the same experiment. For example, in connection with the idea of boiling point, all the students boil water, but each uses a different quantity and some unknowingly get water with various amounts of salt dissolved in it. Each student gets a different graph of temperature versus time, and all of these are placed on the board. We thus have enough information to discuss whether the boiling point depends on the quantity of water or whether there are other significant differences.

Content of the Course

In selecting the topics, we used the same criteria as we did in the construction of the PSSC. That is, we asked: How much does the student benefit by learning this? How useful is it later in the development of the story? We feel that a topic that appears in our outline only once should not appear at all; it has no "mileage," and we can do very well without it.

No particular set of prerequisites was assumed in the students except some general familiarity with our technological society. In other words, we assumed that the students had seen common household instruments and objects. For example, we assumed they would know what a thermometer is, but there is a great difference between that and assuming that they had heard about atoms. The student can hold the thermometer in his hand and see the liquid rise when he puts his thumb on the bulb. The atom is another story; he has never seen one, and we must not rely on things with which he has no association or experience.

We have chosen as a central theme of this course the introductory study of matter. If we look around us we see a bewildering variety of matter; we can try to bring order into this seem-

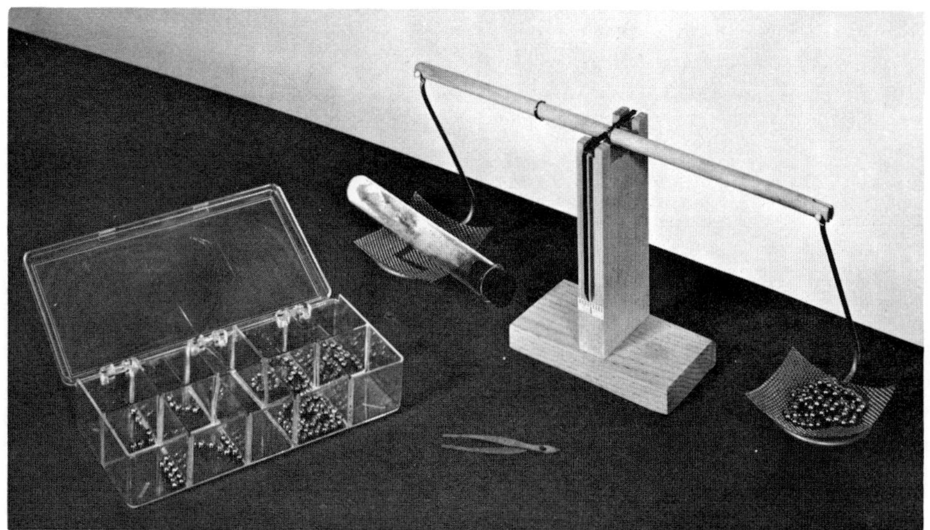

The equal-arm balance designed for the IPS laboratory. Note the box containing bead weights in various amounts.

ing chaos by breaking up the many kinds of matter into simpler components, and then combining these components into a pattern. If we cannot build a pattern, then we can only catalogue things as a collector catalogues stamps.

Characteristic Properties

Scientific inquiry begins when we do things on purpose instead of just compiling our experience as it comes. When we look outdoors, we see different kinds of leaves of different colors and different sizes; we see stones; we see trees. We know that these things are different, because we have touched them many times, held them in our hands, broken them. This is all fine, but then we meet up with two things which on first sight look the same. We ask: Are these two objects the same, or are they not? Then we have to do things to them deliberately in order to find out. To the person working in the field, it is obvious that you do the same thing to both, and you see whether they react the same. Yet, strangely enough, this basic concept — the idea of doing the same thing to two samples to see if they react the same way — is completely missing from most texts.

Perhaps even more fundamental than the idea of differences between substances is the idea of quantity. It is essential to be able to say "how much" without regard to what particular thing we have. How can we compare an amount of chalk with an amount of paper, and an amount of gas or air with an amount of water? The answer lies in the balance: we say that two amounts of matter are the same when they are in equilibrium on the equal-arm balance. We call this property "mass," without elaborating further. The next step is to look for properties which are independent of the amount and the shape and other conditions. We must show first that there are indeed such characteristic properties that do specify a substance as distinguished from other substances.

There is a large variety of characteristic properties to choose from, and we cannot discuss all of them; we choose those which can be used to separate substances from one another. Density is one: some things will float in water; others will sink. Solubility is another: some things will dissolve readily; others will not. Boiling point is another: one can separate substances by fractional distillation.

There is another consideration which influences the choice of characteristic properties; this is their usefulness in building a model or theory of matter. We need properties which can be combined to give us a unified picture of matter. In this context the similarity in the behavior of gases and the diversity in the behavior of liquids and solids is very significant.

Apparatus for collecting gas from the distillation of wood. The basic laboratory setup is a sheet of peg board supported by a heavy base; the smaller pieces of apparatus are held by clips bolted to the peg board. This makes an inexpensive and compact arrangement which can be used on an ordinary desk and eliminates the need for much specialized hardware.

Mixtures, Pure Substances, and Elements

The course proceeds to the separation of mixtures. We use all these characteristic properties to break up what we find in front of us into as many components as we can. We use the available tools quite indiscriminately, and we remind our students that men used these tools long before they knew there were such things as physics and chemistry. For example, people knew about grain alcohol for several thousand years and used it as a solvent, without any chemical theory. We also are going to use it as a solvent, without asking what happens or why. The fact is that if I put one substance into alcohol, it dissolves; some other substance does not. Here I have a way of separating substances.

From the separation of mixtures we get the idea of a pure substance; we define it by certain rules of the game. We start with something; we heat it and freeze it and dissolve it and filter it. We keep doing all kinds of things to it, and we keep getting back the same substance; the material does not separate into two components which react differently. We say that this is a pure substance. With these rules we define pure substances and we see that, unlike the mixtures, they have definite characteristic properties.

Here the rules of the game are applied in practice and in our text: You get something. You try to break it up into components by whatever techniques you have developed. (Other techniques, which are beyond the reach of the student laboratory, are described in the textbook.) Then you measure the characteristic properties of your sample of matter and you check them against a table of data. If there is such a combination of properties tabulated, it has a name, and you say, "Aha, I have so-and-so." And if it does not have a name, you may call it whatever you wish.

Now we add to our arsenal. Instead of just distilling and freezing and crystallizing and so on, we permit a wider range of tools, such as heating with charcoal and boiling in hydrochloric acid to break up those few substances which would not break up under the previous treatment. This is how we get to the idea of elements, by way of an operational definition. Elements are those things that do not break up into simpler components, even when they are put in acids or heated or subjected to electric currents, or treated in certain other ways.

An experiment to demonstrate radioactivity, as a step toward the atomic model of matter. Samples of six different substances in small plastic boxes are placed on a photographic film enclosed in black paper. After three days some parts of the film are found to show effects like that in the photograph at the right.

Radioactivity

Ultimately, we want to get an atomic picture of matter. But if we are really honest and do not just rely on our beliefs, we find very little to suggest atoms in anything which we have described here. When you pour water, it looks continuous; if you look at crystals of salt, the crystals are big; they dissolve, and there are no more crystals, and the resulting liquid looks continuous. We need something to give us some hint, some real indication that there is a discreteness in all matter.

We have chosen a path through radioactivity to the atomic picture, because radioactivity is one area where discreteness is very much in the foreground. Anybody who has ever heard a Geiger counter click knows what I mean by discreteness. Discreteness is apparent in the grains of a photographic film exposed to radioactivity. Even though the intensity of the radiation may vary, the grains are always the same size (with the same kind of film). The tracks in a cloud chamber also give a strong impression of discreteness.

Now you may say this is just radioactivity, a special phenomenon; where does matter come in? Matter comes in because, after many clicks, you find that you have collected a quantity of a new element.

Previously, the word "atom" has nowhere appeared, but now we offer the suggestion that all matter may be made up of particles. We say that we can count individual particles, and if we count long enough we can see a measureable amount of gas. Incidentally, we plan to do this experiment by brute force on film, using a large

Apparatus for measuring the thermal expansion of a long tube. As the tube expands, it moves over a needle which rolls on a glass microscope slide. Attached to the needle is a soda-straw pointer which amplifies the motion by sweeping a large arc on a scale.

amount of radioactivity, a kilocurie. You will see the spectra of the resulting gas and see that it is helium.

The Atomic Model

Now we come to the second part of the course, where we theorize and make a model. We reexamine what we have done before, but now we begin to do some abstraction. We start slowly, building up as we go — which is the way that science works, in fact. The first idea we propose is that there are particles; these are probably very small, because we never notice them in daily life. The minute we make such a statement to the youngsters, we have accepted an obligation to say how many and how small; otherwise it is a meaningless statement.

We say that the atoms are very small things which are different for each element, and that in chemical combination they are grouped together in molecules. This very simple picture already correlates a great deal of information which we have gathered in this course. It explains how we can get an element back out of a chemical combination; all chemical reactions are, in this language, a regrouping of existing things. It makes sense that the total mass remains constant in reactions if we believe that atoms only change positions or change their combinations. Each pure substance, each compound, always has the same composition because we always take so many of one kind of atom and combine it with so many of another kind.

So far we have used only the discreteness, but now we can see also that there are more properties than that. We recall that there are some solids which have high density and are very hard to compress. Apparently these atoms act like hard objects touching each other. Gases are very easy to compress and have a low density. Apparently these atoms are far apart, so the low density and the compressibility also fall in line and make a sensible pattern. With oleic acid we can find the thickness of a monolayer and thus get Avogadro's number. So far, out atoms are static, they have a certain size and are a certain distance apart.

The Kinetic Picture of Heat

Now we come to the next phase, where we let the atoms move. Everybody knows that if you open a bottle of gas, the gas will come out; this leads to the idea of molecular motion, and to the molecular picture of heat. We have been using heat all along, but now we want to relate the thermal properties to the atomic picture just as we did the chemical properties. We start the discussion of heat and the gas model of heat without any detailed laws of mechanics, but we make use of analogy. We theorize a molecular picture of two very basic concepts in physics, the temperature and the quantity of heat (which are confused no end by students). We move from the gas into the solid and get the idea that hot molecules and atoms move faster than cold. We say that if things collide, the fast ones slow down and the slow ones speed up; that if you heat something it becomes warmer, because you make its molecules move faster; and so on. This brings us to the ideas of thermal energy, where we find a common denominator for all forms of energy. We can always convert any form of energy into thermal energy, but not vice versa.

We plan to have these last chapters (they are still being developed) end with some general idea of potential energy: the idea that energy can be stored in different forms, such as chemical, mechanical, etc.

In summary, we believe that this course will greatly facilitate the teaching of physics and chemistry: several chapters of chemistry can be eliminated and much of the first half of PSSC will not be needed. But, most important, we believe that pupils will enter physics and chemistry with an improved orientation and attitude toward science, and that they will be well equipped with essential skills.

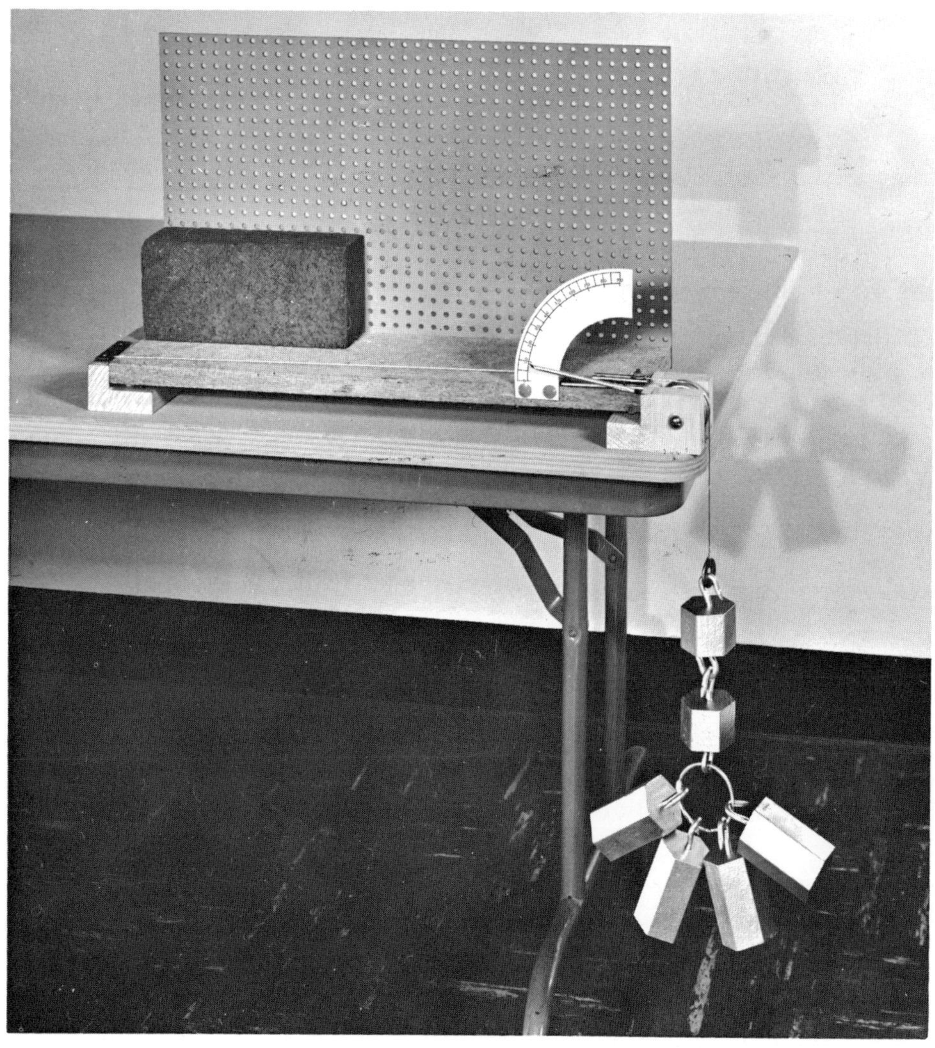

The stretch of a wire when it is pulled can be measured by using a rolling-needle amplifier like the one used in measuring the thermal expansion of a tube.

A special kit to perform the experiments in this section is available from Robert Bentley, Inc. For full particulars, see page 285 in Section XIII, DISTRIBUTORS AND APPROXIMATE PRICES OF ESI CURRICULUM MATERIALS.

The following chapter is reprinted from the Introductory Physical Science text.

II QUANTITY OF MATTER: MASS

II – 1. Volume

Suppose you have some pennies stacked one on top of another in several piles, and you want to know how many pennies are in each pile. The obvious thing to do is to count them. If you had to count the pennies in many piles, you could speed up the counting in the following way. Make a scale by drawing a straight line on a piece of paper and marking it off in spaces equal to the thickness of one penny, indicating the fifth mark, tenth mark, fifteenth mark, etc., as shown in Fig. 1. You can then place this scale vertically alongside each pile and read off the number of pennies. If one of the piles of pennies is higher than the length of your scale, you may find that you can divide it into three equal piles. You can then read off the number of pennies in one pile and multiply by three to get the total number of pennies in the original tall pile.

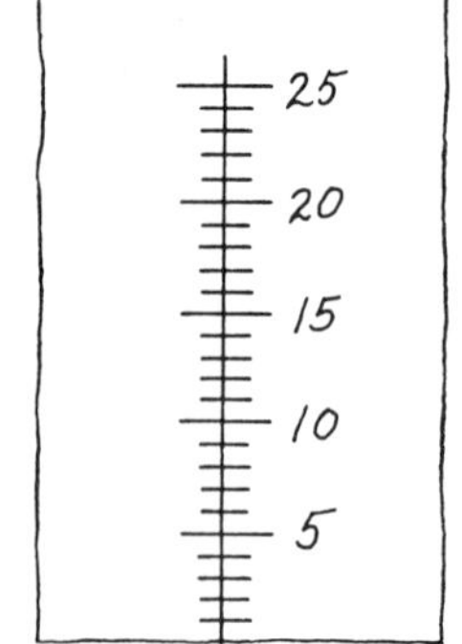

FIG. 1. A scale for counting the number of pennies in a vertical pile. The distance between marks is the thickness of one penny.

If you want to measure the amount of copper in each pile of pennies, you first have to establish a unit in which to measure the amount of copper. If you choose as the unit the amount of copper in one penny, then the amount in the whole pile is expressed by the same number as the number of pennies. Suppose, now, that you want to find out how much copper there is in a rectangular solid bar of copper. You might think of making a box of the same size and shape as the copper bar and then counting the number of pennies needed to fill the box. This scheme will not work, because if you place pennies

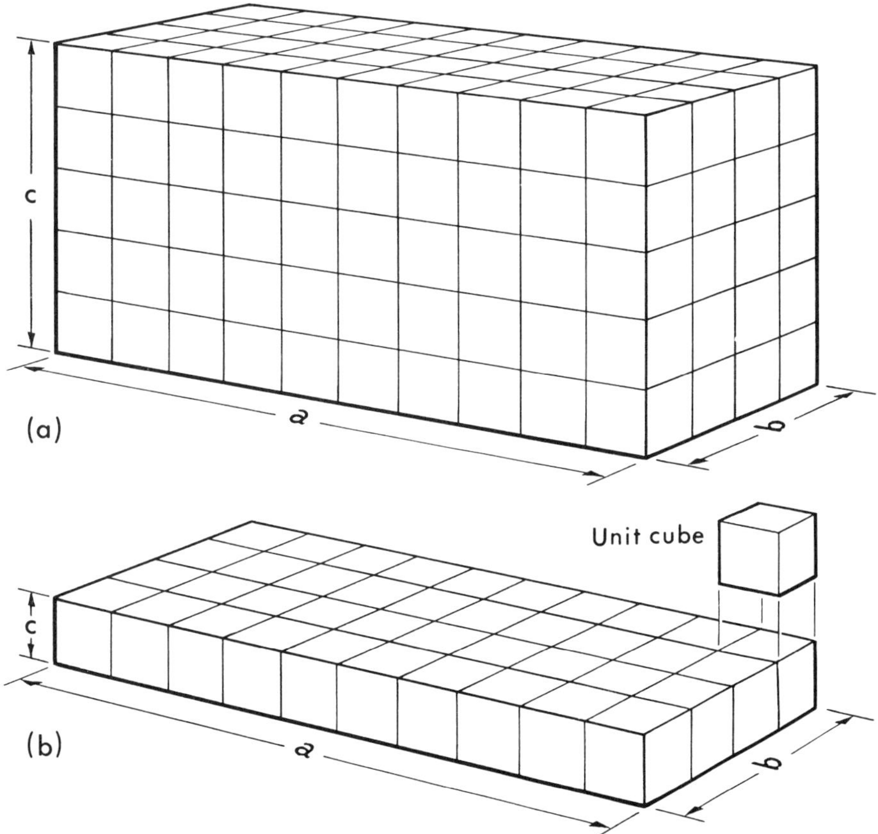

FIG. 2. (a) A bar of copper 10 cubes long, 4 cubes wide, and 5 cubes high. (b) One layer of the bar contains 10 rows of 4 cubes each or 10×4 cubes. We see in (a) that there are 5 layers in the bar, each containing 10×4 cubes. The total number of unit cubes in the bar is therefore $10 \times 4 \times 5 = 200$ cubes. If the unit cube is one centimeter on a side, the volume of the bar is 200 cm^3 (cubic centimeters). For any rectangular solid, therefore, the volume is the product of the three dimensions, $a \times b \times c$.

next to one another in a rectangular box, there is always some empty space between them. A better way is to choose a new unit to measure the amount, such as the volume of a small cube. Then if you find out how many such unit cubes just fit into the solid copper bar, you have a measure of the amount of copper in the bar expressed in units of the cube. If *a* cubes fit along the length of the rectangular bar, *b* along the width, and *c* along the height, then the total number of cubes in

II. QUANTITY OF MATTER: MASS

the bar is $a \times b \times c$. This is the amount of copper in the solid bar expressed in units of cubes. As you probably know, this is also the *volume* of the bar expressed in terms of the volume of the unit cube (Fig. 2). What we choose to be the length of each side of this unit cube is a matter of convenience. We shall choose a unit of length based on the meter, the international standard of the metric system commonly used in scientific work. In this case, as in much of our other work in this course, we shall use the centimeter (1/100 meter). Our unit cube would then be the cubic centimeter (cm^3), a small cube one centimeter on an edge.

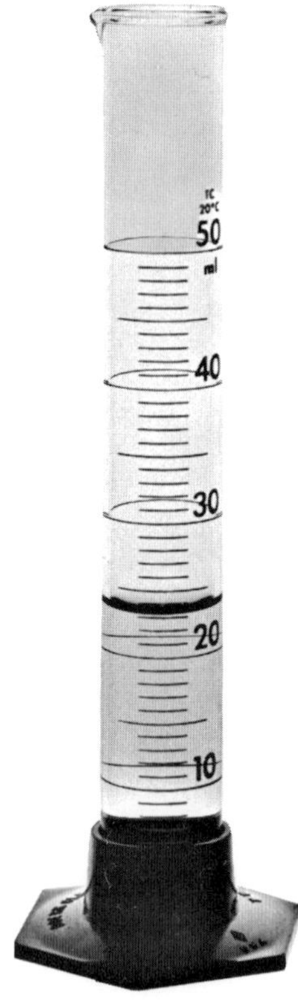

FIG. 3. A graduated cylinder marked off in units of volume. The cubic centimeter marks could be made by filling the cylinder with liquid from a small cubic container, one centimeter on a side, and making a mark at the liquid level each time a containerful of the liquid is poured in.

To sum up, then, we can compare different amounts of the same substance by comparing their volumes — that is, the amounts of space they occupy. When we are dealing with a rectangular solid, we find its volume by measuring its three sides and taking the product of these numbers. We can also calculate the volume of solids of other regular shapes from measurements of their dimensions, but this requires further knowledge of geometry.

The use of volume to compare amounts of substances is particularly convenient when we deal with liquids, because liquids take the shape of their containers. If we wish to compare two amounts of water contained in two bottles of very different shapes, we simply pour the contents of each, one at a time, into a graduated cylinder which has already been marked off with the desired units; we then read off the volumes (Fig. 3). This way of measuring volume is very much like counting pennies all stacked up in a pile.

We can use this ability of a liquid to take any shape when we want to find the volume of a solid of irregular form, such as a small stone. After pouring some water into a graduate and reading its volume, we can submerge the stone in the water and read the combined volume of the water and the stone. The difference between the two readings is the volume of the stone.

A granular solid like sand, though it does not flow so well as a liquid, can be measured by the same method. Suppose we have some sand in a cup. We can find how much space it takes up in the cup by simply pouring it into a graduated cylinder. But does the mark it comes to on the scale of the cylinder really show the volume of the sand? What about the air spaces between the loosely packed grains? What the graduated cylinder really measures is the combined volume of the sand plus the air spaces. However, we can do a simple experiment to find the volume of the sand alone.

II – 2. Experiment: Measuring Volume by Displacement of Water

Pour some sand into a graduated cylinder, until it is about two-thirds full. What is the volume reading on the scale?

Now pour the sand into a beaker and pour water into the graduated cylinder until it is about one-third full. Record the volume of the water and then add the sand to the water. What is the volume of sand plus water?

What is the volume of the sand alone? What is the volume of the air space in the sand? What fraction of a cup of the dry sand is just air space?

• • •

The experiment you have just done shows that we must be careful when we talk about the volume of a sample of a dry substance like sand. We must say how the volume was measured. If we have a bag of dry sand and want to know how many quart bottles it will fill, we need to know its volume dry. But if we want to know the volume of sand alone, not sand plus air space, then we must do an experiment like the one you have just done. We must measure the volume by liquid displacement.

No matter whether a solid is in one piece or granular, when we measure its volume by displacement of water we make the assumption that the volumes of the solid alone and of the water alone add up to the volume of the solid and water together. This assumption may or may not be correct. This will depend on the kind of solid we have. For example, if you measure the volume of a few chunks of rock salt by the displacement of water you will see that the total volume of rock salt and water diminishes as the salt dissolves. (See Fig. 4.)

II. QUANTITY OF MATTER: MASS

II – 3. Shortcomings of Volume as a Measure of Matter

The experiment shown in Fig. 4 strongly suggests that volume is not always a reliable indicator of the amount of a substance. Here are some further difficulties. Suppose you wanted to find the amount of gas released in the distillation of wood which you have performed.

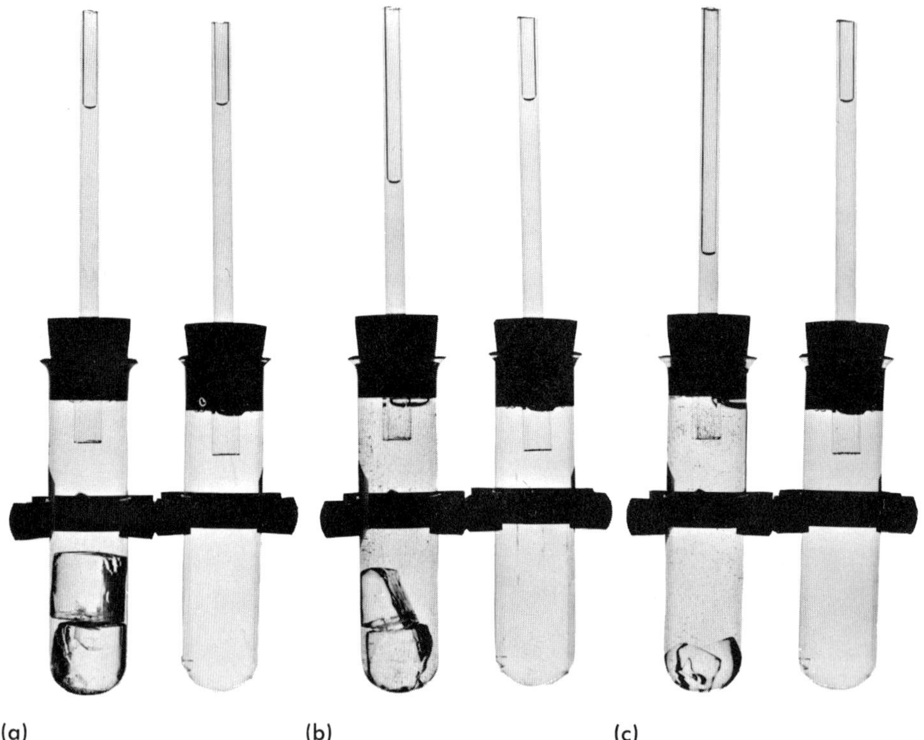

(a) (b) (c)

FIG. 4. (a) A test tube containing only water, and another test tube containing water to which two large pieces of rock salt have just been added. (b) The same test tubes 30 minutes later, after the salt has begun to dissolve. Notice the decrease in the total volume of the rock salt and water, as shown by the water level in the narrow glass tube. The test tube containing the salt was shaken several times to speed up the dissolving. (c) The test tubes after another 30 minutes. The total volume continues to decrease as more salt dissolves.

You could measure the volume of gas you produced by filling bottles until no more gas was left. You could use one bottle as a unit of volume and express the volume as so many bottles of gas. Or you could collect the gas in inverted graduated cylinders instead of bottles, and express the volume in cubic centimeters.

But if you have ever pumped up a bicycle tire, you know that a gas is very compressible. You know that as you push more and more gas into the tire its volume remains almost unchanged. Is there really the same amount of gas in the tire after you pump as there was before?

If you compressed the gas from the distillation of wood into a smaller volume, would there be less of it?

Finally, can we really use volume to compare the amounts of different substances, some of which may be solids, some liquids, and others gases? Consider again the distillation of wood. Does measuring the volume of the wood splints, the ashes, the liquids, and the gas really tell us how much of each of these substances we have?

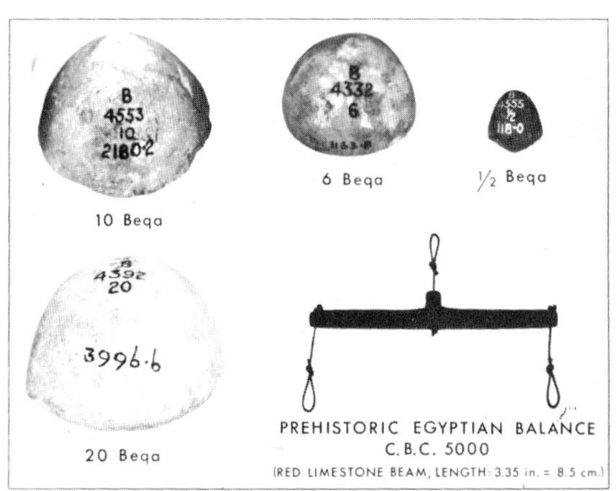

FIG. 5. This balance, the earliest one known, comes from a prehistoric grave at Naqada, Egypt. It may be 7000 years old. The arm and weights are made of limestone. Other limestone masses of different numbers of beqa were also found in these prehistoric graves. Is there any reason why you should not use the beqa as your unit of mass? (Photo courtesy: Science Museum, London.)

II – 4. Mass

The limitations of volume as a measure for the amount of matter must have been known to men many centuries ago, because they developed a method for measuring the amounts of different substances quite independently of their volumes. From an Egyptian tomb several thousand years old, archaeologists have recovered a little balance arm of carved stone, with its carefully made stone masses (Fig. 5). It was almost surely used, in the very dawn of history, for the careful measurement of gold dust. The goldsmiths knew even then that the balance was the best way to determine the amount of solid gold they could cast from any heap of dust or from any pile of irregular nuggets.

The balance could be suspended in the middle by the upper loop so that the horizontal bar was divided exactly into two arms of equal length. The balance bar would then hang horizontally with no objects suspended from either arm. When an object was hung from the loop on the end of one arm, it could be balanced by hanging some other pieces of matter from the end of the other arm.

In using the balance men soon learned, no doubt, that the bar would remain horizontal even though there were drastic changes in the shapes of the objects being weighed. Dividing a chunk of iron into a number of pieces, or filing it into a pile of small grains, does not affect the balance. A balance responds to something quite independent of the form of the object. What it responds to we call *mass.*

If a certain quantity, or mass, of gold just balances a piece of wood, which in turn balances a piece of brass, we say that the masses of all three are equal. If something else balances the piece of brass, it also balances the wood and the gold, and therefore has the same mass. The equal-arm balance gives us a way of comparing masses of objects of any kind regardless of their shape, form, or color, or what substance they are made of.

To record masses we shall need some standard masses to put on one side of the balance, with which various other pieces of matter can be compared. This standard mass is arbitrary — any mass, even the ancient Egyptian beqa, can be chosen — but people must agree upon it. In our work we shall sometimes use as a unit of mass a metal "bead," and sometimes the gram (gm), the fundamental unit of mass in the metric system. The international standard of mass in the metric system is a carefully made cylinder of platinum kept at Sèvres, near Paris, France, which has a mass of a kilogram (kg) or 1000 grams. All other kilogram masses are compared, directly or indirectly, with the standard whenever high precision is required. If we were to place a mass of one kilogram on the grocer's scale, the scale would read 2.2 pounds.

II – 5. Experiment: The Equal-arm Balance

The purpose of this experiment is to make you familiar with an equal-arm balance and to allow you to develop the necessary skill in using it (Fig. 6). Since you will use the balance frequently, it is worth spending the time now to learn its use so that you will not be bothered with the details of operating it later on.

Make sure that the wire pans swing freely and that the vertical pointer in the center does not rub against the wood support. The pointer of the balance should swing very nearly equal distances on both sides of the center of the scale when there is nothing on either pan. In order to adjust the balance so that it does swing in this manner, first make sure that the metal clip on the right arm is as near to the center of the balance as possible. Then move the clip on the left arm until the pointer swings equal distances on both sides of the center of the scale.

Now, with your balance adjusted and a set of bead masses, find the mass in beads of several different objects. Objects whose mass is between 5 beads and 100 beads will be easiest to weigh. Exchange objects with your classmates and compare your measurements of the masses with theirs.

II – 6. Experiment: The Precision of the Balance

Look carefully at several pennies. Do you think they all have the same mass? Would you expect them to differ a little in mass? Now

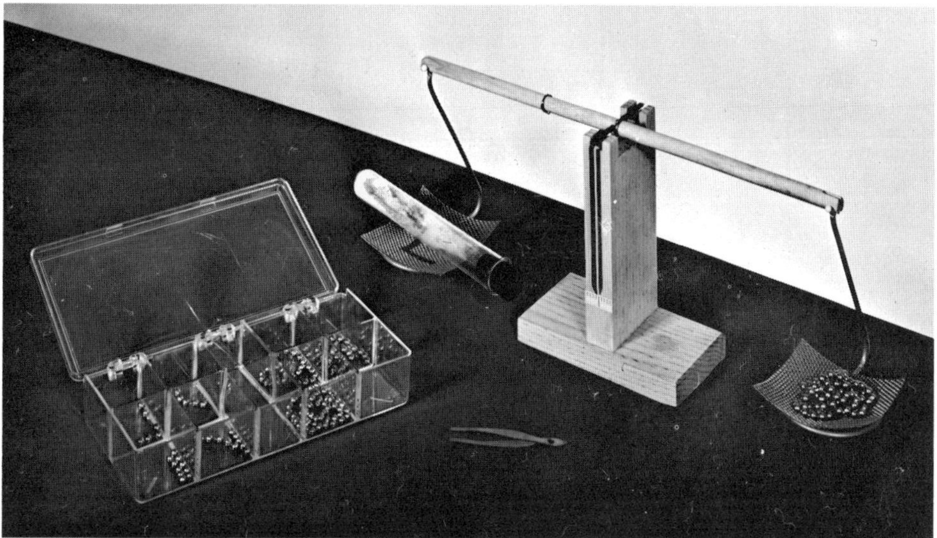

FIG. 6. An equal-arm laboratory balance like the one you will use in your experiments. The object to be weighed is placed on the pan at the left and the standard bead masses are placed on the one at the right. The tip of the pointer hangs vertically down over the scale at the lower end of the center support.

measure the masses of the pennies on your balance. Record the mass of each penny in a table in your notebook and be careful to keep track of which penny is which.

You have weighed the pennies only to the nearest bead. How can they be weighed to a fraction of a bead to see if there are tiny differences in their masses, smaller than one bead? By using the rider (the clip on the right arm of the balance) you can measure masses to a fraction of a bead. Move the rider until it balances one bead placed on the left-hand pan, and mark its position on the arm. Now make pencil marks on the arm, dividing into ten equal spaces the distance between the zero-bead and the one-bead position of the rider. Each mark represents an interval of 0.1 bead on this rider scale. How could you check to see if this is true? If your balance has already been calibrated (that is, if there already is a scale marked on it), check to see if it is accurate.

II. QUANTITY OF MATTER: MASS

Now, using both rider and beads, again measure the mass of each penny. How do their masses compare? How much more precise is the balance when you use a rider than it was without a rider?

To find out how uniform, or really standard, the bead masses are, place an equal number of beads on each pan and adjust the rider until

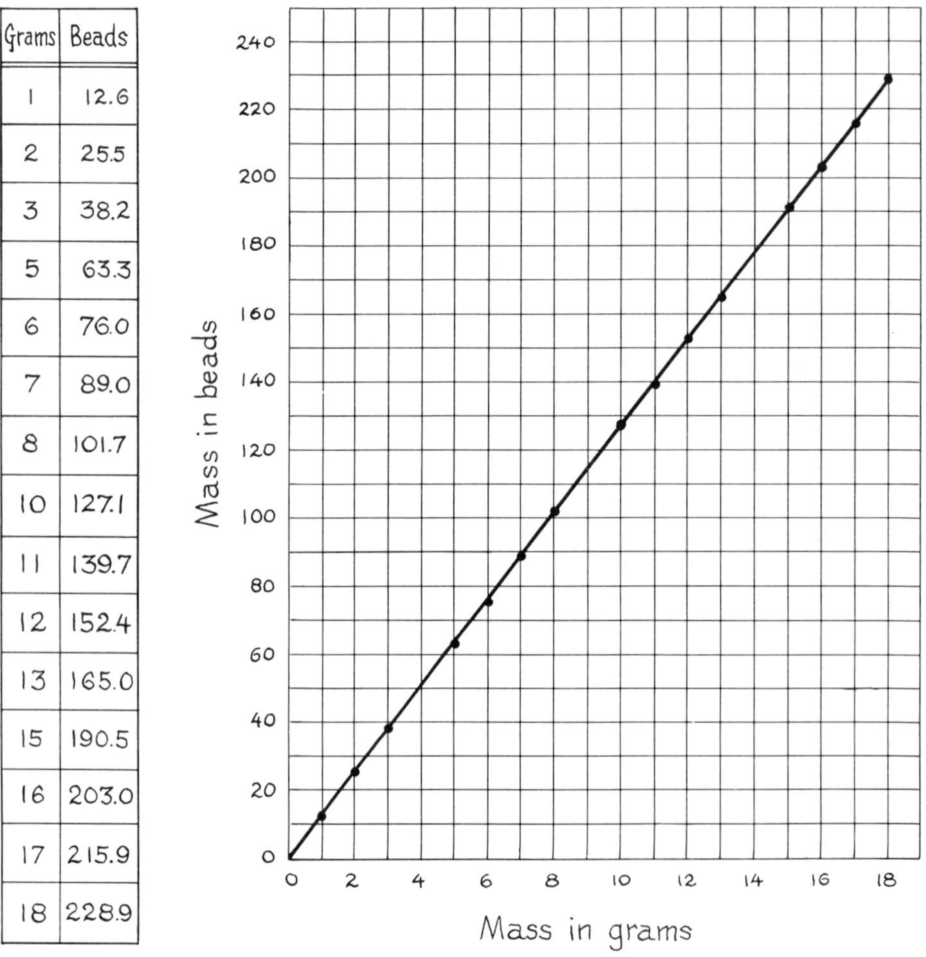

Grams	Beads
1	12.6
2	25.5
3	38.2
5	63.3
6	76.0
7	89.0
8	101.7
10	127.1
11	139.7
12	152.4
13	165.0
15	190.5
16	203.0
17	215.9
18	228.9

FIG. 7. A table of experimental data is shown on the left. The data were obtained by balancing beads against standard gram masses on the equal-arm balance illustrated in Fig. 6. The graph on the right is a plot of the data shown in the table. Such a graph can be used for conversion from beads into grams. The data are for beads of different mass than the beads you use in the laboratory.

they are balanced. If the rider alone will not balance the two pans, switch the beads to opposite pans. If you still cannot balance the scale, count the beads in each pan again to make sure you have the same number. It is worthwhile to repeat this check several times with different numbers of beads.

Sometimes we shall want to know the mass of an object in grams rather than in beads. You can make your own conversion table oı graph in the following way. Weigh masses of 1, 2, 5, and 10 grams, and all possible combinations of these (1 + 2, 1 + 2 + 5, etc.) and make a table in your notebook of the number of beads that balance these different masses. Plot a graph of these values like the one shown in Fig 7, which was plotted from data using beads of different size from those you have used. Save the graph you have made, so that whenever a conversion between grams and beads is needed, the information will be readily available.

II – 7. Experiment: The Mass of Dissolved Salt

In Section 2 of this chapter, you learned that as salt dissolves in water, the combined volume of salt plus water decreases. This leads us to ask whether the mass also decreases when salt is dissolved in water.

Half fill the cap of a small plastic bottle with salt and put it carefully aside. Pour water into the plastic bottle until it is about two-thirds full and find the total mass of the bottle, water, cap, and salt when all are on the balance together but the salt and water are not mixed.

Pour the salt into the bottle and put the cap on. Using the same beads as before, find the mass of the capped bottle of salt and water. Shake the bottle occasionally to speed up the dissolving of the salt. Did the mass change as the salt dissolved? How does this change compare with the accuracy of your weighings?

II – 8. Experiment: The Mass of Ice and Water

Here is another process where there is a volume change. When ice melts, it contracts — its volume decreases. Does its mass also change?

Weigh a small container with its cover; then put an ice cube in the container and weigh it again. What is the mass of the ice? After all the ice has melted (you can tell when by shaking the container, if it is not transparent) weigh it again. Do you notice any condensation of water on the outside of the can? If so, what should you do about it? What do you conclude about change in mass when ice melts?

II – 9. Experiment: The Mass of Mixed Solutions

In the two experiments you have just done, a solid was either dissolved or melted. Now let us ask what happens to the mass when a solid is formed by mixing two liquids.

Pour lead nitrate solution into a small bottle until it is about one-third full. Now pour the same amount of sodium iodide into another bottle of the same size. Find the total mass of the bottles of solution and their caps. Now pour one solution into the same bottle with the other and cap both bottles. Again find the total mass of both bottles. Did the mass change as a result of the mixing?

II – 10. Experiment: The Mass of Copper and Sulfur

The changes you have examined so far were quite mild. A more drastic change in matter takes place when sulfur and copper are heated together. Does the total mass change when these substances are heated together?

Weigh a large pyrex test tube and rubber stopper. Put 10 beads of granular copper and 5 beads of sulfur in the test tube and mix thoroughly. Record the total mass of the stoppered tube. With the test tube tightly stoppered, heat the mixture until the glow that begins inside finally stops. (Let the test tube cool before you touch it.) Has the total mass of the copper and sulfur changed?

Describe the appearance of the material in the test tube. Do you think the substance in the bottom is sulfur, copper, or a new substance?

II – 11. Experiment: The Mass of Gas

In this experiment a solid and a liquid produce a gas. Is there a change in mass?

Place one-eighth of an Alka-Seltzer tablet in a small, heavy bottle one-fifth full of water and immediately cap the bottle very tightly. Wipe off any moisture on the outside and immediately place it on the balance and weigh it. Does what happens inside the bottle affect the mass of the bottle and its contents?

Slowly loosen the cap. Can you hear gas escaping?

Again weigh the cap, the bottle, and its contents. What do you conclude?

II – 12. The Conservation of Mass

What have the last five experiments shown? If you have worked with sufficient care you have shown that in all five changes that you investigated, any apparent changes in mass that you observed were within the experimental error of your equipment. Therefore your results agree with the conclusion that there was no change in mass that you could measure. On the basis of these experiments alone, you are in no position to predict with certainty whether there will be a change in mass under other circumstances. For example, perhaps if we use larger amounts of matter in our experiments and use a balance of higher accuracy we may measure a change greater than the experimental error and conclude that mass really does not remain the same. Furthermore, although we checked five rather different kinds of change, there is an endless variety of other reactions we could have tried, even more violent than the reaction of copper and sulfur.

What would happen, for example, if we set off a small explosion inside a heavy steel case, making sure no mass escapes? The experiments you have performed give no direct answer to this question. But we can make the guess that the results of these five experiments can be generalized in the following way: In all changes mass is exactly conserved, provided nothing is added (like the water that condensed on the outside of the closed container in the experiment with ice and water) or is allowed to escape (like the gas in the last experiment). This generalization is known as the law of conservation of mass. It has been checked to one part in a billion* for a large variety of changes. Still, all this vast amount of evidence in favor of the law of conservation of mass does not prove that it is an absolute law. Surely, if some one claimed that he had made an experiment in which as much as one millionth of the mass disappeared or was created, we should treat the results with great suspicion and first of all make many checks to determine whether he had a leak of some sort in his apparatus from which gas could escape. The chances are that we should find such a leak. On the other hand, if an experiment were made where a change in mass of one part in 100 billion was reported, we might have to conclude after enough scrutiny of the experiment that the law of conservation of mass has its limitations, that it holds to one part in a billion, but not to one part in 100 billion (10^{11}).

We have seen in this chapter that volume is very often a con-

*A billion is 1,000,000,000. Such a number is clumsy to write. Most of the zeros can be dispensed with by writing it as 10^9 and reading it "ten to the ninth." The nine is called an exponent and tells how many times we multiply one by ten to get the number. For example, $1 \times 10 \times 10 = 10^2$, $1 \times 10 \times 10 \times 10 = 10^3$, etc. We shall use this way of expressing numbers, called "powers-of-ten notation," whenever it is convenient.

venient way of measuring the quantity of matter. But we have also found out that when matter changes form (when ice melts, salt dissolves, etc.) there is often an easily measurable change in volume but no observable change in mass: mass is conserved. It is the conservation of mass that makes mass such a useful measure of matter.

II – 13. Laws of Nature

The law of conservation of mass is the first of several laws of nature that we shall study in this course. It is worthwhile to pause at this point and compare the laws of nature with the laws with which you may be more familiar, the laws of our society. Laws of society are legislated; that is, they are agreed upon and then enforced. If evidence is presented that you have violated such a law, you are punished. The laws of society can also be changed or repealed.

Laws of nature are quite different. These are guessed generalizations based on experiments, often even crude experiments. If you perform an experiment which appears to violate a law of nature you are not punished; but if you present convincing evidence that the law is not quite true, the law is changed to take into account the new experience. Only rarely does this amount to a complete repeal of the law; in most cases the change is a recognition of the limitation of the law.

FOR HOME, DESK, AND LAB

1. A student has a large number of cubes which measure 1 cm along an edge.
(a) How many cubes will he need in building a cube that is 2 cm along an edge?
(b) How many cubes will be necessary to build a cube that is 3 cm along an edge?
(c) Express, in cm^3, the volume of the cubes made in (a) and (b).

2. Consider a staircase constructed of the unit cubes illustrated in Fig. 2.
(a) If the staircase is ten cubes wide and ten cubes high, and each step is one cube deep and one cube high, what is the volume of the staircase?
(b) What would be the volume of the solid if each step was filled in so that the face of the staircase became a smooth incline running from the floor at the bottom to the top of the highest layer of cubes?

3. In determining the volume of a rectangular box, five cubes were found to fit exactly along one edge and four cubes fitted exactly along another edge. However, after six horizontal layers had been stacked in the box, a space at the top was left unfilled.
(a) If the height of the space was half the length of a unit cube, what was the volume of the box?
(b) If the height of the space was .23 of the length of a unit cube, what was the volume of the box?

II. QUANTITY OF MATTER: MASS

4. The dimensions of two rectangular solids are measured in meters. The volume of one solid is computed to be three times as large as that of the other. If the dimensions were measured in inches, what difference would it make?

5. A close look at Fig. 8 shows that the top of the liquid contained in the graduated cylinder is not flat, but curved. How do you decide how much water is in the cylinder?

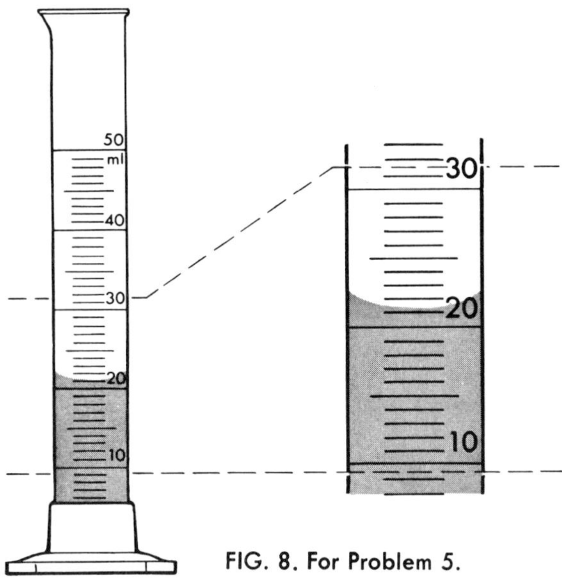

FIG. 8. For Problem 5.

6. We normally use graduated cylinders to measure liquid volumes. Could a conical-shaped container be marked off to measure volume?

7. How would the volume of a piece of glass as measured by displacement of water compare with its volume as measured by displacement of kerosene?

8. How would you measure the volume of granulated sugar?

9. (a) How would you measure the volume of a sponge?
(b) What have you actually measured by your method?
(c) Does this differ from your measurement of the volume of sand?

10. You have a small piece of rock you picked up from the ground, and you wish to determine its volume. You put water in a graduated cylinder and read its volume as 15.2 cm^3. Then you drop in the rock and read the contents of the cylinder as 38.8 cm^3. You put a stopper in the cylinder and set it aside; no one disturbs it. The next day you see that the volume of the contents of the cylinder is 36.4 cm^3.

(a) What would you have recorded for the volume of the rock immediately after you dropped it into the cylinder? On the succeeding day?

(b) What could account for the difference in the two values you have for the volume of the rock?

(c) Would it have made any difference if you had not stoppered the cylinder?

11. When you place a stone in a graduated cylinder containing water in order to measure its volume, you may find small air bubbles clinging to the stone. Is it necessary to try to remove the bubbles before reading the graduate?

II. QUANTITY OF MATTER: MASS

12. (a) Completely fill two small bottles with water. Pour the water into a single larger vessel. Now refill the bottles with the same water. Are they both filled completely?

(b) Now do the same thing again, but fill one bottle with water and the other with burner fuel or rubbing alcohol. (You may have some at home.) Compare the total volume of alcohol and water before and after they were mixed together and poured back into the bottles. Is volume a good measure for the quantity of matter in this case?

13. Fuel oil usually is sold by the gallon, fuel gas by the cubic foot, and coal by the ton. What are the advantages of selling the first two by volume and the last by mass?

14. In the following list of ingredients for a recipe, which are measured by volume, which by mass, and which by other means?

1½ pounds ground chuck	pinch of pepper
1 medium-size onion	3 drops Worcestershire sauce
½ cup chopped green pepper	oregano to taste
4 slices day-old bread	3 tablespoons oil
1 teaspoon salt	1 1-pound can tomato sauce

15. When you buy things at the store, are they measured more often by volume or by mass? Give some examples.

16. (a) What is the volume of an aluminum cube whose sides are 10 cm long?

(b) What is the mass of the aluminum cube? (One cubic centimeter of aluminum has a mass of 2.7 gm.)

17. A 5-cm^3 stone has a mass of 15 gm.

(a) What is the mass of 1 cm^3 of the stone?

(b) What is the mass of a 120-cm^3 stone of the same rock?

18. One cubic centimeter of gold has a mass of 19 gm.

(a) What is the mass of a gold bar 1.0 cm $\times$ 2.0 cm $\times$ 20 cm?

(b) How many of these bars could you carry?

19. A student has a number of identical marbles. He measures their diameter as 1.9 cm and the volume of each as 3.6 cm^3.

(a) What would be the inside dimensions of a covered rectangular box that would just contain a stack of marbles 4 wide, 6 long, and 5 high? The marbles are to be arranged so that the lines joining the centers of any four touching marbles make a square.

(b) What would be the volume of the inside of this box?

(c) With the marbles in the box, what volume of water would just fill all the space in the box not filled by marbles?

(d) With the box filled with marbles and water, what would be the total mass of the contents of the box? (The mass of each marble is 8.5 gm, and that of 1 cm^3 of water is 1.0 gm.)

20. A student took the balance home. When he was ready to use it, he found that he had forgotten his set of bead masses.

(a) How could he make a set of uniform masses from materials likely to be found in his home?

(b) How could he relate his unit of mass to a bead or a gram?

21. When you use the equal-arm balance, can you put the object to be weighed on either pan?

II. QUANTITY OF MATTER: MASS

22. (a) Use the graph you made to find the mass in beads of an object whose mass is 9.0 gm.
(b) What is the mass in grams of a string of 50 beads?
(c) What is the mass in beads of a test tube whose mass is 25 gm?

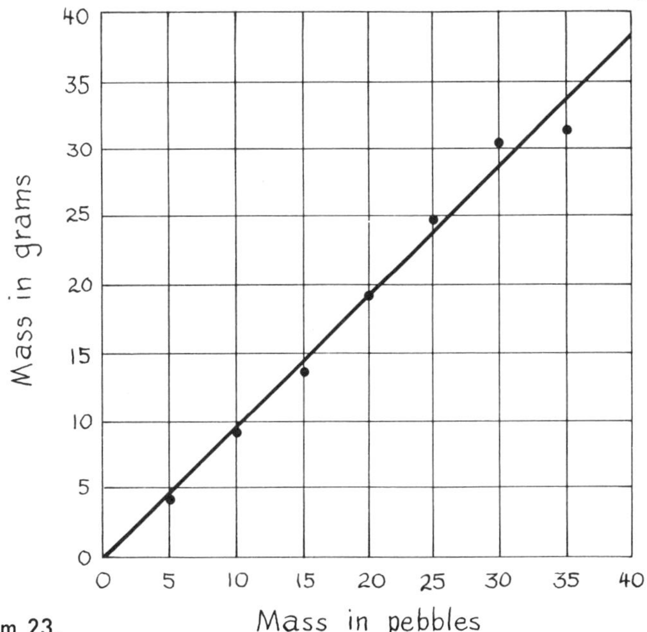

FIG. 9. For Problem 23.

23. A student picks up pebbles that appear to be the same size, to use as standard masses for a balance. He makes the conversion graph for pebbles and grams shown in Fig. 9.
(a) Are the pebbles as good a standard for mass as your beads?
(b) How many beads equal 1 pebble? How many pebbles equal 1 bead?

24. Suppose you lost the rider for your scale. Try to devise another method, not using a rider, by which you could measure tenths of a bead.

25. Five students in turn measured the mass of a small dish on the bead balance; none knew what results the others obtained. The masses they found were

Student	Mass in beads
1	35.7
2	35.6
3	35.8
4	35.6
5	35.7

(a) Can you tell whether any student made an incorrect measurement?
(b) Do you think there is anything wrong with the balance?
(c) What do you think would be the best way to report the mass of the dish?
(d) How precise do you think the measurements were?

26. You can set the rider on your balance by eye to 0.1 of a division on the rider scale.
(a) What fraction of a bead does this correspond to? What fraction of a gram?
(b) Try weighing both a light and a heavy object on the balance, to 0.1

II. QUANTITY OF MATTER: MASS

of a division on the rider scale. Weigh the objects several times, alternating light and heavy. What do you conclude?

(c) How nearly equal in mass are your beads when they are weighed to 0.1 of a division on the rider scale?

27. A bead balance shows that two solid rubber stoppers, one on each pan, have equal masses. Both are placed on the same pan, and a third stopper is found to balance the first two together.

(a) What is the ratio of the mass of one of the first stoppers to the mass of the third?

(b) What is the ratio of the volume of one of the first stoppers to the volume of the third? What assumptions have you made in answering the question?

(c) Could one use the mass of one of the first stoppers as a unit of mass?

(d) Instead of a third stopper, we now find a glass marble that balances both of the first two stoppers together. How do the masses of the marble and the third stopper compare? Can anything be said about the ratio of the volumes of the marble and the third stopper?

28. Suppose you balance a piece of modeling clay against a number of beads on the balance and then reshape it. Will it still balance? If you shape it into a hollow sphere, will it still balance?

29. In Experiment II-7, how could you recover the dissolved salt? How do you think its mass would compare with the mass of dry salt you started with?

30. Suggest a reason for putting the lid on the small container that you used in studying the mass of ice and water.

31. Should the mass of the container used in Experiment II-8 be measured with the container warm or cold, or does it matter?

32. In Experiment II-8, would the mass of the container and its contents stay the same if you started with water and froze it? Try it.

33. Assume that the mass of ice in a closed container does not change when the ice melts, but that the mass increases by 1 per cent when the same water is refrozen. What would happen if you melted the ice, refroze it, and repeated the process many times? What would happen if, on the other hand, the mass decreased when the water froze but stayed the same when it melted?

34. A test tube having 20.0 beads of iron and 12.0 beads of sulfur was heated in a manner similar to the copper-and-sulfur experiment. The total mass of the tube and contents measured on the bead balance before the heating was 182.5 beads. After the heating, its mass was measured again. The mass of the tube and contents was 182.4 beads.

(a) Are you inclined to think it reasonable that mass was conserved during this experiment?

(b) What additional steps would you take to strengthen your inclination?

35. A burning candle grows smaller and finally disappears; it seems to lose mass while it is burning. What would we have to do to show that mass is really conserved when a candle burns?

36. (a) Express the following numbers in powers of ten:

100 10,000 100,000,000

(b) Write the following numbers without using exponents:

10^5 10^6 10^9

37. There is an old saying: "Whatever goes up must come down." Does this express a law of nature? Why, or why not?

IV

PHYSICS IN THE HIGH SCHOOL: The Physical Science Study Committee

THE PHYSICAL SCIENCE STUDY COMMITTEE

by Gilbert C. Finlay

THE Physical Science Study Committee was formed in 1956 as a group of university and secondary-school physics teachers working to develop an improved introductory physics course. The committee is developing interrelated teaching materials for physics in the secondary school. Materials intended for direct instructional use include a textbook, laboratory apparatus and a laboratory guidebook for students, motion picture films, and a set of ten achievement tests. Supporting materials include a four-volume teacher's guide and resource book, and a series of paperback books that provide authoritative science literature for students and adults.

To help teachers who are considering the use of these materials, the committee has encouraged the development of instructional programs that enable teachers to study the new course in detail.

For its various activities, the committee organized teams of university and secondary-school physics teachers. These teams blended teaching experience at several levels with deep insight into the nature and meaning of physics. The materials developed by these teams were used in classes and subjected to close scrutiny by the teachers who used them and by the committee's staff observers. The course materials were tried, evaluated, and revised for three years before they were released for general use in the fall of 1960.

The committee, in the course of its work, thought it wise to establish a permanent organization to provide for revision and related development. A non-profit corporation, Educational Services Incorporated, was formed. This corporation now administers the program of the Physical Science Study Committee.

Science is becoming an increasingly consequential factor in the affairs of man. There are the practical goods: the hand-in-hand advance of science and technology continuously increases human potential for producing, transporting, communicating, healing. The attendant problems of social control and adaptation are pervasive and complex. In business, legislation, and statesmanship, the scientist increasingly is called upon to help unravel the social and economic implications of science. But beyond its technological goods and meanings, science as a humanistic study stands on its own terms as a dynamically stable system with its own ends and procedural styles. As a form of human expression, it is one of the triumphs of the intellect. It lends perspective and direction to other aspects of life. It is a system one can ill afford to ignore if one is to become a whole man in a world of whole men.

Physics, as a parent discipline, stands close to the center of our scientific milieu. What instruction in physics is appropriate for secondary-school students in the mid-twentieth century? The work of the Physical Science Study Committee is an attempt to answer this question operationally.

As an initial target, the committee chose to design a new course to fit into the current pattern of school curriculums. Physics is usually offered as a separate, elective subject for students in the eleventh or twelfth grade. In terms of prior measures of ability, these students are drawn mostly from the upper half of their classes, with the distribution of their abilities skewed toward the top levels. Some of these students will follow careers in science or science-related fields, and further work in science will be a part of their higher education. However, the careers of many secondary-school physics students will be in fields other than science, and they will do no further formal work in physics. The committee judged that the needs of both groups of students could be served with a single course.

The committee chose to plan a course dealing with physics as an explanatory system, a system that extends from the domain inside the atom to the distant galaxies. The course tells a unified story—one in which the successive topics are chosen and developed to lead toward an atomic picture of matter, its motions and interrelations. The aim was to present a view of physics that

---

The late Gilbert C. Finlay was a Professor of Education and Director of the School Science Curriculum Project, both at the University of Illinois, as well as one of the original members of PSSC Planning Committee. He died on April 17, 1964.

Reprinted with permission from "The School Review," Volume 70, No. 1, Spring, 1962, published by The University of Chicago Press. **Copyright, 1962, by the University of Chicago.**

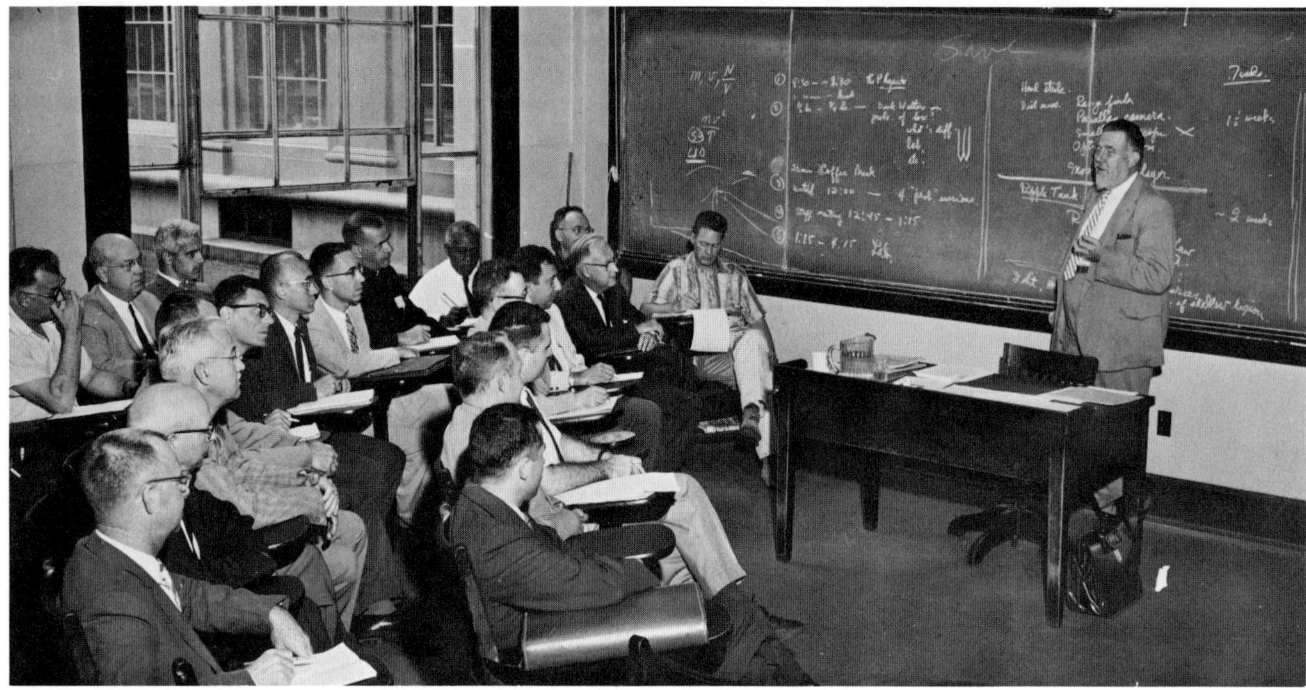

Professor Walter C. Michels, Professor of Physics at Bryn Mawr College, talking to participants at a PSSC staff workshop in August 1958, held at the Massachusetts Institute of Technology.

would bring a student close to the nature of modern physics and to the nature of physical inquiry. Finally, the committee sought to transmit the human character of the story of physics, not simply an up-to-date codification of the findings. The student should see physics as an unfinished and continuing activity. He should experience something of the satisfaction and challenge felt by the scientist when he reaches vantage points from which he can contemplate both charted and uncharted vistas.

Achieving these aims in a one-year course meant that coverage of the field of physics had to be sharply restricted in favor of a deeper development of ideas that are central to a comprehension of the fundamentals of contemporary physical thought. This deeper development meant carrying key concepts to higher levels than have been ordinarily reached in secondary-school courses. Deeper development also meant a more extensive exploration of the substructure of experiment and thought that underlies the basic physical principles.

The student is expected to be an active participant in this course. The textbook, laboratory experiments, and films were developed in a way that reflects this expectation. The course materials do not assert the ideas of physics, then illustrate their utility by exemplifying them in problems and in laboratory exercises. Instead, the student is expected to wrestle with a line (or with converging lines) of inquiry, including his own laboratory investigations, that leads to basic ideas. The power of the fundamental ideas is brought out partially in the student's work on carefully chosen end-of-chapter problems, but more important, the intellectual thrust of the basic ideas is brought out sequentially through using those which are introduced early to illuminate other ideas in a chain that comprises an introductory view of the structure of physics.

As one examines the changes that have occurred in secondary-school physics courses during the past few generations, one is likely to get the feeling that modern technology has found its way into the courses almost to the exclusion of modern physics. Such modern physics as has been worked into many courses is often limited to statements of some of the conclusions. There is little other choice without a preceding development of such subjects as dynamics, wave behavior, and fundamental electricity, that is sufficiently penetrating to permit seeing modern physics as a logical synthesis of ideas emerging from a related structure of experiment, principle, and theory.

No one-year course can give an adequate account of both an expanding physics and the related technology. Planning a course that concentrates on either of these subjects still poses a selection problem of large proportions. As the magnitude of what might be learned grows rapidly, it becomes increasingly clear that the school at any given level, indeed in its entirety, can do little more than provide a base for further learning. The development of a mind is never ending. The function of the school is to provide a fertile start—such a start that the end of formal schooling does not mark the end of further learning. The central problem is to transmit those ideas and styles of thought that have the broadest applicability, the greatest power for further thought and activity. To this end, the Physical Science Study Committee judged it wise to shift the emphasis in secondary-school physics away from technology toward a deeper exploration of the basic ideas of physics and the nature of inquiries that can lead to these ideas. This choice was based on the premise that, for the future scientist as well as for the non-scientist, an introductory course that provides a grasp of the central ideas of physics and the kind of thought that lies behind them is more useful and rewarding than a course that emphasizes a somewhat more ephemeral technology. Technological applications have not been eliminated from the course. But they have been cut back sharply from the role they play in many secondary-school courses. While the course was not specifically developed with college preparation in mind, the course is regarded as providing a sound base for further work in physics.

In this course, experiments—whether they are performed by the student, analyzed in the textbook, or shown on film — are not used simply to confirm an earlier assertion. The laboratory experiments are designed to supply firm rooting for the growth of ideas by providing direct, non-verbal contact with relevant data. Hence, the most common use of laboratory experiments is to introduce a topic or to contribute to the early stages of its development. The students' laboratory guidebook keeps specific instructions to a minimum, directing the students' attention to key points by raising questions. The student is responsible for thinking out the nature and the meaning of what he is to do. The purposes of the experiments vary. Some are qualitative and give general familiarity and introductory experience with a set of phenomena. Many experiments are quantitative but differ extensively in the degree of experimental accuracy that is sought. Students should understand that prior knowledge and experimental purpose influence the precision required to secure new knowledge. Experimentation is a great deal more than establishing the third decimal place. In all cases, students are encouraged to establish or approximate their experimental error.

Clearly a student can have direct laboratory experience with only some aspects of physics. Careful selection of experimental activities can advance the student's understanding of the more important physical ideas. Moreover, presenting these activities in the spirit of experiments rather than as exercises should enhance the student's ability to analyze and appreciate experiments that he reads about or sees on film. Still further, the emphasis in the course on experiment and experimental style is meant to foster insight into the role of experiment in the generation and refinement of physical ideas. While some demonstrations are suggested, more emphasis is placed on experiments performed by students. The apparatus and the laboratory guidebook provide for more than fifty experiments, many of which include optional extensions to provide for variability among students and classes.

A great deal of what might ordinarily be called demonstration is provided by the films produced by the committee. Basically, the films are built around experiments. Films are used to bring to the classroom certain key experiments and a range of experiments that are likely to be too difficult, too time-consuming, or too costly for students to perform or for teachers to demonstrate. For many experiments, films can bring the purposes, techniques, data, and analysis more directly within the students' purview than any other approach can. The films are planned with attention to the general aims of the course and to the particular choices that have been made in the development of related ideas in the students' laboratory and in the textbook. Because the films articulate closely with these resources and because most of the films assume that the viewer is familiar with earlier parts of the course, the scheduling of the films is a matter of consequence. The films are intended as take-off points for teachers and students. They are not intended to replace a teacher. As of October, 1961, forty-four films were available, and sixteen more were being completed.

Some films—such as those on the Millikan experiment, the Rutherford atom, and the Franck-Hertz experiment—are concerned primarily with the presentation and the interpretation of a complex experiment. Other films are more general in purpose and may use a dozen or more experiments or models to develop a set of related ideas. Such films are intended to help integrate and summarize a field of study. Films on crystals, on the relation between mechanical and thermal energy, and on frames of reference are examples. Finally, a few films are intended as introductions to major areas of study. Such films are meant to give the viewer perspective by taking stock of the array of phenomena that require explanation and by suggesting some of the central questions.

The films do not glitter. There is no background

Professor Eric Rogers of the Nuffield Foundation in the film, "Coulomb's Law."

Professor Edward M. Purcell, Harvard University, in the film, "Inertia."

music, and there are no elaborate stage settings. They are frankly teaching films. It should go without saying that the experiments presented are scrupulously honest. The films are not impersonal, neither are they stylized in a personal sense. They present a number of real scientists speaking in their individual ways to students, directing their attention to key points. In this quiet way, the films bring students into closer contact with a group of scientists as persons.

As supplementary sources of authoritative, scientific information, the committee is developing a series of paperback books. These books are appearing as the "Science Study Series." Some deal with individual topics in science or technology. Some are biographical, some historical. As of October, 1961, twenty books had been published in the series. More than thirty were in preparation, and others were planned. An interesting side

light on the pedagogical application of these books is the occasional use of some of the foreign-language translations of the series as reading material for science-oriented students in language classes.

The content of the course of the Physical Science Study Committee has been described in somewhat greater detail in other sources (1, 2, 3). The course is divided into four parts. Part I is an introduction to the principal actor in the physical drama—matter—and its setting, time and space. The course begins with a consideration of the dimensions of time and space and how they are sensed. Through laboratory work the student sees how his senses can be extended by instrumentation and begins to develop a perception of the role, nature, and limitations of measurement. This perception is extended through films that go beyond the usual facilities for measurement available in school laboratories. Familiarity with techniques of defining intervals of space and time leads to a study of motion through space in the course of time. The student learns the relation between distance, velocity, and acceleration, and how to move from one to another through graphical differentiation and integration. The use of vectors to represent these quantities completes this introductory view of the descriptive tools of physics. The course then turns to an introduction to matter, the substance of the universe. Here, the ideas of mass and conservation of mass are considered. The student examines experimental evidence for the existence and the size of atoms. In the laboratory he establishes an upper limit for the size of a molecule and sees how extensions of his experiment can lead to determining the size of an atom. The combination of atoms in molecules is studied, and the ideas of atomicity are extended through a consideration of the arrangement of atoms in solids (crystals) and in gases. A beginning on the molecular interpretation of a gas makes it possible to deal specifically with the idea of a physical model.

In Part II the student begins the process of observation of, and abstraction from, a family of physical phenomena; in this case, light. The natural development of the subject leads to an examination of a particle theory of light. This section of the course illustrates how models are abstracted from experimental observation, how they illuminate further investigation, and how they are established, modified, or rejected. Study shows

Reflection of water waves. Water waves strike a barrier and reflect, much as light is reflected from a mirror. This similarity suggests that a wave model may be useful in describing light. We shall use waves on ropes and springs, too, in our study of wave behavior. And we shall find that what we learn gives us a major key to understanding the structure of atoms.

From the PSSC text

A photograph (magnification 6, 5X) of a piece of zinc. The fanlike group of crystals stands out clearly because, owing to the natural roughness of the specimen, it is on a plane slightly above the rest of the material. The basic crystalline form is not apparent in the darker regions because they are in different planes. This is but one possible illustration of the fact that metals do occur as crystals.

From the PSSC text

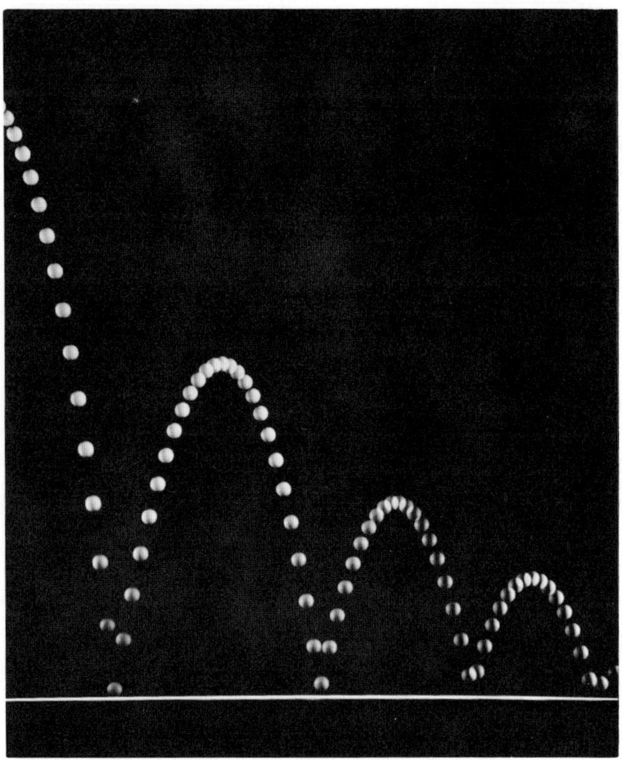

A multiple flash photograph of a bouncing ball. In our study of mechanics we shall study motions of bodies that range in size from enormous suns and planets, through things of ordinary size, like this ball, down to the minute particles in atoms. Throughout this great range we shall find a few basic ideas, such as momentum and energy, that clarify our understanding at any scale. *From the PSSC text*

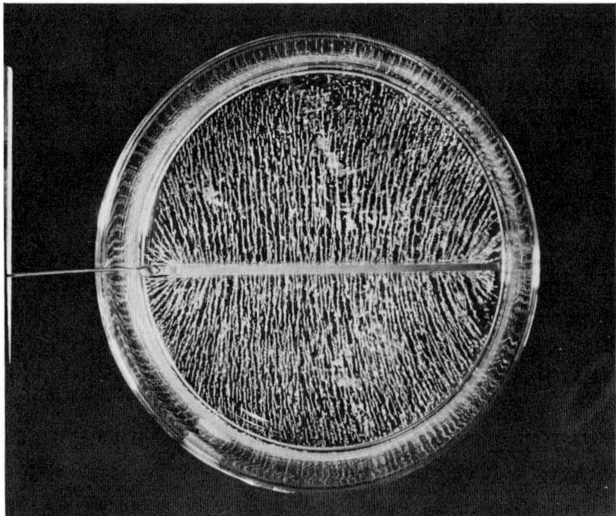

The electric field around a charged conducting plate outlined by grass seeds in an insulating liquid. The study of electric force fields will help us understand the nature of light and the forces that hold atoms together. *From the PSSC text*

that a simple particle model does not fit the behavior of light, and the course turns to another model, waves. Extensive laboratory experience with waves—first in one dimension on ropes and springs, then in two dimensions on the surface of water—shows similarities between wave behavior and light. A detailed study of interference establishes the wave nature of light.

Part III returns to motion, this time from a dynamical point of view. Again depending heavily upon laboratory work, and extensively reinforced with films, the course moves through the relation between force and motion, the story of the discovery of universal gravitation, and the conservation of momentum and energy. The generality of the conservation laws is stressed. The use of the conservation laws in situations where detailed observation of the motion is not possible (as in the molecular turmoil in gases) and emphasis on two-body interactions lay groundwork for exploring the atom in Part IV.

The atomistic character of matter is introduced in Part I and carried further in the kinetic theory of gases in Part III. Part IV develops the nature of electrical forces and energy; begins to bind together dynamics, electricity, and waves in a consideration of electromagnetic radiation; and returns with all these tools to an exploration of the structure of matter, atoms. Analysis of scattering experiments establishes a simple Rutherford model. Some of the inadequacies of this model are pointed out. The particle-wave nature of both light and matter is shown. Experiment discloses the internal energy states in atoms. The energy levels are explained in terms of standing wave patterns, and the course comes to a close with a quantum mechanical view in which both wave and particle characteristics are essential to an understanding of the structure of matter. In this part of the course, because of the difficulty of many of the relevant experiments, films carry a large share of the burden of presenting experimental evidence.

The logical unity of physics has been emphasized in this course. As an alternative to covering the various fields of physics at the same level, the course employs earlier material to clarify that which follows. For example, ideas about waves and particles recur, each time to be carried further in a higher synthesis of ideas. This characteristic plus the exploration of concepts that are clearly unfinished, the tightly related student laboratory, the investigative approach in the films and the frequent analysis of experiments in the text all contribute to a perception of physics as a continuing search for order in a picture of the universe. This coherent, searching character of man's approach to building an explanatory structure of the physical world is one of the course's principal aims and chief pedagogical characteristics [*1: 292*].

The Physical Science Study Committee had its beginning early in 1956 in exploratory discussions, held first at the Massachusetts Institute of Technology and later at other centers. These discussions, led by Jerrold R. Zacharias of the Massachusetts Institute of Technology, established the desirability of rethinking the secondary-school physics program and made it clear that an adequate number of able secondary-school and university physics teachers would be willing to join in such an effort. In November, 1956, an initial grant from the National Science Foundation marked the official beginning of the project. The National Science Foundation has provided the principal financial support. The Ford Foundation and the Alfred P. Sloan Foundation have contributed to the support of the program.

By the time of the initial grant, informal groups had been established at Cambridge, Massachusetts; the Bell Laboratories in New York; the California Institute of Technology; Cornell University; and the University of Illinois. Several of these groups developed tentative outlines for a new physics course. A meeting of most of the people who had participated in these groups, together with other interested individuals, was held in December, 1956 (4). The proposals of the several groups were presented and discussed. General agreement was reached on a broad outline and on the major pedagogical characteristics of the course. Following the December meeting, several of the centers began to prepare detailed outlines and preliminary drafts for a work conference to be held during the summer of 1957 at the Massachusetts Institute of Technology.

About fifty people participated in the 1957 summer work session. Most of this group were high-school and university physics teachers. In addition, there were specialists in such fields as testing, film-making, educational administration, and editorial production. Work was begun on all parts of the project: textbook, laboratory experiments, films, tests, teacher's guides, the "Science Study Series," and instructional programs for teachers. The textbook and the laboratory programs were given priority so that enough material would be ready by the end of the summer to make it possible to use a preliminary version of the course in a few schools during the following year. Early use of the course in

Some Members of the Physical Science Study Committee Staff
Summer 1957

F. Friedman
W. Michels
H. Gross
G. Finlay
B. Richardson

L. Cooper
J. Kaplan
F. Ferris
P. Axel
M. Wilson
C. Hinckley
J. Stubblebine

R. Shult
V. Erilane
S. Wang
L. Roberts
L. Fermi
J. Cross
P. Lund
Unidentified
J. Kane

B. Kingsbury
P. Boylan
E. Smith
R. Donaldson
U. Haber-Schaim
F. Harris
M. DeVoto
G. Carr
B. Griffin

T. Dillon
D. Lazarus
E. Goldwasser
J. Walters
A. Kerman
L. Lewis
J. Marean
A. Peterson

B. Diver
T. Sadowski
J. Halpern
W. Everette
D. Tomer
H. Knauss
J. Paige
R. Jones
Unidentified
A. Josephs

A. Jubenville
R. A. Granger
G. Waltz, Jr.
W. Burton
N. Perkins

B. Richards
R. Marden
E. P. Little
L. Laudecker

schools permitted an almost immediate application of classroom feedback to the problems of revising existing materials and helping to shape materials yet to be developed.

During the 1957-58 school year, eight teachers used preliminary versions of the course with about three hundred students. These teachers had participated in the committee's summer project, and they and their schools were in a position to work closely with other members of the committee in evaluating their teaching experience. During that first year, it was possible to supply teachers with printed versions of Parts I and II of the course, mimeographed copies of Part III, and the materials from which preliminary designs of the laboratory apparatus could be built. Formal materials for Part IV of the course were not available that year. Because of the newness and the tentativeness of the materials, few classes moved fast enough that year to get into Part IV. For those that did, the teachers improvised from their knowledge of the plans for Part IV.

This first year of experience in teaching the course was extremely fruitful. Because the number of classes was small, the committee's staff was able to work intensively with the teachers. In some cases modifications of approach were discussed and tried out on the spot. The over-all evaluation was highly favorable. Teachers and students found the course stimulating and were enthusiastic. The close relation between the laboratory and the textbook and the premium on student initiative in the laboratory were well received. The results of the preliminary achievement tests used that year indicated that students attained the desired levels. The desirability of revising the textbook and the laboratory program was pinpointed at various places in Parts I and III. Part II was judged as markedly successful. In that part of the course, teachers found that the mutual reinforcement of the textbook and the laboratory program enabled them to bring students to a deep understanding of advanced ideas on wave behavior. The year's experience also suggested the desirability of a change in the way in which the committee had expected schools to acquire laboratory apparatus. Originally the committee hoped that the use of simple designs of apparatus to concentrate on fundamentals would not only clarify the subject but make it possible for schools to acquire most of the necessary laboratory material locally with construction to be done by students. While the local acquisition of materials and local construction of apparatus were shown to be possible and instructive, shopping and construction time was costly. This excessive time burden on students and teachers was confirmed in the following year, and the committee turned to the development of easily assembled kits of pre-formed apparatus.

During the summer of 1958, five universities offered institutes on the course. The institutes were from six to eight weeks in duration. These institutes were organized under the National Science Foundation's regular program of support to institutes for teachers of science and mathematics. The institutes enrolled a few more than three hundred teachers. As a part of the experimental development of the course, the preliminary course materials were supplied without cost to any of these teachers who wished to use them during the following year, 1958-59. The course was used by about 270 teachers and 11,000 students.

The course materials available for that school year were not complete, but represented a considerable advance over the year before. The preliminary textbook included a partially revised version of Part I, and the textbook extended through the first half of Part IV. The committee was able to supply preliminary laboratory guidebooks and apparatus for Parts I, II, and III and a partial laboratory program and apparatus for Part IV. A preliminary edition of the teacher's guidebook was distributed for all portions of the course except the latter half of Part IV. A complete set of ten achievement tests was used. Although a number of films had been completed during the year, only a few were available for use in the schools at the most appropriate times.

The feedback from the larger number of schools benefited all parts of the program. Intensive feedback

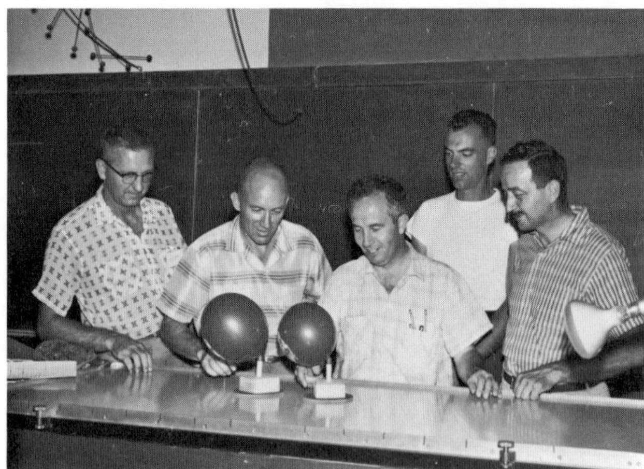

Attending one of the early PSSC institutes, in 1958, at the University of Minnesota, from left to right: Louis B. Buster, Senior High School, Everett, Washington; Darrell Tomer, Union High School, Hanford, California; John Marean, High School, Reno, Nevada (President of the National Science Teachers Association in 1962); John G. McMahon, Garfield High School, Los Angeles, California; Frank Verbrugge, Director of the Institute, School of Physics, University of Minnesota, Minneapolis. In this picture they are studying collisions and momentum with frictionless pucks.

At a 1963 Summer Institute held at Princeton University, Professor Alfred Romer, on the right, Professor of Physics at St. Lawrence University, discusses interference patterns formed by two point sources, with Mr. John J. Parrotta, Cousino High School, Warren, Michigan.

relations were maintained with a few schools. From the rest, information was derived from periodic reports, questionnaires, and regional meetings. Results from the administration of the series of achievement tests also contributed helpful information. In one school, a few students who had gone through the first three parts of the course in the previous year studied Part IV in the fall. This experience contributed several key ideas to the further development that winter of Part IV, which was used by a large number of students in the spring.

During the summer of 1959, about seven hundred teachers studied the course in fifteen institutes. For the 1959-60 school year, the course materials were provided at cost to schools that wished to use them and whose teachers had already taught the course or had studied in one of the institutes. That year about 560 teachers used the course with 22,500 students. Some of the teachers who had taught the course during the year before had moved to administrative positions, enrolled in graduate study, or had otherwise withdrawn (in many cases temporarily) from physics teaching. Of those who continued to teach physics, 96 per cent elected to continue with the PSSC course.

Except for the films (about thirty were available for use at the appropriate showing times), a complete set of preliminary materials was on hand. Feedback arrangements were the same as for the 1958-59 school year. The information gleaned from the use of the course in earlier years had already been used as starting points for some revisions of the textbook and the laboratory experiments, and these were tried out and studied. During the 1959-60 school year, the committee's major effort was directed to a complete revision of all printed materials and the design changes appropriate to the commercial production of kits of laboratory apparatus. By the fall of 1960 the textbook, laboratory guidebook, apparatus, tests, films, and teacher's guidebook had been turned over to commercial suppliers and were available generally.

The institute programs have continued to provide opportunity for teachers to study the course in detail. During 1960-61, the course was used by about eleven hundred teachers with forty-four thousand students. As of October, 1961, a conservative approximation of the number using the course in 1961-62 was eighteen hundred teachers and seventy-two thousand students.†

Evaluation of the course has several aspects. The committee's own evaluations are directed toward the improvement of the course, not comparisons with other courses. The course differs sharply from most secondary-school physics courses both in selection of content and in style of development. Comparison with other

†As of the fall of 1963, fifty-three PSSC films are available; Science Study Series has thirty-three titles in print (see back cover for full listing); and the PSSC course is being taught now by approximately 4,000 teachers to approximately 160,000 students in the United States.

courses is not a matter of evaluating the relative merit of different methods of teaching toward the same objectives. Rather, such a comparison involves questions as to the choice of the objectives themselves. Close scrutiny of the courses is enough to confirm this fundamental difference. Further confirmation comes from the few instances in which standard examinations have been given to PSSC students and PSSC examinations have been given to students in standard courses. The results show that the students have studied different courses. The sharp difference between the PSSC course and other courses has been recognized by the College Entrance Examination Board, which has provided separate examinations in physics for PSSC and non-PSSC students. Certainly it is possible to design an examination on which matched groups of PSSC students and students from other physics courses would achieve equivalent score distributions. This procedure would hardly provide a comparison. It would prove only that such an examination can be prepared. Comparative evaluation requires common objectives—common with reference to fundamentals of substance and intellectual style.

In terms of its own objectives, the committee judges that its present course is successful in the sense that it provides a context for teachers and students through which students have reached the desired goals. Evidence comes from several sources. Performance on the PSSC achievement tests speaks of the students' understanding of content and their power to handle ideas, to apply them broadly. In preparing the achievement tests, the level of difficulty was set so that an average performance of answering half the questions correctly would be regarded as satisfactory achievement. This goal was attained. On the qualitative side, the preponderant testimony of teachers and students who have used the course indicates that it sharply stimulates the development of more powerful styles of inquiry.

The difficulty of the course and its adaptability to students of varying abilities have been the subject of a great deal of discussion by those who have used and/or studied the course and by some who have not. The results of the analysis of achievement test performance by students from various levels of academic aptitude, as measured by conventional aptitude tests, clearly suggest that success in handling the ideas of the PSSC course is not limited to a narrow band of what, by traditional measures, might be called high-aptitude students. The testimony of a majority of the teachers who have used the course supports this view. Most teachers who have used the course feel that it is appropriate for the range of student abilities that typically has been enrolled in physics. Some teachers make the point that, for the less facile student, an exposition based on experiment rather than assertion is especially helpful. Of the teachers who have used the course, a clear minority feel that the course is too difficult for average students and prefer to restrict the use of the course to high-ability students. On the difficulty of the course, the committee is inclined to agree with the student who wrote that "the course is not for those who have difficulty tying their shoelaces." The course was intended to provide a challenging experience. Students and teachers say that it does. Most of them also say that it is highly rewarding. The committee feels that the course is close to the intended mark. Certainly other course structures could be developed that would provide a satisfactory secondary-school physics course. The present course is simply a stage in the development of one satisfactory course. Indeed, through Educational Services Incorporated, the committee expects to give continuing attention to the improvement of secondary-school physics.

The committee fell a bit short of reaching its objectives of providing a one-year course. The course as it stands was prepared so that teachers could omit several sections without seriously undermining the material that follows. These are, however, omissions that most teachers will make only with regret. Without cutting, many teachers feel that the course should extend for more than a year. This problem is being met in various ways. Some teachers are making the possible cuts. Some schools are lengthening the time given to physics by teaching it for more than two semesters or by giving it more class time during the year. Some schools are trying early parts of the course in earlier science courses. The development of improved science courses at lower levels will be one of the factors influencing revision of the current PSSC course.

As of the fall of 1961, the committee has a number of on-going projects. To get information on what and when revision should occur, study of the use of the course continues. In this connection, it is now apparent that improvements in laboratory experiments for Part IV will be sought. The "Science Study Series" is being extended at the rate of nearly a book each month. The film studio of Educational Services Incorporated is continuing its work on the series of films that are a part of the course.

Another current activity is the preparation of a second battery of achievement tests to augment the existing series. In the development of these new tests, techniques are being investigated that are expected to extend the information that can be obtained on the nature as well as the over-all quality of student performance.

In the general area of evaluation, other studies are

planned. While the course was not planned specifically as preparation for college work in physics, it is natural to look at students' performance in college physics for one source of evidence on the effectiveness of the course.

With growing numbers of students completing the PSSC course in secondary schools and continuing physics in college, it will be possible to look more definitely than before at their performance in college physics. To the extent that certain college courses and the PSSC course share common goals, such studies should be helpful in reflecting the contribution of the secondary-school work. There have been a few preliminary studies of this kind, necessarily with small numbers of students. These studies indicated that PSSC students were at no disadvantage and in several respects (grades in one study; flexibility of thought and procedure, particularly in the laboratory, in another) were at an advantage.

Another kind of investigation that is being formulated uses the extensive element of design in the PSSC course (over-all story line with closely related textbook, laboratory, and films) to provide a context for a clinical study of learning over a year-long span. Among other things, this plan contemplates the development of nonverbal as well as verbal measures of performance.

The PSSC course was planned to fit a pattern in which physics is offered as a one-year course during the eleventh or twelfth grades. The achievement of adequate depth in a one-year course required the omission of many topics that logically could have been included and for which the course as it stands lays a powerful base. Some schools are able to offer a somewhat more advanced course either because of the time they give to physics, the ability of their students, the teaching of some of the earlier parts of the PSSC course in earlier grades, or a combination of these reasons. For such courses the committee is developing supplementary textbook material, laboratory experiments, and films for a series of advanced topics.

In the development in the PSSC course of an atomic model, some teachers have found a convenient structure for moving toward the integration of their work in chemistry and physics. Several schools have developed an integrated, two-year sequence in physical science using the PSSC course and a chemistry course, either one of their own devising or one of the chemistry courses recently developed with the support of the National Science Foundation. These activities are worth further effort and support.

The development, including trial and evaluation, of a course such as that of the Physical Science Study

Committee naturally leads to suggestions on the kinds of educational experiences that might logically precede and follow such a course. A number of related activities, some of them partially stimulated by the work of the Physical Science Study Committee, have come into being. Some of those who shared in the PSSC project are now working with the Commission on College Physics, which is concerned with the improvement of physics teaching at the college level. Some are working in individual university centers on the improvement of the physics courses taught at their university. Some are turning to the problems of science instruction in elementary and junior high schools.

A great deal of interest in the work of the committee has been shown by science teachers and scientists from other countries. From the beginning, many foreign visitors have come to observe and discuss the project. This interest has led to the translation of the "Science Study Series" into other languages. Publication rights have been granted in eighteen countries. The books are now appearing in seven languages other than English. As the course materials neared completion, the interest of other countries in the use of the course (in some cases translation and use) quickened. By special arrangement, several dozen educators from abroad have attended some of the regular summer institutes of the Physical Science Study Committee. During the summer of 1961, staff members of the committee accepted three invitations to conduct intensive institute programs in other countries. These institutes enrolled secondary-school teachers, university teachers, and, in some cases, science supervisors. Two of these institutes, in Israel and in New Zealand, were national in character. One, in England, enrolled teachers from half a dozen European countries. One outcome of these institutes was that the course will be used soon in several countries. Also, during the past summer, a planning conference was held in Japan to consider the problems of translation and use of the course in that country. At the invitation of the Australian College of Education, a staff member of the committee recently spent a week in Australia discussing the course with teachers who were convened for that purpose. Similar visits have been made to India and to some of the African and South American countries. These various explorations of the applicability of the course in other countries have been supported by the governments of New Zealand and Israel; the United Nations Educational, Scientific and Cultural Organization; the Carnegie Foundation; the Asia Foundation; the Organization for European Economic Cooperation; the Office of Information Services; and the Organization of American States.

Dr. Uri Haber-Schaim, ESI, lectures at the International PSSC Summer Institute in Montevideo, Uruguay. At left is Professor Gerrado Melcher, Department of Physics, University of Chile, who acted as interpreter and section leader. The Institute was sponsored by the Pan American Union with a grant from the Ford Foundation. Local arrangements were made by the National Council of Secondary Education and the Physics Center of the Institute of Catholic Culture.

The course of the Physical Science Study Committee has proved to be rewarding to a large number of teachers and students. Clearly, its applicability is not confined to highly selected students or to a particular culture. The several hundred men and women who have contributed directly to the course have derived a great deal of satisfaction from that work. The committee looks forward to continuous improvement of the course.

NOTES

1. Gilbert C. Finlay. "Secondary School Physics: The Physical Science Study Committee," *American Journal of Physics,* XXVIII (March, 1960), 286-93.
2. Physical Science Study Committee. *Physics,* pp. v-vi. Boston: D. C. Heath and Co., 1960.
3. Stephen White. "The Physical Science Study Committee (3) The Planning and Structure of the Course," *Contemporary Physics,* II (October, 1960), 39-54.
4. This conference was reported in "Physical Science Study Committee, A Planning Conference Report," *Physics Today,* X (March, 1957), 28-29.

An Excerpt from the PSSC text, Second Edition

A special kit to perform the experiments in this section is available from Robert Bentley, Inc. For full particulars, see page 285 in Section XIII, DISTRIBUTORS AND APPROXIMATE PRICES OF ESI CURRICULUM MATERIALS.

chapter 15

Introduction to waves

15-1 A Wave: Something Else That Travels

In the last chapter we considered at some length a particle model of light, in which we supposed that light consisted of a stream of particles or corpuscles. We found that this model fails to provide completely satisfactory explanations for some of the behavior of light that we observed. We therefore find ourselves faced with a choice: we can try to construct a better particle model that will succeed where the earlier one failed, or we can look for a new model based on a completely different concept. Let us try the second approach.

The most basic thing to be accounted for in *any* model of light is the fact that light travels through space. In looking for a new theory, we first ask whether there is anything except a particle (or stream of particles) that can move from one point to another. The answer is "yes." Consider, for example, what happens when we drop a pebble into a quiet pond. A circular pattern spreads out from the point of impact. Such a disturbance is called a *wave*, and if you watch the water closely enough, as such a wave moves across the surface, you will find that although the water may be churned and jostled locally, it does not move forward with the wave. This is quite clear if you watch a bit of wood or a small patch of oil that may be floating on the pond. The wood or oil moves up and down as the wave passes; it does not travel along with the wave. In other words, a wave can travel for long distances, but once the disturbance has passed, every drop of water is left where it was before.

If we look around us, we can find all sorts of examples of waves. For instance, we notice an American flag as it ripples in the breeze at the top of a flagpole. The ripples or waves travel out along the cloth. Individual spots on the cloth of the flag, however, hold their positions as the waves pass by. The fourth white star in the bottom line on the field of blue always remains the fourth star in the bottom line and its distances from the four edges of the flag remain unchanged. Just as the water does not travel with the water waves, so the cloth of the flag remains in place when the waves have passed through it.

Some waves are periodic or nearly so; the

motion of the material repeats itself over and over. Not all waves, however, have this property. For example, when you slam the door of a room, the air in the doorway is suddenly compressed, and this single short compression passes as a disturbance across the room, where it gives a sudden push to a curtain hanging over the window. Such a wave of short duration is called a *pulse.*

Here is another example of a wave pulse. We place half a dozen pocket-billiard balls (plastic croquet balls will work, too) in a straight line so that each ball is touching the next one. We then roll another ball so that it strikes one end of the row head-on. The ball at the other end of the row moves away at a speed equal to that of the ball we rolled in. A pulse like that on the water surface or on the flag has traveled through the row of balls from one end to the other. Each ball has been disturbed; this disturbance has passed along the entire line of balls; but no ball has moved from one end of the line to the other.

You see another kind of wave—let's call it a "wave of starting"—if you watch a line of cars that has been stopped while waiting for a traffic signal to change from red to green. Shortly after the signal changes to green, the driver of the first car starts his car forward. A moment later, the driver of the second car, seeing that the car ahead of him is in motion, starts his car forward. Still later, the driver of the third car gets his car under way, and so on down the line away from the traffic signal. You can see a "pulse" move down the line of cars. It is interesting that this "starting pulse" travels in one direction while the cars travel in the other direction.

Just how fast the starting pulse travels back depends on how fast the various drivers react, and how their cars respond. If we were able to handpick a group of drivers with identical reaction times, and provide them with cars that accelerated in exactly the same way, the starting pulse would travel backward at a uniform speed.

What is alike in all of these examples? In each case the disturbance travels through some medium—through the water, the cloth of a flag, the billiard balls, or the line of cars; but the medium does not go along with the disturbance. Disturbances which travel through media are what we mean by waves. We can now answer the question we asked at the beginning of this section: is there anything except a particle that can move from one point to another? A wave, a thing which is not itself a particle of matter, can go from one place to another.

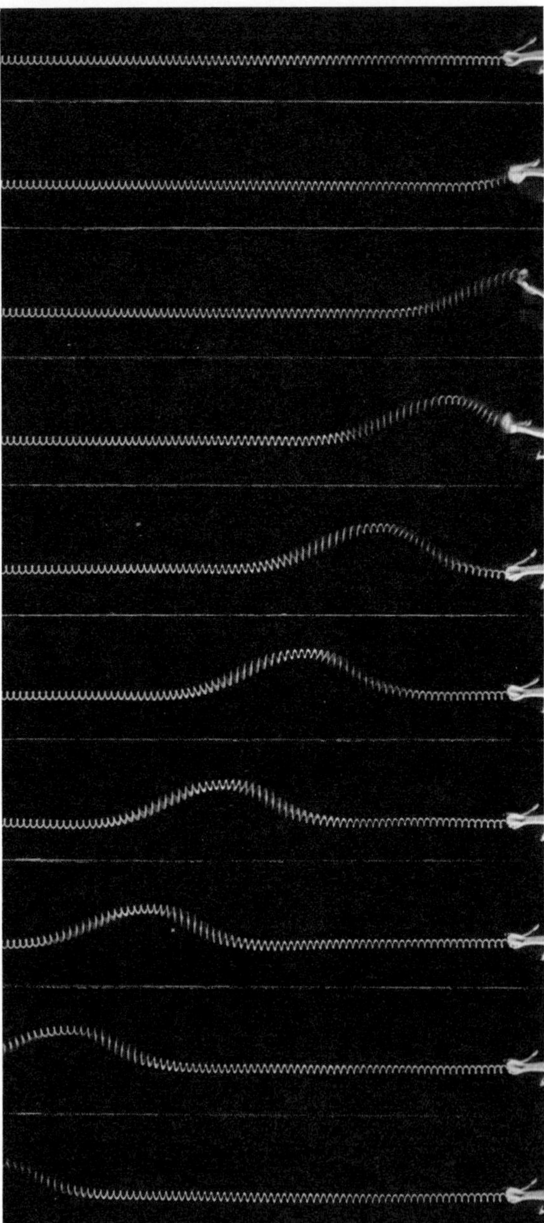

15-1 The generation and motion of a pulse along a spring shown by a series of pictures taken with a movie camera.

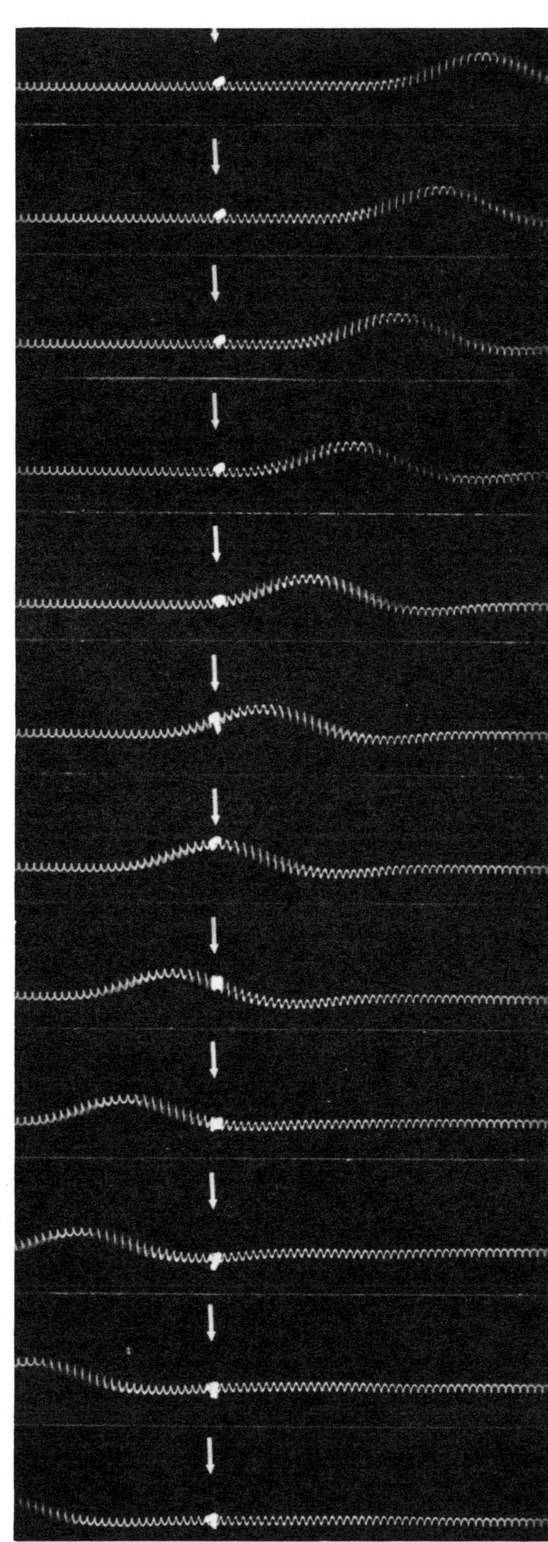

15-2 The motion of a pulse from right to left along a spring with a ribbon around one point. The ribbon moves up and down as the pulse goes by, but does not move in the direction of motion of the pulse.

15-2 Waves on Coil Springs

Do waves really behave like light? To find out, we must know more about them. When we know how they act, we can compare their behavior with what we know about light and with other things that we can find out about it. The variety of examples we have mentioned also suggests that waves are worth studying for their own sake.

It is convenient to start our study of waves with a coil spring.* Figure 15–1 shows pictures of a pulse traveling along such a spring. These pictures were taken by a movie camera at intervals of $\frac{1}{24}$ of a second.

We see that the shape of the pulse does not change as it moves along. Except for the fact that the pulse moves, its picture at one moment is just like a later picture. Also we see that the pulse moves the same distance in each interval between pictures—it moves along the spring at constant speed.

The spring as a whole is not permanently changed by the passage of the pulse. But what happens to each small piece of spring as the pulse goes by? To help us fix our attention on one piece, we can mark the spot by tying on a bit of white string or ribbon as shown in Fig. 15–2. If we then shake the spring to start a pulse moving along it, we can see how the marked spot is displaced. We find that it moves at right angles to the spring as the pulse passes it.

Other pieces of the spring, as well as the marked spot, also move. We can see which pieces are moving and which way they go if we look at two pictures, one of which is taken shortly after the other. Here we shall use two successive pictures taken from Fig. 15–2. We have printed these two pictures together in Fig. 15–3 so that we see the pulse in two successive positions just as we would see it in a rapid double exposure. Below the photo in Fig. 15–3 we have traced the pulse in its earlier position, and the gray line shows the later position. As the arrows show, while the pulse moved from

* If you find it hard to get a coil spring, a flexible clothesline or a rubber tube will also do pretty well. Tie one end to a doorknob and shake the other. If the clothesline or tube is sufficiently heavy, you will get good pulses that travel slowly enough for easy observation.

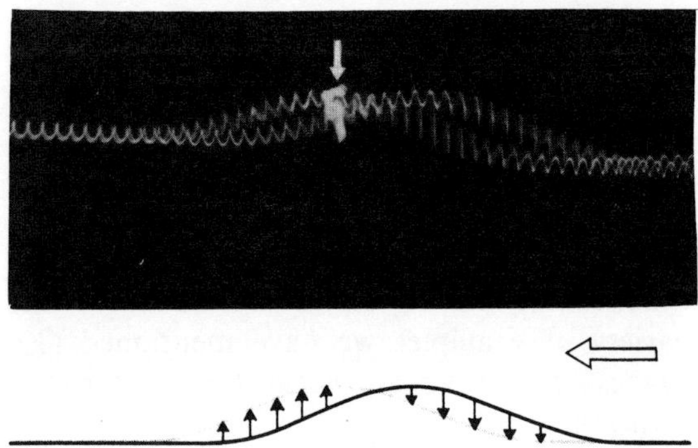

15-3 The relation between the motion of a pulse traveling from right to left and the motion of the coil. The photograph shows the pulse in two successive positions. The arrows in the diagram indicate how the coil moves as the pulse passes. The large, open arrow shows the direction of the motion of the pulse.

right to left, each piece of the coil in the right-hand half of the pulse moved down and each piece of coil in the left-hand half moved up.

If the pulse were moving from left to right, just the reverse would be true, as we show in Fig. 15–4. Here we use a schematic pulse because it is a little easier to work with and we can make the time interval between positions as short as we wish. In this way we can determine the instantaneous motion of the coil. Thus, if we know in which direction the pulse is moving, we can determine how each point of the spring moves at any particular stage in the passage of the pulse. On the other hand, if we know how the parts of the spring move, we can determine the direction in which the pulse is traveling.

We now have a good notion of how the pieces of spring move, even though there is no visible motion in any one of our pictures. Really, what we have done is to observe (1) that any pulse moves undistorted at constant speed along the spring and (2) that the spring itself moves only at right angles to the motion of the pulse. We can combine these two pieces of information to learn how each part of the spring moves at any time. Of course, we have looked only at the simplest waves, and the statement we have just made may not be true of all waves. Even in the cases we have examined, a sharp eye may detect slight deviations from our description. Nevertheless we have formed a useful first picture. With slight changes it applies to many other waves.

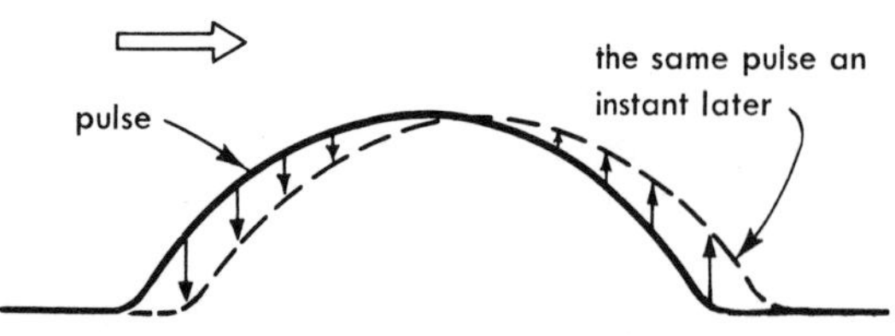

15-4 The relation between the motion of a pulse traveling from left to right and the motion of the spring.

15-3 Superposition: Pulses Crossing

So far we have discussed the behavior of a single pulse traveling in one direction. But what happens when one pulse moves from right to left at the same time that another moves from left to right? Particularly, what happens when the two pulses meet? Do they pass through each other, or do they somehow knock each other out?

The best way to find out is to try. The photographs in Fig. 15–5 show what happens when two pulses are started at opposite ends of a spring at the same time, one traveling from left to right and one from right to left. The top pictures show the pulses approaching each other as if each had the spring to itself. As they cross each other, the two pulses combine to form complicated shapes. But after having crossed, they again assume their original shapes and travel along the spring as if nothing had happened, as is indicated by the pictures at the bottom. The left-going pulse continues to travel to the left with its original shape. The right-going pulse continues to move on to the right with its earlier form. We can perform this experiment over and over with different pulses. We always get the same general result.

The fact that two pulses pass through each other without either being altered is a fundamental property of waves. If we throw two balls in opposite directions, and they hit each other, their motion is violently changed. The crossing of waves and the crossing of streams of balls made of solid matter are thus two very different processes.

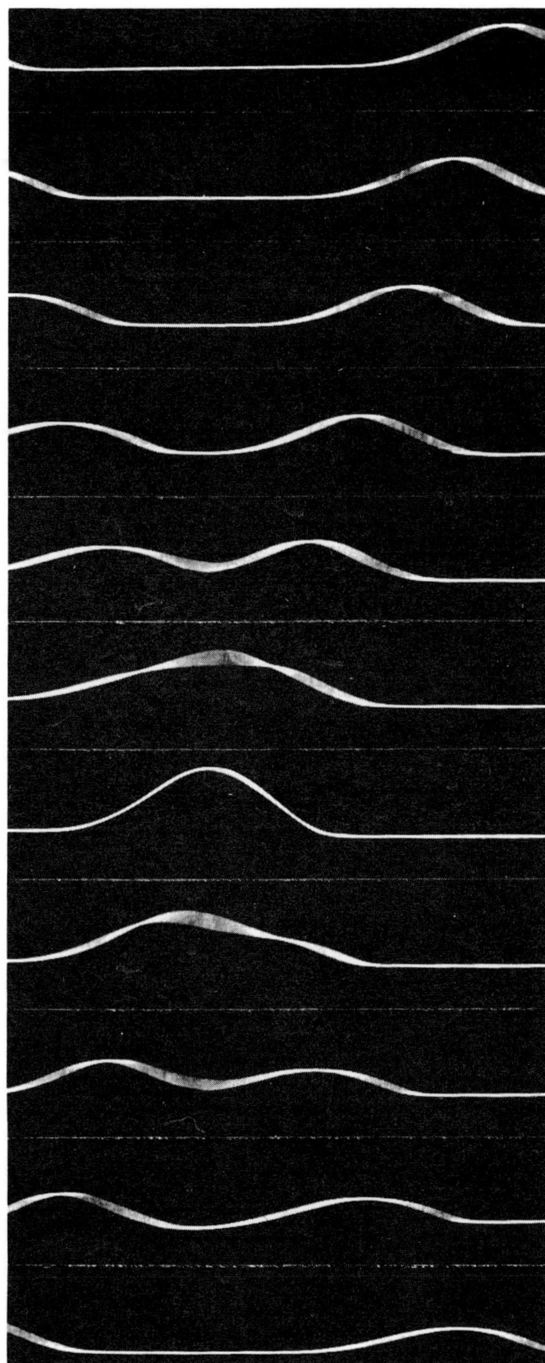

15-5 Two pulses crossing each other. Notice that the two pulses have different shapes. Thus we can see that the one which was on the left at the beginning is on the right after the crossing, and vice versa.

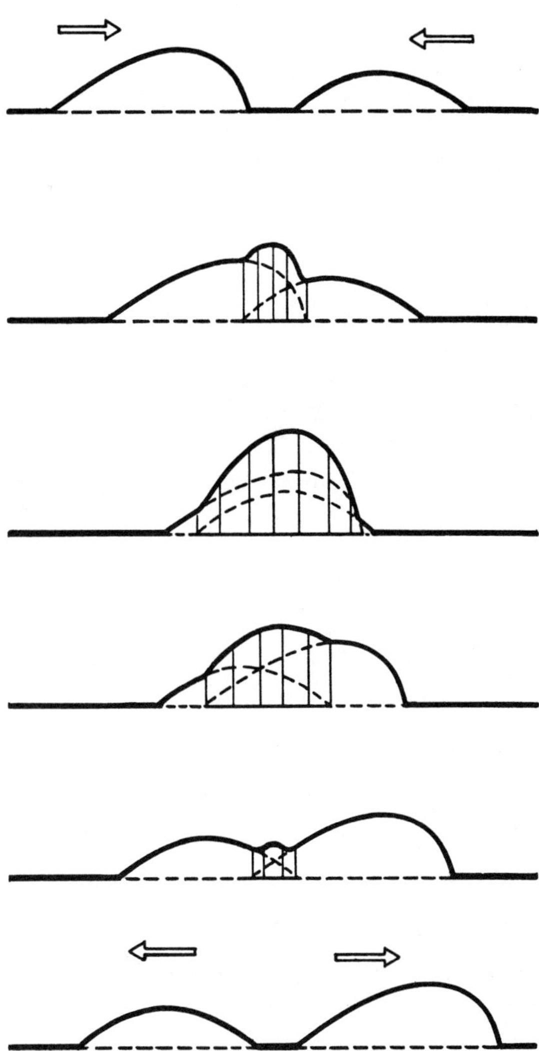

15-6 The superposition of two pulses. The displacement of the combined pulse is the sum of the separate displacements.

Let us now take a closer look at the two pulses crossing each other (Fig. 15–5). Often the shape of the combined pulse does not resemble the shape of either of the original pulses. We can see its relation to them, however, if we visualize each of the original pulses at the position it would occupy if alone; then we add up the displacements of the original pulses to get a new pulse. We find that the total displacement of any point on the spring at any instant is exactly equal to the sum of the displacements that would have been produced by the two pulses independently. The method is illustrated in Fig. 15–6. It works for any two pulses. As a

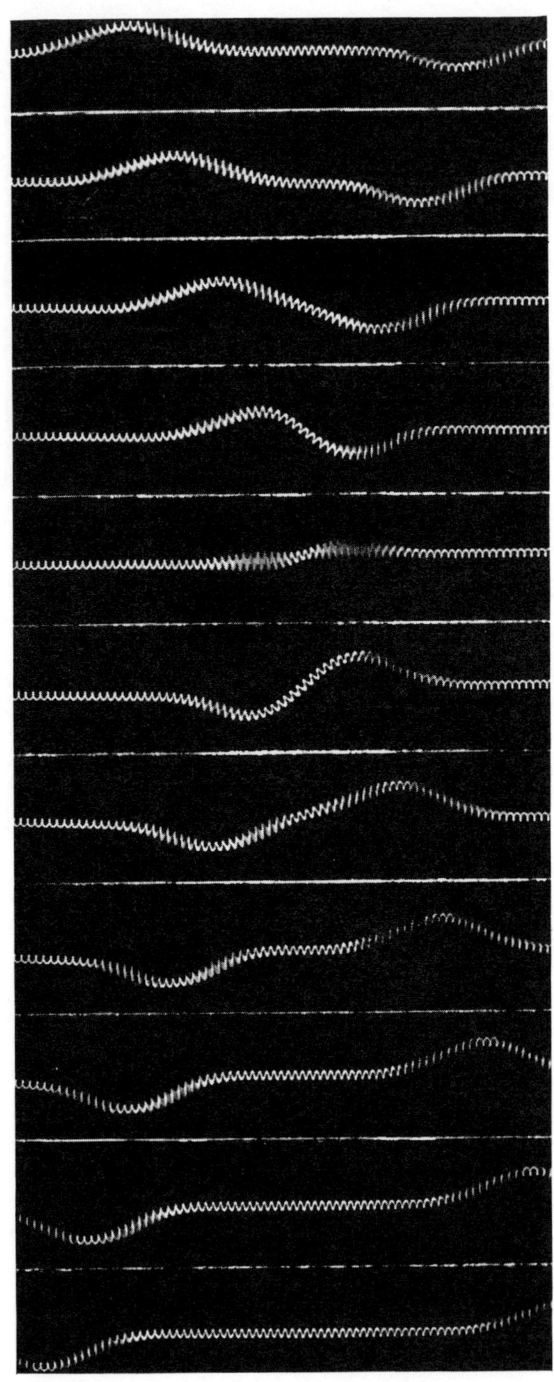

15-7 The superposition of two equal and opposite pulses on a coil spring. In the fifth picture they almost cancel each other.

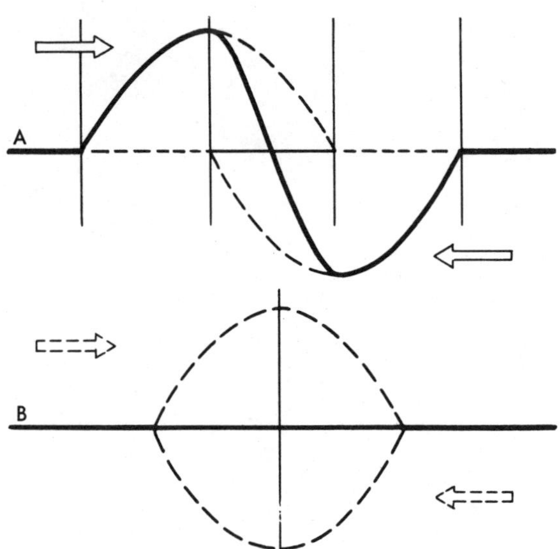

15-8 The superposition of two equal and opposite pulses. (A) Before complete cancellation. (B) At complete cancellation.

matter of fact, it also works for more than two pulses—the displacements due to any number of pulses can be added.

We can summarize the whole situation as follows. To find the form of the total wave disturbance at any time, we add at each point the displacements belonging to each pulse that is passing through the medium. That this simple addition gives the actual displacement of the medium is called the *Superposition Principle*.

Let us apply the Superposition Principle to two special cases. First, let us consider the experiment shown in the sequence of pictures of Fig. 15–7. We consider the combination of a pulse that displaces the spring downward and travels along the spring from the right-hand end with one that displaces the spring upward and travels from the left. Suppose that the two pulses have exactly the same shape and size and that each is symmetrical. Notice that in one picture the addition of equal displacements upward (plus) and downward (minus) leaves us with a net displacement of zero. There is clearly a moment, as the pulses pass each other, when the whole spring appears undisplaced. (See also the drawing of Fig. 15–8.) Why does the picture not look exactly like a spring at rest? Let us consider the difference between an undisplaced spring carrying two equal and oppo-

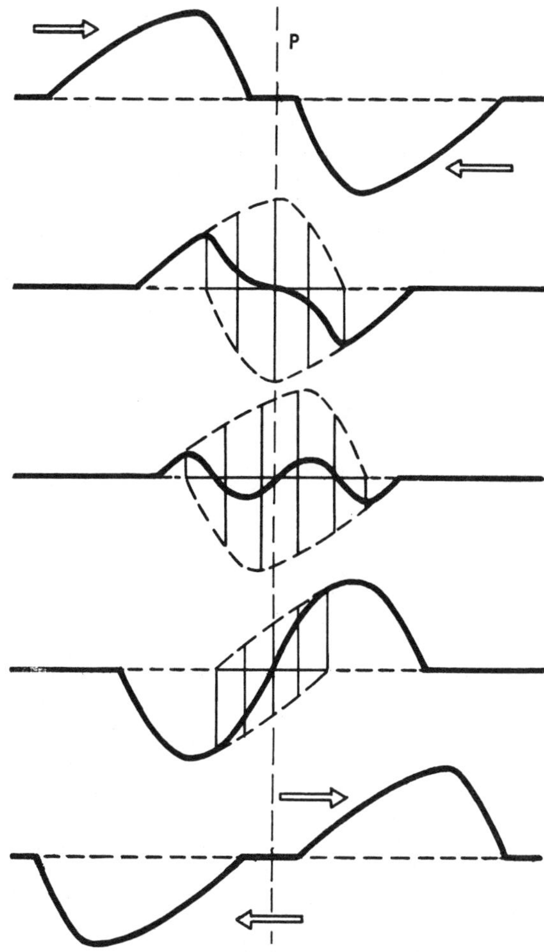

15-9 The superposition of two asymmetrical but similar pulses. Notice that the point midway between them remains at rest at all times.

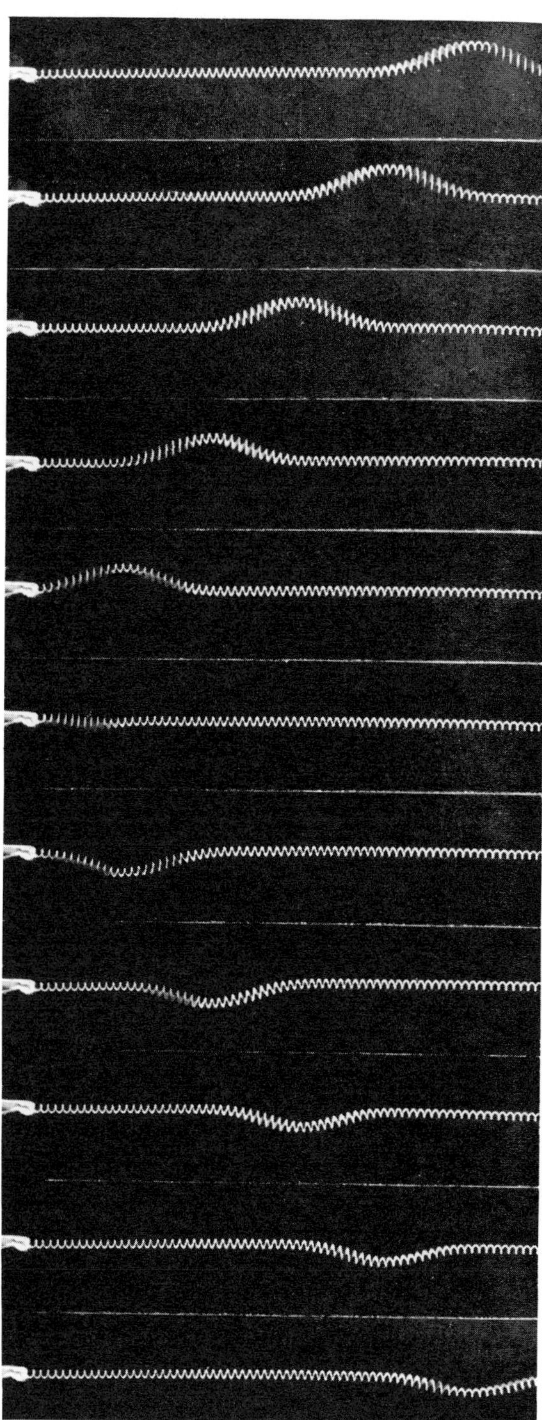

15-10 Reflection of a pulse from a fixed end. The reflected pulse is upside down.

site wave pulses and an undisplaced spring carrying no wave at all. When the spring carries no wave, all the various pieces of spring stand still at all times. On the other hand, when two equal and opposite waves are passing, there is only one instant when the spring is passing through its rest position, and at that instant the spring is moving. The motion shows up as a blur in the pictures, just as a snapshot of a rapidly moving airplane appears blurred.

Our second special case is shown in Fig. 15–9. Here we have two similar pulses, one coming from the right and one from the left. In one the displacements are upward and in the other they are downward. These pulses differ from those of Fig. 15–7 in that neither is symmetrical, although the two are alike in shape and size.

Because neither of the pulses is symmetrically shaped, they never completely cancel each other. But there is always one point P on the spring which will stand still. That point is exactly halfway between the two pulses. As the pulses come together, they pass simultaneously through that halfway point in such a way that the highest point of one pulse and the lowest point of the other just cancel each other out. The same argument applies to any other pair of corresponding points on the pulses. They always arrive at the midpoint of the spring together, one on top and one at the bottom. Consequently, the midpoint stands still.

15-4 Reflection and Transmission

When a pulse moving on a spring comes to an end that is held fixed, it bounces back. This reversal of direction is called *reflection*, and the pulse that comes back is called the *reflected pulse*. In Fig. 15–10 the fixed end is on the left. In the original or *incident pulse*, which moves to the left, the displacement is upward. The returning pulse has its displacement downward. The pulse comes back upside down, but with the same shape that it had before it was reflected.

You may wonder why the reflected pulse is upside down. The reason for this behavior is that one point on the spring, in this case the end point held by the hand, does not move. We have already met a situation where a point on the spring remained at rest; this was the point P in Fig. 15–9. Cover the right-hand half of Fig. 15–9 and you will see an upward pulse moving to the right, "flattening out" as it approaches P, and finally being reflected upside down. Now, at the front of an upward pulse, the spring itself moves upward (Fig. 15–3). When the front of the pulse in Fig. 15–9 gets to P, the point P should move upward. But since P remains at rest, the upward motion of the spring must be canceled by a downward motion. The only difference between the situations shown in Figs. 15–9 and 15–10 is that in Fig. 15–9 we supply the necessary downward motion by sending a downward pulse from the right, whereas in Fig. 15–10 we supply the downward motion by simply holding the end point fixed.

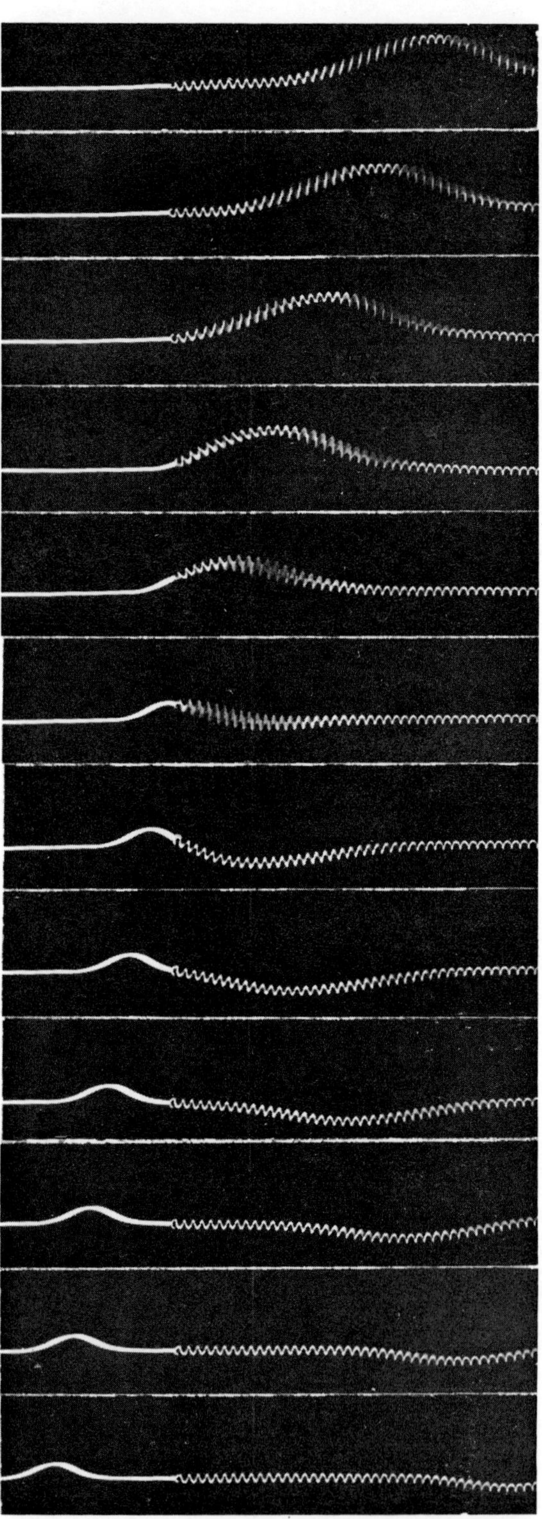

15-11 A pulse passing from a light spring (right) to a heavy spring. At the junction the pulse is partially transmitted and partially reflected. You will note that the reflected pulse is upside down.

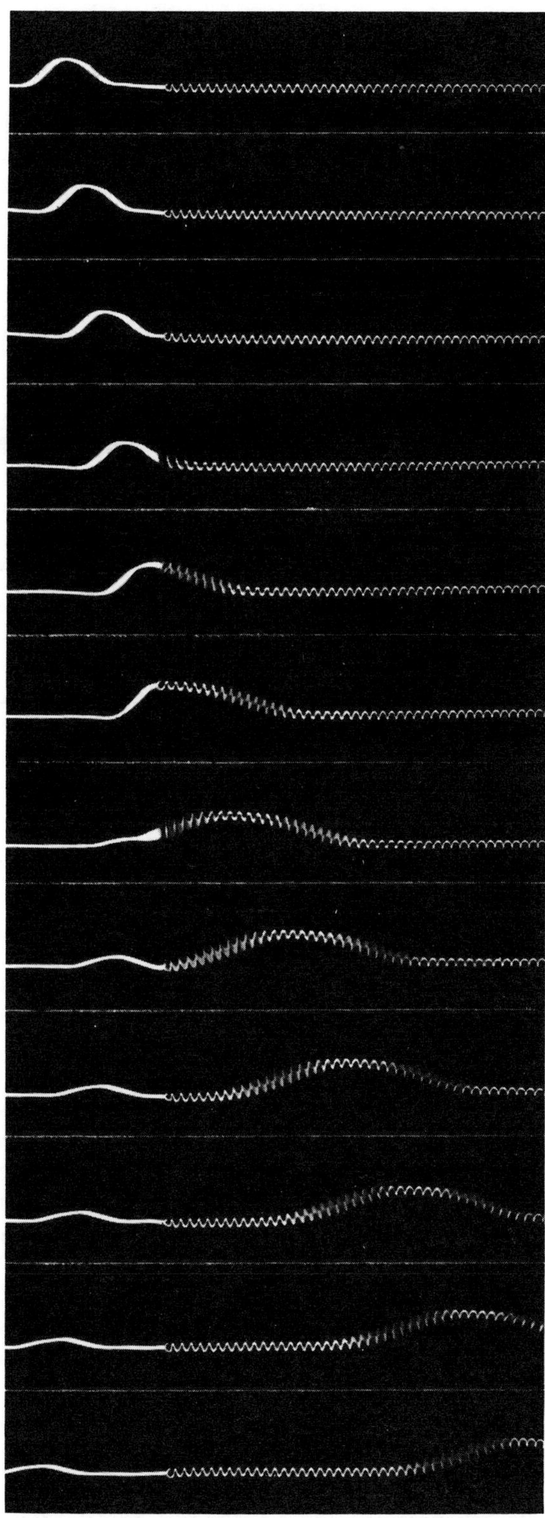

15-12 A pulse passing from a heavy spring (left) to a light spring. At the junction the pulse is partially transmitted and partially reflected. The reflected pulse is right side up.

Forcing the end point to remain at rest is just another way of supplying the downward motion which cancels the motion of the spring due to the original pulse, and then propagates to the right in the form of an upside-down pulse.

Imagine now that instead of fixing our coil spring at one end, we connect it to another spring which is much heavier and therefore harder to move. Our new arrangement will be somewhere in between the two cases (a) the original spring tied down, and (b) the original spring just lengthened by an additional piece of the same material. In case (a) the whole pulse is reflected upside down; in case (b) the whole pulse goes straight on. We may, therefore, expect that under our new arrangement part of the pulse will be *reflected* upside down, and part of it will go on, or as we say, will be *transmitted.* This effect is shown in Fig. 15–11 where the original pulse comes from the right and the heavier spring is on the left. We see that at the junction or boundary between the two springs —which are the media in which the wave travels—the pulse splits into two parts, a reflected and a transmitted pulse. Like superposition, the splitting into a reflected and a transmitted part is a typical wave property.

What happens when a pulse goes the other way, traveling along the heavier spring and arriving at the junction between it and the light spring? This is not so easy to foresee. We no longer can bracket the behavior between two situations in which we know the answer. But experiment tells us what takes place. In Fig. 15–12 we see a pulse moving from the left, from a heavy toward a light spring. Here, as in the opposite case, illustrated in Fig. 15–11, part of the pulse is transmitted and part is reflected, but this time the reflected pulse is right-side up.

In summary, then, when a pulse is sent along a spring toward a junction with a second spring, we observe that the whole pulse is reflected upside down whenever the second spring is very much heavier than the first. As the second spring is replaced by lighter and lighter springs, the reflected pulse becomes small and a larger and larger transmitted pulse is observed to go on beyond the junction. When the second spring is only as massive as the first, no reflected pulse is left and the original pulse is completely transmitted. Then if the second spring is made

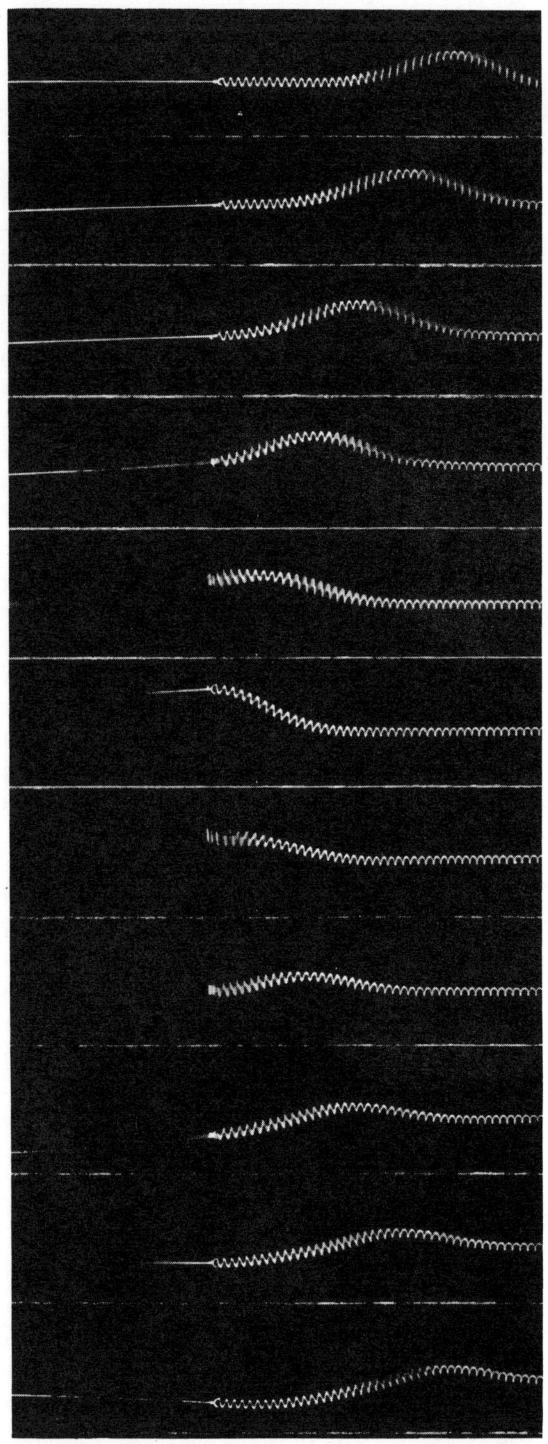

15-13 A pulse on a spring reflected from a junction with a very light thread. The whole pulse returns right side up. The blurring of the thread in the middle frames of the sequence of pictures indicates that the particles of the thread are moving at high speed as the pulse passes. Can you determine the direction of this motion in each of the frames?

still lighter, reflection sets in again, this time with the reflected pulse right-side up. The lighter the second spring, the larger is the reflected pulse. When the second spring is negligible the reflected pulse is nearly the same size as the pulse sent in. This can be demonstrated with a heavy spring tied to a thin nylon thread (Fig. 15–13).

15-5 Idealizations and Approximations

In discussing waves along a spring, we said that their shape or size remains unchanged during the motion. Indeed, if we look again at Fig. 15–1, we can notice hardly any change in the size of the pulse as it travels along. Yet, as you have undoubtedly noticed, a pulse slowly diminishes and after several reflections it dies out completely. Is it reasonable for us to ignore the dying down of the pulse? Or has our description of wave behavior been wrong in some fundamental way?

To answer these questions, we start by observing that the time it takes a pulse to die out varies with circumstances. For example, if the spring is submerged in water, the pulse dies out more rapidly than it does in air. The water offers greater resistance to the motion of the spring than the air does. We may expect that in a vacuum the pulse will require a longer time to disappear than in air; experiments to test this, although not easy to perform, justify our expectation.

Even in a vacuum, the pulse eventually dies out because of internal resistance in the spring. The amount of this resistance depends on the material of the spring. For some materials it is very small and the pulse will keep moving for a long time.

We may imagine a spring with no internal resistance kept in vacuum. On such a spring a pulse would travel forever. By ignoring the dying out of the pulses, we have idealized our real springs and considered them as if they were free from both external and internal friction. We are entitled to do this so long as we consider the behavior of a pulse only for periods of time in which the size of the pulse changes so little that we hardly notice the change. For such times, the ideal resistance-free spring serves as a good *approximation* to the real one and can therefore be made the subject of our discussion. There is a clear advantage in this, since the behavior of the ideal spring is much simpler than that of the real one.

A similar idealization occurs in our discussion of the superposition of two pulses. We learned that the displacement produced by the combined pulse equals the sum of the displacements due to the separate pulses. But if we make the individual pulses too big, we find that the combined displacement is less than the sum of the two displacements. Again, when we ignore this deviation from the simple superposition, we are discussing an ideal spring instead of the real one. We are making an approximation rather than a complete description of the real situation. But as long as we keep our displacements small enough so that we hardly notice these deviations, the ideal spring will be a good approximation to the real one; and it has the advantage of simplicity.

These are not the first idealizations we have made. In Chapter 9, for example, we made an idealized model of a gas which leads to Boyle's gas law. The law is a good approximate description of the behavior of gases in which the molecules are far enough apart; but when the molecules are too close together, a real gas does not behave like an ideal one.

Idealizations and approximations are very frequently made unconsciously. Consider, for example, what we mean when we say that the area of a piece of land is 1000 acres. Usually we get the area by measuring length and width and then calculating the area *as if* the land were completely flat. That is, we ignore the fact that there are little hills and valleys and that the area under consideration is really part of the surface of a sphere. We replace a surface of complicated shape by a simple plane rectangle. This procedure is useful only as long as there are no big mountains and the dimensions of the land are small compared with the radius of the earth. Under those conditions an idealized flat land serves as a good approximation.

Most of the problems we attack in science are fairly complicated, and in order to make progress toward understanding them we have to separate the essential from the inessential: that is, we have to make idealizations. In this chapter we have been studying waves. This is a very complicated matter on a real spring, but by mentally replacing the real spring by the idealized one, we separate the essential from the inessential and simplify the problem to help our understanding. To make the right idealization is one of the secrets of the successful scientist.

15-6 A Wave Model for Light?

In this chapter we learned about two important properties of waves which clearly indicate the advantages of a wave model of light over the particle model. First, we found that waves can pass through one another undisturbed. If we shine two flashlight beams across each other, each proceeds after the point of crossing as if the other had not been there. (See Fig. 12–4.) Similarly, we can see this page despite the light crossing in all directions between us and it. This means that the crossing of light beams resembles the crossing of waves much more than it does the intersection of streams of particles.

The second important wave property is that of partial reflection and partial transmission at a boundary. Recall now what happens when light passes from one medium to another—say from air to glass. Part of the light is reflected and part of it is transmitted, as was shown by Fig. 13–2. This is just what waves do, but streams of particles do not split up this way.

These two wave properties which appear in light lead us to go on exploring a wave model for light; but they are far from demonstrating that a wave picture is an adequate model for light. For example, when a light beam hits a glass surface the angle of reflection equals the angle of incidence, and the direction of the refracted beam is described by Snell's law. On the basis of what we have studied so far, we cannot say whether a wave model accounts for the observed changes of direction. The waves on our spring are confined to move along one line or one dimension. Therefore, there is no way of changing the direction of propagation except to reverse it. To find if waves can really account for the behavior of light, we must have waves which move in space or at least in a plane, so that we can make a direct comparison. This we shall do in the next chapter, where we shall study waves on the surface of water.

FOR HOME, DESK, AND LAB

1.* What is similar in all examples of waves discussed in Section 1? (Section 1.)

2. Suppose you look out your window and see your neighbor across the street sitting on his porch. In how many ways could you do something to attract his attention, make him move, or otherwise influence his actions? Which ways involve mass transmission and which ways wave motion?

3.* According to Fig. 15–4, along what part of the pulse is the spring momentarily at rest? (Section 2.)

4.* In Fig. 15–2, the ribbon first moves up and then down as the wave moves past it from right to left. Would the ribbon move up first or down first if the same pulse traveled from left to right? (Section 2.)

5. Figure 15–2 shows the displacement of a point on a spring as a pulse goes by. Make a graph showing the displacement of this point as a function of time. Plot displacement vertically and time horizontally with $\frac{1}{24}$-sec intervals (the interval between pictures of Fig. 15–2).

6. Sketch the motion of the spring for the pulse in Fig. 15–14.

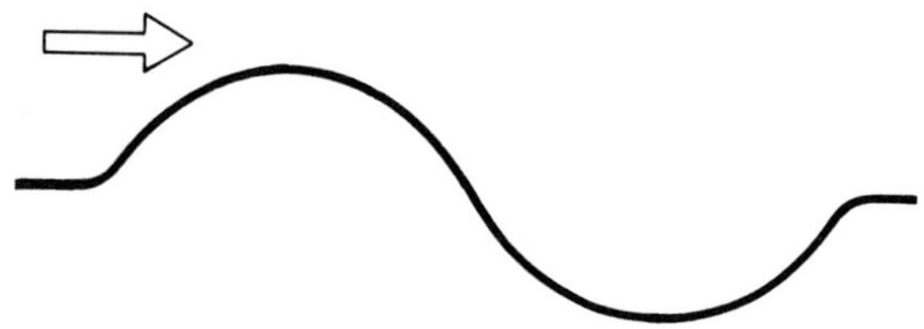

15-14 For Problem 6. A pulse moving to the right.

7.* If two pulses traveling toward each other on a coil have displacements in the same direction, can they cancel each other when they cross? (Section 3.)

8.* Two pulses have maximum displacements of 3 cm and 4 cm in the same direction. What will be the maximum displacement when they pass? (Section 3.)

9. Using the two pulses shown in Fig. 15–15, determine the size and shape of the combined pulse at this moment. Do the same thing for several other positions of the pulses.

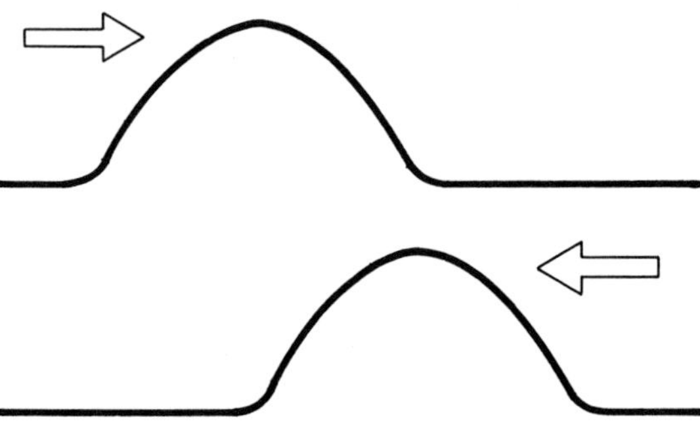

15-15 For Problem 9. Two equal pulses moving in opposite directions.

10. The seventh picture from the top in Fig. 15–5 shows two pulses at the moment of crossing. Specify the pieces of spring that are moving and their direction of motion.

11. In the fifth picture from the top of Fig. 15–7, which points are moving and in which direction do they move?

12.* A pulse, shown in Fig. 15–16, is sent along a coil toward the right. Draw the pulse traveling to the left which could momentarily cancel the pulse shown. (Section 3.)

15-16 For Problem 12.

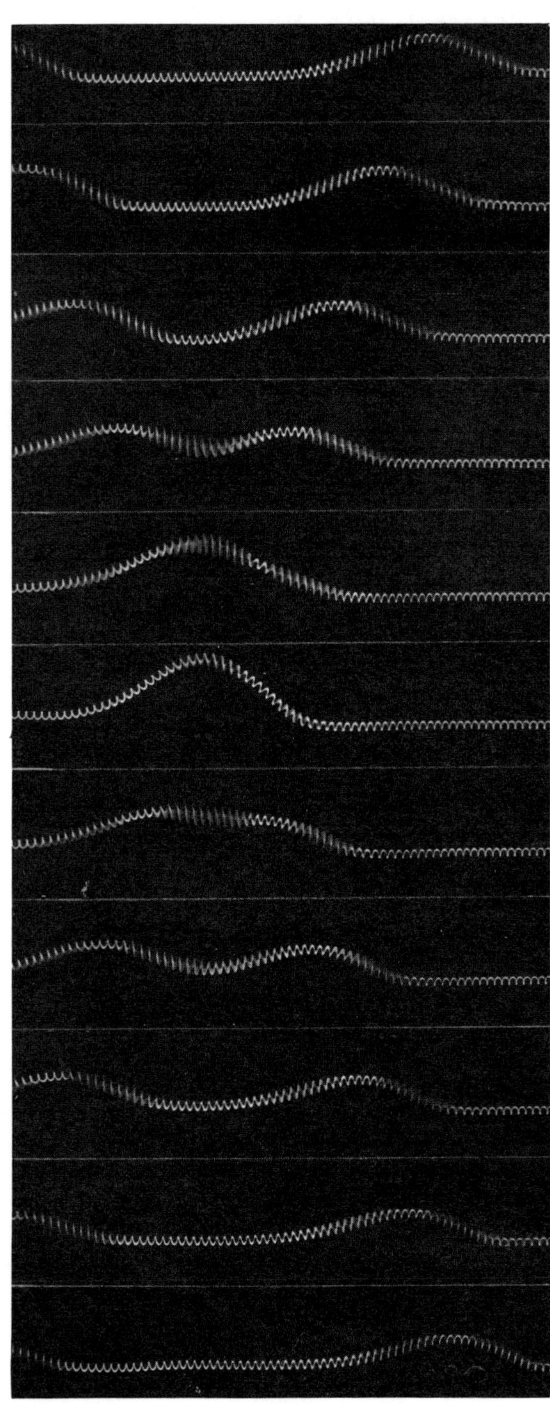

15-17 For Problem 13. Superposition of two equal and symmetric pulses.

13. In the sixth picture, Fig. 15–17, we see the superposition of two equal pulses, each of which is symmetrical about its center line.

    (a) The absence of blur indicates that there is no motion at this instant. Show that this is true by using the principle of superposition.

    (b) Assume that you deform the coil spring in the same manner as shown in the sixth picture. What will happen when it is released?

14. The sixth picture of Fig. 15–10 shows the spring at an instant when the spring is almost straight. Explain why there is an instant when this happens.

15. Consider the asymmetric pulse coming from the left in Fig. 15–6. Draw the shape it will have after being reflected at a fixed end.

16.* In Fig. 15–11, which has the larger displacement, the incident or the transmitted pulse? (Section 4.)

17.* In Fig. 15–11, what is the ratio of the speed of the pulse in the light spring to the speed in the heavy spring? (Section 4.)

18. You send out a pulse at one end of a coil, and it returns to you upside down and smaller in size. What can you deduce about the speed of the pulse on a second coil which is attached to the other end of your coil?

19. Diagram (a) in Fig. 15–18 shows a pulse moving along a rope which has sections of different densities. Diagrams (b) and (c) show the same rope at equal intervals of time later. Where are the junctions, and what are the relative densities of the rope between them?

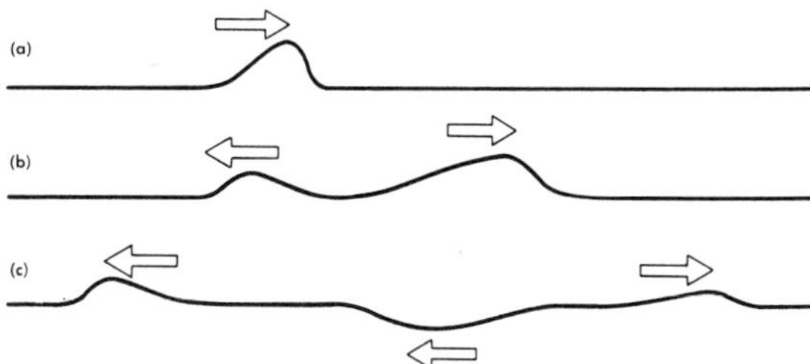

15-18 For Problem 19.

20. When light passes from air to water or vice versa, part of it is reflected. If this situation resembles that of a pulse crossing from one coil spring to another, in which case will you expect the light pulse to be reflected upside down?

21. Hold one end of a long rope with the other end tied to a rigid support. Stand looking along the rope and generate a wave by moving your hand through three fast clockwise circles.
    (a) Describe the wave generated.
    (b) Describe the reflected wave.
    (c) Describe the motion of a particle of the rope as the wave passes forward and back.

22.* How could you tell in Fig. 15–10 that the sequence of events proceeds from top to bottom and not from bottom to top? (Section 5.)

23. Whenever a pulse travels along a spring, its size decreases as it moves along.
    (a) Under what conditions are we justified in neglecting this decrease?
    (b) What is the advantage of neglecting this decrease?

24. What do we mean by an ideal spring in the context of this chapter?

25. We can say that the surface of the sea is approximately flat. Give some examples where this is a good approximation and some examples where it is a bad approximation.

FURTHER READING

These suggestions are not exhaustive but are limited to works that have been found especially useful and at the same time generally available.

BASCOM, WILLARD, *Waves and Beaches.* Doubleday Anchor, 1964: Science Study Series. A good introduction to ripple-tank work.

GRIFFIN, DONALD R., *Echoes of Bats and Men.* Doubleday Anchor, 1959: Science Study Series. A helpful supplement to the treatment of waves and wave phenomena. (Chapter 2)

HOLTON, G., and ROLLER, D. H. D., *Foundations of Modern Physical Science.* Addison-Wesley, 1958. (Chapter 29)

LITTLE, NOEL C., *Physics.* D. C. Heath, 1953. Wave propagation in one dimension; includes an extensive quantitative treatment of water waves and waves in springs. (Chapter 28)

MICHELS, WALTER C., and PATTERSON, A. L., *Elements of Modern Physics.* Van Nostrand, 1951. (Chapter 9)

VAN BERGEIJK, W. A., PIERCE, J. R., and DAVID, E. E., JR., *Waves and the Ear.* Doubleday Anchor, 1960: Science Study Series. Waves from a different point of view.

II-6 Waves on a Coil Spring

You probably have seen various kinds of waves but have not experimented with them. With this experiment you will begin a detailed study of waves.

While your partner holds one end of a coil spring on a smooth floor, pull on the other end until the spring is stretched to a length of about 10 meters. With a little practice you will learn to generate a short, easily observed pulse. Look at the pulse as it moves along the spring. Does its shape change? Does its speed change?

Shake some pulses of different sizes and shapes. Does the speed of propagation depend on the size of the pulse? To find the speed more accurately you can let the pulse go back and forth a few times, assuming that the speed of the pulse does not change upon reflection. How do you check this assumption?

Change the tension in the spring. Does this affect the speed of the pulse? Would you consider two springs of the same material stretched to different lengths to be the same or different media?

You and your partner can send two pulses at the same time. What happens to the pulses as they collide? Try it with pulses of different sizes and shapes, traveling along the same side and along opposite sides of the spring.

When the pulses meet, how does the maximum displacement of the spring compare with the maximum displacement of each pulse alone? You can determine the largest displacement of an individual pulse by moving your hand a measured distance as it generates the pulse. A third partner can mark on the floor with chalk the largest displacement of the spring when the pulses meet.

We can investigate the passage of waves from one medium to another by tying together two coil springs on which waves travel with different speeds (Fig. 1). Send a pulse first in one direction and then in the other. What happens when the pulses reach the junction between the two springs?

Tie a spring to a long, thin thread (Fig. 2). How does a pulse sent along the spring reflect when it reaches the thread? How does this reflection compare with that at a fixed end? Is the speed of the pulse on the thread greater or less than that on the spring?

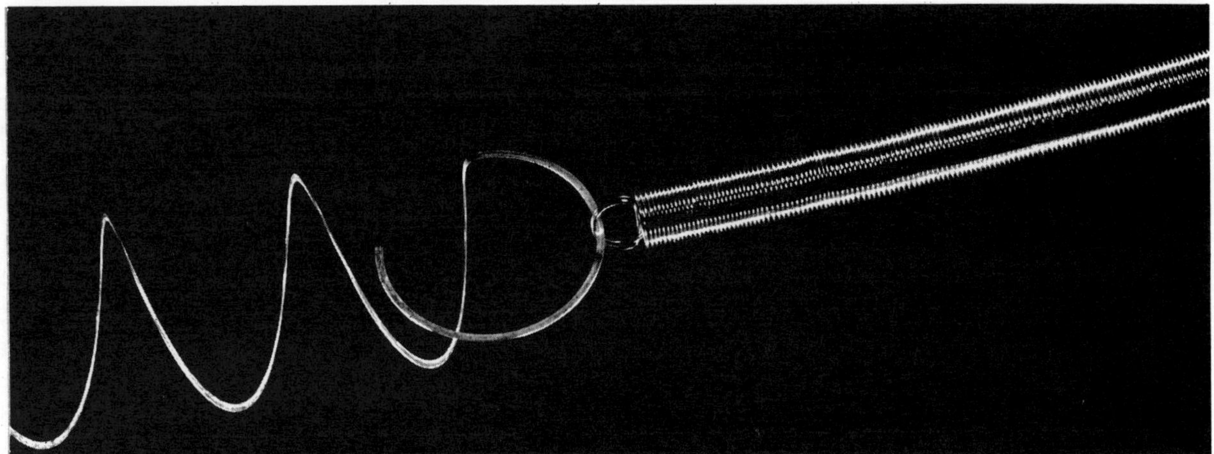

Figure 1

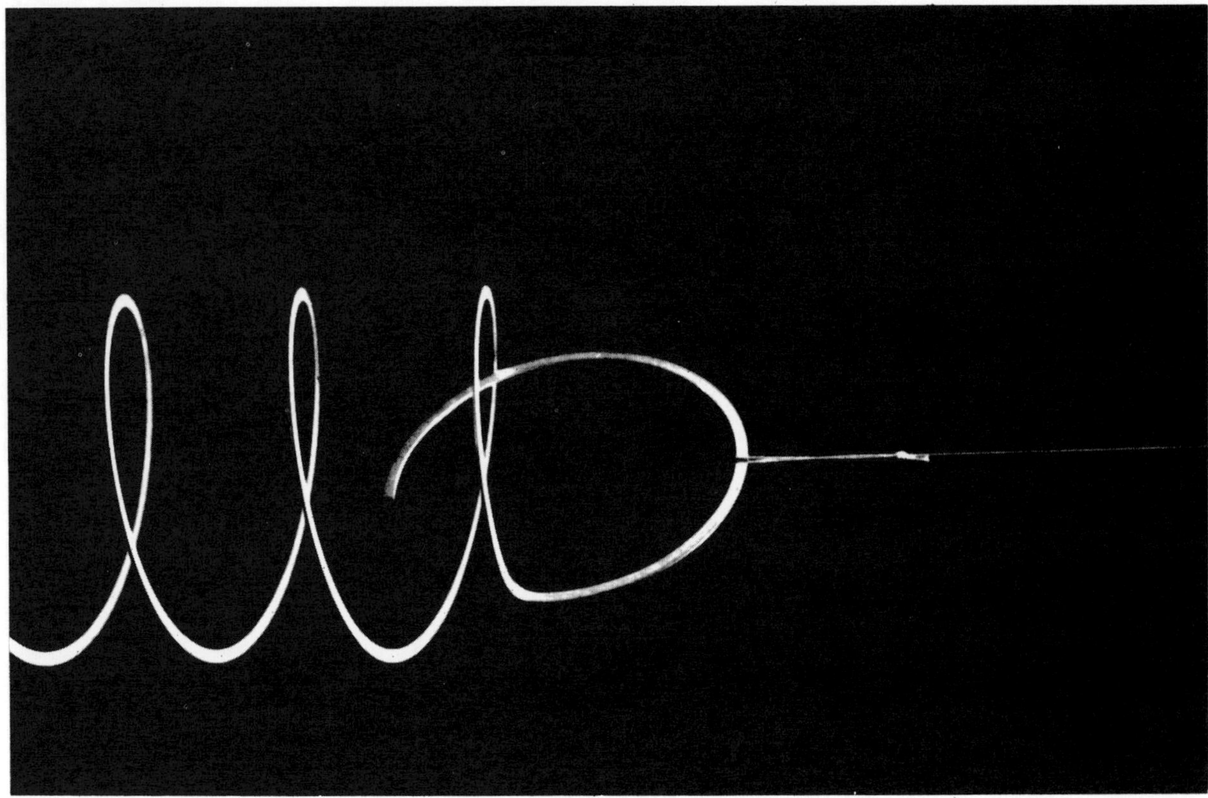

Figure 2

chapter 15

Introduction to Waves

At this point in Part II, some of the major characteristics of the behavior of light have been described and a first step has been taken to develop a model for the behavior of light. A simple particle model has been seen to be inadequate. In the last half of Part II the course turns to another model — waves. The model must describe the travel of light through air, vacuum, glass and water; it must encompass the laws of reflection and refraction; it must cover the noninteraction of intersecting light beams; it must predict the observed speed of light in various media; and it must explain diffraction effects. The next four chapters explore the characteristics of waves and their applicability in a model for light.

If some students show a little irritation at "developing a model, then throwing it away," this is a good sign of their involvement in the subject; the facts of life are that models are hard to give up. The Ptolemaic model of the solar system was clung to for centuries after its inadequacies were shown clearly. In any case, students should not get the idea that, with waves, we are now getting the "right" model. With waves we are taking the next step in the development of a model for light. Part IV returns to this problem to show that, currently, particle and wave concepts must be combined.

Students are fairly familiar with the kinematics of particles. They have watched marbles, baseballs, croquet balls and many other objects speed up, slow down, collide, rebound and fracture. Their knowledge of waves is almost sure to be sketchy. True, they have jumped rope, perhaps thrown a loop along a clothesline, watched ripples on a pond, and seen waves rolling in from the ocean. But it is a rare student who has observed these effects with sufficient care to get a good general feeling for the nature of wave motion. Thus, an important part of the development of Chapters 15–18 in both text and laboratory is the patient building of ideas about waves from concrete examples that can be seen and handled. This gives a firm footing for the concept of waves in light.

Chapter 15 introduces the general characteristics of wave motion in a simple and concrete way. The chapter deals with a pulse on a coiled spring (a piece of a wave moving along only one dimension).

Chapter 15 should be covered thoroughly since it is basic to the rest of Part II. Of the many interesting topics in this chapter, principal emphasis should go to such topics as superposition and reflection. These are essential to later work.

Chapter 15 (and the rest of Part II) is critically dependent upon laboratory work. If you can arrange it, you may want to spend extra time in the laboratory. If you have a fixed amount of laboratory time per week, you may need to augment it with classroom demonstrations.

CHAPTER CONTENT

(a) A wave is something which travels and yet does not necessarily take any matter along with it.

(b) A pulse moving along a coiled spring maintains its shape as it moves. The pulse moves along the spring, but points on the spring move at right angles to the motion of the pulse.

(c) When two pulses cross, the displacement is the sum of the displacements of the individual pulses.

(d) When a pulse reaches a new medium (such as a heavier or lighter rope or a fixed support), part of it may be transmitted and part of it may be reflected. Exactly what happens depends on the relative properties of the two media.

(e) Idealizations are necessary and useful in analyzing many physical phenomena. This is exemplified in the analysis of waves.

(f) A wave model may be suitable for light.

SCHEDULING CHAPTER 15

The following table suggests possible schedules for this chapter, consistent with the schedules outlined in the summary section for Part II.

Chapter 15	*9-week schedule for Part II*			*14-week schedule for Part II*		
SECTIONS	CLASS PERIODS	LAB PERIODS	EXPERIMENTS	CLASS PERIODS	LAB PERIODS	EXPERIMENTS
1, 2, 3	1	—	—	2	—	—
4, 5, 6	1	1	II–6	2	1	II–6

RELATED MATERIALS FOR CHAPTER 15

LABORATORY. Experiment II–6 — *Waves on a Coil Spring*. This experiment uses the coil spring pictured in the text, giving students a chance to see pulse behavior at first hand. If scheduling permits, the experiment might be performed in two parts: first, pulse propagation and superposition, and second, reflection. If it is done in one part, it should be scheduled at about the middle of the chapter. See the Lab Notes for suggestions.

HOME, DESK, AND LAB. See the HDL Notes for answers, solutions, and a table which classifies problems according to their estimated level of difficulty.

FILMS. "Simple Waves," by Dr. John Shive of the Bell Telephone Laboratories. Behavior of waves on ropes and coil springs is used to show velocities in differing media and other elementary characteristics; torsion-bar wave machines are used to repeat these and to demonstrate phenomena of reflection and refraction. Running time: 27 minutes. This film can be shown at any point in your work on this chapter. However, since the film demonstrates all of the phenomena discussed in the chapter, many teachers prefer to use it near the end to help summarize and tie together the ideas.

15–1 A Wave: Something Else That Travels

PURPOSE. To give students the qualitative idea that a disturbance can travel and to introduce the pulse (which is easier to study and analyze than the periodic wave) as a wave of short duration.

CONTENT. A wave is a disturbance which travels without necessarily taking any material along with it. Some waves are periodic, but single pulses can also be waves.

EMPHASIS. Treat thoroughly. Many students have the idea that a wave must be periodic (or repetitive). Be sure that they realize that pulses are waves because they will soon be studying pulses to learn how waves behave.

COMMENT. Some students may quibble over a statement such as at the end of the second paragraph of the chapter: ". . . every drop of water is left where is used to be . . . ." Students should realize that this is an idealization which can be approached quite closely. Waves washing ashore and waves so high that they break are cases where the water is transported short distances. These are cases which are not close to the idealization which is being discussed. Even in these cases, the water particles are transported over only a small bit of the entire path of the wave.

DEVELOPMENT. A good class discussion of this section can center about HDL Problem 2. Students are asked to give examples of how they might get a message from one point to another and list each of these as either mass transmission or wave motion. Some of the examples will require discussion before you can decide in which category they belong. (Some students will not know what "mass transmission" means unless you explain that it merely implies that some object has gone from the starting point to the final point.)

Some arguments will occur over whether a given suggestion is an example of mass transmission or of wave motion. Encourage sensible debate because many students will miss the whole point of the categories unless it is clear to them that the crucial question is one of mechanism. For example, if the suggestion involves opening a jar of coffee and letting the odor spread, before one can decide one must understand what odor is and how it is transmitted. If you know that some gaseous molecules are released from the coffee and eventually go to the nose, odor transmission belongs under mass transmission. But if one were to postulate (incorrectly) that odor is caused by a distinctive oscillatory pattern induced in air molecules and transferred from molecule to molecule (like sound), odor transfer would be wave motion.

Another example which might be either particle transmission or wave motion involves a string running between two windows. If you stretch it tightly and twang at one end, receipt of the twang at the other end is rather clearly due to wave motion. But what if you pull it two feet into your window, thereby removing two feet from the coil in the other window? This sounds like mass transmission in a way, but no piece of string went from one window to the other. Do not let students waste time in a case such as this, fighting over which one category is the best one. The two categories have not been that well defined! Students have learned what they were expected to learn and can go on to other suggestions or a different class activity.

An example that may amuse your class is that of a long, thin-walled rubber tube which, when observed from a distance, clearly has a small region of expanded diameter moving along it. This bulge usually would be an example of wave motion (unless you know that the bulge is caused by an animal running along inside the tube!). It would be rather unimportant and arbitrary to decide whether or not to label it as a wave if the animal were known to be running inside and causing the disturbance.

Some students will almost surely suggest signaling with a light to communicate a message. If this is suggested early, put it in the "questionable" category temporarily. When you have enough examples, return to the classification of light. If the students have gotten the general idea of this section, they should realize that the course has not yet given them enough information to decide. Inasmuch as the course thus far has not found a light particle, and we are just beginning to explore waves, you might place light in the wave category (with a question mark). On the other hand, if the simple particle model had worked, or if a more complex particle theory would work, light might belong in the mass transmission category. Indecision about where light really belongs is one of the reasons for learning more about what waves are like.

COMMENTS. Some students may get the idea that a wave cannot involve mass transmission. They will be less confused if you point out that sometimes, incidental to the wave motion, some mass transfer occurs. A common example is a surfboard carried forward on a water wave. Clearly the surfboard moves, but the waves would exist even though the board were not there. The surfboard is carried by the wave, but it is not the cause of the wave propagation.

Some students may be a bit surprised at the wide variety of phenomena that are called waves. They realize (correctly) that you cannot expect all the characteristics seen in a wave of starting automobiles to carry over to waves on a string, etc. It would be unwise to dwell on which waves have common characteristics.

At this stage we are not defining a wave. Often the term "wave" is reserved for the wide class of phenomena which satisfies the same differential equation, the wave equation. We cannot give students the wave equation, nor can we discuss it. Instead, we choose simple systems in which the wave equation holds, and observe how these systems behave. At this stage, we need only consider that property of a wave which permits the transfer of a signal without involving the sending of a material particle.

CAUTION. If you do not choose varied examples now, you may leave the student with the impression that waves must always have a medium through which to travel. The clearest examples of wave motion are those in which a wave travels in a medium which is clearly visible; everyone can see one end of the rope move up, pull its neighboring piece up, and thereby propagate a wave. Hence students are likely to associate a wave with the medium in which the wave moves. They can most easily visualize a mechanical wave whose propagation depends on the elastic properties of the medium. Eventually, however, they will have to face the idea that light is a wave motion without an apparent medium.

One way to avoid overemphasizing the medium is to be careful in your choice of statement. A phrase like, "We can see the disturbance as it moves along the rope" is probably better than "Each piece of the rope which is disturbed in turn disturbs its neighbor, giving rise to a pulse moving down the rope." Emphasis on the explanation of the propagation (or the dynamics of wave motion) may cause students to overemphasize the importance of the medium.

Another way to de-emphasize the importance of the medium in which the wave travels (aside from merely warning the class that there can be wave phenomena without a medium) is to give examples in which there is no medium. Students will accept the idea that if you twist a little bar magnet through 180°, it takes time for the effect of this new orientation to be felt. (There is no need to mention that the signal speed in this case is the speed of light. The only necessary fact, that there is a finite speed, will probably be accepted by the students without further detail.) Consider the bar magnet being turned just outside a vacuum chamber. If there were small isolated compass needles at various points in the vacuum, each would start to turn when the effect of the rotated magnet became known. This pulse of "awareness" or the pulse of "potential awareness" which would travel through the vacuum is a suitable example of a wave moving without a medium.

15–2 Waves on Coil Springs

PURPOSE. To provide a foundation for the study of waves.

CONTENT. (a) A pulse moves undistorted at constant speed along a tube.

(b) The motion of points on the tube is quite distinct from the motion of the wave.

(c) The graphs drawn of pulses will be approximations of pulses. Real pulses never have very sharp corners (or "sharp" changes in slope).

EMPHASIS. Treat thoroughly. It is important for students to develop, directly from observation, an accurate picture of wave motion. The "content" listed above, including the distinction between the motion and shape of the wave and the motion of the particles of the rope, should be understood clearly. Demonstrations, problems, and laboratory work are particularly helpful.

CAUTION. You will not want to discuss in any detail the dynamics of wave motion on a rope. Students may ask about how one piece of rope affects the next, but they will accept the fact that they cannot expect to understand this quantitatively until they know how forces affect motion (Part III).

Longitudinal waves are almost sure to come up. Students will think of them, or see them on the coil spring. For the class as a whole it will probably be best to stick closely to transverse waves — explaining that longitudinal waves are just another type of wave motion with which we do not now need to be concerned.

DEVELOPMENT. You should demonstrate pulses on a coil spring (or a rope or rubber tube), and have students work with them in laboratory, Experiment II–6 — *Waves on a Coil Spring.* It is recommended that half of two periods be spent on this experiment during the time spent on the chapter. If this is not possible, one full period should be allowed in the middle of the time spent on the chapter. (See supplement to this section for details concerning a Slinky hung on strings.)

You can clarify most of the material in this section through a detailed class discussion of Figures 15–3 and 15–4. In order to understand easily superposition in the next section, it is important for students to understand the difference between a *picture* (or sketch) of a wave and a *graph* of a property of the wave. Students may have some difficulty with this because in Figures 15–3 and 15–4 the graph closely resembles a picture. You can make this distinction clear to students by examples such as the following:

If the following figure is a sketch of an actual wave (pulse) on a rope, it was correct not to draw in the horizontal axis because the rope cannot be in two places at the same time. In making a graph of this wave we can choose whatever vertical and horizontal scales suit our purposes. We might make a graph that looks like this:

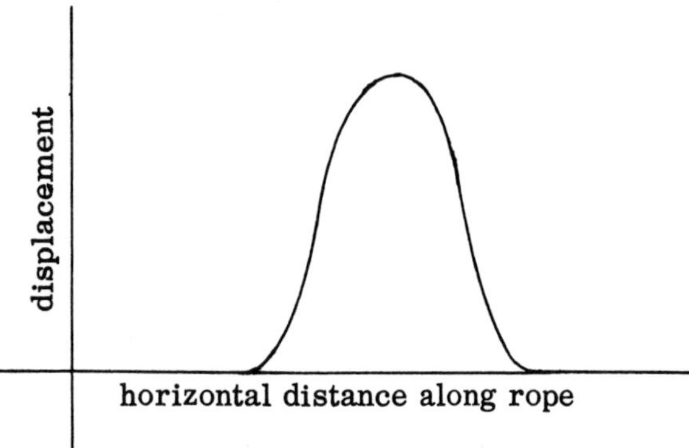

Notice that we are graphing displacement from the "zero position" against horizontal distance along the rope. On another occasion we might watch one point on the rope and graph displacement against time. Both displacement-distance and displacement-time graphs are somewhat deceptive because they have the same general shape as the wave itself. If students still have difficulty with this distinction, you can mention that if the wave looked like this, a graph of the absolute value of the displacement against a horizontal distance would look something like this:

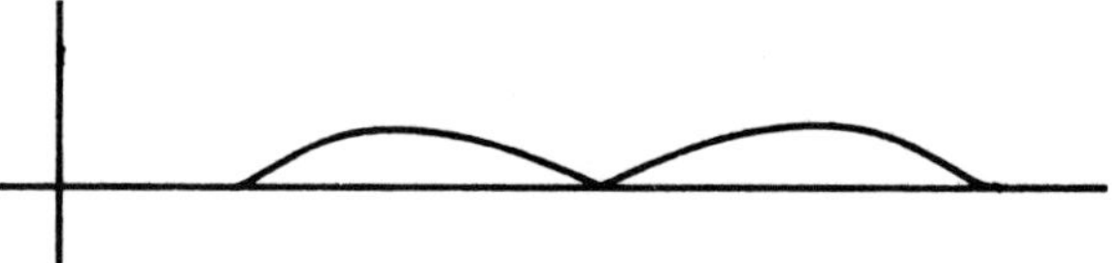

Now the possible difference in appearance should be clear.

Students should consider Figures 15–1 and 15–2 together with subsequent similar figures as basic experimental data. Studying these figures should be like making careful observations in a laboratory. The following points can be made while you discuss these figures or during discussion of some of the problems.

(1) Make it very clear that Figures 15–3 and 15–4 are idealized graphs of displacement of points on the rope from their normal position (plotted vertically) as a function of position of each of these points along the rope (plotted horizontally). Label the two curves with two different times (t_1 and t_2, or 0 and t, or 0 and 1 second, or 0 and 0.1 second). If possible, use differently colored chalk for the axis and for the curves. The portion of the axis below the curve is sometimes a source of confusion. Some students mistake the straight-line axis for the rope.

(2) Ask students whether the graphs in Figures 15–3 and 15–4 really look like one of the instantaneous frames from Figure 15–1 or 15–2. (You can return to the blurring later.) They should realize that an actual pulse would not have a sharp corner. (It is impossible to produce an actual pulse whose slope changes so abruptly.) The sharp corners are used merely as an approximation convenient for preliminary study.

(3) Once you have established that you are working with approximations, you can feel free to give students examples of triangular pulses and other "flat-sided" pulses which they can practice with easily. (Examples later.)

(4) In Figures 15–3 and 15–4, what indicates the average velocity of each point? The arrows. Their direction gives the direction of the piece of rope; their length gives the speed. An optional activity (you may want to defer this until able students have had a chance to try Problem 13 on their own) is to graph the *velocity* of individual points on the rope in

Figure 15–3 against horizontal distance. It would look like this:

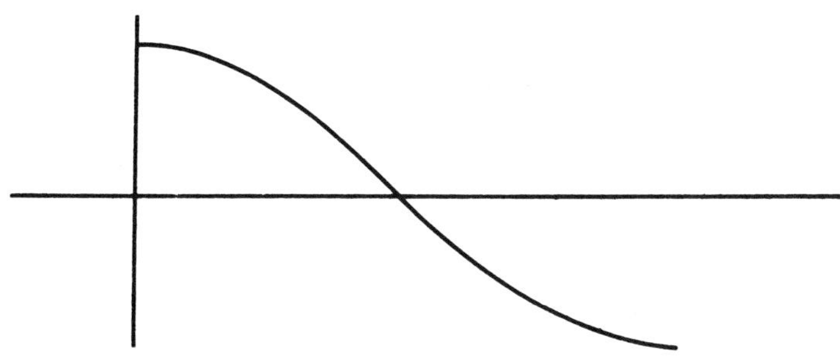

Practice in drawing such graphs will be useful in solving Problem 13(a).

(5) What is the velocity of the wave? Be sure that the students realize that:

(a) The wave itself must have a single velocity; otherwise its shape would change;

(b) The direction of the *wave's velocity* is different from the direction of motion of an individual point on the rope;

(c) The magnitude of the wave velocity is not directly dependent upon the magnitude of the particle velocities. If the displacement of each point were doubled, the particle velocities would double but the wave velocity would be unchanged (or almost unchanged).

(6) Why is there an apparent abrupt change in velocity at the edges of the pulse which is graphed? Is there an abrupt change of velocity (or blurring) in Figures 15–1 and 15–2? Would there be an abrupt change if you drew a displacement graph with rounded corners in place of Figure 15–3?

(7) Be sure to include, either during the previous discussion or now, some quantitative work. An example which can be used is shown below.

Note: If the students object to a complicated pulse like this, remind them it is an idealization. Perhaps the "real" pulse looked like this:

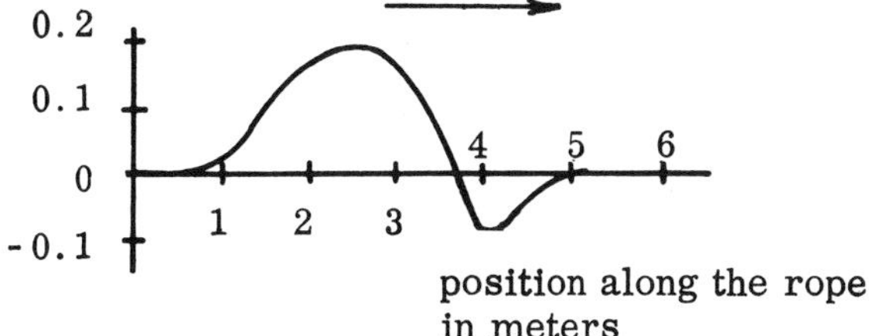

Also note that this is not a drawing but a graph; the vertical and horizontal scales are different.

Consider the qualitative problem first. Ask about points *A*, *B*, *C*, *D*, and *E*. Which ones are moving up, down, or standing still? Many students will know immediately. For other students be sure to

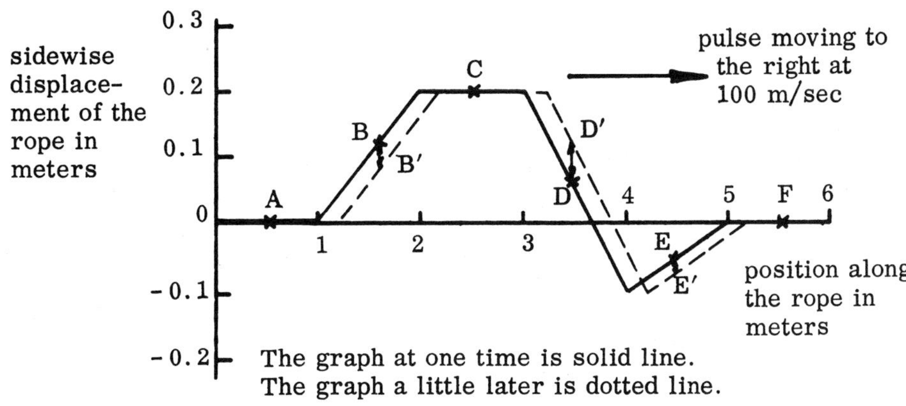

draw in the dotted-line curve showing where the pulse will be 0.002 second later. (At this qualitative stage you don't need to specify the 0.002.) It should be clear immediately that points *A*, *C*, and *F* have not moved and, therefore, that they have zero velocity. Point *B*, during this 0.002 second, moved down and therefore has a velocity down. *D* moved up to *D′* and therefore has a velocity up. *E* to *E′* shows that *E* is moving down.

Next you may inquire about which points are moving fastest. It should be clear, just from the drawing, that *D* moved farthest in the given 0.002 second, *B* next, and *E* the smallest distance — except, of course, for those points that remained at rest.

The next question is a quantitative one. What is the velocity of point *D*? To answer this, refer to a larger graph.

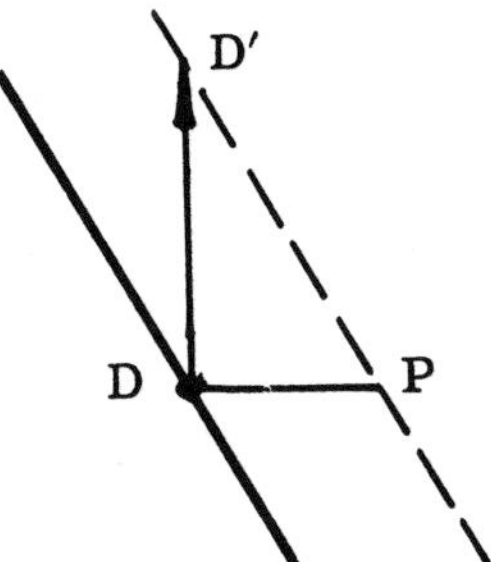

During the given time interval, *D* moved a distance *DD′* while the *wave* moved a distance *DP*. In our particular case, the distance *DP* is 0.002 sec × 100 m/sec = 0.2 meter. Referring to the original graph it is easy to see that $\frac{DD'}{DP} = \frac{0.3 \text{ meter}}{1.0 \text{ meter}}$. Then $\frac{DD'}{DP} = 0.3$. $DD' = 0.3 \times 0.2 = 0.06$ meter. Since this motion occurred in 0.002 second, point *D* is moving with a speed 0.06 ÷ 0.002 = 30 meters/sec. We can do the same for points *B* and *E*, obtaining 20 and 10 meters/sec, respectively.

It is now time to point out, if some student hasn't by this time, that the *whole piece of rope* from 1 to 2 meters is moving with the velocity of point *B*. The whole piece from 2 to 3 meters is standing still, etc.

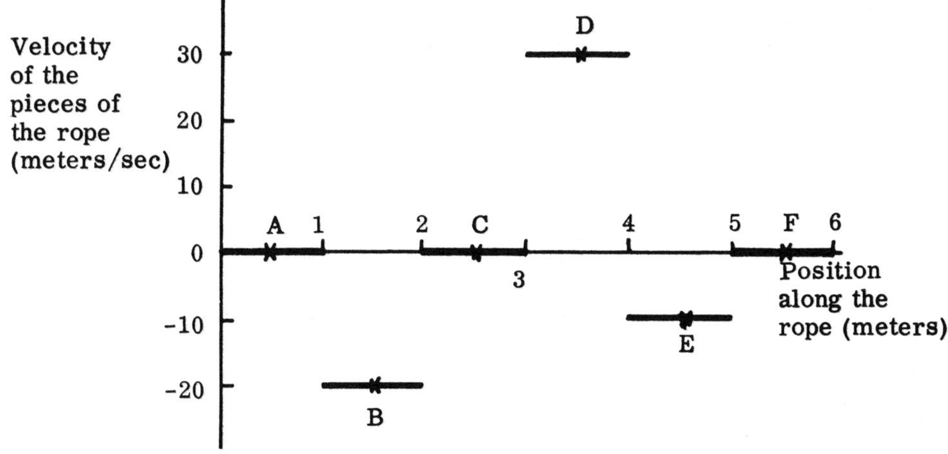

Now a graph of velocity vs. position along the rope can be made. The graph above is discontinuous. This is because our wave had sharp corners. Actual waves do not, so that this velocity graph in a practical case might look like the one to the right:

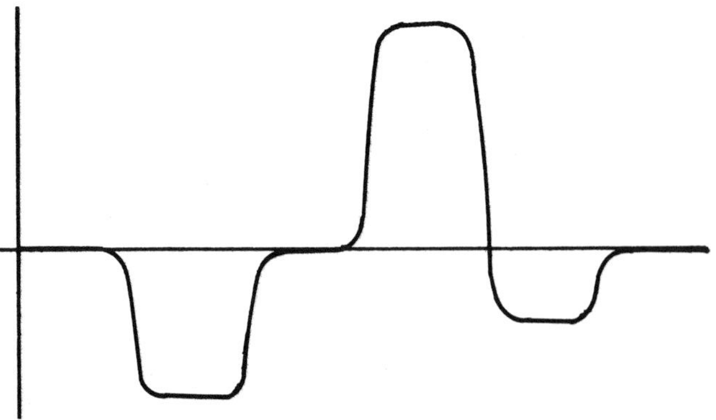

(One reason for including this discussion on graphs is that when two waves come together on a rope, their velocities add vectorially as well as their displacements.)

SUPPLEMENTARY INFORMATION ON SETTING UP A STRING-SUPPORTED COIL SPRING

The triple-length coil spring "Slinky" (supplied as a PSSC laboratory item) is the most satisfactory coil spring for this purpose. About every fifth or sixth coil should be supported by a string. Pick a spacing, say, every fifth coil, and then stick to this spacing. In order to produce waves of high amplitude which can be seen easily by an entire class, the supporting strings should be five or more feet long. When it is being used, the spring will be extended to a length of about 20 feet. In most cases it will need to be on a collapsible mounting, which can be made by running the individual supporting strings up to curtain rings which can slide along a rod or taut cable near the ceiling.

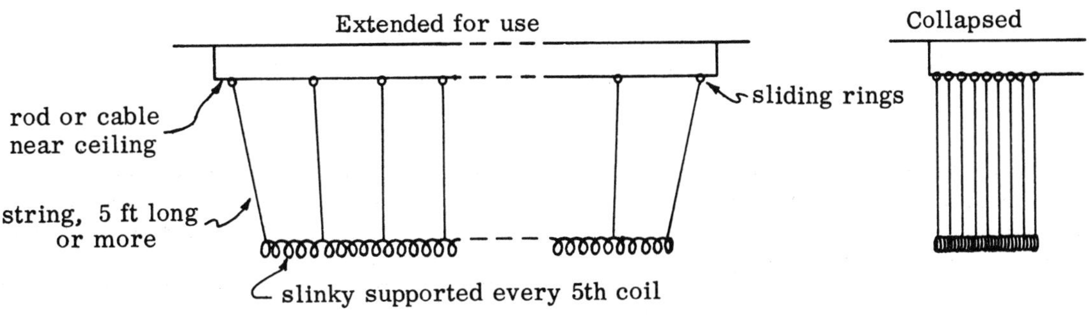

For good viewing, the coil spring should be about waist high. It can be a little higher if it is necessary to clear tables or benches. *Caution:* If you use an overhead cable for the rings to slide on, it needs to be a rather heavy one and stretched tightly. Tight clothesline is a borderline case. This is because waves in the coil spring set up waves in the supporting cable which, in turn, influence the wave on the coil spring. If you support the cable at several points, clothesline will do, but then you cannot collapse the coil spring for storage because the supports will prevent sliding the rings together. Another warning: once you have a coil spring extended 20 feet or so, do not let it snap together. It can become so inextricably tangled that destructive surgery is the only recourse.

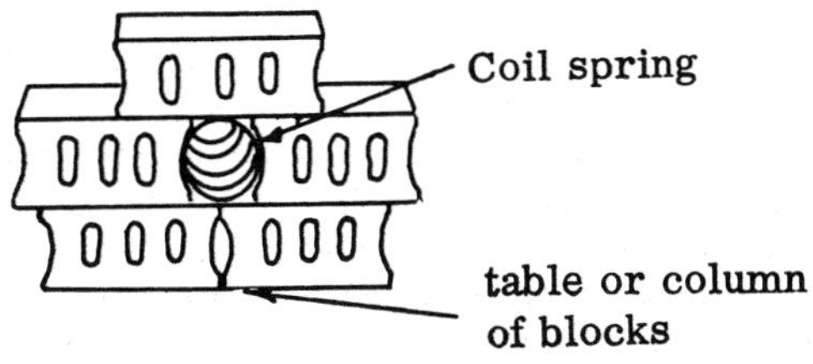

In order to keep the coil spring extended to about twenty feet, some horizontal force must be applied. The figure above shows the end supporting strings somewhat diagonal. Such slanting supports will not keep the coil spring extended. The ends must be held. A fixed end is easy. Use a table or a pillar of concrete blocks to firmly "pinch" the end. Concrete blocks, either starting from the floor or starting on a table, are particularly convenient because they can be made to grip the coil spring rigidly without damaging it.

The person who is generating the pulses can stand at the other end. Shake a pulse into the spring, and it will travel to the fixed end and reflect (coming back on the opposite side) back toward you. If you want the pulse to reflect again from your end, you must grip the end of the spring as rigidly as possible (rest your elbow on a table, etc.). Even so you will not do as well as another pillar of concrete blocks. But holding one end with your hand, you will be able to trace a single pulse up and back between six and a dozen times.

Note: To observe these waves, students need to gather at the ends of the spring. A student near the middle of the spring does not see the wave nearly as well as does a student near an end.

Producing a free end is more difficult than producing a fixed end unless you have an extra long room. Ideally you produce an open end by holding that end with a long string (half the length of the extended spring or more).

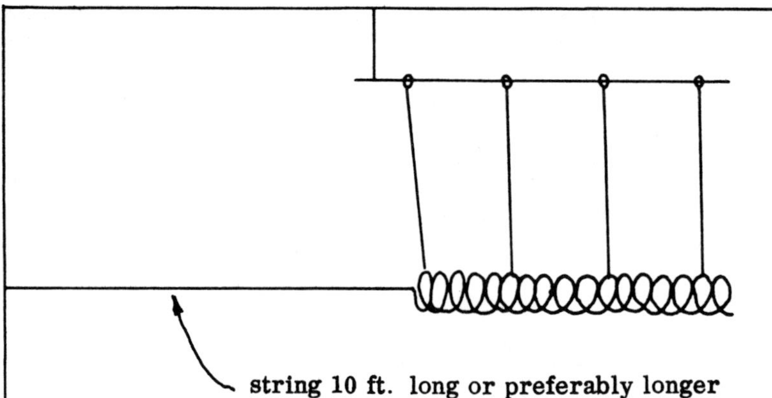

If you do not have a room long enough for both the extended spring and an open end, you will need to experiment with compromises involving shortening the length of the spring in order to increase the length of string at the open end.

Since there is very little natural damping in a suspended spring, one of the first problems you will meet is how to make a "disturbed" spring return quickly to rest. Most attempts to force the spring into a rest position with "bare hands" only result in more total agitation. (If you learn to "trap" the wave near one end, you can cut down its amplitude fairly quickly.) What you need is a way of extracting energy from the spring. Hold a large piece of cardboard or similar material loosely against the spring near the middle. Each time the wave crosses the cardboard the spring should scrape back and forth. The motion will die out quickly. If the cardboard is held so tightly against the spring that it cannot move, the motion will not die out rapidly. Experiments with different materials, and different forces of application, should result in finding a satisfactory method of rapid absorption.

If you suspend a coil spring, you may want to keep it available for the introduction of Chapter 17.

SUPPLEMENTARY NOTE ON SPEED OF TRANSVERSE WAVES ON A ROPE

There is no need to give students an analytic expression for the speed of a wave on the rope. They will not yet know enough about mechanics to recognize the units. But you might find the formula useful if students are doing extra work, measuring speeds in the laboratory in order to get a qualitative idea of what the speed, v, depends on. The speed v is given by $v^2 = \dfrac{\text{Tension in rope}}{\text{Mass per unit length of rope}}$. This shows, for example, that a wave on a coil spring (high mass and low tension) moves slowly. If the tension is expressed in newtons and the mass per unit length is given in kilograms per meter, the speed will have the units meters per second.

In the above relation for waves on ropes we assume that the rope is completely flexible and elastic. Furthermore, we assume that the amplitude of the wave is small enough so that the local tension near the wave shape is the same as the tension on all parts of the rope. (If the stretching were severe and the local tension increased, for example, the velocity would be greatest near the most stretched spot and the wave would not maintain its shape.)

NOTE ON WAVE DYNAMICS: Insofar as you can, you will want to avoid getting into discussions of why a wave moves as it does. Students will need more background in mechanics to make such discussions worthwhile. As background for the teacher, general information on wave dynamics is included in the Appendix at the back of this volume.

15–3 Superposition: Pulses Crossing

PURPOSE. To present the superposition principle.

CONTENT. The net displacement of any point which is affected by several independent pulses is the algebraic sum of the displacements which would have been caused by each of the individual pulses. This is the superposition principle: it is a fundamental property of what physicists call waves.

EMPHASIS. Students need to understand the superposition principle for displacements in order to appreciate interference in ripple tanks (and thus in light). It is not essential that the work be extended to the superposition principle for velocities. However, if you have time, you may want to extend your treatment of this section (and the chapter) to include superposition of velocities.

COMMENT. In discussing the constructions involving superposition such as those given in Figures 15–6, 15–8, and 15–9 it may be well to check to make sure that students understand that the dashed curves represent the displacement which would exist if each pulse were present alone. If they take pictures in laboratory, they will never see the dashed parts of Figure 15–6 in a picture. This point should be mentioned several times as you work with superposition at the blackboard.

Ask a student to explain Figure 15–8B in order to see how well he appreciates the superposition principle and the distinction between a graph of a pulse and a picture of the pulse. Be sure the class realizes that the dashed curves are graphs of the displacements that would be caused by the separate pulses. A picture of the rope at the instant of part B of Figure 15–8 would be merely a horizontal line.

It is possible that when examining Figure 15–17 students may wonder whether two equal pulses pass through each other or whether each just bounces back. Figure 15–5, which shows two pulses of different shape apparently passing through one another, does not settle the question; there is no way of telling whether the small pulse really "penetrated" through the larger one or bounced back, pushing an equal pulse out of it. In general, when two waves are superposed, no particular part of the combined wave describes either of the original waves. Consequently, when the two waves separate again, the identity of the waves is meaningless.

This recognition is particularly important in relation to matter waves (Chapter 33, Sections 8–10). When two waves describing the motion of two electrons are superposed, the combined wave describes both electrons but no particular part of it describes either one. Thus, when the waves are superposed, the individual electrons lose their identity, and when they separate again we cannot say that the electron moving, for example, to the right, is the same one that was moving to the right before the superposition.

The waves describing two unlike particles (say, an electron and a proton) do not superpose, but behave like two waves on separate coil springs.

A qualitative perception of the superposition principle as applied to velocities will deepen students' understanding of Figure 15–7 and the related text. Students who have missed the significance of the blurring as an indication of velocity in Figures 15–1, 15–2, and 15–5 may not realize that the coil spring is essentially undisplaced in the middle (fifth) frame of Figure 15–7. Furthermore, an awareness of superposition of velocities will help with HDL Problems 11, 13, and 14.

DEMONSTRATION EXPERIMENT. PRESSURE OF WAVES. The particle model predicts that light will exert pressure. The fact that waves also exert pressure can be demonstrated with a Slinky. Place a section of cardboard tubing about 2 inches in diameter and six inches long inside a Slinky and shake some pulses. Each time a pulse goes by, the tube will move a little farther away from the source. As it approaches a fixed end, it will slow down, since the reflected pulses push it in the opposite direction. The tube will not move if standing waves are produced, because the pushes balance out when waves are moving in both directions on the spring.

WAVE REFLECTIONS. (Perform upon completion of Experiment II–6.) The following demonstrations have been found helpful in giving the student a better understanding of reflections from free and fixed ends of a spring. The mirrors to be used in these demonstrations should be at least a foot square.

(1) Hold a plane mirror above the end of the spring, as in the diagram, so that the student shaking the spring can see its image in the mirror. When he shakes a pulse, it will seem to go into the mirror and the reflection of the pulse will seem to come out of the mirror and down the spring. The action of the Slinky at the junction will be the same as if two identical pulses from opposite directions met at the mirror. A long thread approximates a free end.

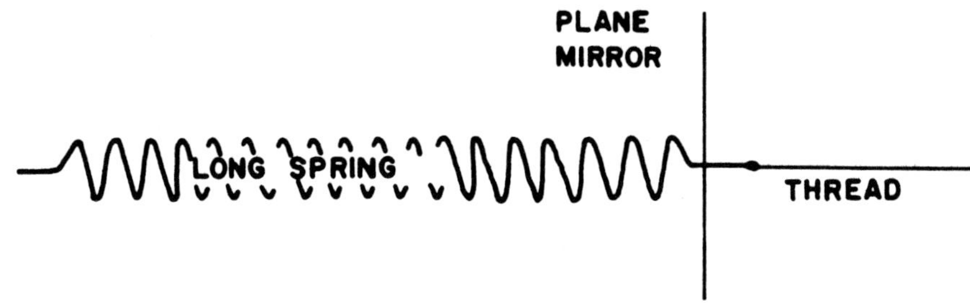

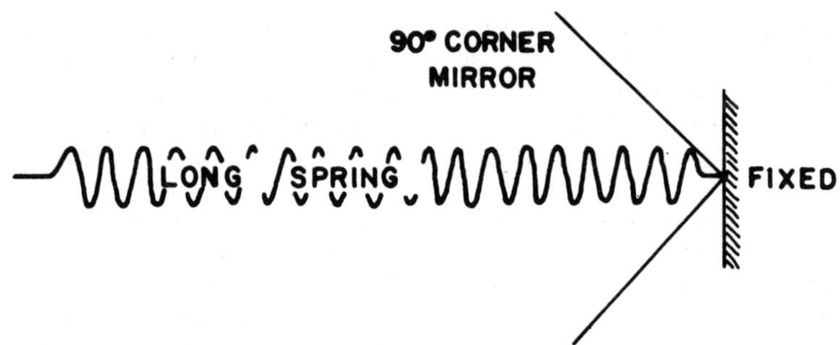

(2) A 90° corner mirror held above the fixed end of a spring, as shown in the diagram, will show the action in the case of a fixed end. This type of mirror is discussed fully in Problem 16–9.

These demonstrations will enable the student to draw a time sequence of the behavior of a pulse at a free or fixed termination by using superposition.

DEVELOPMENT. Give students practice in both wave motion and superposition by drawing two simple wave shapes (rectangular, or triangular, or a mixture) and asking questions such as the following.

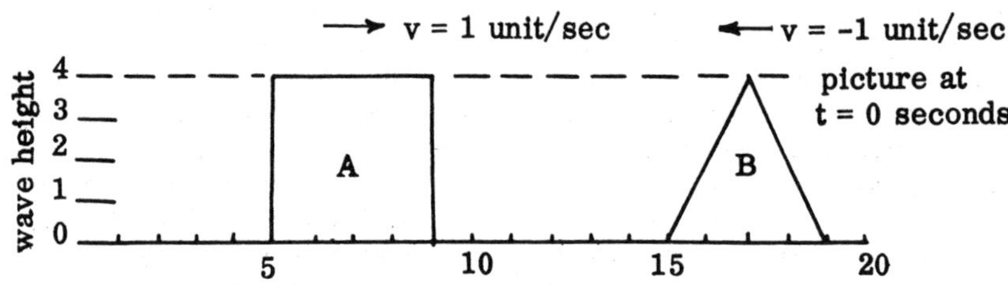

If we had only pulse *A*, what would be the shape of the rope after 1 second? After 2 seconds? After 10 seconds? If we had only pulse *B*, what would be the shape of the rope after 1 second? After 2 seconds? After 5 seconds? After 10 seconds? If only pulse *A* were present, where would the point at horizontal position 12 be after 2 seconds? If only *B* were present? If both were present? Etc.

Although most students will follow readily Figure 15–9 and its explanation in the text, they may have only a hazy idea of what similarity must exist between two pulses if the point at which they meet is to remain undisturbed. Since this same question recurs in the next section and at several places in Chapter 17, it is worthwhile to discuss it in class. You may wish to draw several examples on the board and make sure that the students understand which ones do not leave their midpoint on the rope undisturbed. Those on the left do and those on the right do not:

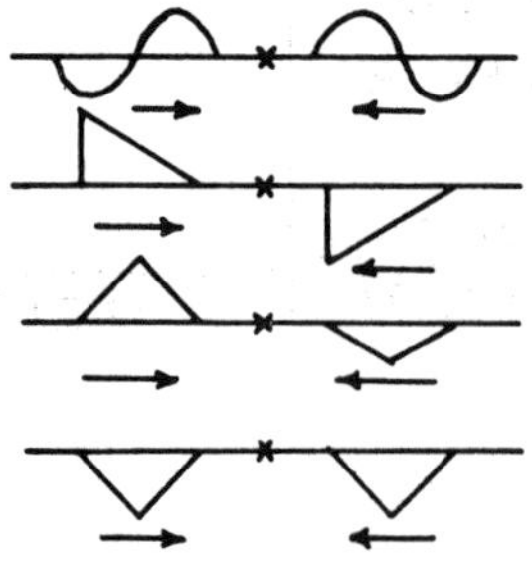

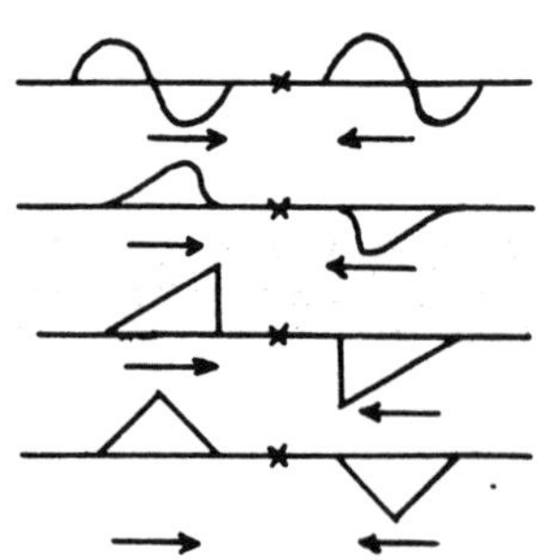

* * *

[*Page 15-10 of the original text*]

If you have time, you may want to give the students some of the following treatment of superposition of velocity.

Two triangular pulses moving towards each other give nice examples for studying velocity superposition if you ignore the sharp corners. (Sharp corners imply extremely high accelerations; if the corners were rounded a little, the velocity changes would be physically realizable.) Consider the two pulses shown below moving toward each other:

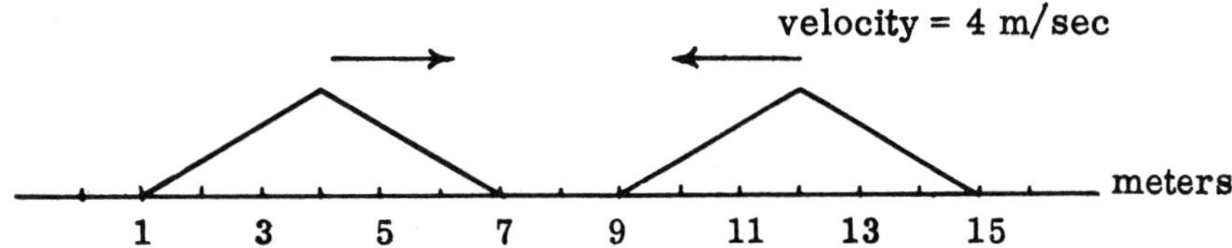

A graph of velocities of points of rope at this time is:

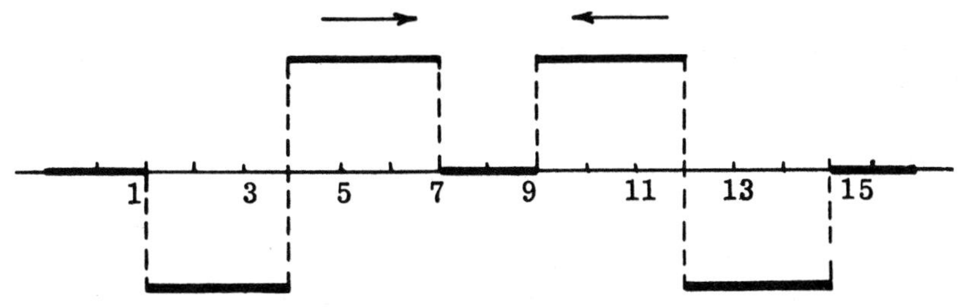

The following sequence of graphs shows points and velocity displacements as the pulses cross each other.

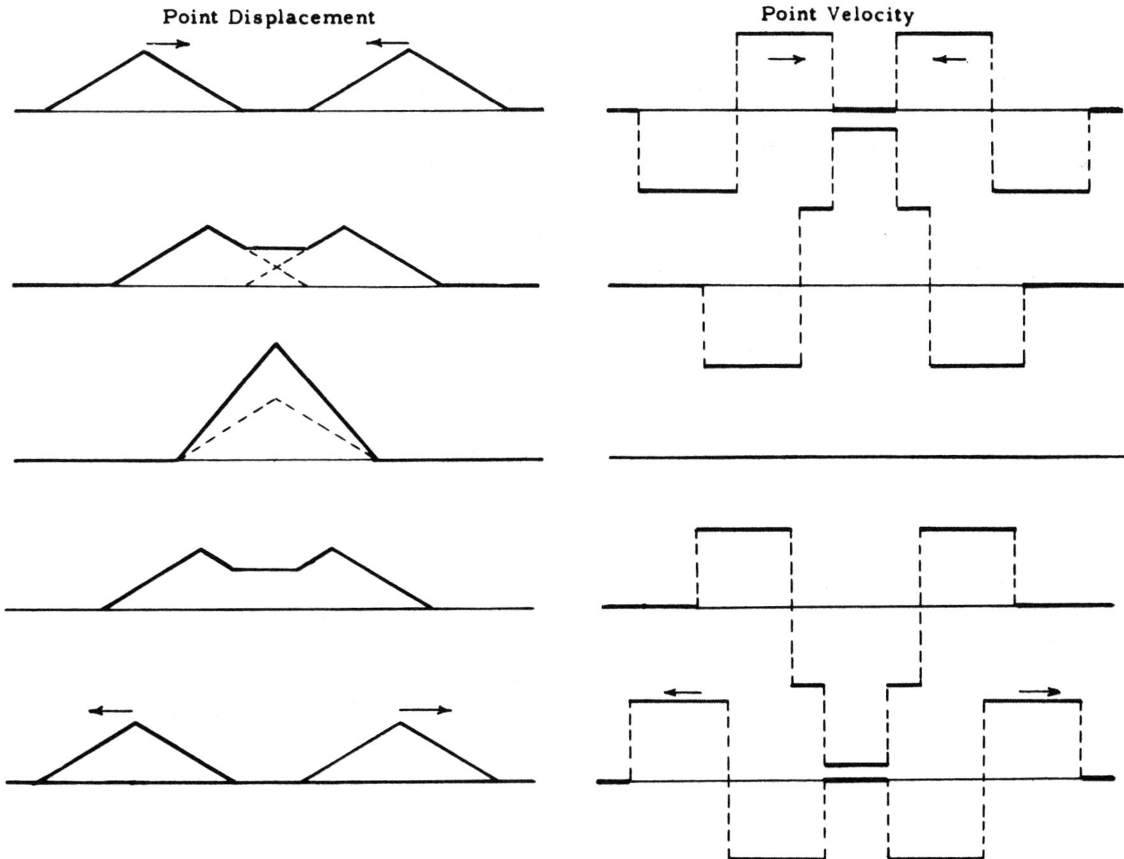

Note that at t = 1 second the two pulses add to be twice as high, but at this instant the velocity everywhere along the rope is zero! Compare this example with Problem 13 and Figure 15–17.

If the two pulses have opposite polarity,

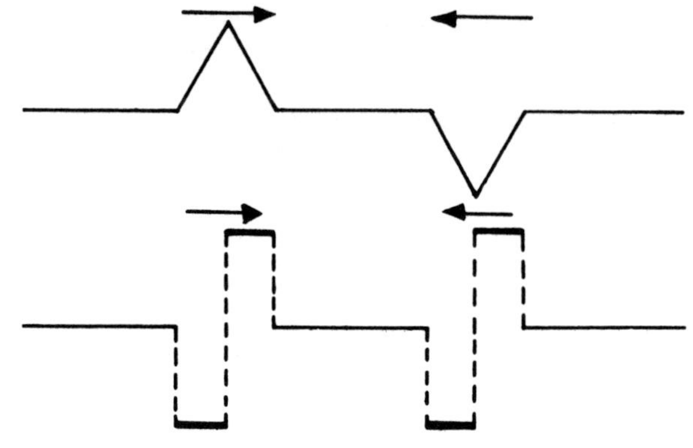

the velocity graph looks like this:

As the two pulses cross, there would be a time when displacements would add to zero giving a displacement graph like this:

but the velocities would be

This is the case in Figure 15–7.

* * *

While it is not at all vital, in an extended treatment of this section with able students, you might want to use triangular pulses to show that the particle velocity is proportional to the instantaneous slope. Once this is established, you can give bright students who ask about Figure 15–7 the semiquantitative explanation below.

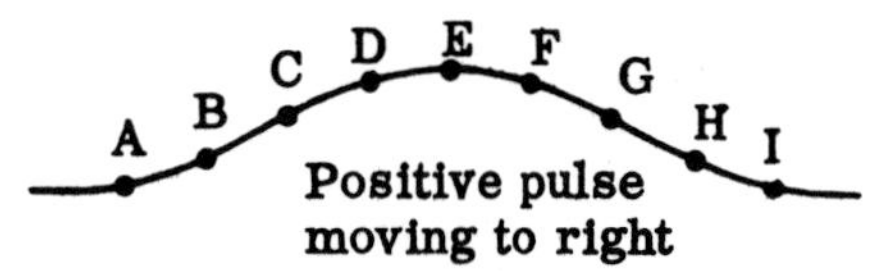

Positive pulse moving to right

(See frame 1 or 2 top, Figure 16–7)

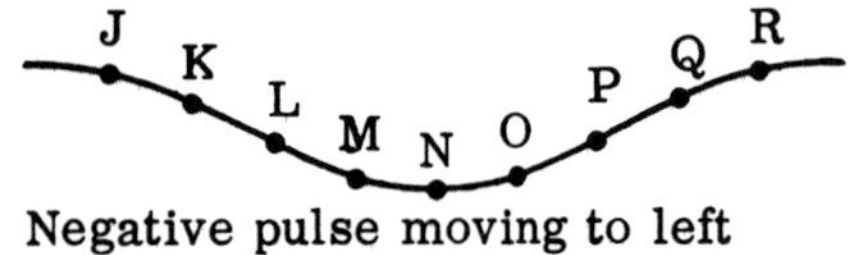

Negative pulse moving to left

Total displacement at overlap is zero (See frame 5 from top, Figure 16–7)

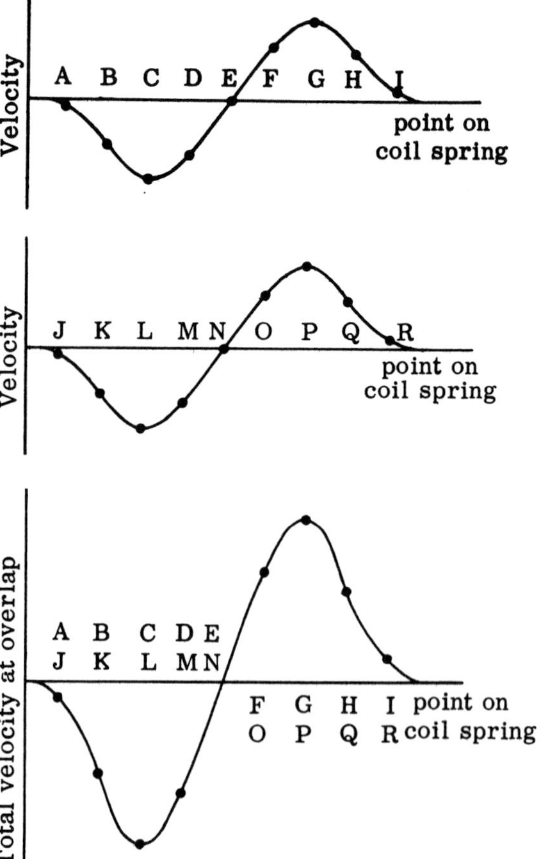

15–4 Reflection and Transmission

PURPOSE. To *describe* (not explain) what happens when a pulse reaches a boundary.

CONTENT. In general, a pulse on a coil spring is partially reflected and partially transmitted if it comes to a boundary between different kinds of materials.

(a) If the boundary is a rigidly fixed end, the pulse is reflected back upside down.

(b) If the boundary is a free end, the pulse is reflected back right side up.

(c) If the pulse goes from a "light" medium to a "heavy" medium, the transmitted pulse continues right side up, the reflected pulse comes back upside down.

(d) If the pulse goes from a "heavy" medium to a "light" medium, both the transmitted and reflected pulses are right side up.

(e) If the two media have nearly the same mass per unit length, most of the pulse is transmitted. If they have equal masses per unit length, there is no boundary (as far as the pulse is concerned) and the whole pulse is "transmitted."

EMPHASIS. It is important for students to realize that partial transmission and partial reflection occur at boundaries. They should also know that the polarity of the reflected wave depends on the exact nature of the boundary. They should not be expected to have a good mechanical idea of why the pulses reflect as they do. Observation of actual reflection and transmission of pulses in laboratory work or in classroom demonstrations is essential.

CAUTION. When you refer to whether a reflected pulse is right side up or upside down, use these phrases, or use "erect" and "inverted," or introduce the term "polarity." Avoid the word "phase." "Phase" is used in Chapter 17 and has meaning only for a periodic wave. If "phase" is used here in place of "right side up," or "erect," or "positive polarity," students may not get a precise notion of phase when they encounter the concept of phase in periodic waves.

COMMENT. While it is important for students to see that the polarities of reflected and transmitted pulses depend upon the nature of the boundaries they encounter, the specific polarity of the reflected pulse on a spring is not important to the later development of waves. However, the idea of change in polarity is interesting in itself, particularly in that it gives the students something else to look for in the laboratory. (When a phase change is invoked to explain the interference pattern from a thin film in Chapter 9, the student needs to carry over the idea that reflection can be quite different at two different types of boundaries. There is no direct analogy between waves on springs, water waves, and light waves which would make the specific polarity of the reflected wave on a rope important.)

When students watch the reflection of waves on, say, a suspended coil spring, they will inevitably press for an "explanation." "Why do waves reflect the way they do at open and closed ends?" Formally, the same old answer applies: "You do not know enough about mechanics yet to understand *why*." However, students will enjoy inventing (or hearing from you) "common sense" explanations. Such explanations are fine as long as they are treated as little more than mnemonic devices.

Some students may reject an explanation of reflection which suggests that the wall generates a canceling pulse. "How does the wall know just what kind of pulse is required, and how does a *fixed* wall know just when to send it out?" Such questions seek to go more deeply into mechanics of reflection than is possible now. As an alternative explanation (the not to be taken very seriously type), consider an "intelligent hand" replacing the fixed wall. If one tries to hold fixed one end of a rope as a pulse comes toward that end, he has to push sideways on the rope an amount equal and opposite to the push on his hand by the pulse. (Take this as straight intuition; don't mention Newton.) Now suppose that he exerted this kind of push on a stationary rope. A pulse of opposite polarity would be generated. Don't go into much detail. Students may have other explanations. See if, in this spirit, students can "explain" reflection at a free end.

15–5 Idealizations and Approximations

PURPOSE. To illustrate how idealizations and approximations are used in science.

CONTENT. Considering a pulse on a perfectly flexible coil spring which has no internal resistance and is kept in a vacuum is an example of an idealization. Since the effects found with real coil springs do not depend on those of its features which are eliminated in the idealization, the idealization can be used to advantage.

COMMENT. Be sure that the students do not confuse an idealization with a simplified experimental setup. Sometimes you use the idealization as a guide to setting up an experiment. At other times you merely use the idealization as a guide for what to observe and what to ignore in the experimental equipment already available. A third use of the idealization, which is not developed in this section, is as a model on which calculations are based.

DEVELOPMENT. You can ask students to give examples of idealizations from earlier parts of the course. The point of such a discussion is not to produce a definition of "idealization" or "approximation." Instead, it should be directed to the idea that, in studying or working with complex phenomena, it is highly important to separate the essential from the inessential. Far from being a superficial explanation, an appropriate idealization or approximation is often a powerful intellectual tool for dealing with a complicated matter. Making the right idealization is often the most important part of the problem.

Here is a partial list of approximations that have been used in studying about light:

(1) Reflection is either completely specular or completely diffuse.

(2) A spherical mirror is like a parabolic mirror.

(3) A spherical mirror provides a sharp focus.

(4) A single index of refraction applies to all white light.

(5) Lenses form perfect images.

15–6 A Wave Model for Light?

PURPOSE. To provide a transition to the study of waves on the surface of water.

CONTENT. Having seen that waves can cross without interfering with each other, and that waves can be partially reflected and partially transmitted at a boundary, we wish to inquire whether waves can be refracted. To do this, we must consider waves which are not confined to a single straight line.

EMPHASIS. Treat briefly.

V

CURRICULUM CHANGE IN THE SOCIAL SCIENCES

MEN AND IDEAS

ESI'S Social Studies and Humanities Program

A Conversation with Elting Morison

THE following conversation with Professor Morison was held at his office in M.I.T.'s Sloan Building on Memorial Drive in Cambridge, Massachusetts.

INTERVIEWER: *When and why did you first become interested in this program, in assuming the responsibility of organizing the group, and setting objectives?*

MORISON: Well, I don't want to be doing hair-splitting, but I, of course, am only sharing the responsibility with a variety of other people on this. I haven't got any *primary* concern as Franklin Patterson does, for example, for a group, but Zach, Fred Burkhardt, and I have a kind of common collective responsibility for seeing that it works.

And why I got interested in it — some of it's personal and some of it's large and philosophical. The second, large and philosophical, part — I have been much interested in the last three or four or five years in what history is like, what useful purpose it can serve today for anybody studying it. I haven't really worked out my answers to this question, or these questions, about the field I'm in, but I thought this would be one way of making me really think seriously toward a goal rather than just speculatively about what the uses of history are. That's one reason. The second is that I have had kids in school recently enough to know that many of the things that they are taught, I, at least, think that they don't need to be taught or that they might be taught differently. Those are the two philosophical reasons, if they *are* philosophical. The third is that I've been terribly impressed as, of course,

---

Elting E. Morison, Professor of History at the Massachusetts Institute of Technology since 1946, is perhaps most widely known for his editorship of "The Letters of Theodore Roosevelt," which was published in eight volumes, from 1951 through 1954. Professor Morison has also written "Turmoil and Tradition: A Study of the Life and Times of Henry L. Stimson," published in 1960; "The American Style," published in 1959; "Cowboys and Kings," published in 1954; and "Admiral Sims and the Modern American Navy," published in 1945. Professor Morison was born in Milwaukee, Wisconsin, December 14, 1909; after graduating from Harvard in 1932, he taught at St. Mark's School, Concord, New Hampshire, served as an assistant dean at Harvard, and was a Lieutenant Commander in the United States Naval Reserve during World War II. He lives at Upland Farm, Peterborough, New Hampshire.

everybody ought to be terribly impressed, by what Zach has accomplished with Francis Friedman and others in the last six or seven years in the sciences in schools. When Zach began to get interested in similar projects in the social sciences and humanities, it seemed to me one could do worse, if one were interested, as I have said I am, in the meaning of the social sciences and humanities and in how you teach them . . . one could do worse than get hooked up with such a force of nature as that. When he does something, things come loose.

All of these things involved me originally in the Endicott House Conference, which is the kind of exercise that I look forward to with immense dread, as he knew, because I'd been to a variety of conferences, as everybody has, at which nothing was accomplished. I think it was the immense success of the Endicott House Conference, not only (which often happens in such exercises) in terms of people coming out, being very fond of each other, but the success in terms of coming out with two or three rather well-developed propositions which could serve at least as a base for future action. This really impressed me a lot, and it seemed to me that anything that could be done so successfully in two weeks suggested the possibility of doing other more ambitious things over a year. So when he proposed that we continue, I yielded.

—*Isn't there a feeling that the social sciences and the humanities are incompatible?*

MORISON: I think I didn't truly realize how different they were until that Dedham conference — in spirit, and in methodology. All the historians pretend that they follow a scientific method, and much of today's literary criticism pretends it does. But the methodology isn't terribly important, and historians really don't proceed in any definable scientific way. But the difference in spirit — it interested me a great deal, and until then, as I say, I didn't realize how different they were. Both, theoretically, of course, are in the same business, which is investigating how human beings, individually and collectively, behave. But they really proceed in quite different ways, and I think they look for quite different ends. I'm trying to decide whether to embark on a considerable irrelevancy, and I guess I will, in order to make my point.

The humanities, up to I don't know how many years ago — ten, fifteen, twenty — were almost the sole way in school curricula for students to investigate human action — individual and collective — in the classics and history and literature. These have been, because of that dominant position which I think they assumed in the eighteenth or nineteenth century, still somewhat the primary methods of looking at individual behavior and collective behavior. With the development of psychology, clearly some part of the total task that the humanities used to take upon themselves has been taken over by the social sciences in a rather more systematic way.

Now large areas of human behavior and of the structure of personality have been taken out of the hands of the humanities by the social sciences. But I think it's fair to say that the contribution of the social sciences to our understanding of how people work, while increasing in colleges, is practically nonexistent still in secondary schools. There is practically no sociology taught. There is practically no psychology taught. There is some political science taught. Under the name of history a certain amount of findings and much more of the attitudes of the social sciences creep into the secondary school curriculum. A teacher will have read *The Lonely Crowd* and — keep your powder dry — *Coming of Age in Samoa* and will infiltrate the study of the French Revolution or the Era of Good Feeling with these findings. And this doesn't seem to me to be really a very useful way of going about it, or as useful a way as perhaps reducing the amount of the humanities which is taught and increasing the amount of the social sciences. There are new ways of looking at the most interesting problems there are, which are how and why human beings behave as they do. Although the humanities are very useful in this, they have limitations which in many ways the social sciences have transcended or gone beyond.

I'll give you an example. For 300 years *Hamlet's* been taught and people have gotten a great deal out of reading *Hamlet,* all kinds of useful experiences have resulted. But I am not sure that *Hamlet* contributed *measurably* to the general understanding of the structure of personality. Each man can make his own interpretation, there have been hundreds of interpretations of Hamlet — that he was mad, that he couldn't make up his mind, that he was a woman, even, which accounted for his failing to take action. There was no settled opinion about him that could be supported by data and transmitted to students and to the intelligence of students. The appeal was rather more directly to the feelings, and the individual interpretations too. Well, Freud devised a method which seemed to suggest that through looking at a succession of people with certain kinds of behavior, one could arrive at a conclusion about some of the determining influences in the structure of a personality. And some of these findings of Freud could be employed most usefully to not only describe actual people, what the structure of their personality was, but also to define in literature the characteristics of certain fully developed characters.

Let us take *Hamlet,* for example. If you've seen the Olivier *Hamlet,* well, this is a highly Freudian interpretation. Now, Olivier's *Hamlet* is not only a Freudian interpretation, but quite possibly, if one looks at the lines of *Hamlet,* a kind of unconscious feeling that Shakespeare had in mind also about the motivations of Hamlet. Now this becomes a way of demonstrating certain truths with far greater economy and efficiency and general acceptance, of demonstrating certain findings rather than truths about a personality.

— Are high school students mature enough to understand these concepts?

MORISON: Well, I can tell you I am encouraged to think about this as a possibility. I would stress the fact that this isn't necessarily the *true* explanation, but that which offers the possibility of thinking about personalities in a more systematic way, deriving evidence from data, and of transmitting certain ideas about human behavior to students in a way which they find it easier to understand. The humanities deal with a single situation, subject to an infinite variety of interpretations. It's the theoretical schemes that can be developed in the social sciences — tentative and approximate, to be sure, but still useful in communicating your findings.

We were talking about the differences between the humanities and the social sciences, and why I do not think it is enough to have history taught in such a way that it just includes some of the random findings and attitudes of the social scientist that the teacher may have picked up. I think there is an area for the systematic study of certain social sciences in the secondary schools. I also think that the social sciences themselves can be (and this is implicit in the whole Hamlet anecdote) of *immense* value to anybody who is teaching the humanities. I find constantly that my friends in the social sciences are of greater help to me in thinking about problems in history than historians are. One reason for this is that the social scientist frequently begins with a hypothesis that he wants to test, which, in effect, is a question that he wants to ask; in my own field the tendency is to what I tend to do — to reconstruct the whole situation without asking yourself anything about it, which means that you tend to organize your information, if you're in history, on a strictly chronological basis, one thing happens after another, which, of course, has its uses and purposes, but frequently if you reorganize the data in a different kind of way, or take only part of it which is relevant to a kind of question you have in mind, you find all different kinds of information coming out which you can't get from the organization of a single situation within a chronological form. And I think that if one *thought* (which I trust this whole ESI venture is designed to do) of ways of reorganizing the immense amount of valuable information that there is in the humanities, both literature and history, in new ways, you could greatly reduce the amount of information you have to teach, which would make it much more assimilable for students.

You would put it in forms which would make much more sense to them so that they could learn much faster. I am puzzled, and *very* puzzled, about one thing. I set store by not knowing history but having an historical sense — just a feeling for the past. I have a feeling, that may be wrong, that without a feeling for the past it's very difficult to have a real feeling for a possible future. Without it you tend to live exclusively and operationally in the present. Whether by this rather dramatic reorganization and curtailment of historical data you can still set up in the student over a short time a feeling for the past, I don't know, but I'm inclined to think you can. You know, this selection of three or four episodes *properly* told out of the past might very well give you exactly the same feeling that things happened before, as you theoretically get from studying two years of world history from Rome to the present.

— Is there not a lack of perspective of the reach of history in our country?

MORISON: Now part of this, of course, may have nothing to do with education. There's hardly a spot in Europe that you can grow up in where the outward, visible signs of the past are not all around you, where a sense of family continuity is not present, at least to a far greater extent than here. In America, we live in a constantly changing environment where even the older cities have lost their sense of permanence because of the obvious changes in construction, etc.; we have been from the very beginning a *constantly* developing culture, starting from scratch, in a way that Europe didn't have to do for a long time; we have had a feeling of living from hand to mouth, which accentuates the present and reduces the emphasis on the past and future. I would like to — because I think it's a very steadying thing, and a very necessary thing in terms of perspectives and evaluations of a situation — at least I would like to feel that out of education students would get a feeling that, even if they were not part of a discernible continuum, at least there was much that had gone on before.

— How far can you profitably study history in subjective terms?

MORISON: I've been wondering whether to make a comparison between the thinking that goes on in the sciences and the thinking that goes on in the humanities, and I guess I won't. I will say that one of the things which I hope this whole program will endeavor to do, also, is to discover ways in which, in a sense, a man can become his own historian within a small enough scale so that he can understand what becoming a historian means; that he can construct for himself, out of raw materials, historical situations and episodes. This is really much more valuable than the exercise of describing the trends over a hundred years, which you can do in a passionless and uninvolved way. Any kind of past situation is *loaded,* even a very small one, even a thing out of local history, with all kinds of problems, or just of organizations with all kinds of conflicts, attitudes and feelings and qualities of mind and thought, and faith. The exercise of separating out from the immense material which can be developed the moment you begin to look at *any* situation, no matter how small, what is relevant, what is irrelevant, what is telling in a dramatic way from what is not useful, and putting these together to make a point, all this exercise will fully engage not only the mind but the feelings of anybody who's working with this material.

I would much rather have a year in which I had the materials from which students could construct an episode in local Massachusetts history and in local Boston history than to have them take that year to study the whole history of the U. S., from 1608 to 1962. And, I really think I mean this. I think you could do more to get across the qualities of thought and the necessary information which I think people today must have about the problems which they are going to deal with today, and the necessary historical information from such an exercise than from the rather large narrative thing. And I am comforted by the thought that enough people at the Endicott House Conference seemed to feel that this is the case, too. So I think that out of these investigations will come some proposals whereby students in various grades in school can have this kind of experience of independent historical training which will stimulate their imaginations, their minds, and their curiosity.

— In your slice, or snapshot, of history would you consider, for example, a book like "1846"?

MORISON: The *"Year of Decision,"* you mean. . . .?

— Yes. In which you take one year and you've really got about sixty.

MORISON: Yes, although I think that's awfully rich fare for all but the most well-informed person to work on. I've said that you could select a case like the building of the battleship *Kentucky* in 1900 and teach as much about the relations of congressmen to the executive officers, to the population that the congressmen represent, to the way in which congressional committees work, the way in which we attempt to relate force to policy, which is the key problem today, as you could by any other method, and this would be one single little episode in which there is an enormous amount of material. So I don't think you have to take a whole slice. The year 1846 was a beautiful slice to take, and it was a beautiful book, but you could take a problem or a situation.

— "The World of Humanism," for instance.

MORISON: I haven't read that book for some time. That's the Renaissance-Reformation, isn't it? Yes, although I would still like to insist on smaller dosages even. If you take the Renaissance, I would rather have students investigate how Cellini got the commission to make the Pope's buttons, for example, and bring in all there was to talk about in the way of art and religion and ecclesiastical administration and the culture of Italy from a smaller episode which would give you your organizing principle and which would enable you to relate a set of rather specific and concrete evidences to a very specific and concrete situation. You would lose from that that straight sense of continuance, certainly, if you followed this out too completely.

— You're slicing history.

MORISON: Yes, although I would happily, I think, just omit large slices. I think one of the great curses of historians is their feeling that they must have total recall and must communicate total recall. We are the least selective of disciplines, and I think we ought to be the most selective, because we have the most data.

— Would these periods in history be selected on the basis of their emotional potential for revealing the politics of the whole age?

MORISON: To take the field that I am most familiar with, American history, it would be possible to begin with this kind of an operating principle, that the really interesting history in America is the history of a process — how the democratic method works, rather than the history of the particular episodes that were developed chronologically through time in the course of the evolution of this process. I know of a particular episode in which Theodore Roosevelt appointed a judge in the Second District of New York, a district judge, which contains, by the time you're through with it, just about all one needs to know about the appointive power of the President and how important it is, and about how he acts to give meaning to that power, and about how he uses Congress to achieve his purposes, and how he puts pressure on Congress to move towards his purposes — all that any student would need to know. And I would like to look for a series of episodes of this sort to reveal all of the methodology of the process that we live in all the time, because I think it's probably much more important for citizens to have a clear feeling, or as clear a feeling as they can have, of how this whole social-political process works, than it is for them to have a knowledge of General Longstreet's behavior at Gettysburg.

I want to conclude this part of social science-history, or humanities, relationship by saying that I think increasingly in the future we will learn many of the things that we used to look to the humanities to get our information about, from the social sciences. I think that increasingly certain areas of our understanding about human beings will be taken over by the social sciences. This does not mean that there is no place for the humanities. I think that it greatly increases the part they can play in a person's education, in two ways. One is that the generalizations of the social sciences can be supported by the data that they develop experimentally through quizzes, polls, and things like that. They can also be supported by striking examples from history or from literature. You know, the striking examples taken out of our own past or out of the imagination of writers, all give an enormous supporting drive to the theoretical considerations of the social sciences. Also, all history and literature is engaged not only with how men behave, but with the question that the social sciences are less prepared to deal with of *why* they behaved as they did — all questions of value and meaning — and that you can find only, I think, in the humanities. Indeed, I think with the increase in what I will call the *rational* rather than the *scientific* method of dealing with life, which is obviously increasing, and is going to increase — the need for these other elements, whatever you call them, I have called them value and meaning, and I guess I would add feeling, the role of feeling — the need for these is going to become more, rather than less, important.

The humanities have a more significant part to play in the education of a student than they ever have had before, precisely because of this tendency of ours to reduce so much of experience to problems that we can solve by the use of intelligence alone. So that we may in time only get to deal with problems which are intellectually soluble and not accessible to these other agencies like intuition and feeling and affection. And so my interest really is to decide how to give the full assistance to the areas which I am most interested in, which are the humanities.

— Are there any target dates set yet in the social studies and humanities program?

MORISON: I have systematically avoided all administrative questions of that type. As my understanding is, a kind of rough chronology has been laid out, that there are already, as you know, a couple of groups of mixed talents working together on special parts of the curriculum. The one I am most familiar with is the one that is trying to think of a seventeenth and eighteenth century course for the junior high school, and this includes a political scientist, an anthropologist, and a couple of historians, and a classicist. That was one of the most extraordinary and refreshing things to me about Endicott House; I have worked in conferences of mixed disciplines which invariably have fallen apart into the separate groupings of training. And at Endicott House it was demonstrated that within a reasonably short time — although with an immense amount of pain originally, and I think, in many instances, of even actual hostility — a group of mixed talents could set a special problem, could work together not only with great harmony and even elan, but with a transfer of information and attitude and training amongst the group, something such as I had never received before. The way that we in that seventeenth and eighteenth century group made use of a geographer, and the way the geographer made use of the historians, and the way we all made use of the classicist, was the most refreshing and, to me, delightful thing about the whole works, and the best augury for the future . . . that actually, if you define the areas that you want to work in, you can get people of widely different intellectual trainings and with widely different kinds of information, working together, once you've defined the area you want to work in, with immense success.

These groups are working now — two of them; I understand that they may have one in the classics and one in the seventeenth and eighteenth centuries. There is a third, *Stones and Bones,* as you know, for the grades 1-6 social sciences. There is an intention to put together a group which will deal with the tenth, eleventh, and twelfth grades social studies, shortly. The whole bit is that these groups, three in being and one to be appointed, will have done enough work by June so that what will be called "writing conferences" can be called together to really lay out not just the skeleton but the actual course material in these various areas over the course of a summer in such a way that they can be tried experimentally next fall. Now I think this is a most ambitious schedule, because it does involve movies, in some instances; it involves the creation of artifacts of all kinds; it involves the writing of at least, if not textbooks, new kinds of material for the student to read. And whether all this can be done in the course of a year in which you have part-time operations with members of the committees who are only able to meet part-time, and then a three-months full-time operation, I don't know. But this is the hope. But I don't think it makes much difference whether it's this fall or next fall. People do not seem to be losing their steam about this; indeed, they seem to be getting more steamed up rather than less, and more anxious to go forward, and I don't think they will feel, if they fall short of a deadline, that the thing is not finishable. I think they will go on and finish it as soon as they can. And I wouldn't be at all surprised if within a year and a half they had testable materials that could be put into various schools like the Newton school system to see whether they work.

— Were you entirely satisfied with the accomplishments of the Dedham conference?

MORISON: If I have any feeling of failure in that conference, and I do, it is that nobody dealt with English adequately and that nobody dealt with writing adequately. I think that if an opportunity were given to me to teach anything that I wanted to teach in the secondary schools I would say that I would rather teach them to read and write than any other single thing.

— Some persons at the Dedham conference said that they hope to succeed in breaking down the provincialism of the student and to enable him to see men of other cultures without the clouding which the use of smoked glasses of his own "culture-bound value system" is bound to produce.

MORISON: Well, I've got this response to that. There was an awful lot of talk at Endicott House about how vitally important it was that we understand the state of the emerging societies, that we understand that Timbuctoo was there and was different; that England was different. I have a certain resistance to this notion. I think we grow up in a highly relativistic society, I think that we are not in danger of becoming rootedly provincial in the sense that we think that nothing exists outside the small town and the small prejudice that we have. I think that we're aware in a way that we have never been before of all kinds of alternative solutions. I think that this should be certainly *in* education, this sense of alternative solutions, but I think it's so much more important for us to really understand the nature of our own situation. I think that if we could produce a good description of what this country is, by what process it operates, and what we think it is and ought to be — which we gloss over in our teaching by giving the students a whole lot of hand-me-down cliches about America — then it would not be possible for a person to grow up in our school and college system without having any idea that democracy is the most painful experience that a man can have as a way of life, but also the most indispensable.

— One of the Dedham reports says, "even in the teaching of as bookish a discipline as history is commonly supposed to be, there is room for the use of 'hardware.'"

MORISON: I'm a great believer in hardware, and was one of the great pluggers for it. I had an idea some years ago when I was talking with some friends about what we might do in this area. It isn't a large idea, but it was to take a thing like — to give a classic example — Jackson's war on the Bank, the Second National Bank, and to get, not bound up into a book of readings, but to have in photostated form or reproduced form, so that they looked like what they were at the time — pieces of evidence: the Presidential veto as it was, all written out, a speech from the Congressional Record, Nicholas Biddle's bank account, newspaper clippings, all kinds of, well, private correspondence at the time, either people connected with it directly, which would throw a light on it, or people who were just responding to it. Having a bale of loose data — all loose — and then say to the kid, "Make your own statement about what you would have done if you were Jackson, or what happened here, or who was the writer" — ask him any question, but give him the data to organize in any way he wants. We then at Endicott House propounded this notion of putting in irrelevant data also. In this way, we would deal with the problem, you see, of getting him to feel the thing itself.

— Is there anything we've missed?

MORISON: I have rather more than shot my bolt.

FROM SUBJECT TO CITIZEN

by Peter C. Wolff

ONE of the major efforts which ESI's Social Studies Curriculum Program group made in its initial year was planning a course for junior high school students. Traditionally, the seventh or eighth year of school is one in which American history is taught. It seemed important, therefore, to develop a course of study which would fit into existing patterns while avoiding stereotypes of junior high school history courses.

At the suggestion of Dr. Franklin Patterson, Director of the Lincoln Filene Center at Tufts University, the Planning Committee (which has overall responsibility for the Social Studies Curriculum Program) adopted a course which does not follow a strictly sequential historical narrative. Instead, it concentrates on a few important episodes that are of special significance. It is concerned with the period from roughly 1600 to 1800 and has been given the title *From Subject to Citizen.* This course has a number of advantages from the point of view of curriculum developers. (1) Since only a few episodes are considered, these episodes can be studied in considerable detail and depth. The feeling of frustration that often overwhelms a teacher faced with the task of "covering" large periods of history can be avoided. (2) It becomes possible to suggest that history is not just an unrelated series of events but the product of a number of causal factors operative in history. (3) Ideas and concepts from various areas of political science can be introduced into the course. Instead of studying sequential history, the students deal with concepts: "government," "empire," "liberty," "self-government," etc. As the title *From Subject to Citizen* implies, the course traces the political developments which caused a group of English subjects to become American citizens.

The course assumes the following principles:

1. Secondary school students — in fact all students — should grapple with the nature of their political culture.

   "The term political culture . . . refers to the specifically political orientations — attitudes toward the political system and its various parts, and attitudes toward the role of the self in the system. We speak of a political culture just as we can speak of an economic culture or a religious culture. It is a set of orientations toward a special set of social objects and processes." (Gabriel A. Almond and Sidney Verba, *The Civic Culture,* Princeton, New Jersey, 1963: Princeton University Press, page 13.)

2. English and American history of the seventeenth and eighteenth centuries document revolutionary developments in the American political culture.

3. Students should, therefore, study those crucial events of the seventeenth and eighteenth centuries which dramatize the developments of the American political culture — developments which caused a shift from a "subject political culture" to a "citizen" or "participant political culture."[1]

If the above three principles are true, then the political development *From Subject to Citizen* in the seventeenth century might well be dramatized by the following episodes:

A. The English subject reveres Queen Elizabeth and is willing to defend her against the Armada.

B. The English subject is alienated from his ruler to the extent that he tries Charles I, finds him guilty, and beheads him.

---

[1]For a contemporary discussion of the meaning of these political cultures and how they can be measured in a comparative study of five nations, see *op. cit.,* pp. 3-43, 473-509, 526-551.

Mr. Wolff is the Social Studies Curriculum Program Administrator.

C. The English subject finds it necessary to establish a new relationship with his ruler. He makes Parliament supreme and invites a new ruler, William III, to take the throne.

The political development *From Subject to Citizen* in the eighteenth century can be similarly shown:

D. The American colonists accept London as the hub of their world, as the center for regulating their economic activities and their political life.

E. The Americans are alienated from the British Parliament and King. They revolt against them.

F. The Americans find it necessary to establish a new national order; they have a new vision as to the nature of the relationship between an individual man and his government.

These six episodes—three from seventeenth century England and three from eighteenth century America—are the focal points for six units that are being planned for the course.

Experience has shown that three units can be handled simultaneously; the three units are always at different stages of development. For example, the 1688 Unit ("C" above) is currently the least advanced; research is just beginning in this area. The Colonial American Unit ("D") is further along; some of its material has already been tried in the classroom and work continues during this summer. It is expected that by this fall a preliminary edition will be ready for trial in some five or six classrooms.

The American Revolution Unit ("E") is closest to completion; it has already been taught in several classrooms and has gone through two editions. It is being taught again this summer under the careful scrutiny of teachers, researchers and evaluators. As a result of this work, this material can be tried in as many as thirty classrooms in selected schools across the nation during the year 1964-1965. There exists reason to hope that the American Revolution Unit will be in finished form by June, 1965.

As one unit is finished, another one will be started. At all times, three units will be in various stages of development for this junior high school course in American history.

Core of "The American Revolution Against British Authority" →

Composed and written by Richard McCann, with the assistance of researchers, including Mrs. Grace Jager and Miss Terry Knopf.

The core of the unit is divided into two parts. It places the student first in London to view the British Empire from economic and political standpoints, to consider the British version of the events of the 1770's, and to examine the issue in conflict as it was debated in Parliament in 1775. The unit then places the student in the American colonies to consider the American version of the events of the 1770's and to examine the issue in conflict as it was debated in 1776 and written into the Declaration of Independence. The parts of the core are as follows:

PART III

London — 1773-1776: How It Looks From Here

Students are given a set of cards which give a British view of events in Britain and America between 1773 and 1776. Using these cards, students work out the chronology of the period and identify the recurrent biases of the British view.

PART V

In the American Colonies — 1773-1776:
How It Looks From Here

Students are given a set of cards which give an American view of the events in Britain and America between 1773 and 1776. Using these cards, students review the chronology of the period, identify the recurrent biases of the American view, and compare the American and British versions to see how they are similar and how they are different.

Core of "The American Revolution Against British Authority"

PART III

1

PARLIAMENT'S TEA ACT ATTACKS TRADE -- TAX ON TEA REMAINS

American colonies, Summer 1773: News has arrived that Parliament has passed a new Tea Act. The Act, which became law on May 10, lowers the price of East India Company tea and keeps the despised three-cent import tax per pound of tea. There is no question why Parliament has passed this Act. It is Parliament's evil design to use the East India Company, which can now sell tea cheaper than anyone else, to undercut colonial merchants and eliminate them from the tea trade. At the same time, Parliament will use the low-priced tea to trick the colonists into paying a tax without the consent of their legislatures.

Writings of Samuel Adams, ed. H. A. Cushing (New York, 1907), III, 67-69; Richard B. Morris, Encyclopedia of American History (New York, 1953), I, 80-81.

2

BRITISH LEAVE COLONISTS NO CHOICE -- TEA DUMPED

Boston, December, 16, 1773: Tonight a group of "Mohawk Indians" boarded three ships lying at anchor in Boston harbor. They carefully took the ships' cargoes--chests of East India Company tea--and emptied them into the water, without the least damage to any other property on the ships.

This drastic action was taken only when the townsmen knew that they had no other choice. Ever since November, they had made it clear to the local British officials that they could not permit the landing of the East India Company's tea. To do so would be to submit to the tea tax without the consent of their colonial legislature. In addition, they tried every course of action to convince both the customs officials and Governor Hutchinson that the ships and their cargoes of tea should be allowed to return to Britain. But, both customs officials and the Governor refused to give the ships clearance to sail. The townsmen, knowing that if the ships remained in the harbor a few more days the tax on tea would be collected, made their decision--the only one possible. They destroyed the tea.

Writings of S. Adams, III, 75-76.

3

PARLIAMENT PUNISHES BOSTON AS WARSHIPS CLOSE PORT

Boston, June 1774: His Majesty's warships took position in the Boston harbor on June 1st to shut off that city from the outside world--putting into effect the Boston Port Bill passed by Parliament on March 31, 1774. Throughout the ports and towns of the American colonies, men debate the meaning of the British warships in Boston. Does Parliament expect to empty the purse of Boston? To crush the spirit of that great trading city? What port will be next?

The colonists who debate these questions marked June 1st by sending promises of food and money to the people of Boston and praying for Boston's speedy deliverance from cruel British tyranny.

Richard Frothingham, Rise of the Republic of the United States, 5th ed. (Boston, 1890), p. 324; Writings of S. Adams, III, 107-125, 146.

PART V

1

PARLIAMENT'S TEA ACT GOES INTO EFFECT -- EAST INDIA COMPANY TO BENEFIT

London, May 10, 1773: Today Parliament's new Tea Act becomes law. The Act will help the East India Company, which is almost bankrupt and has millions of pounds of unsold tea in its warehouses. The Act allows the Company (1) to ship the tea in its British warehouses to America free of any British export duty, and (2) to ship tea directly from India to the American colonies. The Act keeps the American import duty of three cents per pound of tea, which Parliament had placed on tea in 1767.

Because this new Act removes export duties and allows the direct shipping of tea, the East India Company will be able to sell its tea cheaper than anyone in America. By being in such a good position, the Company should be able to improve its financial situation.

William Cobbett, Parliamentary History of England (London, 1806-1820), XVII, 840-841; Richard B. Morris, Encyclopedia of American History (New York, 1953), I, 80-81.

2

BOSTON MOB DESTROYS TEA, DEFIES TEA ACT

London, January 22, 1774: News has arrived that the tea exported to America by the East India Company, under an Act of Parliament passed last year, has produced a wave of anger throughout America.

The town of Boston, which has been so long obnoxious to the British government, was the scene of the first outrage. When three ships carrying tea arrived in the harbor, the Bostonians demanded that they return to Britain with their cargo. British officials, not willing to be dictated to by a mob, refused to give the ships clearance to sail. Then the mob of angry Bostonians, disguised as Mohawk Indians, boarded the ships on the night of December 16th. In less than four hours the mob hurled into the sea 342 chests of tea, valued at £18,000.

By their violent and outrageous proceedings, the Bostonians have destroyed the East India Company's property and defied the law and authority of Parliament.

Cobbett, Parliamentary History, XVII, 939-940, 1164-1165; An Eighteenth-Century Journal, comp. John Hampden (London, 1940), pp. 14-15.

3

PARLIAMENT PASSES BOSTON PORT BILL

London, March 31, 1774: Today Parliament passed the Boston Port Bill, which will go into effect June 1st. On that date, the port of Boston will be closed to all trade until the Bostonians pay the East India Company for the tea they destroyed, and until British officials feel that once again they can collect the taxes on goods arriving in Boston.

In the debates on this bill, Lord North explained why this strong measure was necessary:

> "The people at Boston [began] . . . many years ago . . . to throw off all obedience to this country . . . [and this is] the first time Parliament [has] proceeded to punish them. . . . The good of this Act is, that four or five [warships] will do the business without any military force; but if it is necessary, I should not hesitate a moment to enforce a due obedience to the laws of this country."

Morris, Encyclopedia, I, 82; Cobbett, Parliamentary History, XVII, 1171-1172.

THE DEATH OF THE ROMAN REPUBLIC: A SOCIAL STUDIES UNIT

by Arleigh Richardson, III

In the Junior High School Social Studies Program, a sequence aimed at approximately the seventh grade level will be entitled *Inventing the Western World.* Under the direction of Professor Erich Gruen of Harvard and Professor Robert O'Neil of Berkeley a unit in this sequence entitled *The Death of the Roman Republic* is now nearing completion, and should be produced in an experimental edition for rather widespread use in schools during the academic year 1966-67. This unit, one of our earliest in conception, has gone through some significant sea changes as it has been worked on during the past two and one-half years.

Originally during the summer of 1963, it was thought of as a relatively simple exercise, which we called the Caesar Unit for convenience. Its nominal subject was a dramatic political event of the classical world: the desperate gamble which Julius Caesar made at the beginning of 49 B.C. for supreme control of the Roman state. Early that year Caesar decided to leave his jurisdiction in Gaul, and moved swiftly down into Italy with only one legion to cut off his rival, Pompey, and assume complete power in the Roman government. By this time the Republic was corrupt and chaotic. The practical question was whether Caesar or Pompey would control the state. Both men decided the question in their own favor, but Caesar made his decision stick. In these narrow terms, the first version of the unit focused on the first three months of 49 B.C., and on Caesar's audacity as a political and military actor.

The event was described in a number of ancient sources: Plutarch, Suetonius, Lucan, Appian, and Dio. We drew selections carefully from some of these sources for use as data in the unit. More importantly, the event was described at the time from two completely divergent political points of view by two of the principals in the struggle over power in the Roman state: Caesar himself, and Cicero, Pompey's advocate—scholar, literary man, and sensitive indecisive man of peace. Caesar's *Civil War* and Cicero's *Letters* give contrasting reports of the same series of events, seen from quite different perspectives. We drew parallel brief selections from Caesar and Cicero as the heart of the unit data and, on field testing, found them manageable by seventh grade students who were reading at approximately their normal grade level.

In addition to these documentary data, the early version included other simple tools. One was a modern auto map of Italy; with this each student could easily trace Caesar's swift march down the eastern coast to Brindisi and then to Rome. Another kind of simple but helpful aid was afforded by United States Army topographic maps of Italy. These are relatively small, very light sectional relief maps pressed out of plastic material. An important set of materials for the unit in its earlier form was a series of color slides made from pictures taken for us by a *Life Magazine* photographer. These were not employed simply for pictorial ornamentation, but as part of the problem-solving exercises in which the unit engaged students. For example, they were used to examine Caesar's decision to leave Gaul, cross the Rubicon, and enter Rimini. In addition to the study of his main decision to move at all, the records gave children a chance to try out their minds on a number of smaller, essentially historiographic puzzles.

Take the crossing of the Rubicon, for instance. Plutarch—who certainly wasn't there—tells us that Caesar crossed the stream which runs between Ravenna and Rimini and said, "The die is cast." Lucan—who wasn't there—makes a big thing of the crossing in his *Pharsalia,* describing in detail how Caesar stood his cavalry

---

Dr. Richardson is Associate Director of the Junior High School Division of ESI's Social Studies Curriculum Program.

across the stream "to break the current's force" so foot soldiers could get over, and quoting exactly what he thought Caesar said once he was across. But Caesar's own description of his move from Ravenna into Rimini is most matter of fact and makes no mention of the Rubicon, crossing it, or saying anything quotable for the occasion. And Cicero's correspondence immediately after learning of Caesar's move mentions nothing about the Rubicon. As students dug into reference works and more detailed maps, they learned that the river now called the Rubicon is not necessarily the Rubicon that Caesar crossed. It was Mussolini who arbitrarily decided on the present Rubicon, sometime after having crossed his own. In all of this little study which has long been one of our symbolic cliches, the "crossing of the Rubicon" turns out to be a more complex puzzle than one might have thought. How much can we be sure of? How? Students in effect were faced with the historian's own problem and even with some of the data he would be likely to analyze.

The first, or "Caesar," version gave seventh grade students a microcosmic politico-historical episode to work on, principally through textual analysis of some carefully selected bits of material: Caesar, Cicero, and later Latin writers. Wherever this version was tried it certainly engaged children. But, in handling these written documents, it often seemed that children failed to detect ambiguity where it existed, that they too easily fell into over-interpretation from very limited evidence, that they frequently misinterpreted, and that often what was inherently a conflict of evidence became indeed a conflict of students. The signs pointed toward a need to teach in ways that would increase the linguistic capability of children to interact with problem-filled materials.

A second cause which handicapped children in handling the early version of the Caesar materials was that the episode of 49 B.C. stood alone, out of any historical context. The episode was in a kind of intellectual limbo which left children unexposed to the larger setting within which it occurred. We concluded that the episode could not stand alone. We decided that it should become an exercise within a larger unit on the death of the Roman Republic. By the end of this summer we should have a Roman unit of much more relevance to children and to the ideas of our whole sequence than we have had heretofore. At its simplest level, what the unit is "about" may well be the difference between "ought" and "is", between the ideal and real in politics. Again, what the unit is "about" may be the idea that a system of power can sicken and die, that a republic can have a death, that a new system of power may arise. The late period of the Roman Republic is a good case study of the disintegration of a system and its transformation through turmoil into something quite different. How and why these things happened are not matters of anything like complete agreement among present-day ancient historians. But as George Homans once said when we were talking about this, the fact that complete agreement does not exist among scholars is no reason not to raise the questions for children. The new version of the Roman unit, on which much groundwork was done during the summer of '64 and a great deal more has been done since, will have five parts.

Part I, which will serve as an introduction, is not yet fully developed. It seemed better to defer work on an introduction until the basic materials of the rest of the unit have been fully developed. But the chances are that Part I will introduce children to general features of Rome and Roman history, will acquaint students with the governmental and political structure of Rome, and will, perhaps through selections from Polybius, convey some idea of the Roman Republican system in its ideal form.

Part II plunges students into the political realities of the Republic in Cicero's time. This section takes up real campaigning for public office, the conduct of the elections and the practice of bringing one's political enemies to trial. Marcus Tullius Cicero is followed, in original sources, through a campaign for the consulship and into the aftermath of a campaign in a bribery trial. Among other things, this section includes Quintus Cicero's advice to his brother on how to campaign, much of which has a startling familiarity to us in the twentieth century, as perhaps just two extracts may suggest:

> . . . Show that you [know men's names], and practice so that you get better at it from day to day. Nothing is so popular or pleasing.
> . . . Last, you must take care that your whole campaign is brilliant and splendid, well-suited to the popular taste. . . . Also, if possible, see that some new scandal is started against your opponents for crime or immorality or corruption—whatever their characters suggest.

Through investigating a real campaign, through a game simulating an election, and through role playing a real trial for bribery children experience some of the political realities of the times.

In Part III the unit moves from a study of elections, corruption, and bribery to a study of violence. Through the materials of Part III the dichotomy between the violent solution and the orderly legal solution of problems of state emerges quite clearly. These materials include selections dealing with the Cataline conspiracy, the Cato-Caesar debate over the fate of the conspirators, the exile of Cicero and the *Pro Sestio.* In the latter, Cicero's defense of Sestius depicts violence, disorder, and the breakdown of the kind of systematic government which sounded so fine in Polybius' descriptions. For example the *Pro Sestio* contains the following passage:

> As that excellent and steadfast tribune Marcus Cispius was coming into the Forum, they drove him away with force, and caused great slaughter in the Forum. Then all together, their swords drawn and dripping with blood, they searched every corner of the Forum for that most excellent man my most brave and devoted brother. Yet he could not escape the violence of those wicked bandits because he had come to beg the Roman people for his brother's recall. Driven from the Rostra, he lay down in the Comitium, sheltering himself behind the bodies of slaves and freedmen, and then saved his life under the protection of darkness and flight, not of law and justice. You remember, gentlemen, how the Tiber was filled that day with the bodies of citizens, how the sewers were choked, how blood was mopped from the Forum with sponges. But neither before that time, nor even on that very day of disorder, did you bring any charge against Sestius.

Student exercises with these materials involve questions about the antithesis between violence and law as methods for settling disputes. The tendency of violence, once used, to breed more violence. The consequences of allowing or requiring private citizens to take law into their own hands. The responsibilities of those who are in government. How and why political conditions in the later period of the Roman Republic became so unstable.

Part IV deals with the Civil War and grows out of what was described earlier as the original "Caesar Unit." The materials here plus some additions give children an opportunity to examine the problems of the Civil War as a whole.

Part V uses materials from Caesar's dictatorship. The reforms instituted during the dictatorship, Caesar's use of power, reactions of men like Cicero, and evidence of the increasing tension of events which culminate in assassination are dealt with. Students will come to the end of the unit facing questions about government, politics, and change that the assassination and all that preceded it in earlier parts of the unit have raised. In the light of Caesar's assassination, they are asked to look back, for example, at such words as these from Cicero's *De Republica:*

> When there is equality under the law, only then is government truly the property of the people. . . . There are those who prefer the efficiency of monarchy to this form of government. It is true that a monarch can be merciful as well as oppressive to his subjects. But in either case, the subject remains a subject. A master can be kind or cruel to his slaves. But in either case, the slave remains a slave.

As we begin to approach the time when the *Death of the Roman Republic* can be tried in schools as a complete unit, we hope to be successful not only in having devised a unit of work for students along the general lines of the ESI philosophy, exposing students to primary source materials, asking them to employ an inductive approach, etc. We hope that we have not only stimulated them to think about some very basic questions concerning power and political culture. But also we hope that we may have made a rather unique contribution in asking school children to consider a number of problems which fall in the realm of political science through the use of some of the vastly rich materials of ancient history.

THE NEWTON SOCIAL SCIENCE SEQUENCE

by Wayne Altree
and
Richard M. Douglas

THE DEPARTMENT OF SOCIAL SCIENCE in the Newton (Mass.) public schools recently started the second part of a new three-year sequence in history, which is now being offered to Curriculum I students in Grades X and XI. Preparation of the next syllabus (for Grade XII) is expected to begin in November. This sequence, planned as if it were a single course, is primarily concerned with the study of historical tradition. Although most of its materials are readily familiar to historians, the Newton course is also being built out of other materials borrowed from literature and the social sciences. The high school teachers are all historians, but some of the college and university consultants who have helped plan parts of the syllabus represent disciplines as diverse as anthropology, art history, English, political science, and sociology. None of these cognate fields is studied for itself, but rather for the illuminations each can add to the understanding of history and social behavior.

The Newton history curriculum is based on the assumption that history is one of the most humanistic of the liberal arts disciplines. If it is reasonable to say that the humanities in their briefest definition are about other lives, then it is reasonable to argue that the value of history for the education of high school students lies partly in its capacity to generate awareness and consciousness of experience other than one's own. The uses of history in high school are surely not to be limited only to methodology or to "finding out what the historian does." Seriousiness about the rules of the discipline obviously has its place, but history as methodology can be no less tedious a sobriety to a high school student than history as unending chronology. The Newton teachers also argue that history is not simply a language of inquiry but also a unique kind of perception; when it works well, it has the effect of expanding one's powers of vision into the competing interests, ideologies and experiences which constitute society. The sense of history can be a special kind of sensibility. And at a time when competitive rewards go so much to the mastery of "functional skills," "conceptual ability," and analytic "sophistication," the case for a humanistic history is singularly strong. When it works well, it is an extension of social experience which expands awareness of life beyond one's own. In this sense, history both informs opinion and creates judgment.

Perhaps the most unorthodox feature of the Newton course, in pursuit of these purposes, is to be found in the opening five months of Grade X. In the first unit (four or five weeks) students read a series of short stories and memoirs, most of them written during the past thirty years, describing a moment of adolescence in which a youngster and a parent confront one another across some gap of self-interest or contention. These stories describe episodes, widely different from one another, in which members of two generations simply don't see things in the same way. (The current syllabus includes stories and essays by Pär Lagerquist, Allan Wheelis, Herbert Gold, James Baldwin, George Orwell, and Mark Twain.) The point of using these stories is simply to open the course with statements about individuals in present time, living in small arenas of experience from the village to the city. The variety of the stories suggests something of the variety of ways in which the historical present can be experienced. The theme of division between generations may also suggest something about the energy of history itself.

The second unit opens with a series of life histories from simple societies (compiled by Radin, Mead, Mur-

Mr. Altree has been chairman of the Newton High Schools' History Department for the past five years. A native of Oregon, he is a graduate of Reed College and has studied at Harvard in the China Regional Studies Program and at the University of Hong Kong. Professor Douglas is Head of the Department of Humanities of the Massachusetts Institute of Technology.

Attending a summer Committee meeting were (clockwise from left) Newton and Amherst teachers Allan Gartner, John Livingston, Professor Charles Hale, Professor Theodore Greene, Elizabeth Roetter, Professor John Ratté, and Emily Thatch.

doch, Weyer, Laye) in which the young assume the burden of an undebated tradition, and where an individual's life is not regarded as a personal artifact but as the renewal of ancestral archetypes. From these accounts the course moves on to different statements about the "culture concept" (Goldschmidt, Lee, Kluckhohn) and the first effort to conceptualize the functions of "custom," "tradition," and the rules which hold a society together.

The following unit proceeds backwards in time to the invention of the city in the ancient Near East, or to the origins of complex social organization in archaic societies characterized by the specialization of skills, writing and literacy, metallurgy, priestcraft and so on. The effort here is once again to examine the variability and diversity of human societies, and the achievements of the city as a system of cooperation, interdependence, and conflict. This unit is to be elaborated in 1964 into a comparative study of Greek and Roman society as contrasting social systems and traditions, but without reference to their histories.

Only with the final unit of Grade X, lasting nearly five months, does the course become formally historical. Between late January and June the syllabus turns to the formation of a European tradition out of Mediterranean and Germanic elements, and the elaboration of that tradition in the Carolingian era, the High Middle Ages, and the early Renaissance.

Grade XI begins with a six-week unit on the High Renaissance and the Reformation, treated as a major fracture of tradition and the beginning of new kinds of opinion about society, piety, politics and history. The purpose of the first month is to suggest something of the range of new perspectives created in the minds of sixteenth-century Europeans. The material includes a picaresque novel, selections from historical writing, essays, accounts of utopias, and extracts from the literature of discovery and exploration. (A special topic on the development of perspective painting, as a new kind of seeing, has also been completed for use next year, along with another visual unit on "The Head of Christ" as portrayed from the art of the early Romanesque through the late Baroque.) This unit, like the latter half of Grade X, is supplemented by assignments in W. H. McNeill, *Handbook of Western Civilization.*

Unit II in the second year is about Tudor-Stuart England and the divisions which produced not only the Civil War and the Revolution of 1688, but the Puritan migration to America. Here the effort is to examine colonial America as a derivation from European tradition, or as a selection from it; and then to develop the uniquenesses of American institutions through three generations of Puritans. A long unit will deal with the life of Benjamin Franklin prior to his career at Passy and Paris, and a separate unit on both the American and French Revolutions (treated again as turning points in the history of a common tradition) will follow. The syllabus for Grade XI will close with a unit on the American Civil War. Grade XII will open in 1965 with a series of interpretations of the factory system in England between 1830-50—in essays, novels, parliamentary debates, social theory, and socialist polemic. Grade XII will include a unit on the impact of Europe and America on the social traditions of Asia and Africa, and will close with a new set of short stories, memoirs, and personal essays similar to those used at the beginning of Grade X three years earlier.

THE IDEA for the Newton sequence began during one of several visits to Amherst College by Wayne Altree in the spring of 1962. Dean Van R. Halsey of Amherst arranged for collaboration with the Department of History at Amherst through Richard M. Douglas and later through Theodore P. Greene, John Ratté, and Edwin C. Rozwenc. Reginald Arragon, Professor Emeritus of History at Reed College, served as resident consultant for six months in 1963-64; and more recently, Professor Marvin Meyers of Brandeis has been working with William Hollman and other teachers on the American History unit of Grade XI. Alan Gartner's group of tenth-grade teachers has had consulting support from Dorothy Lee (San Fernando Valley State College), Sydney Mintz (Professor of Anthropology at Yale, and currently at M.I.T.), Frank A. Trapp (Art History, Amherst), and Peter Ferguson (Art History, Harvard). Norman Pettit (M.I.T.) has contributed source materials and commentaries to the curriculum of Grade XI, and the general design of the program has also been reviewed in discussions with David Riesman (Harvard), Benjamin DeMott (Amherst), and John R. Seelye (University of Toronto). Summer workshops have produced materials for the past two years in collaboration with Professors Douglas and Meyers, and the third workshop is to take place in August 1965. To date, however, the materials produced for the new sequence exist only in mimeograph form; until the syllabus for each course has been used and revised, no effort will be made to publish documents, commentaries, introductions, or teachers' guides.

Professor Edwin Rozwenc, Edward Hollman, and Irving Schwartz discuss the history program's progress.

This is a course in history organized around major periods of equilibrium in the growth of Western tradition and around certain historical turning points or reconstructions of this tradition. It is not a survey course, and textbook assignments are infrequent. It has many features of the "close-reading" course, since there is time to move through the source material deliberately and even slowly, and because the syllabi recurrently use documents of the same kind, restating variations of a few common themes.

Probably the most obvious accomplishment of the course to date lies in the response of the teachers. Unlike some other programs in the social sciences which have been prepared almost exclusively by university people working by themselves without any steady association with teachers, we have maintained a consistent working arrangement between teachers and consultants in the preparation of material, leaving rights of veto and choice to the teachers. Consultants have written a good deal of introductory material, proposed considerable reading and interpretation, and drafted a number of syllabi. But final decisions about the choice of course content have been made in each of the eleven units prepared to date not by consultants, but by our participating staff. As a result, the teachers trust its principles and enjoy the freshness of its materials.

patterns
of learning
in the public schools
of Newton

January 1966 Newton Public Schools Volume 5 No. 3

A NEW APPROACH TO HISTORY

During the past few years a new three-year sequence in Social Studies has been taking shape in the Newton High Schools. Supported in part by outside grants, this work has been directed by Mr. Wayne Altree, Department Head in Social Studies with close cooperation from Dr. Richard Douglas, Chairman Humanities Department, MIT. Because this program is new and different, teachers recognized the importance of communicating with students in advance. The article which follows was first prepared as a mimeographed message which was given to all 10th grade students in Curriculum I as they started their studies in history. We present it here in recognition of the important things it has to say regarding not only history, but also education itself.

Change And Continuity

High school is a new beginning, an event of change within a process of continuity. It is a historical moment in your life, marking your entry into a new place, and a new environment of experience. It represents a significant moment of personal history in the sense that it takes you into something new, not wholly of your own choice or making; unfamiliar, though in this case predictable; unsettling for a while, though not forever to be looked back on in the same way you see it now.

History is complicated that way. The event of entering high school is a fact. The hour and the date, the room and the teacher of your first class, are already a matter of public record. These are already facts in the past. Why you are in high school, and how you feel about it, are different matters. You are here of course because law and custom require it for your own advantage and the good of your society. In another sense it is assumed that through knowing more, and by acquiring more knowledge about the traditions and the intellectual skills our society has developed, you will enter its life with greater choice of freedom in it because you are building up greater knowledge of it. And in still another respect the purpose of the institution of the school is to accelerate the rate at which you learn. To learn alone is hard and not very efficient. School is a way of getting into history, presumably of entering a society more effectively.

It is odd but true that although the fact of going to high school won't change, your own sense of what it's like inevitably will. Thoughts *about* the past seem to be more variable than its facts or sequences. Yet your thoughts belong to your own history just as much as your enrollment in the 10th grade in September. You already see the fact differently from the way you saw it last June, and next June your interpretation of it, through the passage of time and changes in your own way of seeing things, will show still another version. Furthermore, all of us may expect by then to live in a world historically other than what it was this morning. There will be continuities — in our institutions, in our thoughts, in the language we use, in our habits and customs and traditions — but the human environment will in some measure have changed.

The purpose of this course is not merely to give you fresh facts about the past and the tradition to which you belong, but also to educate your attention and to enable you to see and hear the world you live in with an idea of its history. For we live in a world never before so historical — never before so man-made, and never before so subject to rapid and intensive change. A sense of history, it would seem, has never been so imperative to us, both as individuals and collectively as a nation.

"It may seen complicated at first, but you'll be all right after you learn what to look for." The statement applies just as well to a bullfight as to the ballet, archeology, or a new course. Learning has a lot to do with the education of the eye, with learning how to see and what to look for. And education, when it works well, is a process of learning to connect the powers of the mind with the versatility of the eye. It is a process of increasing the number of windows or perspectives through which you are able to look intelligently at the world outside yourself. The young child lives in a private little universe not much more than a thousand yards wide and only a few hours long. "Yesterday" and "tomorrow" are rather meaningless terms to him, or at best confusing abstractions. For strange reasons, the same words can also mean Monday

A monthly publication of the public schools of Newton, Massachusetts.

THE SCHOOL COMMITTEE

MONTE G. BASBAS, Mayor, *ex-officio*

HUGH M. TOMB, *Chairman* — EDWIN HAWKRIDGE
MANUEL BECKWITH — NORMA W. MINTZ
HAROLD J. BERMAN — GRACE C. WHITMORE
FRANCIS P. FRAZIER — WAY DONG WOO

Superintendent of Schools — CHARLES E. BROWN
Production consultant — STANLEY RUSSELL
Technical consultant — ERNEST P. REPPUCCI
P.T.A. Council Consultants — MR. AND MRS. B. I. KAPLAN

or Tuesday. His capacity to understand simple relations of time and space is still crude and limited, though it grows suddenly as he learns to read. But his capacity to pay attention to experience other than his own is virtually nil. He is scarcely able to look beyond himself.

One of your own great achievements during the past ten years is a growing ability to imagine and understand distinctions between past and present, here and there, the self and the other person. You have already learned, and you have been taught, to put questions to yourself about connections between the terms in each of these sets. One purpose of this course is to enlarge your command over such distinctions, helping you to see as well as to ask where you are in historical time and space. Another is to help you ask who you are as someone on whom history has acted, and whose life has been conditioned by custom and culture. To ignore the fact that we live in history, or that we are conditioned by the society around us, is to settle for the attitudes of childhood, never seeing beyond the corners of personal experience.

Questions And Answers

Your history course this year will also confront you with questions too large to answer suddenly or with final certainity. It is not a course in answers merely, nor will you find it one in which you can achieve very much by mere memorizing. Dates and facts will be there, inevitably; they are as necessary to history as numbers are to mathematics. But the measure of your skill and accomplishment will depend just as much on the quality of the questions you learn to ask about what you read and about what you observe in the world around you. Charles Darwin once said that the great lesson of his life was the discovery that the scientist's function is to look not for answers but for *questions.* | Useful answers come only from powerful questions. For thousands of years the biological "answers" had swarmed beneath the eyes of human observers — in every pond, forest, meadow and ocean. But it was not until Darwin's time that the billions of living answers were made intelligible by the elegant simplicity of his theory of the origin and development of the species. And although his questions about the remote beginnings of life were essentially historical, they were produced by observing living phenomena.

In this course you will often find that your own experience and your own puzzlement, your own observations of your own life, can be a rich source of usable curiosity about history and human behavior. We hope you will discover how much can be achieved if you trust your own curiosity; if you cultivate those latent powers of vision, perception, and observation which you already have.

What answers, for example, would you offer to someone who asks the question, in what ways do you live in the same world today that you lived in yesterday? Why can you assume that you will find it familiar tomorrow after losing sight and touch with the world in sleep? To the astronomer and the geologist the passage of an average day makes little difference, despite the fact that the universe is older or that the earth itself — like its animal and vegetable cover — is never identical now to what it was yesterday. Everything has changed a little. Things and persons are older. Yet the basic structure persists.

Strictly speaking, we know we cannot enter the same woods twice, or step again into the same river. In what ways then do we, and in what ways do we not, return to the same world in the morning that we left in sleep the night before? How many different worlds of experience do people enter at the start of each day in Boston? How are we to explain whatever it is that holds a society together from one day to the next? "Custom," is one common-sense answer, like "habit," "law," "institutions," or "tradition." But what kind of words are these? What do these sounds stand for? Is it possible to touch a tradition? Can a tradition be changed? What is its purpose? Even though your mood may change from bright to dark between Sunday and Monday, you will still drive on the right, comb your hair, exchange green paper for goods, and expect the routine of home, city, and school to be repeated from one day to the next. We share these expectations and read the papers for a record of yesterday's exception to the rule — for "news" or breaks in the routine. But you won't get in the papers by getting to class on time or for brushing your teeth.

In its simplest terms the original question asks about both continuity and change — about what keeps a given human society intact, and about what it is that necessitates, permits or forces change of behavior and opinion in human history. The fact of change itself is a great curiosity. In America women's fashions are made deliberately different from one season to another, from year to year. But in Puritan New England, traditional Japan, and most of the Middle East such practice would be unthinkable. To the reflective mind, very little is gained by explaining consistencies of this sort by one-word proclamations about "habit" or "custom." These words do not explain what the terms stand for, or how social habit is established, or why the patterns of custom vary so immensely from one society to the next. Nor do they explain why the fabric of custom and habit can suddenly be changed through time to make history. Such words also fail to explain such phenomena as revolution, when things do change virtually overnight. They do not tell why, although the U.S. and U.S.S.R. share in almost identical technology, our ideas about its management and ownership can be so immensely different from theirs.

Through the centuries the most interesting and orginal historians have been alerted to their own experience, and willing to learn, like Darwin, from what thy were able to see first-hand. Thucydides, Tacitus, Ibn-Khaldun, Machiavelli, Gibbon, Macaulay, Tocqueville, and Henry Adams were all shrewd and steady observers of the immediate scene and as much interested in the details of ordinary life as they were in finding patterns among random events, habits and opinions. The best historians — those whom the literate layman and professional scholar have been quickest to trust and respect — have always combined a passion for fact and a wide tolerance for diversity in their data with a desire to make life itself more intelligible. Like the physicist they look for order behind surface chaos. The curiosity of these historians did not stop with the past or with what had already happened, but they were all eager to observe and to create a useable past for the better comprehension of human nature itself. For all the great historians, history is more than a record of the thoughts and deeds of the dead. It is a form of understanding, a way of seeing and knowing which goes beyond the isolation and narrow vision of those who live only in the corner of their own moment of time, like the child in his sandbox.

Futhermore, the historians, social scientists, novelists, and poets who have made a difference seem to have been gifted or tortured by impatience with the kind of answers which satisfy other minds. They distrust borrowed certainties and explanations. They reject stale opinon. And they are not sure about what is really "obvious" or self-evident." Those who add something to understanding and knowledge are often those who reject some accepted version of the obvious as a result of being able to look around it or by finding a new way to talk about an old question—a new place to stand, in order to see better or at least to see differently.

What Is History?

Never — literally never — in all human history has the question, "What is history?," been so serious or so important. Behind the political and military rivalry between East and West, and behind the rivalry between the U.S.S.R. and China lies an argument elaborated a century ago by Karl Marx—an argument defining the nature of the historical process—which has released energies of revolution on a scale never known before. Whether interpreted by Lenin, Stalin, Khrushchev, Mao Tse-tung, Castro or Ho Chi Min, Marxist's doctrine reports to be a gigantic history lesson which defines all human history as the record of class conflict, or as the class struggle, where classes are defined according to their economic relations with one another. Marxist versions of history are not confined to schoolrooms. They become a basis of policy, and policy the basis of action. In their most recent declaration on the nature of history (September 1, 1965) the Chinese Communists state that "the contemporary world revolution presents a picture of encirclement of cities" (meaning North America and Western Europe) by "rural areas" (meaning Asia, Africa and Latin America). For the Chinese therefore the revolutionary class does not consist of factory workers, but rather of the peasant populations in the pre-industrial regions of the world. Marx, on the other hand, had almost nothing to say about the peasants, and everything to say about the class struggle beween the revolutionary industrial proletariat and the middle classes. So the Communists have recently brought to a head a new quarrel among themselves about the nature of history.

When physicists from the West meet to discuss physics with scientists from the East, they have no quarrel. When historians from West and East confront each other, however, there is no significant area of agreement either about the facts of the past or about why they happened. The entire understanding of what history is, and how human society functions, becomes caught up in irreconcilable debate and disagreement. Our entire tradition of social thought and values, our entire sense of the meaning of human life and experience, now separates us from a second world of meaning and from a new revolutionary tradition whose whole ideology is based on claims about the nature of history — that is, about the record of how men behave in society through time in relation to one another.

Whether you "like history" or not, you belong to it. In many ways, of course, none of us wholly likes the experience of history. None of us likes everything that makes one day or one year different from the one before it. In the city of Florence during the terrible plague year of 1348, a chronicler wrote, "May it please God that great change come not to our city." His city had already suffered from immense disorder, political conflict and violence, famine and unemployment. Like most of us the chronicler found much to deplore in the living events which add up to history. It is not a question, however, or whether we "like history" or not. It is a question of how we are to think about the process of change in the environment around us and in the human record behind us.

History is both (1) a record of significant change through time; a record of past events and ideas; (2) it also consists of what we say about the meaning of such events and ideas in the past. History is (1) the effort to establish what happened, and to explain (2) how or why it happened. It consists of antecedent facts and present thought about such facts. History is therefore an effort to construct the record of society through time. History is not only what is dug up from the earth or out of old libraries; it is also what *we* say about what *they* thought and did. What is said about what is dug up creates the problem of historical meaning and explanation, and therefore the disagreement which divides historians. Otherwise, everyone would agree with everyone else about the history of anything. In some ways, moreover, everyone every day, is a "working historian," for it is impossible to live without some version of past time. There may also be something to claim of a novelist that "Isolation compels every man, all alone like a savage, to invent his idea of society."

But novelists are not historians, however much they may occupy themselves with the experience of history of society. Historians in our tradition do not, like the Communist historians, insist on a single allowable and "scientific" theory of history. Neither do they, nor could they, invite every historian to invent his own idea of the past. Historians in our tradition acknowledge a degree of complexity in the interpretation of history that Marxists deny, and they insist upon the existence of questions about human behavor and the historical process which the Marxists claim already to have answered. This course will not prescribe a single view of history, on the one hand; nor will it invite everyone to create his own opinion on the other. It will often be more concerned with asking than with telling you what history is, what society is.

Conflict In Human Society

In the largest sense, this course has been derived from the question, "What is the most effective way to study and to understand the growth of urban civilization and its social traditions in the Western world?" What kind of knowledge must we seek, what kinds of questions must we ask, what kind of understanding may we expect? How are we to create a useful and intelligible past? We are not after history for its own sake, but after a history that enables us to read our own moment coherently, responsibly, and even shrewdly. We are after a kind of history and a course in it that will help to comprehend the historical present, that will enable us to act in it and on it. We are concerned with the kind of history that will enable us to advance toward greater comprehension of conflict in human society — the condition of history above all others which the Communists claim to have explained for all time — without the unhistorical simplifications of those willing to reduce complex questions to one-factor analysis. Unlike the Marxists, Western historians often find that situations of historical conflict in human society are easier to describe than to explain. They recognize the city not only as a form of social organization which involves conflict, but also as one which depends upon cooperation and interdependence. In their willingness to accept a far greater degree of complexity in historical study, analysis and explanation, however, historians in our tradition face their own kind of perplexity or risk, which is that of treating every episode of historical change (and all historical events signify both change and some measure of conflict) as a special case or as a unique event. The Marxists, as it were, insist that all snowflakes are six-sided crystals; Western historians, on the other hand, tend to say that no two sets of points on the crystals, and no two snowflakes, are alike.

We are also to be concerned with what holds social tradition together in continuity, and with the structure of society as a community of values and institutions. Basically, however, we are to be concerned with the structure of society and its processes of change through time. The study of history is in many ways the most difficult of the social sciences or the humanities simply because the subject entails and includes potentially every aspect of human behavior throughout the human record. Your course this year is confined primarily to the West (the ancient Mediterranean and Europe before 1500) and to the origins and development of its social traditions. We shall examine those traditions historically in the large, and also as they were experienced and expressed by individual men, for the unit of history can be the lives of individual men and women as well the record of dynasties, cities or nations.

Finally, you are going to find that studying history is like driving a streetcar through and around an entire city. You pass through all sectors of experience, all degrees of power and wealth, grandeur and squalor, rapid change and no change. You will find that different parts of a city and its society operate with different kinds of cultural clocks, some of which run faster than others. Part of your task will involve learning to see the city — a city — as a whole system; to ask what holds it together, what divides it, and what induces change within it. In looking at the historical city, or a Boston from the Prudential Tower, you may sometimes incline toward the language of the social scientist, who finds patterns and regularities which can be expressed statistically (about population change, crime, traffic, income, employment, taxation, and so on). And in other situations you will incline toward the language of the novelist or the idiom of the painter, seeking to express a snse of meaning through a particular version of experience. History seems to lie somewhere between science and art. Its purpose combines analytical skills and precise knowledge with insight and even compassion.

To The Past Through The Present

In many ways this course will be new and unfamiliar. For a while you may even wonder why it was ever called history in the first place. For one thing, it starts in the present and moves backward before beginning to proceed chronologically. It starts with modern short stories and autobiographies, completely disregarding war, politics, and the usual subject matter of history. It starts with what might be called the world of fathers and sons, with the remembered responses of adolescents to the demands of custom, habit or tradition as the young discover it in amusement or anger, in their encounters with the adult world. We have worked out these assignments in the belief that fiction in particular often discloses some of those differences between the generations which produce the energies of history. One test of historical change in any era is the degree of difference between the old and the young. In the Middle Ages, for example, the son's future was assumed to be his father's past. In the Renaissance, the future was considered to be an artifact of the son's own invention rather than a repetition of his father's craft or profession. In our society, the space between the generations is even wider. In some respects, they don't speak the same languge. Literature can often be read as a record of such differences. It will be up to you to determine in Unit I how much history, if any, you can find in the stories you read during the opening weeks, when the subject will not be civilizations but individuals. You will be asked what you recognize in their lives, language, and point of view, and how to account for the variety of the lives you will meet in these stories about adolescents.

Simple Societies

The second part of the course makes an abrupt and sudden departure both from contemporary fiction and the relatively familiar setting of Europe and America in the modern world. In Unit II you will turn to the description of adolescents and early adulthood in so-called pre-literate societies among peoples with least experience of steady historical change from one generation to the next. Here you will be able to see how ancestral custom and tradition are maintained from father to son, generation to generation, in rituals of continuity. The purpose of this unit, for one thing is to offer you the advantage of seeing contrasts and comparison between your own culture, where the pace of change and innovation is rapid, and cultures in which roughly the same technology — along with the same set of beliefs and customs — has prevailed almost undisturbed for generations. Pre-literate societies offer the further advantage for our purpose of small size and small scale. They are easier to see and take in as a whole, or as a system of coherent parts, because their tools and economic resources are limited and their ways of living, from day to day, less diversified than in a highly complex industrial and urban society. You will also be asked to read some life histories, drawn out of simple societies, in which you will have a chance to see how culture conditions the lives of individuals. But you will also find yourself asking how we are to account for the simplicity and small scale of so-called "backward" or pre-literate societies. There has been no major physiological change in human animal for 500,000 years. Why then the immense variety of cultures and societies maintained by members of the same species? We know that Spaniards are different from Swedes. But how are such differences maintained over time? The Greeks explained such differences by climate and geography. Racists presume to say they are genetic. But neither of these "obvious" answers any longer make sense.

In even the simplest society you will be able to identify elements of organiztion and structure common to all human societies, once you learn how to look for regularities or patterns of this kind. Even in those remaining pockets of greatest geographic isolation you will find rules and religion, a form of law and government, custom and authority, economic production and distribution, just as you will recognize a sacred system and body of myths and science by which people in the culture explain the big mysteries of human experience and the physical world. So too will you find shared agreements and values, giving a society its own style of form and identity. Pre-literate culture — we will try later to define the word more rigorously — can be profitably studied in order to draw our own society into greater relief and perspective, and to clarify certain basic questions about the nature of human institutions and historical change. You will be expected to look for evidence both of what seems to be universal in all human societies, and of those features which seem to be unique in particular societies. You may find that uniformity may appear at one moment and uniqueness at another. You will also find elements of value and behavior which seem wild or bizarre, only to discover by looking more closely that they have thier own human dignity within the system in which they exist.

Ancient Cities To Western Europe

In Unit III of the course we will move back to the earliest beginnings of civilization and thus to the earliest evidence of the city in the river valleys of the Ancient Near East. The city was an extraordinary human invention and actually a very recent one. If you were to place a dime on top of the Prudential Tower, the height of the building would still be too little to represent the duration of man's presence on earth and the thickness of the coin too great to represent the brevity of time since the first cities — or history — began. And because the invention of writing came slightly after the invention of the earliest cities, our knowledge of the past derived from written records remains only a slight fragment of the human story. Although we try to determine something about the origins of acient cities some 7,000 years ago, we will be largely concerned in this unit with the variety of their structures and organization. Before turning to more complex questions about historical change, we shall try to learn something about the traditions which held the ancient cities together, investigating their form and structure without going on to the next step, which would be to examine their evolution, development and decline.

Unit IV is explicitly concerned with the history of Western Europe. It is the longest part of the course and will start with the origins of a distinctly European tradition, gradually formed out of the diverse Mediterranean and Germanic elements. The unit will then exmine the development of European society from the end of the Roman Empire to the of Columbus, Machiavelli and Luther. It will deal with changes in the structure of European society and tradition from the early Middle ages to the early Reformation.

The Mind's Vision

By the middle of the year you ought to be far more skillful in knowing what to look for in understanding how social traditions function, than if you were suddenly to start in September, at the beginning of European history in the Middle Ages. We will ask you instead to start your explorations of human time with your own moment in the present, with the discovery and interpretation of tradition and traditions in the living world in order to see something in the diversity of experience to which we have become so accustomed. The examination of pre-literate and ancient society will confront you with material much less familiar in specific detail but often starkly recognizable as a different version of being human. You will have to change your focus without changing the lens, because you will always be looking at human beings. Your eyes ought to improve in the process, your mind's vision not only of things remote in time and space but of the environment you live in, just as observant traveler comes home to see it differently and often more acutely as the result of being somewhere else.

What strikes the eye in ordinary life are individual human beings and simple events. What we see on the streets are people and things. The eye does not directly observe such abstractions as "civilization," "society," "authority." But the mind's vision can see patterns in the behavior of individuals and the possibility of order in events which to the eye of the child are chaotic and meaningless. Your responsibility in this course is to extend your own inner vision of human action, thought and feeling, while you increase your sense of history and your knowledge of human record in some of its variety.

As you study the course you may want to reflect on the following quotations:

> "No man can sit down to write about the history of his own time — or perhaps of any time — without bringing to the task the preconceptions which spring from his own character and experience."[1]

> "History has no meaning, in the sense that it has a clear pattern or a determinate plot; but it is not simply meaningless or pointless. It has no certain meaning because man is free to give it various possible meanings."[2]

> "Man alone of all the animals dose not live in the present. Culture makes it impossible for him to live a hand-to-hand existence, from moment to moment, in the spiritual as in the material sense."[3]

> "Human life is a moral life precisely because it is a social life and because in the case of human species the minimum necessities for order and co-operative behavior are not provided by biologically inherited instincts. In other words, all moral orders are human artifacts, the products of the cultural process."[4]

1Allan Bullock. *Hitler: A Study in Tyranny* (New York, 1959) p. 9.
2Herbert J. Muller. *The Uses of the Past* (New York 1952), p. 73.
3B. Malinowski. *The Dynamics of Cultural Change* (New Haven, 1945), p. 45.
4Clyde Kluckhohn. in *City Invincible* (Chicago, 1961), p. 391.

VI
CURRICULUM CHANGE IN MATHEMATICS

THE MATHEMATICS CURRICULUM STUDY

by W. T. Martin

During the past five to ten years a number of curricular reform groups in mathematics have developed. Among these are the massive School Mathematics Study Group (SMSG), the Stanford Arithmetic Project, the University of Illinois Arithmetic Project, the University of Illinois Committee on School Mathematics, the Syracuse University-Webster College Madison Project, the Minnemath Center of the University of Minnesota and other groups. In the summer of 1962 a small group met in Cambridge with representatives of the National Science Foundation to discuss informally the state of mathematics instruction in primary and secondary schools. The group recognized the important and excellent work already underway by various groups but at the same time felt it advisable to begin at once to move toward a more radical revision than any at that time underway. With this in mind Educational Services Incorporated, with financial support from the National Science Foundation, held a conference in the summer of 1963, called the Cambridge Conference on School Mathematics, which was attended by twenty-five mathematicians and scientists from universities and industrial firms. The conference participants considered the structure of mathematics education and sketched a rough outline of possible new frameworks for primary and secondary school instruction. The report of that study is given in a booklet entitled *Goals for School Mathematics,* published by Houghton Mifflin Co., in the fall of 1963. The caveat to that book stated:

"The reader is urged to recognize the report that follows for what it is and for nothing more. A small number of professional mathematicians have attempted to express their tentative views upon the shape and content of a pre-college mathematics curriculum that might be brought into being over the next few decades. These views are intended to serve as a basis for widespread further discussion, and, above all, experimentation by mathematicians, teachers, and all others who share the responsibility for the processes and goals of American education. At this stage of their development they cannot pretend to represent guidelines for school administrators or mathematics teachers, and they should not be read as such. If this report, however, fulfills its purposes by provoking general debate and bold experimentation, those guidelines may ultimately emerge."

In the foreword to the *Goals* book, Dr. Francis Keppel, United States Commissioner of Education, wrote:

"If one were to look for the most significant development in education over the past decade, it would be reasonable to single out the wave of curriculum reform which has swept the school system, and appears to be maintaining its vigor undiminished. Beginning with mathematics and the physical sciences, it has spread in scope until almost every discipline represented in the primary and secondary school curriculum has been in some degree affected.

These recent reforms have several characteristics that differentiate them from the steady stream of curriculum reform of earlier years. They have been for the most part national, or at least regional, efforts. They have drawn on university scholarship and skilled teachers not only for leadership but for the immediate demands of day-to-day operation; to some extent they have served to destroy (or at least to lower) the wall that has traditionally separated the scholar from the teacher. Almost without exception they have passed from the determination of policy and program directly into the preparation of materials for use in the schools.

For the most part, they have been eminently successful, and in the light of their successes it has sometimes been difficult to distinguish their shortcomings. Yet the shortcomings are there, and they are by no means insignificant. It can be argued, in fact, that

---

Dr. Martin is the Chairman of the Mathematics Curriculum Study and Chairman of the Mathematics Committee of ESI's African Education Program. He is the head of the Department of Mathematics at the Massachusetts Institute of Technology.

the deficiencies of the present reform movement are grave enough to threaten the expressed goals of the movements themselves.

These deficiencies derive from the inherent inconsistency that characterizes most curriculum reforms. On the one hand, there is the intention to represent in the revised curriculum the discipline in question as the scholar himself regards that discipline, complete with its sense of adventure, its unsolved questions, and its groping toward the future. Inseparably associated with this intention is the belief that the student can be brought into contact with the frontiers of knowledge, and that his capacity to learn is far beyond anything we have been accustomed to attribute to him.

But these ambitions are immediately dampened by the awareness that serious limitations are imposed upon the student's ability to learn by the instructor's ability to teach. If the student is to be brought to the frontiers of knowledge, the teacher must know the whereabouts of those frontiers. If the student is to be encouraged to grope, the teacher must at least be able to suggest which of his roads are likely to be blind alleys.

Most curriculum reforms, practically enough, have chosen to limit their ambitions in the light of these realities. They have tended to create such new courses as existing teachers, after enjoying the benefits of brief retraining, can competently handle. They have done so fully aware that they are thus setting an upper limit, and an upper limit that is uncomfortably close.

If the matter were to end there, the result might well be disastrous. New curricula would be frozen into the educational system that would come to possess, in time, all the deficiencies of curricula that are now being swept away. And in all likelihood, the present enthusiasm for curriculum reform will have long since been spent; the "new" curricula might remain in the system until, like the old, they become not only inadequate but in fact intolerable. Given the relative conservatism of the educational system, and the tendency of the scholar to retreat to his own direct concerns, the lag may well be at least as long as it has been during the first half of this century.

The present report is a bold step toward meeting this problem. It is characterized by a complete impatience with the present capacities of the educational system. It is not only that most teachers will be completely incapable of teaching much of the mathematics set forth in the curricula proposed here; most teachers would be hard put to comprehend it. No brief period of retraining will suffice. Even the first grade curriculum embodies notions with which the average teacher is totally unfamiliar."

The participants found themselves essentially in agreement on the mathematical aims of the elementary school. Through the introduction of the number line the child would be started immediately on the study of the whole real number system including negatives. By a wedding of arithmetic and geometry the intuition of the child could be developed and exploited and the significance of the arithmetical operations enriched for him. In the suggested curriculum, the order properties of the real number system would be studied from the earliest school years and would be used in the study of inequalities, approximation, and order of magnitude estimates. The group felt that an early development of the child's spatial intuition was essential and that it was important also for children to study the standard shapes in two- and three-dimensions including a discussion of their symmetries. The group recommended that the notions of function and set be used throughout the elementary school sequence. This does not mean that set theory and formal logic should be emphasized as such but that the child should be able to build his early mathematics experience into his habitual language. It was hoped that informal algebra could be studied with arithmetic operations.

The conference agreed that reasonable proficiency in arithmetic computation and algebraic manipulation is essential to the student of mathematics, but the group also felt that adequate practice in computation could be built into problems which genuinely attract the student's interest.

Because of both their intuitive appeal and their basic importance there should be an introduction of the elementary ideas of probability and statistical judgment accompanied by concrete experimentation with random processes. The concern for motivation, applications and the interplay between mathematics and the physical world is a constant theme in the conference's report. The group felt that the one constraint on this theme was the limited science experience available in the elementary school. This will likely be changed as elementary school science programs develop throughout the nation. Geometry also offers a rich area within which younger students can explore the relationship between physical objects and their idealized mathematical abstractions. As the student's experience deepens, more sophisticated problems can be introduced.

Having studied arithmetic and geometry, mostly informally, in the elementary school, the students should be prepared for a sound treatment of geometry and the algebra of polynomials beginning in the seventh grade. The program of a student who elected mathematics each year would at the end of the twelfth year have contained a closely knit presentation of calculus, linear algebra and probability as well as a brief introduction to other mathematical topics. In addition to the topics mentioned above, the conference also arrived at a recommendation which dealt more with methods of presentation. It was felt that it was desirable, for example, to adopt a spiral approach in which each new topic is introduced early, in less complex forms, and is then reconsidered repeatedly, each time with more sophistication and each time illuminating more of a particular topic's interconnection with the rest of the subject. The result should be a sort of guided tour of mathematics. A second aspect of the same precept led to the suggestion that topics receive multiple motivation. It was suggested that it would be wise to use several different informal approaches, each one leading to the desired goal—for instance, the rules for multiplication of negatives—rather than leave students with the feeling that there is only one correct road.

One would hope to strengthen the impression that a mathematical idea appears first as the solution to some problem by some person. The problems thus become a matter of importance equal to, or even greater than, that of the textual material itself. This would also help the student to develop the facility to pose problems.

The conference operated quite differently in making recommendations for the upper grades from the way it did for the primary grades. It was recognized that the feasibility of the program designed for the upper grades would depend on the success of the elementary school program. Since no one has had any experience with a class that has had seven years of well-organized pre-mathematical training the participants simply had to guess what level of sophistication would be appropriate. The conference proposed two alternative, ambitious programs.

Following the publication of *Goals for School Mathematics* there have been a number of conferences and experimental classes conducted concerned with material proposed in the report. During the summer of 1964 course development and trial teaching were conducted at the Morse School in Cambridge, Massachusetts, in Miss Mason's School in Princeton, New Jersey, and in an eighth grade geometry class at Palo Alto, California. In the way of classroom testing as a follow-through to the Morse School summer session, trial teaching has been conducted this academic year at several grade levels, at the Estabrook School in Lexington, Massachusetts, and in a sixth grade class at the Hosmer School in Watertown, Massachusetts. Work continues on mathematics at the nursery school level at Miss Mason's School.

In March, 1965, the SMSG and the Cambridge Conference jointly sponsored a three-day conference, held in Cambridge, Massachusetts. The conference was attended by representatives of most of the major curricular reform groups in mathematics in the United States, as well as by the President of the National Council of Teachers of Mathematics and by Dr. Bryan Thwaites, Director of the School Mathematics Project at the University, Southampton, England. The main purpose of the conference was to establish better communication among the various individuals and groups concerned with educational reform in mathematics. Brief reports were given by representatives of each group. Their reports were followed by a discussion of various problems faced by individual projects and by the entire mathematics curriculum reform movement. Among these problems are:

1. What should be the basis for deciding upon the content of a strong mathematics curriculum, given that pupils at a given grade level can clearly master a wide variety of mathematical concepts?
2. What is the place of sets and functions in elementary school mathematics?
3. How much geometry is needed, and of what type?
4. How can manipulative and computational skills best be developed? Can these skills be developed as a by-product of otherwise interesting work such as number theory?
5. How can the number of mathematicians involved in work of this nature be significantly enlarged?
6. How best can school systems be advised of work in progress?
7. How can better communication be established a) among mathematics curricula reform groups; b) between teachers and university mathematicians concerned with these problems; c) with parents, the public and the press?

The large and important problem of teacher education entered into nearly every aspect of the discussion.

The participants agreed that they would meet again in approximately a year to continue their discussion of these and related topics.

Last January, the Steering Committee of the Cambridge Conference invited other interested mathematicians to a special meeting held in Denver, Colorado, concurrently with the Annual Meeting of the American Mathematical Society and the Mathematical Association of America. At the special meeting, plans for two further activities of the Cambridge Conference were made. The first involved the consideration of preparing material for the primary grades in geometry, in applications and, where feasible, in an introduction to the calculus. The second involved the problem of teacher education. During the summer of 1965 a small workshop is planned to tackle the first of these problems. The group does not plan to produce text material in these three topics but it does hope to prepare broad outlines with exercises and examples of the three topics; the three topics should be interwoven. There will be applications of geometry to problems of indirect measurement and areas and volumes. The use of graphs, interpolation and extrapolation should lead to the idea of rate of change. It is intended that the material produced in the summer of 1965 on these three topics can serve as the basis for text material either by other writing groups or to be produced by commercial publishers. As one participant described it, perhaps the material can be prepared in a way similar to modules for furniture, that is the material could be inserted in the primary school curriculum wherever it seemed appropriate in a given school.

The next topic, teacher training, is to be considered at a conference to be held during the summer of 1966. This conference will consider and develop suggestions regarding the education of mathematics teachers. The conference will not be primarily concerned with the problems of the present but rather will look to the not so distant future of mathematics education even twenty or thirty years from now. The topic of the meeting will be the level of mathematical understanding needed on the part of the classroom teacher in order to instruct students in the materials being produced by the various curriculum groups. It will also study the implications of the *Goals* report for teacher training. The hoped-for results of the conference will be a report similar to *Goals for School Mathematics*. This report would consider the long-term future but not without substantial consideration of the in-service training of teachers. The "bench mark" of this conference would be "What does the teacher have to know to teach the K-6 recommended materials as outlined in *Goals for School Mathematics?*" This is probably the most difficult of the various mathematical tasks which we face in this country largely because of the huge number of teachers involved. The *Goals* report contained outlines of curricula toward which the schools should be aiming. As Dr. Keppel said in his foreword, "If teachers cannot achieve them today, they must set their courses so that they may begin to achieve them in ten years, or twenty years, or thirty. If this is what the teacher of the future must know, the schools of education of the present must begin at once to think how to prepare those teachers. There must still be short-term curriculum reforms, they must look upon themselves as constituting a stage toward the larger goals, and they must at all costs be consistent with those larger goals." Dr. Keppel continued, "As the years pass, these goals may well change, but at least we will be in motion in the general direction of the new goals and in a fair way to get there sooner or later." In the body of the *Goals* book a further statement is made, namely, "Our program makes even heavier demands on teachers than our remarks so far would suggest. Almost any drill material can be taught by almost any good drillmaster. But we do not propose to teach by drill. At every level we propose to present mathematics as the pursuit of truth by process of inquiry; we propose to elicit all the insight and all the creative responses the student is capable of. Just how much they will turn out to be capable of we do not know; but the experience of a few bold experimenters amply proves that the present apparent limits on the insight and creativity of children are being set by the materials presented to them, and not by the native talent of the children." Later the report states, "Thus the training of teachers involves a threshold phenomenon. The point is that we propose to teach ideas. The mechanical processes of arithmetic can be taught, after a fashion, by rote and drill. Ideas cannot be. If the elementary teachers in the next generation do not understand the ideas that they are supposed to be teaching, then the results may easily be worse than the results that we are getting now." And finally, "Much of our work will be wasted unless curriculum development and teacher training keep pace with each other."

In the April 1965 issue of *The Mathematics Teacher,* (Volume 58, Number 4, pages 353-360) Professor Marshall H. Stone of the University of Chicago published a review of the report *Goals for School Mathematics: The Report of the Cambridge Conference on School Mathematics.* It seems appropriate to close this article by quoting the final paragraph of that review:

"The challenge of the Cambridge Report is real, and it should be accepted by our profession. I hope and believe that a better answer can be given to the challenge than any the Cambridge conferees have themselves offered. I am convinced that such a better answer can be given long before 1990. The real obstacle lies not in our knowledge of mathematics or our knowledge of pedagogy, but in the outmoded and inadequate preparation we are still giving to our future mathematics teachers. It is high time that we stop prating about this obstacle and take counsel as to how we can remove it."

ESI'S PROGRAM IN MATHEMATICS FOR THE ELEMENTARY GRADES

For five years Professor David A. Page directed the University of Illinois Arithmetic Project at Illinois. Now, in order to communicate with larger numbers of teachers via the creation of a course in mathematics on paper and on film, Professor Page has been given leave to move the project to Educational Services Incorporated.

To continue the basic work of inventing and innovating which had previously characterized the project, he located a co-operative school system, school, teacher and class where he could work directly with grade school children. Professor Page shared the mathematics instruction of a fifth-grade class at the James Russell Lowell School in Watertown, Massachusetts, about equally with their regular teacher, Mrs. Marjorie Skülley. The principal, Mr. William D. Corbett, recently reported:

> *Stanford Achievement Tests had been administered to the children of this class in March, 1963, and again this year in May. In arithmetic computation (March, 1963) the average grade level score was 5.3. In May, 1964, the average computation score was 6.8. Arithmetic reasoning grade level scores rose from 4.5 in 1963 to 7.0 in 1964.*
>
> *Mrs. Sculley noticed an unusual rapidity with which the children completed and checked their achievement tests.*
>
> *While aware of the limitations of arithmetic averages and the several shortcomings of achievement tests, I feel that the results indicate significant growth.*
>
> *The tests administered did not specifically measure many of the topics taught in class viz. negative numbers, other bases of numeration, maneuvers on lattices, functions (number line jumping rules), "the greatest integer not greater than" function and graphing of same, work in a two-dimensional co-ordinate system and exponents.*

Professor Page also taught the three sixth-grade classes at the Lowell School several times as well as meeting for five sessions with all the teachers of the school to help them improve their mathematics instruction.

In Concord, Massachusetts, as a pilot program for the forthcoming course for teachers, Professor Page and his associates conducted a sixteen-week workshop for nearly all of the teachers in the system in grades 1 through 6. The Concord school provided released time each Wednesday so that during working time their teachers could observe and study a demonstration class deal with a topic in mathematics new to the elementary school. The demonstration class was followed by another hour of lecture-discussion concerning mathematics and how mathematical ideas of importance can be communicated to children. At most of these sessions related "homework" papers were handed out to the teachers. The teachers spent an average of two to three hours on each homework assignment. The homework was corrected and graded and only teachers who had satisfactorily completed a majority of their homework were certified to receive salary increment "credit" for the workshop.

During the week of March 9, 1964, Page taught three classes daily in front of cameras at the ESI Film Studios in Watertown. Jack Churchill, associate director of the project, was the producer and director of this filming. Mrs. Skulley's class and Miss Mary Donald's fifth-grade class each came to the Studio for an hour of filmed instruction each of the five days. The third class that came to the Studios was Mrs. Catherine Marks' fourth grade from the Paul A. Dever School at Columbia Point in South Boston.

From this fifteen hours of filming, one 45-minute film, *Three A's, Three B's and One C,* has been completed as a sample. Additional films will be completed when the project expands this fall.

In the fall of 1964 the project has agreed to conduct two more pilot programs for elementary school teachers—one in Newton and one in Wellesley, Massachusetts. These courses will follow the general pattern of the Concord workshop except that films will be used to replace some of the demonstration classes. Further programs will progressively replace all demonstration classes and much of the lecture-discussion periods with films.

MANEUVERS ON LATTICES

by David A. Page

This "intermediate invention" has come about through the active cooperation of children ranging from first grade to high school. The author prefers not to estimate the fraction of the content here which is attributable to the collection of children in schools who have worked with it.

* * *

As presented here, this topic begins in first grade. A teacher starting it for the first time with a fourth grade class would need to enter the topic by a faster, more complex route.

The presentation here is necessarily continuous. In schools, on the other hand, it should be assigned a week here and there over the several years.

The student first coming to this topic, whatever his grade level, is assumed to be familiar with the physical interpretation of number-symbols (hereafter called numbers) such as 1, 2, 3, . . . , 100, . . . He should be able to get 17 blocks out of a box upon request. If he "sees and hears" whole numbers easily, it is not necessary that he can "make his figures well" at the outset.

1. First Grade

Put on the board, as pupils watch, the following table ("lattice") of numbers:

				.	.				
60	61	62	.						
50	51	52	53	54	55	56	57	58	59
40	41	42	43	44	45	46	47	48	49
30	31	32	33	34	35	36	37	38	39
20	21	22	23	24	25	26	27	28	29
10	11	12	13	14	15	16	17	18	19
	1	2	3	4	5	6	7	8	9

After completing the first row or two, have students tell "what number comes next". Do this several times, and then complete the table by skipping around among the various unfilled places with students telling what number goes there. Include for example:

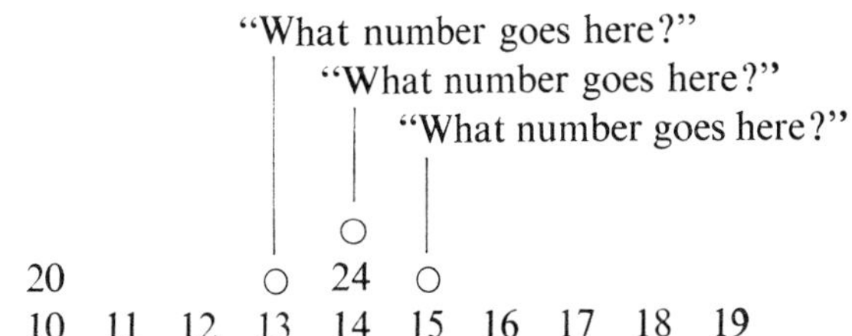

and several other examples where students tell what number goes directly to the right, left, above, or beneath a given number. Do not use many words at all. As a challenge, do it all in pantomime. Start the table, and after a couple of rows, hesitate and point to a spot and look puzzled instead of saying anything. (And so on.)

The table is complete to somewhere up above 50. (The more experienced and brighter the students, the less table needed on the board.)

> "We are going to have a sort of secret code for writing numbers. It uses that table. Here is a number in code:
>
> $5\uparrow$
>
> What number do you guess this stands for?"

In most of the classes in which this has been tried, a response in agreement with the teacher's plan has been forthcoming. It is important for the teacher to know and

© 1962 by David A. Page

Professor David A. Page, Director of the University of Illinois Arithmetic Project, joined Educational Services Incorporated in August, 1963, on leave from the University of Illinois. At ESI Professor Page is developing materials and techniques for instructing elementary school teachers in mathematics teaching. **This paper was prepared for the Conference on Mathematical Learning held May 4-6, 1962, Berkeley, California, sponsored by the Social Science Research Council. Reprints are available from ESI.**

express indirectly (or directly) that "this is mind reading and not mathematics". No student's reply should be dealt with as a mistake. The children cannot possibly *know* what this means. Asking children to guess here is better than "explaining", because guessing gets them involved quickly and produces more students who, five minutes later, really know what these symbols mean.

Here are some examples of guesses which do not correctly read the teacher's mind, and suggested replies:

(TEACHER: What do you guess for 5↑?)

(1) STUDENT: 5
TEACHER: Well, that could be right — but we wouldn't have gone to all the work to make a chart and use an arrow if that were just going to be 5.

(2) STUDENT: 6
TEACHER: You have almost got the idea. Only 6 would be (writes on board) 5 →. What do you think 5↑ is?

(3) Sometimes (especially in higher grades) trouble arises because students over-guess instead of under-guess. Here it can be difficult to tell what a student has in mind. (A fifth grade class entering the topic in this fashion may need to be told: "Don't think much; this is just a simple-minded code.")
STUDENT: 515
TEACHER: (after a five minute interrogation): No, it's not as fancy as sliding the 5 up alongside of the 15 and then using 515 as the number. But that would make a good code to use some other day! Let's see, in your system, what would (draws) 15↑ be?
(Ans. 1,525)*

In most cases the desired reply, 15, is obtained and less than five minutes of class time is expended. Next:

TEACHER: 5 →
STUDENT: 6
TEACHER: Right.

TEACHER: 9↑
STUDENT: 19
TEACHER: Yes.

*This happened in one class of sixth grade students. When the suggestion was rejected, others of similar sophistication were proposed. Example: 20. (Move the 5 up to the 15 and add.) The teacher finally had to announce his code — in order to avoid these systems which he was not prepared to handle.

TEACHER: 9 ←
STUDENT: 8
TEACHER: Right.

TEACHER: 15↓
STUDENT: 25
TEACHER: Look at it again.
STUDENT: Oh, 5.
TEACHER: Right.

Give more practice of this type until students have the idea well in mind. Less than ten examples are usually plenty, however. During the first few questions and correct replies, other students who at first were mystified will catch on to the idea. Notice that there is no formal pronunciation for this notation as it is learned.

If a student remains mystified, have another student come to the board and show how he finds the "number he starts with" and then does (moves his finger) what the arrow says to get his answer. A flurry of words from the teacher will not help.

More exercises:

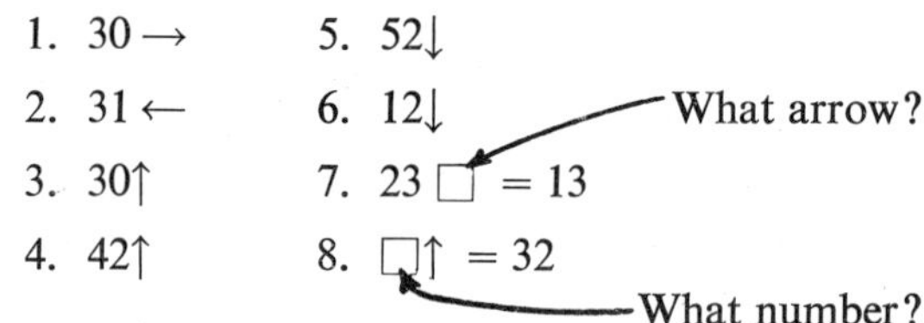

From 6-year-olds, especially if the = sign is unfamiliar, a wrong answer to expect on (8.) about half of the time is 42. The child saw 32 and ↑ and acted. Check by putting 42 in □ and seeing if the resulting statement is true.

Some students will quickly interpret ↑ as "add 10" and → as "add one". Others will keep the geometric interpretation and use the chart, either looking at it directly or seeing it in their minds. First graders are less likely to make the "add 10" interpretation than are third graders. Don't commit yourself on the way *you*, as the teacher, do it. In fact, don't dwell on the two ways at all. Just be aware of them. Later, the relative advantages of these methods will be an important element of the plot.

Note: If, after doing problems such as 27 → and 28 →, students are given 29 →, most of them will reply 29 → = 30 for understandable reasons. In order *not* to fix this as *the correct* answer and because it is a topic of considerable importance later, we are here avoiding problems which deal with the *edges* of the chart.

Most of the teaching suggestions so far have been aimed at preventing "too much teaching" and too much talking. Just get on down the road and let *correct answers to significant questions be your guide* to student "understanding". For example:

TEACHER*: 5 + 13↓
STUDENT: 8

TEACHER: Right. Who can give the answer in our code?

STUDENT: 18↓

TEACHER: Good. Who can do it another way in code?

STUDENT: 7→

TEACHER: Good.

Now any ordinary arithmetic problem can be given in code instead. Do a few. Suit the level to the age and ability of the students. In the following examples, many may feel that some problems are for second or third grade rather than first grade. The teacher must decide this, but if your students are in avid pursuit, you may be able to survive harder problems than you thought.

1. 11↓ + 11↓ + 11↓
2. 11↓ + 12↓ + 13↓ + 14↓
3. 11↓ + 12↓ + 13↓ + 14
4. 11↓ + 12↓ + 13 + 14
5. 11 + 12 + 13 + 14
6. 13↓ + 4← + 2→
7. 10 + 17↓
8. 10 + 53↓
9. 10 + 98↓
10. 14↑ + 26↓
11. 14↑ + 27↓
12. 17↑ −7

*Few first grades are familiar with the so-called horizontal notation. They will need to see

$$5 + 6 = 11$$
$$10 = 5 + 5$$

and other expressions like these before tackling this problem. It should cause only a few minutes delay.

13**. 107↑

14. 1,672↑ −3 −3 −3

(The possibilities for such exercises are endless. Other types must wait for a thorough treatment.)

2. *Several Arrows*

Students may have brought up the idea:

TEACHER: What was 7↑?
STUDENT: 17.

TEACHER: Yes, and now if I put on another arrow (adds an arrow to the 7↑), what is this: 7↑↑?

STUDENT: 27.
(or 17↑ or 37↓ or 26→ . . .)

TEACHER: Yes. How about 15↑↑?
STUDENT: 35.

TEACHER: Yes. And 50↓↓?
STUDENT: 30.

TEACHER: Yes. And 39↑↓?
STUDENT: (class laughs) Still 39.

TEACHER: 63→→→ ?
STUDENT: 66.

TEACHER: (By now the teacher can often omit saying, "right" or "yes", and smile or nod instead — with a watchful eye for unhappy faces.)
63→← ?

STUDENT: 63.
(Again, amusement.)

TEACHER: 762 ←→ ?
STUDENT: 762.

TEACHER: 4 →↑ ?
STUDENT: 15.

TEACHER: 4 →↑←↓ ?
STUDENT: 4.
(With luck, someone points out that these successive moves take you around a square:

14 ← 15
↓ ↑
4 → 5

**This exercise is introduced to warn against a common student error. Namely, 107↑ = 207. Apparently, the unexpressed rule that is operating is "increase the left-most digit by one". To set students straight, draw a piece of the chart including 107 and the number above it and actually make the move. From time to time other pieces "up high" may need to be drawn.

Another student may point out that "each one there has a reverse, so you stay where you started".*)

TEACHER: 22↑↓↑↓↑↓↑↓ ?
STUDENT: 22.

TEACHER: 44↑↓↓↓↑↑↓ ?
STUDENT: 34.

Here there are likely to be several methods worth noting. Of course, a few students are tediously taking it step by step, saying to themselves "44, 54, 44, 34, 24, 34, 44 34". From their words you may not be able to tell who they are, however, for you will frequently find a student who has an answer instantly and who then *explains how he did it* by this tedious procedure! He is giving the "explanation" he thinks the teacher wants even though *he* did not really do it that way — and is thereby inadvertently telling you that he has a secret intellectual life which he does not admit to — in school.

Predominant fast methods:

(1) Cancel as many pairs of opposites as possible and then do what's left:

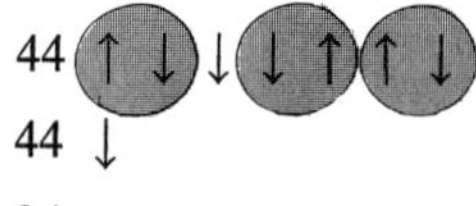

44 ↓

34

(2) Count the "ups", count the "downs". Subtract. Here, three "ups" and four "downs". Subtract and get one "down".

Answer: 44 and a "down", or 34.**

Interesting psychology(?):

TEACHER: 35↑↑↑↑ ?
STUDENT: 75.
TEACHER: Now, I will only change the last arrow (erases just the tip of the last arrow and puts on an arrowhead at the bottom):

35 ↑ ↑ ↑ ↑

35 ↑ ↑ ↑ ↓

The student now, four times in five, gives the incorrect answer, 65.

Now students are ready for these:

1. 16↑↑↓↑↑↑↓
2. 39↑↑↓↑↑↑↓
3. 2↑↑↓↑↑↑↓
4. 2↑↑↑↑↑↓↓
5. 17↑↑↑↑↑↓↓
6. 25↓↓↑↑↑↑↑
7. 100↓↓↑↑↑↑↑↑
8. 14→↑↑↓→↓←↑→↑←
9. 36→↑↑↓→↓←↑→↑←
10.*** 36→→→↑↑↑↑←←↓↓
11. 23→↑←↓ →↑←↓ →↑←↓

WARNING: Close sequencing ends. Exercises skip fast. Grade claims end. From here on we chase ideas as seems fit.

---

*Clearly, one is playing here for shortcuts, recognition of generalities — elegance. Notice, however, that the student who is not up to this kind of contribution can desperately go to the chart and make each move, step by step. Thus, he can see what the correct answer *is*. He is still in a position to genuinely appreciate the student who has an almost instant answer. He may be perplexed at the ideas popping around him, but he is still "in the game". He is thinking something like, "How on earth are they doing it so fast?" rather than the sad thought, "What on earth are they talking about?"

**Implicit in this very notation is that these arrow symbols are *associative*. Most students with shortcut procedures are assuming that they also *commute*. It is clearly a mistake with early grade students to introduce such ideas in a general way or to use this technical vocabulary. (Saying "5↑→ = 5→↑ reminds one of $11 + 2 + 7 = 11 + 7 + 2$" if called for — but little more.)

Experience shows that it is also a mistake to offer these technical terms to elementary school teachers who are exploring this material on their own. Such people are so hard pressed by their administrative environment to come up with vocabulary items sounding esoteric and modern in order to impress the school board, P.T.A.-Modern Math Committee, or the local school system's Curriculum Committee that they generally cannot resist seizing these words and putting them to work. The words fly on; the ideas quickly fall from mind. Soon, documents abound with vocabulary and starve for ideas. Then, properly, critics cry out "false modernism"! The working solution is to suppress the standard technical vocabulary. At least for a time.

***We have been suggesting here the similarity between exercises such as 8, 9, and 10. In a word, the eleven arrows consisting of three "right arrows", two "left arrows", four "up arrows", and two "down arrows" produce the same change (namely, add 21) with respect to the starting number no matter how they are arranged.

Some mathematicians, seeing this material actually presented to children during a single class period, have objected that students are coming to think that "all operations commute". These arrows do not commute freely if the "don't go off the edge" rule is followed strictly. For example, 15↑→↓↓ = 6 while 15↓↓→↑ is meaningless because you go off the edge at 15↓↓. Further details ahead.

3. *Diagonal Arrows*

Guess 5↗. 16 is correct. Four kinds of diagonals only ↖, ↗, ↘, and ↙. Sometimes students have written ↑ + → = ↗.

SAMPLE EXERCISES
(Samples for adults — now.)

1. 14↗↙↗↙↗↙
2. 72↗↗↙↗↗↗↙
3. 5↗↖ (Be ready for 5 as an answer.)
4. 13↗↖↗↖↗↖
5. 52↗↓←
6. 2,607↑→↙
7. 85↗↓←↗↓←↗↓←
8. 85↗↗↗↓↓↓←←←

(Contrast the actual paths in 7. and 8.)

Now come problems that are made up of long series of all kinds of arrows. No special technique is suggested to solve them. Students will suggest a variety of techniques. The student who has been working problems arrow by arrow is under extreme pressure to catch on to some shortcuts. There will still be a contrast between geometric and arithmetic preferences; however, most students with elegant techniques will be leaning heavily on the geometric interpretation. (Whether or not one can go off the edge "legally" must be carefully specified by now.)

Sample:

46↗↘→↓↙↖↓→↖→↓↖↑

One typical solution (look for opposites):

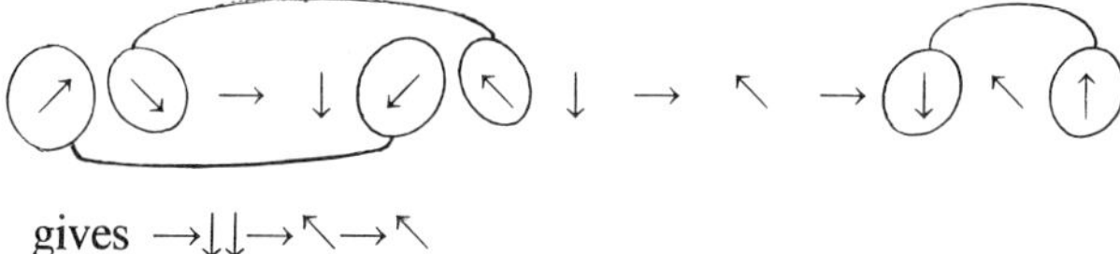

gives →↓↓→↖→↖

or →→→↓↓↖↖

and now proceed.*

Another typical solution (look for nice combinations; each connected group of arrows cancels out**):

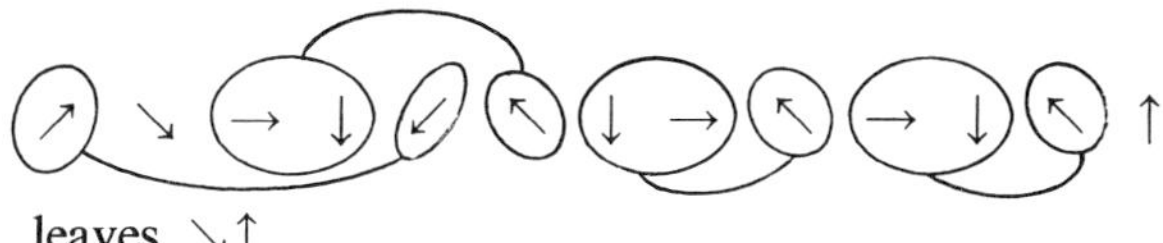

leaves ↘↑

or →

46→ = 47

Some students will break everything into horizontal and vertical components and then sum each component separately. With a little practice they will be able to do this as they scan the problem by eye without recopying it into vertical and horizontal arrows. For example, scanning vertical components, the student keeps a "running total":

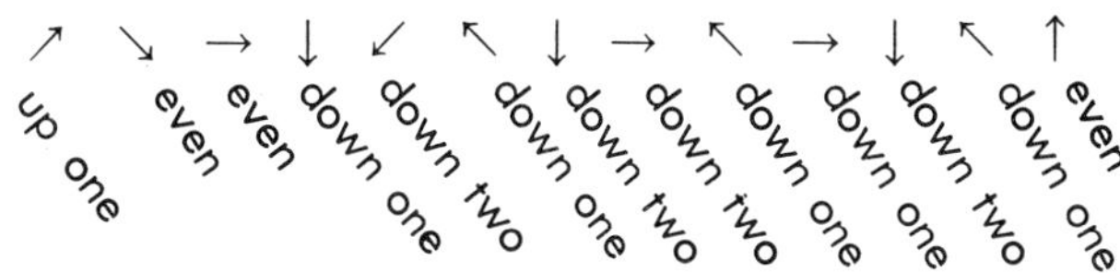

The vertical components cancel out.

This method of components is particularly useful when the teacher holds strictly to the "off the edge is nonsense" rule where students must always be on guard as to whether, even in the middle of a problem, they run off the edge of the lattice. (Best procedure is some days to be strict in this way, some days forget about edge-worries. But students must know the Rule of the Day!)*

4. *Other Types of Problems*

With this much notation understood, many problems are around the corner. The following ones suggest a few types. (Grade and ability level fluctuate widely here — this is just an attempt to suggest part of the "natural" span. Without lead-in exercises many of these would be too hard for most elementary school students.)

1. Put arrows into the frame in many ways to give true statements.

   25 [   ] = 41

   What is the smallest number of arrows that you can use?

---

*A standard error of incompletion in such problems is to give the answer 1 here. The student computed the increment and forgot that he *started at 46* and thus should have 47 for an answer.

**"Cancel out" means "is equivalent to the identity". Note that we have not dealt much with the notion of an identity element. It could be assigned a symbol and emphasized.

*Another easy rule to play by: Surround the lattice with unlabeled dots spaced as numbers would be. These are empty positions. You may travel into them and back to the lattice for an answer. If the problem takes you to an empty position and leaves you there, the answer is "nonsense!".

What is the largest number of arrows that you can use? Show some ways to fill in the frame using only diagonal arrows. Using only vertical and horizontal arrows.

2. Suppose you have many problems to do of this kind:

22↑↑→↑ + 1,047↓↓←↓↑ = ?

Are there any shortcuts that can be depended upon — or must one work out 22↑↑→↑ and 1,047↓↓←↓↑ separately and then add?

3. If we say that ↑→↑ is a route different from ↑↑→, using only horizontal and vertical arrows how many different routes of two arrows each are there all together that start at 23 and land anywhere possible? Of three arrows each? Four? Include diagonal arrows also and repeat.

4. Whenever two frames of the same shape occur in one equation, whatever number is chosen to fill one of the frames must also be used to fill the other frames of that same shape.

Example: Fill the frames with numbers to make a true statement:

⏢ ↑→ + ⏢ →↑↑ = 100

Solution:

⏢ 34 ↑→ + ⏢ 34 →↑↑ = 100

(*check*) 45 + 55 = 100

Note that filling the frames this way:

⏢ 30 ↑→ + ⏢ 38 →↑↑ = 100

is incorrect because it breaks the rule of "same number for same shaped frame" even though, otherwise, it checks.

a. ☐ ↗↗ + ☐ ↗↗ = 58

b. ☐ ↘↓ + ☐ ↖↑ = 86

c. ⬭ ↑→ + ⬭ ↑↑ = 100

(When will answer be a whole number? When not?)

5. Use same arrows for same shaped frame and make a true statement.

a. 192 ⏢ + 65 ⏢ = 215

b. 192 ⏢ − 65 ⏢ = 130

(prove b. is impossible)

6. Suppose that we decide to put in another number so that 10↓ and 1← do not take us off the edge. What number should we put in?

7. Suppose we want to put in a number so that 3↓ does not take us off the edge. What number should we put in for 3↓? (This hints at the topic of *extensions* of a system. It will come up again.)

5. *Different Folds*

A variation that might well come up next is (or if this kind of material is to be presented for the first time to students in, say, a fifth grade, it could probably *start with*) this lattice as the "playing field":

				.
			.	
15	16	.		
10	11	12	13	14
5	6	7	8	9
0	1	2	3	4

Then 2↑ = 7, 12→ = 13, and 13↖ = 17. Run through introductory exercises similar to those given for the lattice folding with ten. For students who have had experience with both lattices, one of the main themes begins:

> In doing problems on these two kinds of lattices, what stays the same and what changes? That is, can you still use any of the tricks and techniques which you invented when you worked on the other lattice? Which ones?

For example, 15↑ is not the same number on the two different lattices, but 15→↑↙ is the same number on both lattices. Students should be encouraged to pursue this matter of "sameness vs. differentness" in considerable detail. We shall move on.

* * *

One of the common complaints of 4th, 5th, or 6th grade teachers is that students do not *really know* their multiplication tables. Moreover, many of the students who are weak with their tables are supposedly able students. In all likelihood, the teacher has been drilling on the tables for the last half year and the results are the standard ones: The students who knew them before still know them; the students who didn't, still don't.

How can we break this deadly cycle? One prescription is to concoct problems where the individual student will really care what the answer is and where knowledge of the multiplication tables is of conspicuous help. Working on the lattice most recently introduced (folding with five), give students this problem:

$$2\uparrow\uparrow\uparrow\uparrow\uparrow\uparrow\uparrow$$

One student will snap out "37" while another student thinks laboriously 2, 7, 12, . . . for six steps, and more than likely gets a wrong final answer through careless errors. The first student counted the arrows and said "seven times five is thirty-five — plus two is 37". He knew what 7 × 5 was — fast!

Of course 7 × 5 or any of the □ × 5 tables are not usually the ones in which students lack skill. To pick up students' proficiency in the "difficult" parts of the tables, fold the lattice accordingly. For example, fold with 7:

.

.

14 15 16 .

7 8 9 10 11 12 13

0 1 2 3 4 5 6

Now give the student a problem such as:

$$2\uparrow\uparrow\uparrow\uparrow\uparrow\uparrow$$

The student who knows what 6 × 7 is (and who also knows what is going on, generally) is ready to announce "44" quickly. By folding lattices in various ways and using the previously suggested exercise types as well as many other types that can be constructed based upon lattices, large numbers of exercises which are related but which "feel" different can be constructed, all of which require knowledge of the "difficult" multiplication facts. In several cases where this has been tried, teachers have reported informally of an easily noticeable improvement in multiplication skills.*

Next, work on this lattice:

.

.

.

12 13 14 15 16 17 18

5 6 7 8 9 10 11

0 1 2 3 4

or on this one:

.

.

.

10 11 12

7 8 9

4 5 6

1 2 3

or on this one:

.

.

24 25 .

12 13 14 15 16 17 18 19 20 21 22 23

0 1 2 3 4 5 6 7 8 9 10 11

and the lattices "in between". In each case a full selection of exercises should be examined, both to strengthen multiplication facts and to push forward the main idea. The question of what is different and what is the same, should continually be examined. (And are there things that are "kind of the same" but not exactly?)

6. *Lattices With Fractions*

There is no need to keep to whole numbers. Maneuver on this lattice:

.

.

15 $15\frac{1}{2}$.

10 $10\frac{1}{2}$ 11 $11\frac{1}{2}$ 12 $12\frac{1}{2}$ 13 $13\frac{1}{2}$ 14 $14\frac{1}{2}$

5 $5\frac{1}{2}$ 6 $6\frac{1}{2}$ 7 $7\frac{1}{2}$ 8 $8\frac{1}{2}$ 9 $9\frac{1}{2}$

0 $\frac{1}{2}$ 1 $1\frac{1}{2}$ 2 $2\frac{1}{2}$ 3 $3\frac{1}{2}$ 4 $4\frac{1}{2}$

In addition to the exercises described earlier, an interesting new kind is:

Look at:

$$36\tfrac{1}{2}\rightarrow\rightarrow\uparrow\nwarrow\swarrow\downarrow\leftarrow\nearrow\nearrow$$

*This is an example of one of the many "chicken or egg" questions in education. Students would do these exercises better if they already knew their multiplication facts well. On the other hand, such problems promote "unintended" retention of the facts. Which first? As a nation we spend too much time getting ready.

Never mind the exact numerical answer.
Is the answer a whole number or not?*
Is the answer bigger or smaller than $36\frac{1}{2}$?
Where is $36\frac{1}{2}$? That is, what column is it in?
Are we in trouble if we can't go off the edge?

Notice that $36\frac{1}{2}\nearrow\searrow\downarrow\leftarrow\nwarrow = ?$ can be answered almost immediately and with confidence by the student who "sees" a closed trip whereas the student who interprets the symbols numerically has a bit more work to do. For the latter student the key matter is whether he gets an answer of $36\frac{1}{2}$ and stops passively or whether starting with $36\frac{1}{2}$ and ending with $36\frac{1}{2}$ makes him curious so that he keeps thinking until, in one of several ways, he sees — "of course!".

More lattices:

.

.

$5\frac{1}{3}$.

$2\frac{2}{3}$ $2\frac{3}{3}$ $2\frac{4}{3}$ $3\frac{2}{3}$ $\frac{12}{3}$ $4\frac{1}{3}$ $4\frac{2}{3}$ 5

0 $\frac{1}{3}$ $\frac{2}{3}$ $\frac{3}{3}$ $\frac{4}{3}$ $\frac{5}{3}$ $\frac{6}{3}$ $\frac{7}{3}$

* * *

.

.

6 .

3 $3\frac{3}{7}$ $3\frac{6}{7}$ $4\frac{2}{7}$ $4\frac{5}{7}$ $5\frac{1}{7}$ $5\frac{4}{7}$

0 $\frac{3}{7}$ $\frac{6}{7}$ $1\frac{2}{7}$ $1\frac{5}{7}$ $2\frac{1}{7}$ $2\frac{4}{7}$

The computational intricacies can be made as "messy" as desired. It is worthwhile, at least once, to use a lattice such as the following one:

.

.

1112.40 .

741.60 815.76 889.92 964.08 1038.24

370.80 444.96 519.12 593.28 667.44

0 74.16 148.32 222.48 296.64

On this lattice, given an expression such as:

$$964.08\uparrow\uparrow\rightarrow\swarrow\swarrow\leftarrow\uparrow\nearrow$$

a student is "strongly encouraged" to use simplifying procedures before computing with numbers. Also, if considerable work on this lattice is done, students often use the "isomorphism" between it and the chart:

.

.

15 .

10 11 12 13 14

5 6 7 8 9

0 1 2 3 4

where the more complicated lattice is obtained by multiplying each element of this integer-lattice by 74.16. A problem given on the complicated lattice is solved on the integer-lattice and then converted by multiplying by 74.16. (Also this suggests the test for deciding whether a given number occurs in the complicated lattice: Does division of that number by 74.16 give a whole number?)

7. *Non-Rectangular Lattices*

Here is a problem worth the attention of high school students. Given the lattice:

.

.

.

16 17 18 19 20 21

11 12 13 14 15

7 8 9 10

4 5 6

2 3

1

Find $1{,}096\uparrow$. Notice that although $6\downarrow$ or $10\rightarrow$ are (at least initially) meaningless because they take us off the lattice, $n\uparrow$ is always defined (for each positive integer n). But what is $n\uparrow$, in general terms? No fair building a huge table! It is worthwhile to look for (gross and fine) approximations to $1{,}096\uparrow$ and $1{,}000{,}000\uparrow$ and $n\uparrow$ before looking for exact solutions.

Consider this lattice:

10 . . . 20 . . . 30 .

6 9 . . 16 19 . . 26 29 .

3 5 8 . 13 15 18 . 23 25 28 . . . .

1 2 4 7 11 12 14 17 21 22 24 27 31

Here, some early intuition for periodic functions can be developed. (For now, you are permitted to move over the unnumbered dots, but if you stop on a dot instead of

---

*Of course, this question is equivalent to asking "even or odd" on the lattice of integers first introduced — the one which folded with 10. A search for more ways of asking this "same question" is worthwhile if the teacher has a taste for it.

a number, the answer is undefined.) This "periodic" lattice has been treated successfully with third grade students. There are many interesting problems but the main idea is that of the *period* of this array; that is:

$7 \rightarrow\rightarrow\rightarrow\rightarrow = 17$

$7 \rightarrow\rightarrow\rightarrow\rightarrow\rightarrow\rightarrow\rightarrow\rightarrow = 27$

$n \rightarrow\rightarrow\rightarrow\rightarrow$ is always defined.

(abbreviate $n \rightarrow\rightarrow\rightarrow\rightarrow$ as $n \overset{④}{\rightarrow}$)

$n \overset{④}{\rightarrow}\overset{④}{\rightarrow} \ldots \overset{④}{\rightarrow}$ is always defined and has the same last digit as n.

etc.

8. *Extensions at the Edge*

One of the important ideas in mathematics is that of *extending* a system to include more objects or more operations with an eye to whether the rules which held in the original system can be imposed on the enlarged system or whether some of them must be altered or given up. Too often the student meets this idea repeatedly in situations where he feels familiar with both the original and the extended system — for example, extending from the integers to the rational numbers. (I have in mind "extension by fiat", not the careful method of partitioning ordered pairs of integers into equivalence classes.) Also, too often, the student can remark with understandable naïveté, "How else would you *ever* do it?" Work with lattices permits some insight into the idea of *extending* a system.

Return to the lattice:

```
        .
      .
20  21  22  .
10  11  12  13  14  15  16  17  18  19
 0   1   2   3   4   5   6   7   8   9
```

Take $22 \rightarrow$ to mean explicitly: Go to 22 and move one space to the right. Then $29 \rightarrow$ is meaningless. We are off the lattice.*

Now, can we assign a meaning to $29 \rightarrow$? We could, of course, just pick any old number at will and say $29 \rightarrow = 95$. (The student protests are temporarily ignored!) Then we would have to decide on a meaning for $39 \rightarrow$. Suppose we choose $39 \rightarrow = 11$. Without bothering to see what havoc we are creating otherwise, one trouble is immediately clear. Without some kind of general, orderly procedure, we are faced with supplying, one by one, all the entries in an infinite table ($49 \rightarrow = ?$, $59 \rightarrow = ?$, $69 \rightarrow = ?$, . . . , $10 \leftarrow = ?$, $20 \leftarrow = ?$, $30 \leftarrow = ?$, . . .) — an unpleasant task. Thus any meaning proposed for $29 \rightarrow$ must be part of a general scheme of assigning meaning to similar "edge problems". (We are concerned, for the moment, with the vertical edges and not necessarily with giving meaning to $6\downarrow$.)

Of course, the most "natural" general system is to say that $29 \rightarrow = 30$. The reasoning here is that in every meaningful case until now it has been that $n \rightarrow = n + 1$. Let this rule continue to apply at the edge. Geometrically this turns out to be the "reversed typewriter" extension (at the right margin go up a space and back to the left margin). What other systems might we use? Adults frequently feel that $29 \rightarrow$ MUST mean 30 and that any other suggestions are heresy. Faced with this question, 4th through 6th graders have suggested the following systems:

I. Reversed typewriter (as already discussed).

examples: $29 \rightarrow = 30$
$20 \leftarrow = 19$
$29 \nearrow = 40$

II. Marching men at a cliff — don't go!

examples: $29 \rightarrow = 29$
$20 \leftarrow = 20$
$29 \nearrow = 29$
$27 \rightarrow = 28$
$27 \rightarrow\rightarrow = 29$
$27 \rightarrow\rightarrow\rightarrow = 29$

III. If you fall off, go directly to zero and start over.

examples: $29 \rightarrow = 0$
$29 \nearrow = 0$
$29 \rightarrow\rightarrow = 1$
$28 \rightarrow\rightarrow\rightarrow\rightarrow = 2$
$29 \rightarrow\rightarrow\uparrow\downarrow = 1$

IV. Bounce back the way you came.

examples: $29 \rightarrow = 28$
$29 \nearrow = 18$
$29 \nearrow\leftarrow = 17$

*In earlier work, problems might well have been given where rather than to find a numerical answer, the student was to answer, "in bounds", or "out of bounds". $7 \nearrow\nearrow$ is in bounds; $7 \nearrow\nearrow\nearrow$ is out of bounds.

V. Billiard-ball bounce (reflection).

examples: 29 → = 29
29 ↗ = 49
(This often splits into two camps, one as above and the other wanting 29 ↗ = 39.)

VI. Cut and paste to a cylinder.

examples: 29 → = 20
10 ← = 19
9 ↗ = 10

VII. (From an 11th grader) Take a band and make a Möbius strip.

A	30	31	32	. . .	39	B
	20	21	22	. . .	29	
	10	11	12	. . .	19	
B	0	1	2	. . .	9	A

examples: 39 → = 0
9 → = 30
19 → = 20
10 ← = 29
19 ↗ = 30 (or is it 10?)

VIII. Make a quilt.

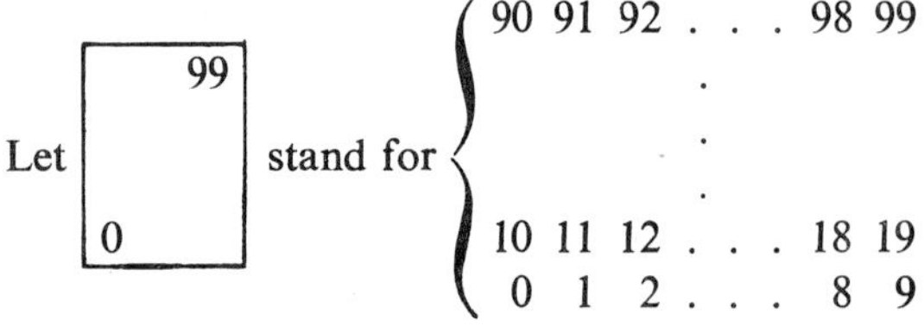

Then make the chart:

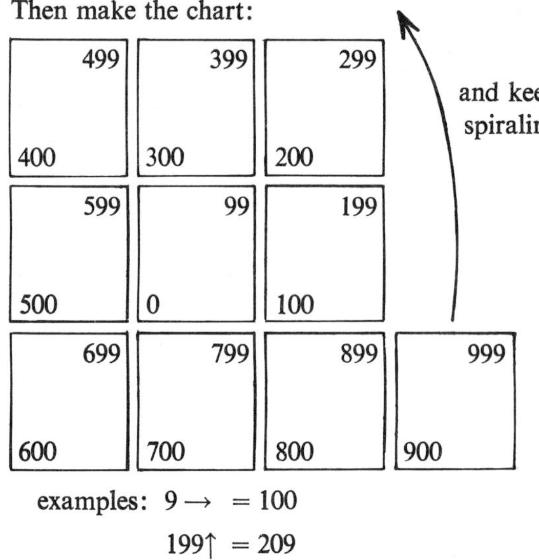

examples: 9 → = 100
199↑ = 209
0 ← = 509

IX. If a move would take you off the lattice, turn it counterclockwise the least amount that will keep you on.

examples: 29 → = 39
29 ↗ = 39
29 ↘ = 39
29 ↓ = 19
29 ↓ → ↗ = 39

X. Supply yourself with an unnumbered framework of dots surrounding the lattice. Move as directed. Expressions only have meaning when they land you in the *numbered* part of the chart.

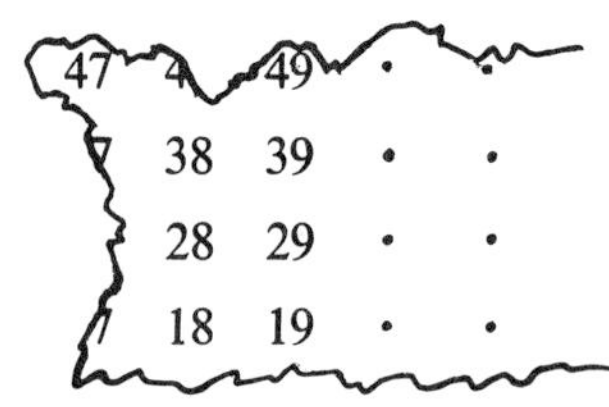

examples: 39 → = meaningless
18 → → → ↑ ↖ ↖ = 49

(It should be pointed out that stüdents seldom characterize these systems neatly. Frequently, they have an extension for → at the edge and not for ↗. Often an intricacy comes up requiring that the student proposing a system must explain it further and give more examples.

Also, although this is cold, arid mathematics in the abstract (?), there is often much heat generated by students in doing this work. Many students object violently to certain systems as they are proposed — often for reasons that will be considered subsequently. It has seemed good teaching strategy to hold off objections until a reasonably varied list has been suggested.

Many other suggestions have come from students but these ten will serve here.)

Now begin doing some exercises in each system (still on a lattice folding with ten). If there is time, spend a day working in each system. In particular, consider such exercises as these:

1. 6 → → ← ←	6. 5 → ↑ ↙
2. 8 → → ← ←	7. 9 → ↑ ↙
3. 8 ← ← → →	8. 9 ↗ ↖
4. 9 → ←	9. 9 ↖ ↗
5. 9 ← →	10. 87 ↗ ↗ ↗ ↗ ← ↓ ← ↓ ↙ ↓ ← ← ←

(Consider other lattices also.)

* * *

At this point it would be appropriate to talk about *commutativity* and *inverses*, etc. For elementary grades the author prefers to avoid these words, summarizing the ideas in this way:

For which systems is it always true (i.e. true for all starting numbers* put in □) that

□ → ← = □ ← → ?

□ ↑ → = □ → ↑ ?

□ → ← = □ ?

□ ↗ ↙ = □ ?

etc.

If one wants to have these properties obtain — and the others like them — extensions must be chosen accordingly. Change to a lattice that folds with 7. In how many systems, I through X, can one compute 1,019↑↑→↗↘ without bothering to see where 1,019 is in the lattice?

A comprehensive study of which properties fail in which of the ten extensions and why (in the sense that a student could classify an eleventh mode of extension by inspection) might be a good way for junior high school or high school students to spend a few weeks. (Concerning high school students, since there is a full ladder of simpler but related activities underneath this work, it may be of value in giving some relief to the lower ability half of high school students whose lower ability is currently matched by insufferably dull courses just for them — "general math", and the other horrors.)

Worries about the lower edge could have been eliminated by extending the lattice itself in the downward direction. One can again ask students for "nominations" and then check the consequences. Students are often surprised at the most "natural" lower extension of a five-folding lattice:

.
.
.

10	11	12	13	14
5	6	7	8	9
0	1	2	3	4
−5	−4	−3	−2	−1
−10	−9	−8	−7	−6
−15	−14	−13	−12	−11

.
.
.

since their last-digit rule of thumb is upset. Whether this is a third, seventh, or ninth grade topic depends upon how soon one gets into negative numbers. (It should be third grade or lower.)

9. *Multiplicative Lattices*

Consider this lattice:

.
.
.

	$\frac{27}{8}$	$\frac{27}{4}$	$\frac{27}{2}$	27	54	108	216	432	
	$\frac{9}{8}$	$\frac{9}{4}$	$\frac{9}{2}$	9	18	36	72	144	
. . .	$\frac{3}{8}$	$\frac{3}{4}$	$\frac{3}{2}$	3	6	12	24	48	. . .
	$\frac{1}{8}$	$\frac{1}{4}$	$\frac{1}{2}$	1	2	4	8	16	
	$\frac{1}{24}$	$\frac{1}{12}$	$\frac{1}{6}$	$\frac{1}{3}$	$\frac{2}{3}$	$\frac{4}{3}$	$\frac{8}{3}$	$\frac{16}{3}$	
	$\frac{1}{72}$	$\frac{1}{36}$	$\frac{1}{18}$	$\frac{1}{9}$	$\frac{2}{9}$	$\frac{4}{9}$	$\frac{8}{9}$	$\frac{16}{9}$	

.
.
.

*In this development, we have not yet worried about the lower edge. Thus, "all starting numbers" here means, in effect, all expressions that do not become entangled in the lower edge.

Students can profit from a detailed examination of it. It has no edges — goes on infinitely in all directions. Where are all the numbers, one and larger? Where are all the numbers between $\frac{1}{2}$ and 1? Could you draw a loop around all these numbers — or would it have to be a loop of infinite length? Consider various diagonal paths on the lattice. Which take you from smaller to larger numbers? Does another path parallel to such a path always go from smaller to larger numbers also?

On this lattice, ↑ means × 3 and → means × 2. In fact, if we assume the expected "natural" consistencies, we can define the lattice by merely saying

1 is in it
↑ : × 3
→ : × 2

Go through the same kinds of problems as before. What stays the same? What shortcuts are still valid for $\frac{1}{18}$↓↓←↙↘↑↗→↑ ?

On the earlier additive lattices, a problem with repeated addition such as ↑↑↑↑↑ suggested multiplication. On a multiplicative lattice, ↑↑↑↑↑ suggests exponentiation. That is, on this lattice □ ↑↑↑↑↑ = □ · 3^5 where the exponent gives the number of arrows. If many exercises like these come up, either with additive or multiplicative lattices, a suggestion to abbreviate in some manner such as this is probable:

$\overset{⑤}{\uparrow}$ means ↑↑↑↑↑

For multiplicative lattices the ⑤ is an exponent — its base depends on the construction of the particular lattice involved. Here, $\overset{⑤}{\uparrow} = 3^5$ and $\overset{⑤}{\rightarrow} = 2^5$.

A variety of lattices of different kinds and a variety of exercises should be investigated. Among possible lattices to investigate are:

1. $\frac{1}{2}$ is in
   ↑ : × 3
   → : × 2

2. 2 is in
   ↑ : × $\frac{1}{3}$
   → : × $\frac{1}{2}$

3. $\frac{3}{7}$ is in
   ↑ : × 5
   → : ÷ 3

4. 2 is in
   ↑ : × 3
   → : + 4

10. A Non-Existence Proof

If Lattice (4.) above is given to students as homework among other lattices to be constructed, there should be trouble. Any student who has (4.) done *is* in trouble. Why?

STUDENT: "It won't work!"
"It disagrees with itself!"
"If you go around different ways, you get different answers!"

TEACHER: "You mean it is too hard for you? Well, I'll give you another night to work on it. This time each of you get plenty of paper and work hard and *do* it!"

STUDENT: "No, it's not like that. It isn't too hard. It's just impossible. Nobody could ever do it with those rules — unless you put in some tricks like putting two numbers in one place, or one behind the other, and then I don't see how you'd know which number to pick when you land there."

TEACHER: "No, no tricks like that. Let's see if we can *prove* that it is impossible — that there is no point in anyone spending more time on it."

Here is a summary of an informal proof which sometimes can be rather well formulated by children:

If we have any kinds of numbers or things on a flat surface (paper, blackboard, etc.) and arranged in the following fashion:

```
                 .
                 .
                 .

          .   .   .   .   .
          .   .   .   .   .
  . . .   .   .   .   .   .   . . .
          .   .   .   .   .
          .   .   .   .   .

                 .
                 .
                 .
```

then in the physical world, with arrows meaning to move from dot to dot as they have before, if you

> start somewhere and do ↑→, you get to the same place as if you start at the same original place and do →↑. Thus, for any chart we construct with numbers, if □ is in the chart, then □ ↑→ must equal □ →↑. But in (4.) above, 2↑→ = 10 and 2→↑ = 18. No chart is possible.

Of course, this is just a long-winded version of "You get different answers when you go around different ways." However, once students are well captured by mathematics, it seems a good idea to work on sharpening their use of words — despite the clamor these days urging not to verbalize. Perhaps a better rule is: devote the time and effort to saying something carefully when there is something moderately worth saying.

11. Three-Dimensional Lattices

An obvious development that could have been started much earlier is work in three dimensions:

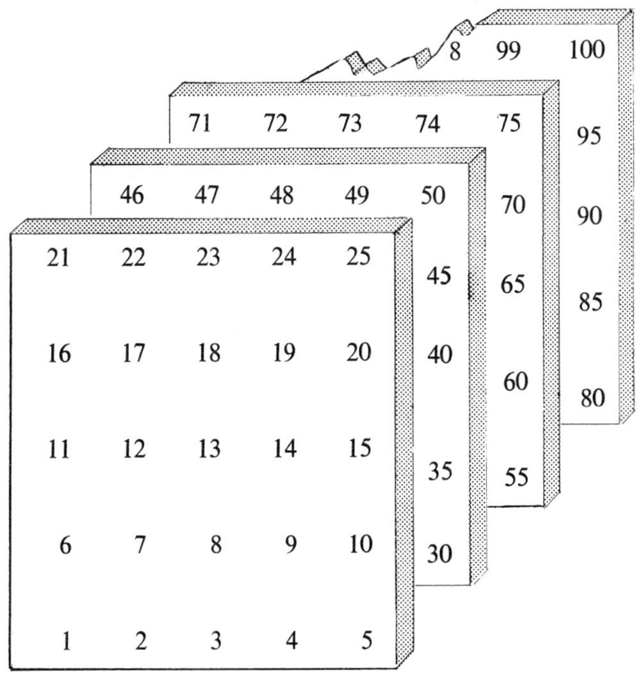

One notation that has been used is illustrated:

25 ∗ = 50 (∗ is the tail of an arrow going away.)

50 • = 25 (• is the point of an arrow coming out of the paper.)

19 ∗↗ = 50 (i.e. ∗ and ↗ = ∗↗)

19 ∗↕ = 49

19 ∗ ↑↙ •↗←∗ = 48

Techniques of simplification now apply to three dimensions. Problems analogous to all the two-dimensional ones illustrated can be constructed: folding at a variety of numbers, using non-whole numbers, various extensions at the edges, multiplicative lattices, non-rectangular and "periodic" lattices. Interplay between "space perception" and abstract, algebraic treatment can be carried as far as one chooses. For example: in a lattice with no edge restrictions how many times does the following path intersect itself?

• •↗↑← ∗ ←∗← ←•↓•→ → → ↗→ ∗

If you know the path crosses over itself, how can you use that information to help work a typical problem (no edge difficulties)?

176 • •↗↑← ∗ ←∗← ←•↓•→ → → ↗→ ∗

(IT DOES NOT END; BUT, FOR NOW, WE DO.)

VII
NEW CURRICULA FOR THE DISADVANTAGED

POOLING EDUCATION'S RESOURCES

by Saville R. Davis

THE deepest moral commitment of Americans is to the work of liberating and developing men and women. A group of Negro colleges and a group of large universities in the United States are banding together and pooling resources for this purpose.

They will begin this summer to adapt the latest techniques for improved education to meet the special problems of students who are deprived and segregated. Their aim is not to help a limited few. They are confident they can develop and test, under forced draft, systems that can be multiplied much more rapidly than anyone in specialized Negro education had dared to hope.

The starting point will be summer institutes for teachers of college freshmen. The attack on the problem begins there because a new generation of freshmen can be drawn through the college system and then fed back as teachers into the secondary and ultimately the primary schools. The institutes will be in Biology (University of North Carolina), English (Indiana University), History (Carnegie Institute of Technology), Mathematics (University of Wisconsin), and Physics (Princeton University).

-:- -:- -:-

Plans for the institutes were completed at a conference last month at the Massachusetts Institute of Technology between university officials and specialists in education and the heads of some 55 predominantly Negro colleges. It is announced that the Carnegie Corporation of New York and the Rockefeller Foundation will support the institutes financially by grants to Educational Services Incorporated, a nonprofit organization headed by James R. Killian, Jr., of M.I.T.

Several strands of recent history have led to this current attack on the problems of teaching the segregated and deprived groups. They are all part of the intellectual revolution that is sweeping the world of education, compelling a reassessment of old methods and bringing waves of experiment with new.

The concept of a university adopting, so to speak, a smaller college and bringing the full power of its abilities to bear on a quick development program, goes back to 1959. Oklahoma City University came to M.I.T. for help. The result was an exchange of faculty, new curriculum and teaching techniques, aid in getting funds — and the germ of an idea on the retail level that could later be expanded into a program at wholesale.

Meanwhile a series of radical changes in dull and outdated science teaching were boldly developed and took fire across the country. They have had enough success, now, to send sparks into the citadels of the humanities. There is a growing conviction that a similar creative approach to these less obviously backward studies might yield a similar result through a better understanding of the learning process.

No one claims to have definite blueprints or answers, Dr. Julius A. Stratton, president of M.I.T., told last month's conference. But the great accomplishment in science teaching has been to demonstrate to the secondary schools that something can be done. Now this confidence is spreading not only to the colleges themselves but from the sciences to the humanities. We should not begrudge the new affluence of the sciences, Dr. Stratton said; we should make the humanities equally exciting so they can compete.

As these various strands were carried forward, at numerous conferences on different educational levels and in various departments of education, a new conviction has more recently emerged.

This article, by Saville R. Davis, Chief Editorial Writer of the "Christian Science Monitor" and a participant at the M.I.T. Conference, appeared in that paper on Saturday, May 9, 1964. It is reprinted with the permission of the "Christian Science Monitor."

1

2

6

3

1. *Dr. J. R. Coleman, Dean, Division of Humanities, Carnegie Institute of Technology, Pittsburgh, Pennsylvania.*

2. *Dr. George W. Hunter, left, Dean of the School of Arts and Sciences of South Carolina State College, Orangeburg, South Carolina, and Dr. Howard E. Wright, President of Allen University, Columbia, South Carolina.*

3. *Dr. T. H. E. Jones, Dean, St. Paul's College, Lawrenceville, Virginia.*

4. *Dr. Carlon W. Pryor, left, Chairman of the Department of Biology and Director of the Division of Natural Sciences at Philander Smith College, Little Rock, Arkansas, and Dr. Sankey C. Chao, Dean of Florida Memorial College, St. Augustine.*

5. *Dr. Leedell W. Neyland, Florida A & M University, Tallahassee, left, in background; Dr. Jacob L. Reddix, President of Jackson State College, Jackson, Mississippi, center, with Dr. Alan J. Lazarus of M.I.T.*

6. *Mr. Dan C. Pinck, Secretary, Educational Services Incorporated, left, and Dr. Earl L. Cole, Dean of College, Grambling College, Grambling, Louisiana.*

The greatest challenge facing education now is not in the normal educational process but in the greatest challenge to society itself: that of equal opportunity for the segregated and the deprived. A study, in which Negro college leaders joined, showed how towering was the need and the opportunity.

-:- -:- -:-

Here are a few sample findings:

"Students come to the colleges from secondary schools that are understaffed, underequipped and taught by men and women who have themselves been the victims of the same system. Neither in his school nor in his home has the Negro student been encouraged to acquire the habits of crisp, economical speech or attentive listening. He is not the master of his own language and it does not serve him efficiently as a tool.

"He has learned to read but is likely to read obediently, in response to a directive. He is the servant of his books rather than their master. He does not know how to seek, on his own initiative, for knowledge or for delight in printed matter.

"Somewhere during his schooling the relationship has been lost that should link formal education with his own human development as an individual within society. History, literature, and the arts are mastered, if they are mastered at all, in relation to examinations and promotion. Their true significance to the whole man is lost. They cease, in short, to be humanistic studies and become items in a curriculum that exists only for its own sake."

These statements are from a working paper for the M.I.T. conference by Dr. Samuel M. Nabrit, president of Texas Southern University, Mr. Stephen White of Educational Services Incorporated, and Dr. Jerrold R. Zacharias of M.I.T., who conceived and directed much of the recent modernization in science teaching.

"The mathematics the student may have mastered is barren of its true import," the report also said. "That it has relevance to the real world and utility in dealing with the real world has never been made clear. The student has learned to compute, and perhaps to state formal proofs, but these achievements, like his achievement in the humanities, constitute a closed system referring in every instance to nothing but themselves.

"His academic knowledge, for the most part, rests on the authority of his teacher or his teacher's textbook. In the disciplines of school and college he has little notion of how one sets out to elicit information which has not first been codified by someone else. Necessarily he is quite capable of learning by means of experiment and mother wit how one manipulates

7. Left to right: Dr. Sankey C. Chao, Dean of the College, Florida Memorial College, St. Augustine; Dr. Gordon S. Brown, Dean of the School of Engineering at M.I.T.; Dr. Ozell K. Beatty, Chairman of Livingstone College, Salisbury, North Carolina; and Dr. Vance E. Gray, Administrative Assistant to the President of North Carolina Agricultural and Technical College, Greensboro.

8. Dr. John H. Taylor, Head of the Science Department of Cheyney State College, Cheyney, Pennsylvania, with Mrs. Emily Morrison of Educational Services Incorporated.

7

8

9

12

10

11

9. *Left to right: Dr. Prince Jackson, Jr., Assistant Professor of Math-Physics, Savannah State College, Savannah, Georgia; Dr. O. B. Edwards, Dean of the College, Oakwood College, Huntsville, Alabama; Dr. William E. Anderson, Acting President, Elizabeth City State College, Elizabeth City, North Carolina.*

10. *Dr. Japheth Hall, Jr., Chairman, Division of Mathematics and Science, Stillman College, Tuscaloosa, Alabama, and Mrs. Barbara D. Finberg, Carnegie Corporation of New York.*

11. *Dr. Leedell W. Neyland of Florida A & M University, Tallahassee, Florida, left, with Dr. Sankey C. Chao, Dean of Florida Memorial College, St. Augustine, Florida.*

12. *Dr. E. C. Harrison, left, Dean of Southern University, Baton Rouge, Louisiana, with Dr. Alan J. Lazarus of M.I.T.*

13. *Dr. Cohen T. Simpson, left, Dean of Instruction at Talladega College, Talladega, Alabama, and Dr. R. D. Morrison, President of Alabama A & M College, Normal, Alabama.*

his social and domestic environment, but his approach to formal education is artificial and unreal."

-:- -:- -:-

One result is a staggering dropout rate among freshmen in Negro colleges. One-third or more of the entering class "is likely to surrender its aspirations for higher education before the first term of the freshman year has been completed. But even more deplorable, the presence in overwhelming numbers of unprepared students forces the Negro college to set its sights far lower than anything a college can honorably justify. The college to a large degree becomes a second high school, imparting the education that the student should have received two or four or even six years earlier." He cannot qualify for graduate work.

At the same time, these Negro students and their teachers suddenly find themselves at the vortex of the greatest national problem. As the struggle for equal opportunity flames around them, and while they wait for the barriers of race and poverty to be broken down, they can hardly be expected to give enough attention to the equally great problem of tomorrow: once freedom is won, what about skills and training and the developed mind that will produce salable judgment and initiative and social poise?

The program launched at the M.I.T. conference is designed to attack tomorrow's problem today.

It is hoped, too, that the benefits of collaboration between the large institution and the small will cut both ways. The large university is advanced enough in its own fields today but it can also be remote and smug and self-contained with respect to the main currents of the times. Through this program it will have the opportunity to become directly involved in one of the deepest maladjustments in society, at its most sensitive point.

-:- -:- -:-

Six of 10 universities and large colleges that have been approached have already appointed faculty and administrative committees, according to Mina Rees, Dean of the School of Graduate Studies of the University of the City of New York. In California 18 colleges have joined forces for this purpose, and some 25-30 liberal arts colleges across the country are interested.

The conference at M.I.T. heard the directors of the five summer institutes outline their plans. Since promising new developments in the sciences are more generally understood, it was the spokesmen for the new experiment in the humanities that drew special attention. English departments, said Prof. Michael Wolff, are not in revolution. They consider that they should

14

15

14. *Dr. Leonard Price of Xavier University, New Orleans, Louisiana.*

15. *Left to right: Dr. James R. Killian, Jr., Chairman, M.I.T. and Chairman of the Board, Educational Services Incorporated; Dr. O. B. Edwards, Dean of the College, Oakwood College, Huntsville, Alabama; Dr. C. C. Armstrong, Chairman of the Department of Social Science, Alcorn A & M College, Lorman, Mississippi.*

16

18

17

20

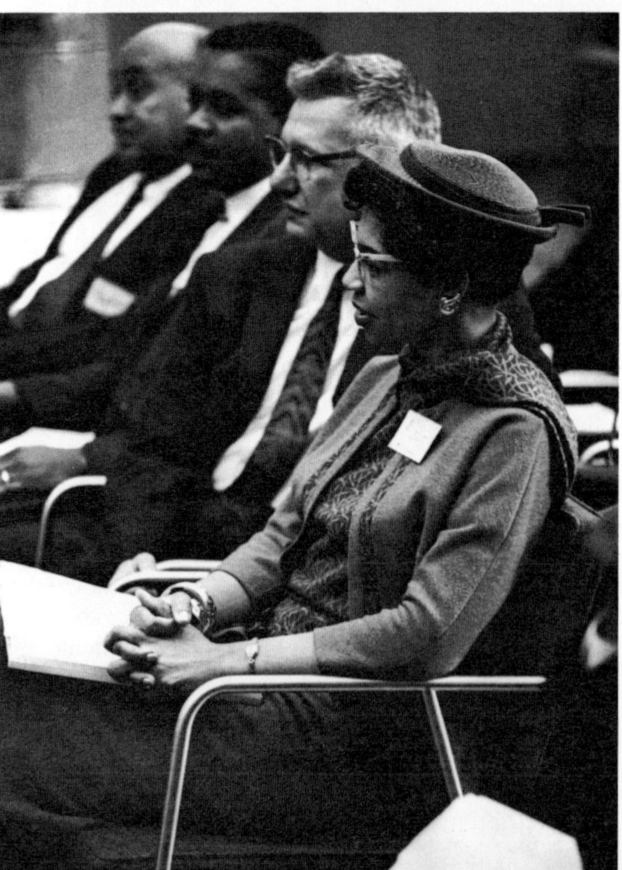

16. *Dr. Prince Jackson, Jr., left, Savannah State College, Savannah, Georgia, with Drs. Marion Smith and Simon Hellerstein of the University of Wisconsin.*

17. *Left to right: Dr. Herman Branson, Head of the Department of Physics, Howard University, Washington, D. C.; Dr. Leland C. DeVinney, Rockefeller Foundation, New York, N. Y.*

18. *Dr. A. D. Beittel, left, President of Tougaloo State College, Tougaloo, Mississippi, with Dr. L. S. Cozart, President of Barber-Scotia College, Concord, North Carolina.*

19. *Left to right: Dr. L. S. Cozart, President of Barber-Scotia College, Concord, North Carolina; Dr. Herman Stone, Jr., Dean of Lane College, Jackson, Tennessee; and Dr. William H. Hale, President of Langston University, Langston, Oklahoma.*

20. *Dr. John H. Taylor, left, Head of the Science Department of Cheyney State College, Cheyney, Pennsylvania; Dr. James T. Guines, Head of the Department of Education of St. Augustine's College, Raleigh, North Carolina; Dr. Cyrus Levinthal of the Department of Biology, M.I.T.; and Dr. Lettie J. Austin of the Department of English, Howard University, Washington, D. C.*

on the contrary preserve prerevolutionary values in the face of the materialism of the times. It is necessary to be patient with them. They have had no break-through like those in physics. And yet it is necessary to help the deprived student because he is apt not to be reached by traditional teaching.

What should we tell the Negro student about the conventional idea of becoming part of middle-class America? Should he? Haven't his parents decided they are not going to get these things?

Freshmen come to college from poor communities crowded with experience and cannot express it, Mr. Wolff said. This is an unrecognized agony. We can only bring these things out with the subject matter of literature, by reading and discussion that is relevant. We must make them feel part of mankind.

The conventional methods have not done this, he continued.

Literature is subversive. To stress this is to run risks. How much ought we to provoke?

We will learn from the people you send us, he told the heads of the Negro colleges. We must find new questions, new ways to bring literature into modernity.

-:- -:- -:-

Prof. David Fowler said the history institute would seek better ways to reach the poorly equipped student than the traditional textbook course. They hoped to select central themes, ideas, around which to organize a course in American history that would encourage work in depth. For out of depth comes understanding of the historical process, he said.

They should be important themes, and not too many, such as: the immigrant experience, progressive urbanization, social mobility in American life, progressive centralization, the fulfillment of the principle of liberty, or conflict and consensus in American life. He plans to look at documentary sources rather than jump at conclusions.

This kind of approach will catch the interest of the unprepared student, Mr. Fowler said. It is a kind of case method inducing the student to ask why, and how his conclusions can be applied elsewhere.

To plan experiments like these, said Dr. Herman Branson of Howard University, one of the prime movers of the conference and its purposes, is not to condemn the old. It is to face problems that are different. We are not abandoning old values. These experiments are transitions, he said. Or expansions, he agreed. They will generate enthusiasm and we expect that the teachers who come to these institutes will pass it along to their students.

21. *Dr. Lawrence Howard, left, of the American Council on Education with Dr. Philip Morrison of M.I.T.*

22. *Left to right: Dr. Charles L. Knight, Dean of Bishop College, Dallas, Texas; Dr. Cecil L. Patterson, Acting Director of the Summer School of North Carolina College at Durham, Durham, North Carolina; Mr. Saville R. Davis of the "Christian Science Monitor"; and Dr. Leonard Price of Xavier University, New Orleans, Louisiana.*

21

22

PAPER COMPUTING MACHINES

by William L. Barclay, III

Introduction

This unit on Paper Computing Machines starts with a consideration of exponents and standard operations with exponents and then proceeds to develop paper machines, first ones that will add and then, later, machines that will multiply. In effect, the student is given the opportunity to invent his own slide rule.

The materials that will be needed for a class of 20 students include:

100 sheets of linear graph paper, preferably ruled 10 × 10 to the inch; 7 × 10, such as K & E 46-0700

40 sheets of 1 cycle semi-log paper such as K & E 46-4650

20 slide rules (optional) such as Sterling Slide Rules #589

Sterling Plastics Company
Sheffield St.
Mountainside, New Jersey

This write-up has been written for teachers and is meant to be read with pencil in hand. There are many places where questions are posed and blanks are left in the text. The teacher should answer these questions as they come up and write in information wherever there is a blank. The hope is that by becoming an active participant in the development of the material the teacher will get a sense of the possible insights and potential difficulties his students will experience. In addition, this form of written presentation more closely resembles the mode of classroom approach for which the unit was designed, an approach in which the teacher's role is to stimulate inquiry and exploration rather than preside as an authoritative source of answers.

I. The Notational Basis

Starting with a pattern of numbers arranged in a lattice:

			–	–	
–	8	–	–	–	
2	4	8	16	–	–
	–	–	8	–	

fill in all the spots marked by a "–".

The mathematics unit reproduced on these pages was developed by William L. Barclay, III, a teacher at Boston's Commonwealth School and a mathematics consultant to the Pre-College Program. The Pre-College Program for Students from Low-Income Families was initiated in the summer of 1964 with the object of preparing challenging course materials of high quality for prospective college students from low-income families, as an alternative to the "remedial" fare more usually offered these students. About eighty teaching units in English and in mathematics are in development or completed; the Program works closely with Pre-College Centers located at colleges and universities, six in the South and two in New England, at which college-bound high school seniors attend eight-week resident summer sessions and Saturday programs during the school year, using these course materials.

Now expand the lattice, keeping the same pattern, moving to the left and down.

This can all be presented with a minimum of explanation, starting the lattice on the board and asking for the numbers that go in various empty positions. A further question that tests understanding can be: "How do you know that's right?"

Sometimes, when moving to the left, students will suggest:

			2	4	8	
−2	−1	0	1	2	4	8
−4	−2					

This is a place where it is possible to accept wrong answers without comment, and test the logic of the system that results from these suggestions. One way to pursue this is to look at questions of the type 4 → = □. The symbol "→" means move one place to the right in the lattice; arithmetically it means multiply by 2 for this particular lattice. Now questions such as the following bring about the confrontation:

4 → = □ and 4 × 2 = □

1 → = □ and 1 × 2 = □

16 → = □ and 16 × 2 = □

−2 → = □ and −2 × 2 = □

−1 → = □ and −1 × 2 = □

If students suggest for negative numbers that the arithmetic interpretation of → be changed to multiply by $\frac{1}{2}$, test this:

−2 → = □ and $-2 \times \frac{1}{2}$ = □

−1 → = □ and $-1 \times \frac{1}{2}$ = □

△ → = 1 and △ $\times \frac{1}{2} = 1$

Once the lattice has been expanded, additional problems can be explored just for the fun of it.

1. 4 →→↓↓←← = □

2. 4 →→→→→→ = □

   (And if you get tired of writing all those arrows to the right, invent a short-hand.)

3. $\frac{1}{2}$ ↑→↓← = □

4. $\frac{1}{16}$ ↗↗→↙ = □

5. Build a lattice that contains 1 and for which → means times $\frac{1}{2}$ and ↑ means times 2. Maneuver around the lattice.

6. Build a lattice that contains 1 and for which → means times 3 and ↑ means times 2. Maneuver around.

7. Build a lattice that contains 1 and involves multiplying by a negative. Investigate.

If the question comes up, as it sometimes does, of why lattices are important, or how they are useful, something like the following answer might be given:

> "One of the nice things about these lattices is that they really aren't important by themselves. Certainly there are no facts or formulas that you should memorize for some test or future college course. Their beauty is that they provide a mathematical system in which what counts is how you think, the questions you ask, and the ideas for exploration you come up with. It isn't what you know that is nearly so important as how you know it."

After multiplicative lattices have been explored, the move can be made to writing them exponentially. Thus the lattice

		4	8	16		
$\frac{1}{2}$	1	2	4	8		
$\frac{1}{4}$	$\frac{1}{2}$	1	2	4	8	16

becomes

				2^2	2^3	2^4		
		–	–	2^1	2^2	2^3		
–	–	–	–	–	2^1	2^2	2^3	2^4
		–	–	–				
				–				

Complete this exponential lattice, filling in the spots marked by a "–".*

If the class has trouble expressing 1, $\frac{1}{2}$, and $\frac{1}{4}$ or $\frac{1}{8}$ exponentially, the system is self-correcting, and the students should be given the opportunity to test suggestions against the logic of the lattice.

Once the proper notation has been established, further questions can be explored.

$2^2 \rightarrow\rightarrow\downarrow\downarrow\leftarrow \quad = \square$

$2^{-3} \rightarrow\rightarrow\rightarrow \quad = \square$

$2^{-3} \nearrow\swarrow\leftarrow\uparrow\rightarrow\downarrow = \square$

What is an easy way to find the answer to the following questions?

$2^5 \rightarrow\rightarrow\rightarrow\rightarrow\rightarrow = \square$

$2^0 \leftarrow\leftarrow\leftarrow\leftarrow\leftarrow = \square$

What would the rules for the lattice have to be if one of the diagonals were like this?

			2^2
		2^2	
	2^2		
2^2			

Fill in more of this lattice.

Build an exponential lattice that contains 1 and for which $\rightarrow$ means times 3 and $\uparrow$ means times 2.

---

*Notice that when you want to move to exponential notation, it is easier to use a lattice with the same rule for moving both up and to the right. A lattice where this does not hold, such as:

9	18	36		
3	6	12	25	
1	2	4	8	16

becomes

3^2	$(2^1 \cdot 3^2)$	$(2^2 \cdot 3^2)$	$(2^3 \cdot 3^2)$	
3^1	$(2^1 \cdot 3^1)$	$(2^2 \cdot 3^1)$	$(2^3 \cdot 3^1)$	$(2^4 \cdot 3^1)$
2^0	2^1	2^2	2^3	2^4

which is far more complicated.

II. Exploring Explanations of Exponents

There is need for an interplay back and forth among many different modes of teaching and ways of learning, not only as one goes from topic to topic but also within each topic to reinforce concepts. The previous sheets on lattices have been written as the concepts might develop in class, sometimes on the blackboard and other times with each student working independently at his seat.

Certainly each student can profit from the discussions in class, but it is also important that he get a chance to be alone with the quiet of a pencil, some paper and his intellect, wrestling to formulate, translate and express the concepts involved.

The following work sheets continue to present the development of the unit while simultaneously representing an example of the sort of written material that might evolve from a class' investigations. While there is no formal text that prescribes what questions shall be investigated, it can be important for each teacher to write his own dittoed or mimeographed material that recapitulates what already has been investigated. These sheets can be important for several reasons:

1. they provide an organization of the material that gives the student a sense of accomplishment;

2. they provide a reference for checking back when previous investigations pertain to current questions;

3. they give the student who has not understood the class discussions, or less drastically, has not understood some aspects, a chance to go back over the reasoning;

4. by writing these as work sheets, they involve the student in further thinking about the materials;

5. inclusion of questions and exercises gives the students practice with the concepts;

6. open-ended questions can lead to exploration of the extensions and implications of concepts discussed in class, and

7. they provide a check for those whose verbal knowledge surpasses their written understanding.

Bear in mind, then, that the following notes serve two purposes: (1) they are a continuing development of the concepts involved in this unit, and (2) they are an illustration of sheets that might evolve from a specific class.

Notes on Exploring Explanations of Exponents

These are notes on some of the ideas we have covered in class. They are not supposed to stand independent of those class discussions, but rather as a summary and pulling together of what we have talked about.

1. We started with lattices and began writing out these lattices using exponential notation, as in the piece of a lattice shown below:

$$\begin{array}{ccccccccc} & & & & 3^3 & 3^4 & & & \\ & 3^{-1} & 3^0 & 3^1 & 3^2 & 3^3 & & & \\ & 3^{-2} & 3^{-1} & 3^0 & 3^1 & 3^2 & 3^3 & 3^4 & \\ 3^{-4} & 3^{-3} & 3^{-2} & 3^{-1} & 3^0 & 3^1 & & & \end{array}$$

2. As you all know now (and knew then?) $3^0 = 1$. But how do you know that $3^0 = 1$? What is a reasonable argument that might convince someone that $3^0 = 1$? We used three such arguments:

   a. From the lattices (a different lattice this time):

$$\begin{array}{cccccccc} \frac{1}{8} & \frac{1}{4} & \frac{1}{2} & 1 & 2 & 4 & 8 & 16 \\ \frac{1}{16} & \frac{1}{8} & \frac{1}{4} & \frac{1}{2} & 1 & 2 & 4 & 8 \leftarrow \\ & & \frac{1}{8} & \frac{1}{4} & \frac{1}{2} & & & \end{array}$$

   If you start at the arrow and begin writing out the numbers in exponent form:

$$\ldots \quad \ldots \quad 2^1 \quad 2^2 \quad 2^3$$

   you see a natural progression of the exponents going down from 3, to 2, to 1. One would expect the next number in this sequence to be 0, making $2^0 = 1$.

   b. Our second argument was more involved, and you will need a pencil here because I am going to leave many blanks for you to fill in. (I am convinced that a simultaneous combination of reading and writing is a much more productive way to wrestle with mathematical ideas than reading first and then doing exercises.)

   (i) Starting with what we mean by an exponent, namely that 4^3 means $4 \cdot 4 \cdot 4$, we first considered the rule for multiplication:

$$4^4 \cdot 4^3 = 4^{4+3} = 4^7$$

   which makes sense because

   $4^4 \cdot 4^3 = (4 \cdot 4 \cdot 4 \cdot 4)(4 \cdot 4 \cdot 4)$

   which is what we mean by 4^7.

   (ii) Next we affirmed the rule for division. In a fashion similar to (i) above show a convincing argument for why $4^4 \div 4^3 = 4^1$.

   (iii) With this rule for division, we can show that $3^0 = 1$, or 4^0 or $(-7)^0 = 1$, makes good sense. We did this by starting with a fraction we knew

   equaled 1, such as $\frac{3^4}{3^4}$.

$$\frac{3^4}{3^4} = 1 \quad \text{but also} \quad \frac{3^4}{3^4} = 3^{4-4} \text{ which equals } 3^0$$

   therefore, 3^0 must equal 1.

   (iv) How about n^0? Does $n^0 = 1$? Convince me with a reasonable argument that $n^0 = 1$.

   c. The third method for seeing that a number to the zero power = 1 involved multiplying two numbers together, one with a positive exponent the other with a negative exponent, so that their product gave 4^0 (let's change base this time). Write such a product:

   Now convince me that this product is also equal to 1.

3. Negative Exponents

   a. Suppose though that no one had suggested that 2^{-1} equals $\frac{1}{2}$. How could we have worked to discover what 2^{-1} meant? With the reverse of our previous argument—we could have set up a statement that we knew equaled 2^{-1} and then seen if we could find another way of looking at it. Thus:

$$2^3 \div 2^4 = 2^{-1}$$

but $$2^3 \div 2^4 = \frac{2\cdot 2\cdot 2}{2\cdot 2\cdot 2\cdot 2}$$

and by cancellation that equals $\frac{1}{2}$.

Therefore, $2^{-1} = \frac{1}{2}$

b. Another approach:

$$2^{-1} = 2^{0-1}$$

but subtraction of exponents is what you do in division so

$$2^{0-1} = \frac{?}{?}$$

and the numerator of this fraction =
and the denominator = . Therefore,
$2^{-1} =$.

4. Raising a Power to a Power.

What, for instance, does $(2^3)^2$ equal? You may know, but maybe I don't, so I still want you to write out a logical argument to convince me.

5. Fractional Exponents.

a. The argument we used to discover the meaning of fractional exponents, as "$\frac{1}{2}$" in $4^{1/2}$, was the most complicated explanation we got into. Therefore, it is more important than ever that you create as much of the argument as possible for yourself rather than just reading my way of rattling it off.

Our method of approach in all these arguments has been to find two alternative ways of looking at an expression so that we might fathom its meaning. $2^{1/2}$ is an expression containing a fractional exponent, but I couldn't think of any alternative way of attacking this.

$2^{4/2}$, however, can be pushed in two ways:

$$2^{4/2} = 2^2 = 4$$

but another way

$$2^{4/2} = (2^4)^? = (\qquad)^{1/2}$$

which must equal 4 from the first statement above.

Therefore, raising to the $\frac{1}{2}$ power must mean (?) .

$2^{6/2}$ can also be handled in these two ways. Do it.

How about $3^{4/2}$? Show me that the same argument either can or cannot be applied.

b. Another nice argument builds this up from a direct consideration of square root.

If a number times itself = 2,
then that number = $\sqrt{2}$.

Since $2^{0.5}\cdot 2^{0.5} = 2^{(\ +\ )} = 2^1$
$\sqrt{2}$ must equal $2^?$

c. Can you build an explanation that will show me what raising to the $\frac{1}{3}$ power means?

6. Some Exercises.

Knowing all this about exponents and being able to use them in complicated combinations is not always synonymous. The trick is to find simplifications. One concept worth being familiar with is what an expression such as $\frac{y}{4^{-2}}$ can simplify to.

Note that $4^{-2} = \frac{1}{4^2}$

Therefore $\frac{y}{4^{-2}} = \frac{y}{1/4^2}$

dealing with this complicated fraction

$$\frac{y}{1/4^2} \cdot \frac{4^2}{4^2} = \frac{4^2 y}{1} \text{ or } 16\,y$$

so $$\frac{y}{4^{-2}} = 4^2 y$$

The main trick is often to see what order of operations is best. For instance, in this problem

$$\left(\frac{4^2 \cdot 4^3}{4^4}\right)^{1/2}$$

you could expand to

$$\left(\frac{16 \cdot 64}{256}\right)^{1/2}$$

then multiply

$$\left(\frac{1024}{256}\right)^{1/2}$$

now divide, $256\,\overline{)\,1024}$ (quotient 4), and finally,

take the square root: $\sqrt{4} = 2$.

BUT THAT IS NOT THE EASIEST WAY.

$$\text{Better: } \left(\frac{4^2 \cdot 4^3}{4^4}\right)^{1/2} = \left(\frac{4^5}{4^4}\right)^{1/2} = (4^1)^{1/2} = 4^{1/2} = 2$$

Another Example:

$$\frac{3^{-4} \cdot 3^6}{(3^{-2})^{1/2}}$$

You could expand this one out, too, but I'm not even going to show you how complicated that can get. Far easier are either of the following ways:

$$\frac{3^{-4} \cdot 3^6}{(3^{-2})^{1/2}} = \frac{3^2}{3^{-1}} = 3^{2-(-1)} = 3^3$$

or

$$\frac{3^{-4} \cdot 3^6}{(3^{-2})^{1/2}} = \frac{3^6}{3^4 \cdot 3^{-1}} = \frac{3^6 \cdot 3^1}{3^4} = 3^{6+1-4} = 3^3$$

Be sure you see what is happening in each of the steps above and why.

Now you try a few.

1. $\dfrac{4^2 \cdot 4^{-3}}{4^{1/2}} =$

2. $(2^3 \cdot 2^4)^{-3}\,(2^{-3} \cdot 2^{-4})^3 =$

3. How many ways can you find to make the product in problem 2 equal 1 by only changing the exponents?

4. $\dfrac{(4^2 \cdot 4^{-3})^{1/2}}{4^{1/2}} = \dfrac{1}{\sqrt{2}}$. (work out the left side of this equation to show that it is correct)

5. $\dfrac{3^{-1} + 3^2}{3 + 3^{-2}} =$ (Don't be tricked by this one)

6. $\dfrac{64 \cdot 16}{2^4 \cdot 4^3} = 1$

7. Arrange these numbers in descending order of magnitude.

   3^{-2} $\quad \frac{1}{3}^{-2}$ $\quad (\frac{1}{3}^{-2})^{-2}$ $\quad (3^{-2})^{-2}$ $(3^{-2})^{1/2}$

   $(3^{-2})^{1/2}$ & $(\frac{1}{3}^{-2})^{-1/2}$.

A different lattice to play with:

256
16 256
– – – 2 4 16 256
– – – –
– –

Fill in the places marked.

What does 2↑↑↑ mean arithmetically?

What does 16↓↓↓↓ mean arithmetically?

Rewrite the lattice exponentially below.

III. A Machine That Adds

A number line gives a clear way of representing the real numbers.

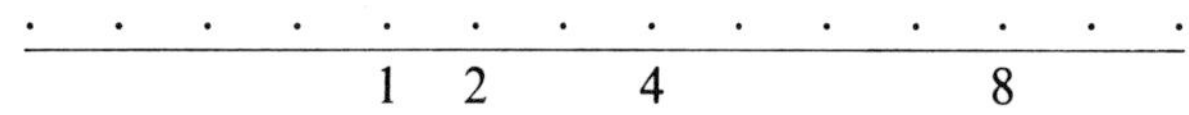

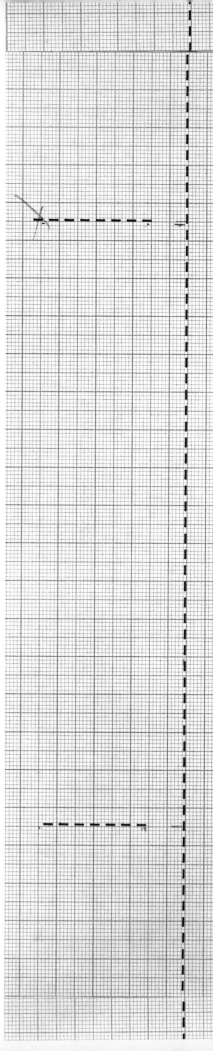

Shown above are some of the numbers taken from a row in a base 2 exponential lattice and shown on a linear scale.

Where are the lattice numbers that come to the left of 1, such as $\frac{1}{2}$, $\frac{1}{4}$, and $\frac{1}{8}$?

What about other numbers such as $3\frac{1}{2}$ or $5\frac{3}{4}$? What number is half-way between 3 and $3\frac{1}{2}$? half-way between this new number and $3\frac{1}{2}$?

Once everyone is clear on number lines, paper strips can be handed out to each student with the statement "See if you can invent a machine that will add." It often helps to give a specific problem as a starter—"one that will add 7 and 2, for instance." The paper strips can be cut from lined, notebook paper, but it is simpler to use graph paper such as K & E 46-0700 which is ruled off 10 × 10 to the inch; 7 × 10 inches. Paper with 10 divisions, each sub-divided into tenths, gives a scale that more readily handles problems that go off the end, such as 9 + 5, where you read the answer back at 4 which is easily recognized as 14. If your scale is 24 units long (when using paper lined with 25 lines) then for a problem such as 19 + 13 the answer is read back at 8, which is not so easily recognized as 32. Other confusions that arise as students invent paper adding machines include:

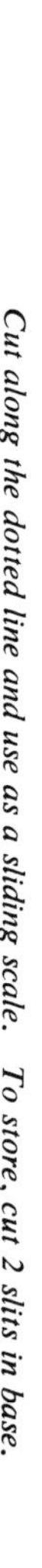

Cut along the dotted line and use as a sliding scale. To store, cut 2 slits in base.

(a) labeling the spaces, . 1 . 2 . 3 . 4 . 5 .,

instead of the dividing lines, 0 1 2 3 4 5;

(b) starting with 1 instead of 0;

(c) if not given pre-lined paper, failure to keep a consistent unit distance along the scale;

(d) writing out an addition table instead of making a machine that will work for all 2 or 3 digit numbers.

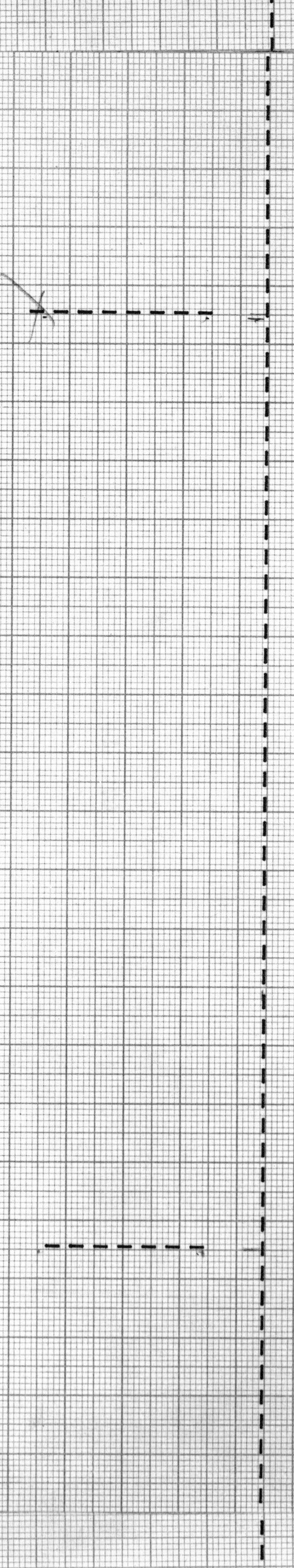

The simplest form of paper adding machines is analogous to using two meter sticks or a set Cuisinaire Rods. Other forms include circular and cylindrical models. The latter can be made on a tin can such as a coffee can, but unfortunately none of the standard cans have a 10 inch circumference so the graph paper cannot be used for the scales.

When you want to demonstrate the use of the adding machine, or later the multiplying machine, a combination of a stick and a blackboard drawing is very handy. You need one movable scale, but you do not want to have to juggle two long sticks. The metric scale works well for the adding machine, and masking tape can be used to apply a logarithmic scale for multiplying.

Questions such as the following cause one to grapple with the basic concepts and problems of these adding machines.

(a) $2 + 7$

(b) $20 + 70$

(c) $3\frac{1}{2} + 4$

(d) $1.4 + 3.7$

(e) $314 + 560$

(f) $7 - 2$

(g) $310 - 190$

(h) $35 + 7.7$

(i) $3.5 - 2.1$

(j) $5 + 7$

(k) $78 + 56$

(l) $11 - 7$

(m) $130 - 75$

(n) $52 - 7.8$

The following illustrates the two ways students commonly explain how to use the linear strips for problems that go off the end.

(a) In adding 8 plus 6

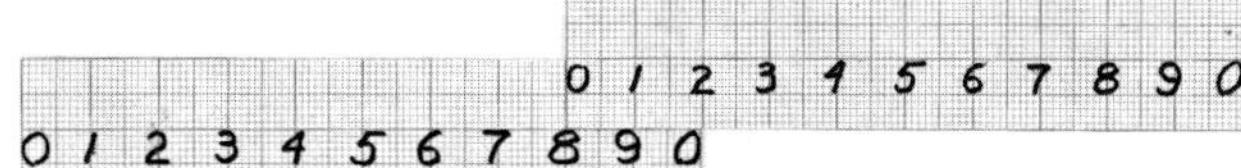

The 6 is still 4 units past the end of the base, and this extra distance must be brought back and added on at the very beginning:

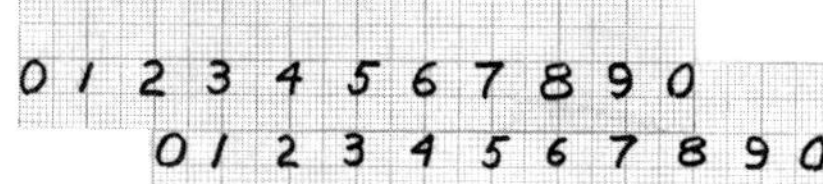

The answer, now below the 6, is 14, not 4.

(b) A cylindrical slide rule handles the problem of going off the end easily. Using scotch tape, two strips can be nested together.

In each case the goal is to observe that the right index on the slider allows one to handle these problems simply.

IV. A Machine That Multiplies

If we want to multiply numbers together, such as 32×16, the paper adding machines seem to be of little help. Note, though, that these numbers are both powers of 2: $2^5 \times 2^4$ which equals 2^9. A table of powers of 2 makes problems like this very easy.

power of 2	number
10	
9	
8	
7	
6	
5	
4	
3	8
2	4
1	2
0	
−1	
−2	
−3	
−4	
−5	

Complete this table.

Now use it to work problems such as:

64×8

$1024 \div 32$

$512 \times .25 \times \frac{1}{16}$

$256 \div 32 \times 8$

In each case the process involves adding and subtracting exponents, and addition and subtraction are exactly the operations the paper strips perform. It should be possible to adapt the paper adding machines to make them into multiplying machines. To do this requires a re-labeling of the scales. Do you see how you would re-label the addition scale below?

0 1 2 3 4 5 6 7 8 9 10

An empirical way to develop a multiplying scale is to start with unmarked strips and label the scales to correctly give products. By marking a 2 on both scales and using the strips as before, the result can be marked 4, only now this is the product not the sum. Going on to set 2 times 4, the result is marked 8, and so on.

This leaves undetermined the scale markings to the left of "2". If each student has been generating his own scale, some will probably write a "1" and then an "0" here:

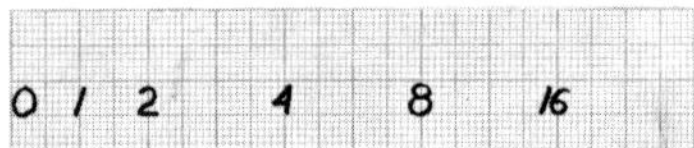

Using two such scales, what do you get when you multiply $8 \cdot 0$ and $8 \cdot 1$?

To be able to correctly handle problems such as the above, the left index must be labeled with the value of the identity element for the operation involved. This is an interesting difference between the adding and the multiplying machine. A fundamental commonness, though, is that both machines find the answer by adding two distances (or subtracting for the inverse operation). This is worth discussing.

The multiplication machine as now constructed is seriously limited because it only includes numbers that are integral powers of 2. Where does 3 go on this scale? Is it here?

If you put 3 mid-way between 2 and 4, note what happens when you multiply 3×3:

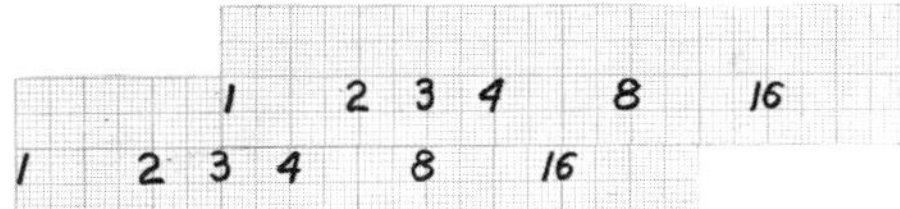

But if 3 does not go mid-way between 2 and 4, what does? and where does 3 go? There are several approaches that get at the answers to these questions.

(a) Least imaginative is to give out semi-log graph paper with its scale all figured out ahead of time for each student.

(b) The approach that most closely parallels the historical development of logarithms is to pursue the question of what number does go mid-way between 2 and 4. This is explained below.

(c) A graphical basis for filling in the scale involves plotting the graph of 2^x vs. x.

Jumping directly to the second alternative, note that the number mid-way between 2 and 4 satisfies the equation: $\square \times \square = 8$. Obviously $\square = ?$ or $2\sqrt{2}$ which equals 2.828.

Looking at it a little differently, the number mid-way between 2^1 and 2^2 should be $2^{3/2}$ which equals $(2^3)^{1/2}$ or $\sqrt{8}$. If $2^{3/2} = 8$, then in the equation $2^{\square} = 9$, $\square$ must be greater than 3/2. It is not too easy to compute the value of fractional powers of 2, but it may be worth pursuing as a demonstration or even a student exercise to show how successive square roots of 2 can be used to find where to place the in-between numbers such as 3, 5, 6, 7, 9, and 10.

Here is a table of the first seven successive square roots of 2:

$$\sqrt{2} = 2^{1/2} = 1.414$$

$$\sqrt{\sqrt{2}} = 2^{1/4} = 1.189$$

$$\sqrt{\sqrt{\sqrt{2}}} = 2^{1/8} = 1.090$$

$$= 2^{1/16} = 1.044$$

$$2^{1/32} = 1.022$$

$$2^{1/64} = 1.011$$

$$2^{1/128} = 1.0055$$

Using this table, it is possible to find more exactly where to place 3. The following computations show how this can be done, starting at $2^{3/2}$ and getting closer and closer approximations of 3:

$$2^{3/2} = 2^1 \cdot 2^{1/2} = 2 \times 1.414 = 2.828$$
which is too small.

$$2^{7/4} = 2^{3/2} \cdot 2^{1/4} = 2.828 \times 1.189 = 3.362$$
which is too large.

$$2^{3/2} \cdot 2^{1/8} = 2.828 \times 1.090 = 3.083$$

$$2^{3/2} \cdot 2^{1/16} = 2.828 \times 1.044 = 2.9525$$

$$(2^{3/2} \cdot 2^{1/16}) \cdot 2^{1/32} = 2.9525 \times 1.022 = 3.017$$

$$(2^{3/2} \cdot 2^{1/16}) \cdot 2^{1/64} = 2.9525 \times 1.011 = 2.985$$

$$(2^{3/2} \cdot 2^{1/16} \cdot 2^{1/64}) \cdot 2^{1/128} = 2.985 \times 1.0055 = 3.001$$

Surely this is close enough to satisfy everyone in the class, but clearly one could also get closer to 3 by working with further successive square roots of 2; in fact, as close as desired. Actually $2^{25/16}$ or $2^{51/32}$ is as fine as you can mark on the paper scale. Note that $51/32 = 1.6$; in other words, 3 is 0.6 of the way between 2 and 4. Now that you know where 3 is, what other numbers can you find? (6 and 9).

To complete the scale between 1 and 10, it is necessary to know the powers of 2 that give the other included primes, 5 and 7.

$$2^2 \cdot 2^{1/4} \cdot 2^{1/16} = 4.965$$

$$2^2 \cdot 2^{1/2} \cdot 2^{1/4} \cdot 2^{1/16} = 7.021$$

For the graphical approach, the graph of 2^x vs. x is shown on the following page. The multiplication scale can be developed using this graph, and such an approach nicely supplements the preceding one. By interpolating and extrapolating, you can find the value of x that corresponds to any value between 1 and 10. Note that the graph is plotted using only integral powers of 2: 2^0, 2^1, 2^2 and 2^3, yet the power of 2 that gives any value between 1 and 10 can be read directly from the graph. Lines on the graph illustrate finding the power corresponding to 3; i. e., $2^{1.6} = 3$. By laying a paper strip along the x-axis of this graph, you can mark all the distances needed to make an exponential scale for 1 to 10.

The use of the graph has the advantage of including only the needed portion of the logarithmic scale, namely from 1 to 10. One could set up a base 10 scale by taking successive square roots of 10. This, in fact, was the method Henry Briggs used in 1624 when he computed the first table of logarithms. Briggs took the square root of 10 fifty-four successive times and as a result was able to compute to fourteen places the logarithms of the numbers between 1 and 20,000 and between 10,000 and 100,000. What a fantastic computational task that must have been. The gap was filled in by Adrian Vlacg, a Dutch bookseller living in London, who published a table of logarithms in 1628 for the numbers 1 to 100,000.

If you empirically find a multiplying scale by marking it so it correctly shows products, as already described, a simple geometric method can be used to expand the relevant portion (1 to 10). Two versions of this process are illustrated.

The aim here is not to produce a perfect scale, but rather to give the students a feel for how such a scale can be made and faith that if required they could make such a scale for themselves. The semi-logarithmic graph paper can be used for a final paper version of the slide rule. After students have had a chance to work with this, plastic slide rules can be distributed—perhaps the next week.

A. Analogous to a Photo Enlarger

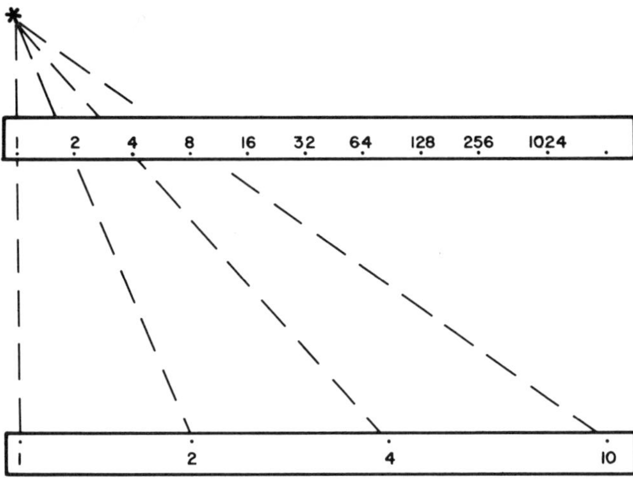

B. Geometric Construction for Dividing a Line Segment:

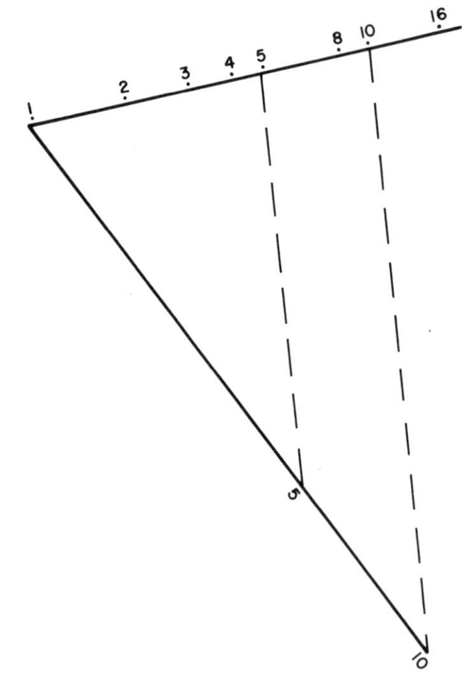

This line as long as the graph paper

Additional Questions and Explorations:

1. Construct a set of base 3 scales for multiplying and dividing. Compare this scale with the base 2 scale and the base 10 scale.

2. One student suggested making a multiplication scale that included fractions to the left of 1. Make a set of these scales, base 2, and explore their use.

3. Make a C-inverted scale (the log scale backwards) for a 1 to 10 multiplying machine and note how it simplifies handling problems that go off the end.

4. After developing the concept of a logarithm, invent an L-scale.

5. Continue with a development of logarithms, using the slide rule rather than a table of logs to find the log of any number, and getting the students to find and refine the rules for logarithmic operations.

6. Remembering that distances along an exponential scale are proportional to powers of the base, and noting the way one takes square roots using exponents, invent a square root scale to use with your multiplication machine.

VIII
CURRICULUM DEVELOPMENT FOR THE UNIVERSITY AND COLLEGE

THE COOPERATIVE PROGRAM IN TEACHER EDUCATION

by Nathaniel H. Frank

During the past decade, a growing and increasingly successful pattern of curriculum development activities has come into being, encompassing a wide range of disciplines and aimed at students of many age levels. Characteristic of all these efforts has been the early creation of programs of experimental testing of the materials and methods of learning with selected groups of teachers and students. From these trial periods comes valuable feedback concerning the feasibility and effectiveness of the new patterns of education.

In some cases members of the curriculum development groups teach such experimental classes. In addition, professional classroom teachers have been introduced to the new materials so that they might also participate in these pilot programs. In general, however, involving a relatively few teachers in the process of curriculum development will make only a small contribution to the massive problem of teacher education.

We now find ourselves in the situation where there is real danger that the very large investment, both in money and in talent, in generating first-class course-content improvement projects will be largely wasted unless adequate numbers of teachers are educated to teach effectively both the currently developed new materials and those that will emerge in the future. The task of satisfying this critical need for highly competent teachers is almost overwhelming. The present number of pupils in elementary schools (through Grade 8) is about 35,000,000; the number in secondary schools about 13,000,000; and the total corps of teachers for these students approximates 1,900,000. About 200,000 new teachers must enter the profession every year because of the growth in the school population and as staff replacements for teachers who retire for various reasons.

One approach to the solution to the problem of finding capable teachers is to retrain teachers in service to handle adequately the new curriculum materials. This has been and is being done with the help of special summer institutes, in-service institutes and the exhibition of teacher-training films such as those being created by Professor Page for the University of Illinois Arithmetic Project (ESI). In fact, such voluntary retraining of teachers has been the sole means of obtaining for the PSSC physics course the four thousand men and women who are presently teaching the course.

Valuable as this retraining process is, it cannot begin to satisfy the over-all need. It is also subject to definite limitations. In the case of the PSSC physics, retraining certainly has been successful to a great extent because the teachers involved have the professional identification of physics, having extensive college training in the subject, and because teacher turnover at the high school level is comparatively small. Turning to the elementary grades, however, where the number of teachers is so much greater and the turnover correspondingly larger, one finds no comparable professional "handle" to give support in the retraining process. Furthermore, the fact that most teachers have themselves been educated along widely different lines from those that characterize the new programs adds to the difficulty of preparing these teachers to cope effectively with the rapidly evolving new course materials.

It is clear then that the crux of the problem of providing large numbers of competent teachers lies in the adequate education of these teachers while they are still in college. It is the purpose of the Cooperative Teacher Education Program to assist the institutions that educate a large proportion of our teachers. Not only is it most efficient to introduce the prospective teacher to new materials and educational patterns while he or she is still a student, but, since people often teach in the same way they themselves have been taught, this early intro-

Professor of Physics at the Massachusetts Institute of Technology and former head of the Institute's Department of Physics, Dr. Frank was one of the original contributors to the PSSC. He is also associated with the Institute's Science Teaching Center. He is the director of ESI's Cooperative Program in Teacher Education.

duction to the newly devised schemes of communication and learning aids, together with the underlying rationale of curriculum reform, is truly essential. Thus, one must face squarely the task of expending a major effort to reform the curricula and courses in the relevant colleges, working collaboratively with the faculties of these institutions. This kind of college curriculum reform, to be effective, must involve eventually the entire educational experience of the prospective teacher, including the courses in education. Because the new curriculum offerings, particularly for elementary and high-school students, generally comprise an inextricable mixture of content and of methods of learning, the changes that must be accomplished in the colleges for teachers will be far reaching indeed. Not only must courses be updated and improved, but the very structure of the college curriculum must be recast.

The programs leading to the kind of college curriculum reform that has been suggested require intimate and continuing interaction between faculty members of the colleges involved and individuals representing the groups that are responsible for and active in the preparation of new educational materials. One way of establishing such mutual interaction is to involve faculty members, on a part-time basis, in the development work of the curriculum improvement groups and conversely to involve members of the latter groups in the actual teaching and course-content improvement in the colleges. With the help of joint or part-time appointments, cooperative schemes such as this will lead not only to improvement of the education of future teachers and those who teach them, but also to valuable feedback to the curriculum development projects themselves. This feedback will be just as essential in judging the usefulness of the newly developed materials as that now obtained by members of curriculum development groups who conduct experimental classes with students and in-service teachers.

It is essential to recognize that the recasting of college curricula will involve far more than the skillful introduction of new materials and new methods of presenting them. While this is a necessary first step to exemplify the spirit, character and rationale of the new developments, the education of teachers must go far beyond this sort of sampling. There must emerge first-rate courses that prepare the student adequately, not only to teach the new educational material effectively but also to exercise critical judgment of such material and to contribute to its further growth. The development of such courses, suitably structured and geared to the background and intellectual level of these college students, constitutes a major goal of the Cooperative Teacher Education Program. It is not necessary, nor is it desirable, to develop these courses as totally new ventures. Rather, one will lean heavily on the rich store of excellent material—written, experimental and visual—that has been fashioned for all levels of education and by an adroit synthesis of appropriate parts of these, create a very effective initial pattern. The initial phase of embarking on a cooperative program is of necessity modest in size. However, it is large enough to be meaningful and to generate a workable model for the solution of the national problem. It is the intent of this project to move as rapidly as possible from this beginning effort to the broader arena of national needs.

This first phase comprises a limited number of collaborative programs with a number of the state colleges of Massachusetts. There are eleven of these colleges, and all of them, except the Massachusetts College of Art and the Massachusetts Maritime Academy, offer four-year programs for students majoring in elementary education. These colleges are a very rich source of public school teachers in Massachusetts. About eighty-five per cent of the graduates enter the field of teaching, and approximately seventy-two per cent remain to teach in Massachusetts. In 1964 some 2,645 degrees were granted by these colleges. The establishment of cooperative programs between the state colleges and Educational Services Incorporated was authorized by the Board of Trustees of these colleges in July of 1964. During the summer of 1964, a number of conferences and visits by ESI personnel to some of the state colleges took place. Possible pilot programs for the fall of 1964 were discussed. As a result, the following activities have been carried out during this academic year:

1. At the State College at Lowell, three members of the Elementary Science Study staff (Clifford Anastasiou, Costa Leodas and Edward Prenowitz) participated in the instruction of students in the physical science and biology laboratory courses required for all prospective elementary teachers. Working with Professor William H. Malone of the Lowell physics department and with Dr. Ethel Kamien of the biology department, they have introduced experimental materials from the Elementary Science Study into these laboratories. Stimulated by the favorable student response to these new patterns of learning, we are making plans for the continuation and expansion of this type of operation. In these, Professor Marguerite Gourville, head of teacher training and of the Department of Education at Lowell, is cooperating actively to bring about early practice teaching by students in these experimental classes as well as to set up a collaborative effort in a seminar for seniors who have had practice teaching experience.

2. At the State College at Bridgewater, Professor David A. Page and members of the staff of the University of Illinois Arithmetic Project have taught an elective course (ESI) to juniors and seniors majoring in elementary education in cooperation with the mathematics department of the college.

3. At the State College at Framingham, Malcolm Smith of Educational Services Incorporated and the Massachusetts Institute of Technology is collaborating actively with Prof. Paul Boylan of Framingham in the preparation of a new one-year physics course for students majoring in biology and in medical technology. This course, which will be based on existing materials developed at ESI, will be taught for the first time starting in the fall of 1965.

During the spring semester of 1965, an experimental section of elementary education majors was directed jointly by Ervin Hoffart of ESI and by Dr. Alice Glover and her staff at the college. Arrangements were made with Dr. George King and Dr. Mary Stapleton of the Framingham School System to have a class of sixth grade students brought to this experimental section once a week. Here the college students taught the sixth grade pupils, using the materials with which they had been working. This served as a trial of a scheme of evaluation of progress made by the college students different from the traditional written examinations.

4. At the State College at Fitchburg, which prepares teachers of Industrial Arts, initial steps have been taken toward a program of collaboration among President James J. Hammond and his industrial arts faculty and members of the Department of Mechanical Engineering at the Massachusetts Institute of Technology (in particular with Professors Henry Paynter and Thomas Sheridan), and plans for an expanded program are being formulated. This program is aimed at improving the teaching of industrial arts, by emphasizing a scientific base that includes the fundamental concepts and techniques of modern technology and engineering.

5. During the summer of 1965, the Elementary Science Study and the Cooperative Teacher Education Program have engaged seven faculty members of the state colleges as staff members of the Elementary Science Study. It is expected that this personal involvement in curriculum reform will provide means by which these faculty members can initiate innovations in education at their colleges. These faculty members are:

DR. FRANK J. HILFERTY, *Chairman, Biology Department, Commonwealth Professor of Botany, State College at Bridgewater;* MRS. JOAN BRENNER, *Physics Department, State College at Boston;* MRS. COLLEEN SCHWITZGEBEL, *Physics Department, State College at Framingham;* DR. ETHEL KAMIEN, *Biology Department, State College at Lowell;* PROF. THOMAS I. RYAN, *Chairman, Biology Department, State College at Salem;* PROF. ALFRED L. BORGATTI, *Biology Department, State College at Salem;* and PROF. J. KENNETH TAYLOR, *Biology Department, State College at Westfield.*

These activities have been made possible by initial grants from Sanders Associates Inc. and from the Carnegie Corporation of New York. It should be made clear that, although the first steps reported here involve primarily those curriculum developments now in existence under the aegis of Educational Services Incorporated, it is the intent of this program to work eventually with many new curriculum developments of merit.

EDUCATIONAL FILMS IN FLUID MECHANICS

by Ascher H. Shapiro

Why Films?

A REMARKABLE ANOMALY exists in the usual courses of lectures on applied science and engineering. Although the subjects considered rest on experimental foundations, and the topics treated relate to tangible physical phenomena, the experimental phenomena generally are absent from the lecture hall. Instead, the lecture is constructed of words, gestures, chalk, sketches, and mathematics.

If a course of lectures in comparative music were given without musical examples, it would be all too evident that something vital was missing. But, surprisingly, there is little conscious recognition that in engineering lectures the equally vital ingredient of experimental phenomena is absent. Perhaps it would be more accurate to say that we take for granted the extraordinary practical difficulties of doing experimental demonstrations in a lecture course and we have become reconciled—even more, habituated—to the easier way of the lecturer and his blackboard.

The emphasis is therefore on the *conceptual* side of the subject. By forfeit, the *perceptual* side is relegated to the background. In many subtle ways, this attention to the conceptual and the relative neglect of the perceptual must have serious effects on the student's acquisition of knowledge and, even more, on the development of his attitudes and critical faculties. What to the lecturer's experienced mind seems like a perfectly clear description of an apparatus or of an experimental observation evokes in the innocent mind of the student an image that is hazy or distorted. Experimental phenomena that are dramatic and unforgettable in their unfolding can never be conveyed with equal force by words alone, any more than could a piece of exciting music. All too often, students become proficient in the formalities of analysis, without having any idea as to what the analysis is all about. Worst of all for engineers is the occasional confusion as to which represents reality: the mathematical analysis, or the experimental evidence.

Students live and grow by example. If they do not grasp the complementary roles of experiment and theory, if they feel that first-class experimental work is of lesser status than first-class theoretical work, then perhaps the reason inheres in the relative emphasis given in lectures to theory and experimental manifestation.

I have, of course, exaggerated somewhat, in order to sharpen the point. But there will be little disagreement with the assertion that lectures in applied science and engineering could be more effective if supplemented by experimental demonstrations which provide the percepts to go with the concepts.

The practical and economic problems of performing demonstrations *in vivo* in the lecture hall are many and too well known to be enumerated. If this were not true, experimental illustration of lectures would be commonplace. Such is far from the case.

This brings us to films. For the past three years we have labored to see whether, in the field of fluid mechanics at least, the pedagogical dilemma that I have posed could be solved by putting demonstration experiments on film. The outlook, I think it fair to say, is hopeful, not only in fluid mechanics, but also in most branches of applied science.

To be sure, seeing a demonstration on film is not the same as doing it with one's own hands. But films may with advantage use such techniques as high-speed and time-lapse photography; they may include experiments which in variety and scope would not normally be avail-

---

Dr. Shapiro is a Ford Professor of Engineering and the Head of the Department of Mechanical Engineering at the Massachusetts Institute of Technology. A founder of the National Committee for Fluid Mechanics Films, he served as its chairman from 1961 to 1964. **This article reproduces the text of a Nominated Lecture delivered in Cambridge, England to the Institution of Mechanical Engineers of London, in April 1964. Statements on film production progress have been updated to July 1965.**

able in a university laboratory. As compared with *in vivo* demonstrations in the lecture hall, all students get a front-row seat, or better still, a roving view by virtue of close-ups and shots from several angles. Good camera work, together with animation and optical treatments, can enhance dramatic impact and leave images even more unforgettable than the experiment seen live. Once an experiment has been properly filmed, the apparatus can be jettisoned; the nuisance of storage, maintenance, and preparation for action disappears forever. The experiment stored in the can of film never fails to work promptly and without fumblings, excuses, or wasted time.

The National Committee For Fluid Mechanics Films

The cost of producing motion-picture films of professional quality would at first appear forbiddingly large. The most elementary calculation shows that no single university could justifiably afford the expense of producing film merely for its own use. If there is any economic sense at all in films, it comes from the replication of prints for use in tens or hundreds of institutions, with a further replication in time over a period of many years. The total audience for a film even in so specialized a subject as fluid mechanics is vast, at least of the order of hundreds of thousands.

The National Committee for Fluid Mechanics Films (N.C.F.M.F.)* constituted itself for the purpose of producing educational films in fluid mechanics. It works in concert with Educational Services Incorporated, a non-profit organization of Watertown, Massachusetts, which provides administrative services, professional film production facilities, and technical staff. Financial support for the project has been provided by grants from the National Science Foundation.

The N.C.F.M.F. has developed several lines of policy worthy of discussion:

(1) We attempt to avoid such parochialisms as might arise if some films were directed toward civil engineers, others toward aeronautical engineers, others toward meteorologists, and so on. One of the fascinating aspects of fluid mechanics is its ramification. Film, with its great powers of condensation, is ideally suited for suggesting breadth and scope. We try to exploit this quality by drawing in each film on examples from diverse areas of engineering and applied science.

(2) Our goal is not the production of "teaching films" in the ordinary use of the phrase, because the films are not designed to replace lectures, or to do what lecturers are ordinarily able to do. Rather, they are aids to the lecturer which enable him to bring in the element now missing: experimental illustrations of the topics he deals with theoretically. To digress briefly, it is still a moot point whether effective lecture films could be produced which, like the lecturer, would develop the concepts and theory of a technical subject; thus far it seems not to have been done. But our own experience shows that films built on experimental demonstrations are effective in that they use the strongest qualities of the film medium to support the weakest point of the lecture system. The experiments must, of course, be related to a conceptual framework which gives them significance. But the conceptual and theoretical allusions are brief, mainly in the nature of reminders of material heard in lectures or read in texts.

(3) It would be entirely out of keeping with our general purpose if demonstration-experiment films were viewed as a means for reducing personal contact with laboratory work. To the degree that laboratory courses have repetitively exposed students to well-known experiments for purely illustrative ends, they have obscured the true purpose of an experimental laboratory. Our films are not intended to displace laboratory experience. Instead we hope that they will help free the laboratory to do its proper job of giving students an appreciation of the place of experimental research in the work of the engineer and the scientist.

(4) The films are "introductory" in the sense that they are intended to relate to the student's first study of a particular topic. Therefore, certain films may be relatively elementary, others more advanced. In any case, since they are built around experimental demonstrations, students at both elementary and advanced levels seem to get something out of them.

(5) The films do not form an ordered sequence associated with a particular curriculum. Fluid mechanics courses vary so greatly that it was deemed best that the films be independent of any specific lecture treatment. Moreover, the rapid contrast capability of films can well be used to offset the slow, orderly, disciplined unfolding of a long series of lectures.

For the large intellectual resources needed to produce an extensive series of films we have drawn heavily on the academic and professional communities. They have responded with great generosity of time and effort. Each film has a "principal" who is combined author-

* *A. E. Bryson, Harvard University (Chairman); D. Coles, California Institute of Technology; S. Corrsin, The Johns Hopkins University; D. Fultz, University of Chicago; R. A. Gross, Columbia University; S. J. Kline, Stanford University; E. L. Mollo-Christensen, Massachusetts Institute of Technology; W. L. Moore, University of Texas; A. H. Shapiro, Massachusetts Institute of Technology; H. Yeh, University of Pennsylvania.*

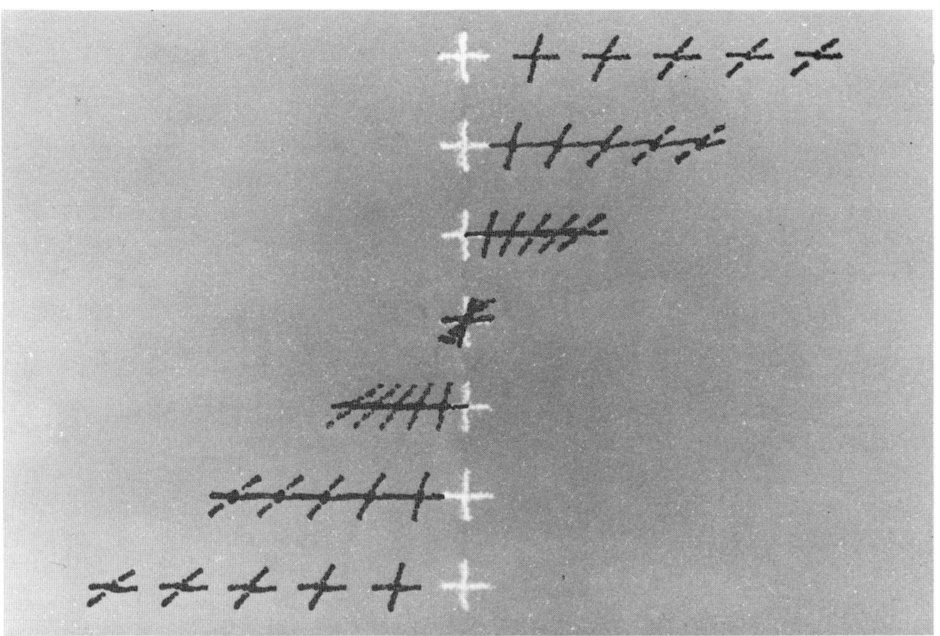

A row of crosses (in white) is initially dropped on the surface. The photograph is a composite of still frames at equal time intervals. The successive positions of the black crosses show the linear velocity profile, the vorticity, and the fluid deformation.

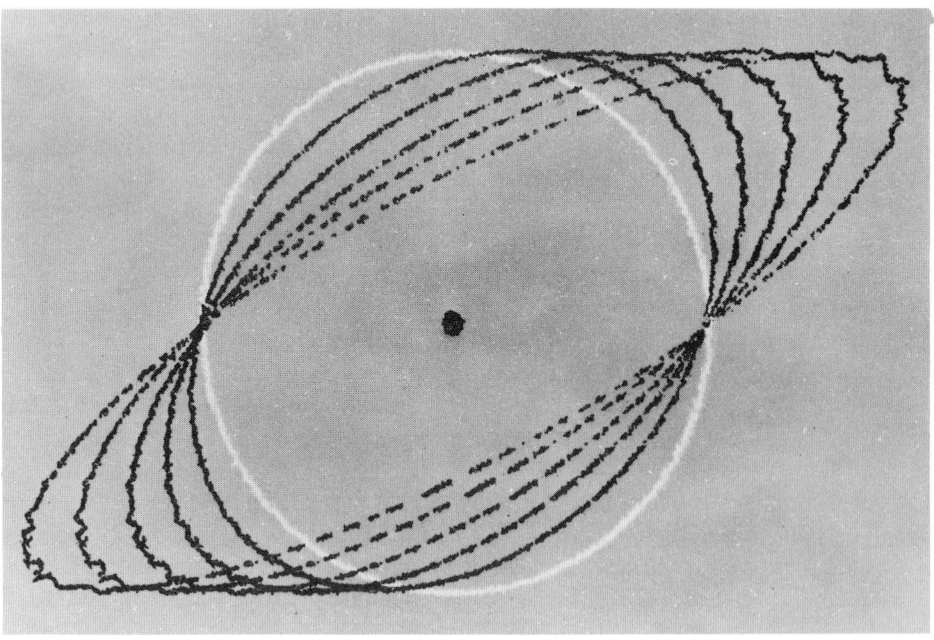

A circle in (white) is initially dropped on the surface. The photograph is a composite of still frames at equal time intervals. The successive positions of the distorted circle show the fluid rotation and the strain ellipse.

A two-dimensional linear Couette flow of glycerine is established between two moving belts having equal speeds in opposite directions. Using a silk-screen technique, various patterns of powder are dropped on the free surface.

Fig. 1. From "Kinematics of Deformation" (J. Lumley)

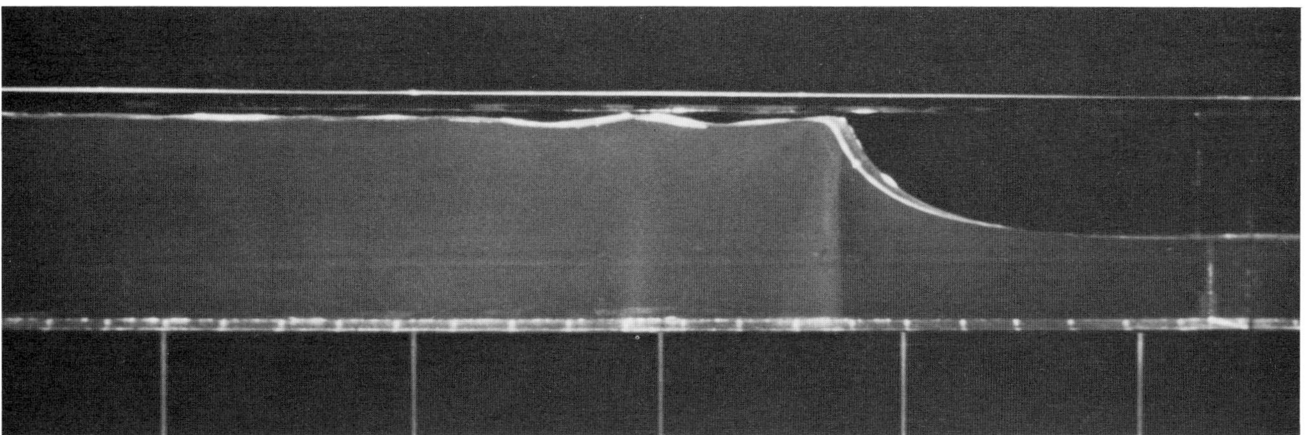

Steepening compression wave of finite amplitude.

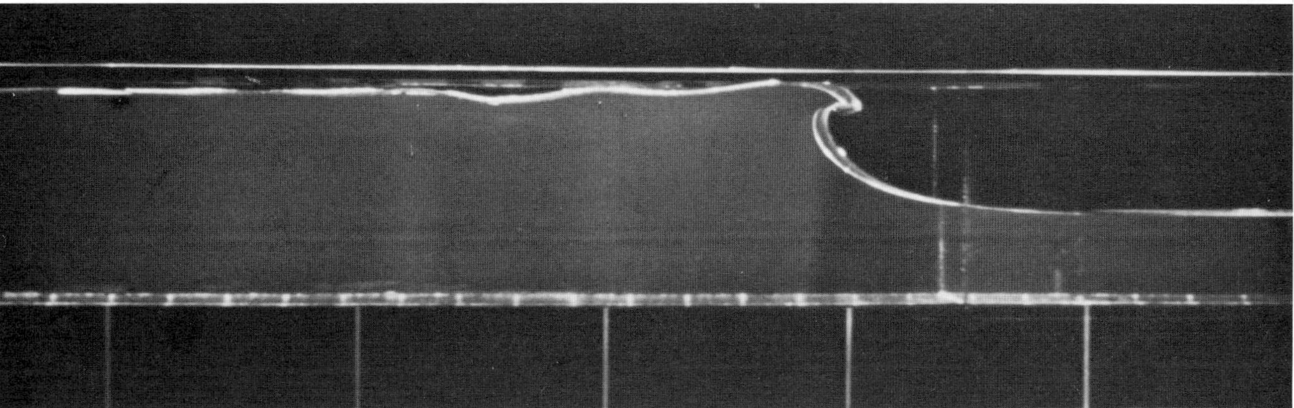

Toppling over of steepened compression wave as it tends toward a stationary surge wave.

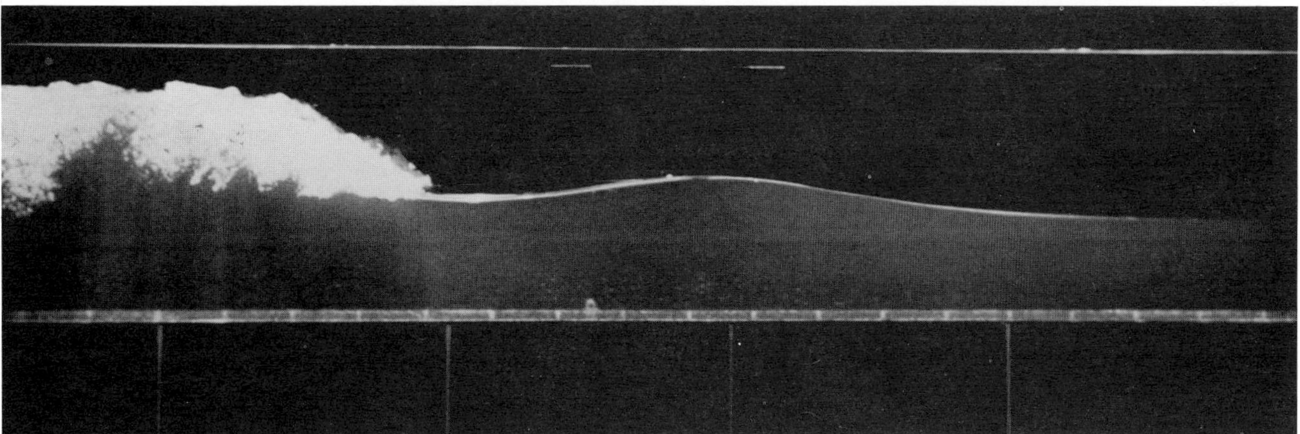

A surge wave of finite amplitude (at left) overtaking a wave of small amplitude (at center).

Propagation of gravity waves in a two-dimensional flume.

Fig. 2. From "Waves" (A. E. Bryson)

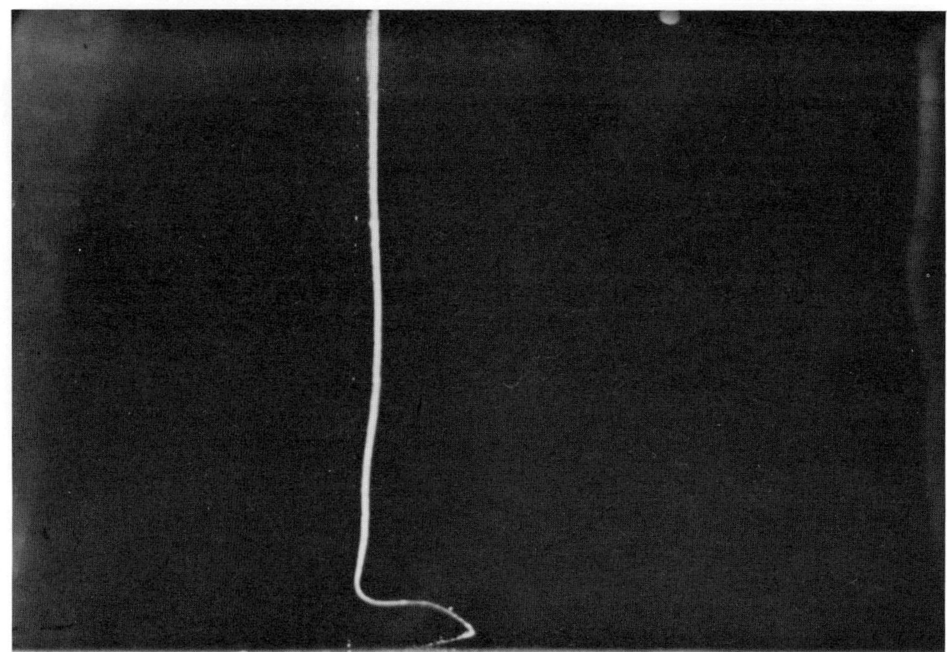

A view showing the radial velocity profile (the axis is off to the right). Secondary flow, radially inward, is seen in the viscous layer on the floor.

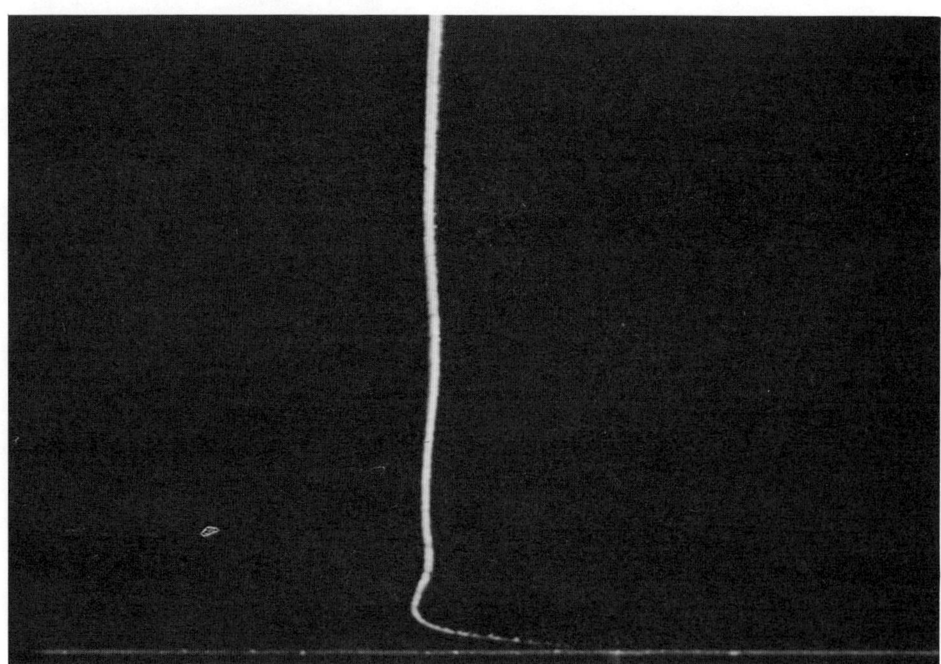

A view showing the circumferential velocity profile (the axis is behind the picture). The viscous layer near the floor is seen; the velocity at the end of the viscous layer is greater than that of the inviscid flow.

Demonstration of the "teacup effect" (tea leaves collecting at the middle). An open cylindrical tank of Plexiglas, filled with water, rotates on a turntable. When the water has reached a condition of solid-body rotation, the turntable is stopped. A vertical wire in the water emits, periodically, a fluid line of hydrogen bubbles.

Fig. 3. From "Secondary Flow" (E. S. Taylor)

An oblique view looking from upstream and above. The flow is toward the upper left. A reflection of the cylinder in the floor of the channel is visible. The vorticity in the shear layer is distorted into a horseshoe vortex.

A side view, illuminated in the mid-plane of the channel. The front of the cylinder is at the left.

A vertical circular cylinder stands in an open horizontal flume carrying water. There is a thick viscous boundary layer on the floor. A horizontal wire stretched across the channel, and in the viscous layer, sheds a continuous sheet of hydrogen bubbles.

Fig. 4. From "Secondary Flow" (E. S. Taylor)

A Newtonian fluid. The pressure increases with radius, owing to the centrifugal field.

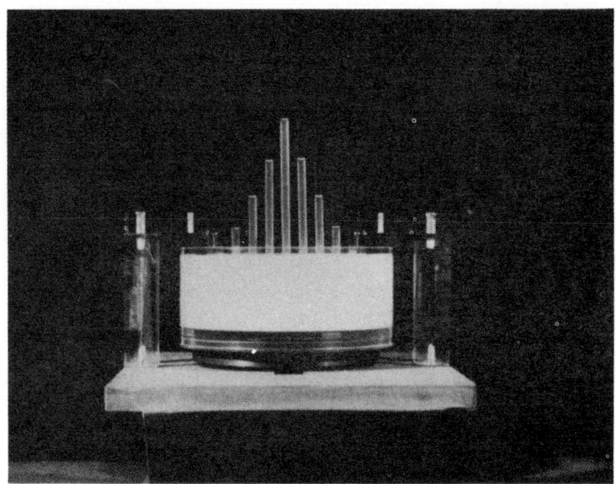

A fluid with non-linear behavior. The pressure decreases with radius, owing to the "normal stress" effect, which at the speed employed is much greater than the effect of the centrifugal field.

Illustration of the "normal stress" effect. A cylinder of fluid is contained between two circular plates. The lower plate is rotated by a turntable; the upper plate is stationary. Piezometer tubes in the upper plate show the pressure distribution.

Fig. 5. From "Rheological Behavior" (H. Markovitz)

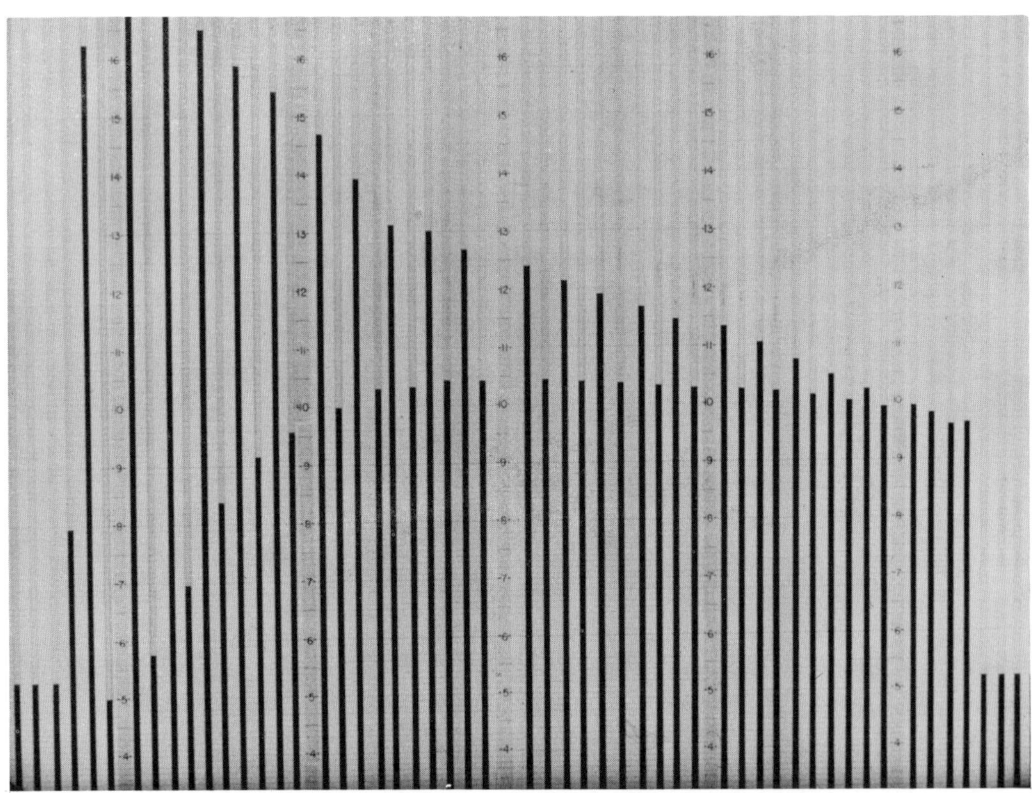

Pressure distributions on upper and lower surfaces of an aerofoil.

Fig. 6. From "Boundary Layer Control" (D. Hazen)

Upper surface is stalled because of excessive incidence.

At same incidence, stalling is prevented by boundary-layer suction through slots in upper surface.

Smoke streaklines past a two-dimensional aerofoil at high incidence.

Fig. 7. From "Boundary Layer Control" (D. Hazen)

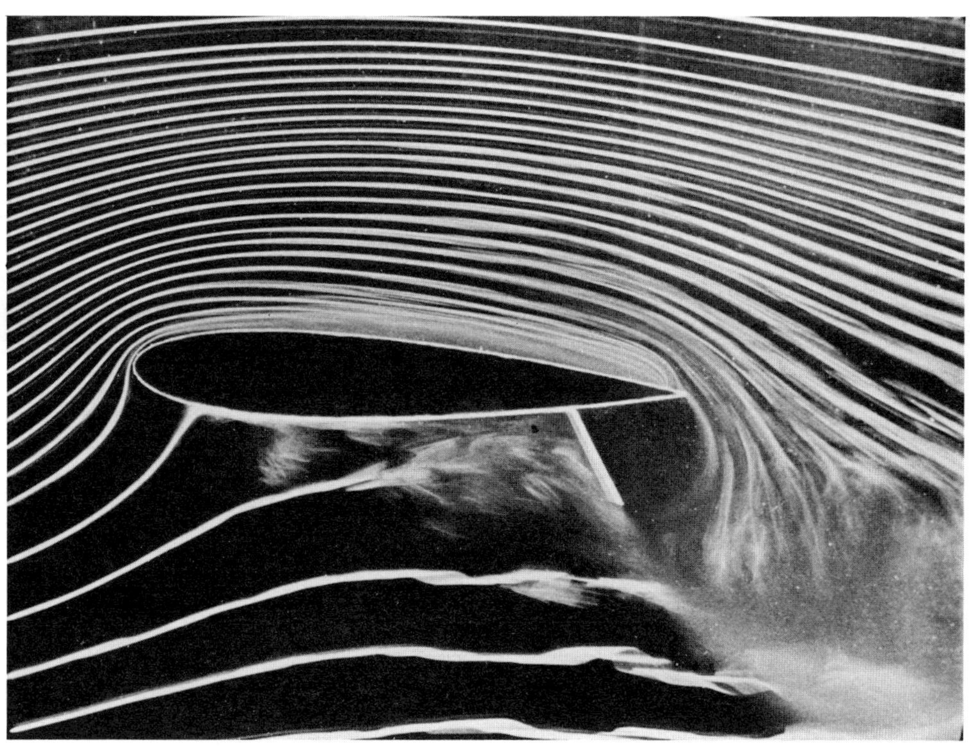

Smoke streaklines past a two-dimensional aerofoil with a high-lift flap. There is suction at a slot near the rear upper surface, and there is blowing near the flap.

Fig. 8. From "Boundary Layer Control" (D. Hazen)

No magnetic field. The jet is turbulent, and the protuberance is unsteady, propagating surface waves across the pool.

A vertical magnetic field is present (note edge of round pole face at top of picture). The transverse turbulent velocities in the jet cause eddy currents which damp the turbulent motion. The protuberance is smooth and unsteady, and the surface waves are nearly eliminated.

A submerged jet of mercury moves vertically upward through a pool of mercury, producing a protuberance above the free surface.

Fig. 9. From "Magnetohydrodynamics" (J. A. Shercliff)

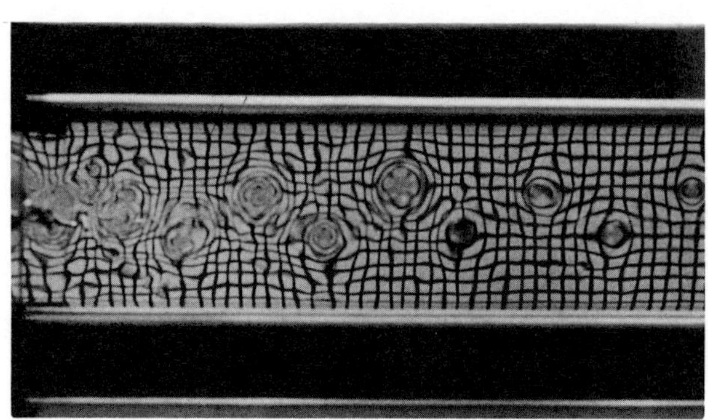

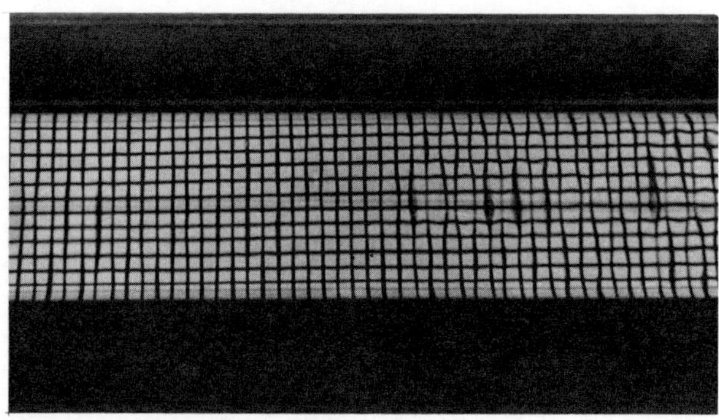

No magnetic field. The plate has passed out of view at the right, leaving a trail of vortices.

A transverse field is applied, normal to the plate motion and to the axes of the vortices. The induced currents, and the corresponding Lorentz forces, destroy the vorticity.

A long narrow trough contains mercury with a free surface. The free surface of the mercury is used as a mirror to reflect a square grid of lines. Distortion of the grid gives an impression of heights and depression in the free surface. A flat plate is drawn at steady speed from left to right through the mercury, the plate being normal to the motion.

Fig. 10. From "Magnetohydrodynamics" (J. A. Shercliff)

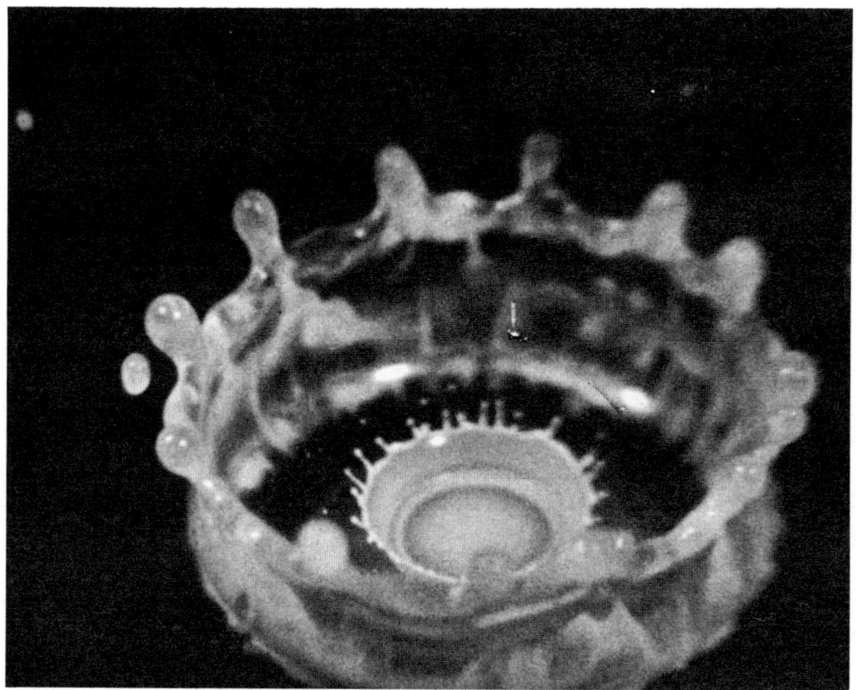

Two coronets are formed in succession. Capillary instability causes the rims to break up into droplets.

At a later stage, a rod of liquid is thrust up. Again capillary instability causes jet break-up, and one droplet is tossed free.

High-speed photography of a drop of milk falling into a glass of water.

Fig. 11. From "Surface Tension" (L. Trefethen)

experimenter-actor, and who holds technical responsibility. In addition, each film has an advisory committee which provides ideas and constructive criticism and which takes responsibility for approval of the film prior to release.

The film production program of the N.C.F.M.F. falls into two categories: "major" films, and "cartridge loops." These are discussed separately.

Major Films

Major films are 16 mm sound films, approximately 30 minutes in length, each aimed towards a concept, a topic area, or a theme in fluid mechanics.

Table 1 shows, in various categories of progress, the entire program of some 25 "major" films which we envisage.

Figs 1-20 are still photographs selected from films in release or in production.

Cartridge Loops

Cartridge loops are four-minute, silent clips of 8 mm film loaded permanently into a plastic cartridge that fits the Technicolor Cartridge Projector. The projector is light and small, and simple to operate. One merely pushes the cartridge into a slot in the projector, and turns the "On" switch. Neither threading nor rewinding is necessary.

The "cartridge loops," so called, while serving the same purposes as the "major" films, obviously are to be used in a different way.

The 30-minute sound film treats its subject at length; it can include a number of experiments, integrated by a common theme. The four-minute silent film, on the other hand, is basically a single demonstration with little explanation. For spot use to illustrate particular points in a lecture, the cartridge loop is ideal. It also provides food for argument and discussion.

We think that the major film and the cartridge loop are complementary to each other. Both are useful.

We have thus far released 35 cartridge loops. Some 50 more are in production, and ultimately we anticipate a total number in the neighborhood of 160.

Problems of Educational Film-Making

Film production is an uncommon venture for academics. We have had to learn much, and of course we grossly underestimated most of the difficulties.

Those individuals who have been asked to serve as principals have, with surprisingly few exceptions, agreed enthusiastically to take on the job. But the job is not a minor one. The demands on time and energy are unexpectedly large. To be effective, the principal must make substantial room in his professional life for the effort required by the project.

Experimental apparatus that has been developed for research purposes is, almost categorically, unsuitable for use in an educational film. It is too cluttered with wires, pipes, and instruments, and the most important part of the apparatus may hardly show at all. Furthermore, a piece of experimental research may be most elegant and

Table 1. Major films: 16 mm; sound; about 30 minutes

Film	Principal
1. Films in release	
THE FLUID DYNAMICS OF DRAG	A. H. Shapiro, Massachusetts Institute of Technology
VORTICITY	A. H. Shapiro, Massachusetts Institute of Technology
FLOW VISUALIZATION	S. J. Kline, Stanford University
DEFORMATION OF CONTINUOUS MEDIA	J. Lumley, Pennsylvania State University
PRESSURE FIELDS AND FLUID ACCELERATION	A. H. Shapiro, Massachusetts Institute of Technology
SURFACE TENSION IN FLUID MECHANICS	L. M. Trefethen, Tufts University
WAVES IN FLUIDS	A. E. Bryson, Harvard University
SECONDARY FLOW	E. S. Taylor, Massachusetts Institute of Technology
RHEOLOGICAL BEHAVIOR OF FLUIDS	H. Markovitz, Mellon Institute
2. Films in advanced editing stages	
BOUNDARY LAYER CONTROL	D. Hazen, Princeton University
MAGNETOHYDRODYNAMICS	J. A. Shercliff, University of Warwick
CHANNEL FLOW OF A COMPRESSIBLE FLUID	D. Coles, California Institute of Technology
3. Films in active production	
LOW-REYNOLDS-NUMBER FLOWS	G. I. Taylor, Cambridge University
FLOW INSTABILITIES	E. L. Mollo-Christensen, Massachusetts Institute of Technology
EULERIAN AND LAGRANGIAN DESCRIPTIONS	J. Lumley, Pennsylvania State University
FUNDAMENTALS OF BOUNDARY LAYERS	F. Abernathy, Harvard University
RAREFIED GAS DYNAMICS	F. Sherman and F. Hurlbut, University of California (Berkeley)
4. Films in early stages of production	
STRATIFIED FLUIDS AND OPEN CHANNEL FLOW	R. R. Long, The Johns Hopkins University
FLUID MOTION IN ROTATING SYSTEMS	D. Fultz, University of Chicago
CAVITATION	P. Eisenberg, Hydronautics, Inc.
SOUND GENERATION AND FLUID MOTION	M. J. Lighthill, University of London
5. Other films to be produced (tentative)	
TURBULENCE	FORCES ON BODIES
SUPERSONIC GAS DYNAMICS	FREE CONVECTION

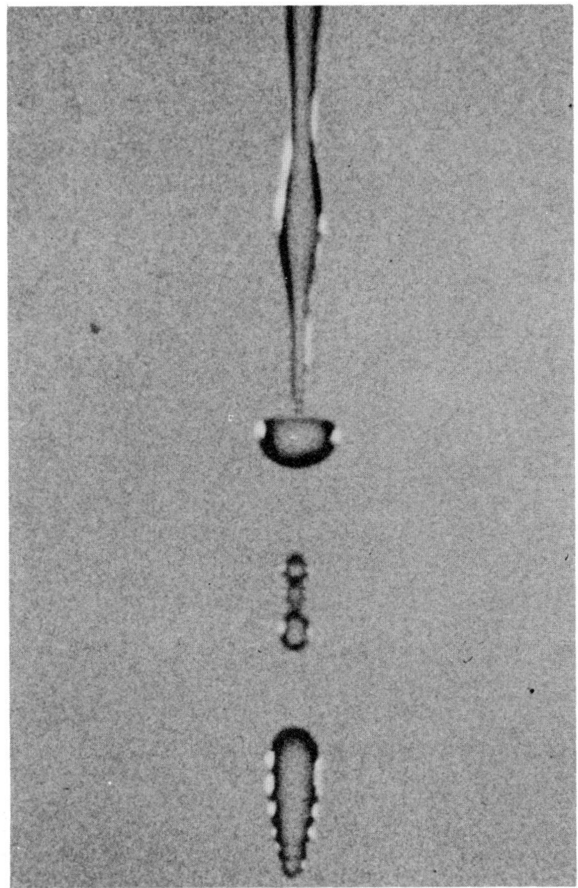

Capillary instablity of a liquid cylinder causes a falling liquid jet to execute oscillatory swellings of increasing amplitude, leading to break-up into drops. Viewed with high-speed photography.

Fig. 12. From "Surface Tension" (L. Trefethen)

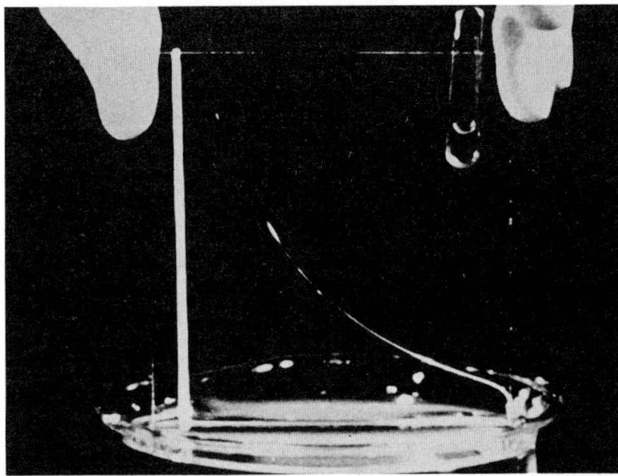

Two glass plates, clamped with a rubber band at the right, are separated by a paper clip at the left, thus forming a wedge-shaped air gap. When the plates are dipped into soap solution and then withdrawn, the capillary rise produces a hyperbolic free surface.

Fig. 13. From "Surface Tension" (L. Trefethen)

interesting yet unsuited to the elucidation of fundamentals for the beginner. In brief, the experiments, and to a large degree the experimental apparatus, for an educational film have to be developed from scratch. On the screen, the demonstration apparatus should be instantly comprehensible, the audience's attention should go immediately to the significant area, and the phenomenon to be displayed should appear bold and clean, without the myriad side effects to which fluid mechanics experiments are prone. The practiced experimentalist soon discovers that it is as difficult to create a clean demonstration of a fundamental concept as it is to do a piece of quantitative research. The less complicated the action on the screen, the greater usually has been the experimental effort. New techniques have been developed as being especially suitable for visual demonstration. The hydrogen bubble method of flow visualization has been greatly advanced, and has been effectively used in several films. The sodium resonance technique is being developed for visualization of low-density gas flows. In "Eulerian and Lagrangian Descriptions," all the fluid motions are programmed on a computer; most of the film will be shots of the scope face.

As a good lecture differs in style from a good book, so a good film differs from both. In the film, the visual takes precedence over the aural. In one's first try at script writing, on the contrary, there is a tendency to neglect altogether the image on the screen. It takes some practice with style to achieve a written script which is in correct relation to the visual action. The demonstration-experiment film is also characterized by a rapid pace which makes for great compression. Perhaps most troublesome to the academic is that he may not turn to mathematics to do the explaining for him. The story line must be so organized that all the physical phenomena can be explained in simple verbal language. To do this is no mean feat of composition or thought. It requires a most discerning attention to what, after all, *are* the fundamentals of the subject. One principal described the successive stages of script writing as 'a chastening experience'. Needless to say, each film exhibits an individual style, dictated by the subject matter and by the personality and interests of the principal.

Production of cartridge loops would appear to be nothing more than splicing together various pieces of action footage, with a few silent titles of explanation. We have learned instead that, even given suitable action footage, good cartridge loops are challengingly difficult to produce within the limitations of four minutes and no sound.

Audience Reaction

Both the use of our films and the comments that have been submitted to us indicate that there is indeed a large audience which will accept and use demonstration-experiment films in fluid mechanics. In the first two years after "Vorticity" was released, nearly 100 prints had been sold or placed in university or government repositories; over and above this, there were loans to a number exceeding 500. Most purchases were by universities in the U.S.A., but about 20 per cent were by universities abroad, and about 5 per cent by industry and government. In the loan category, about half went to universities in the U.S.A., and about half to industry and government, with a sprinkling going abroad.

During the first year after 10 cartridge loops had been released, the total sales were in the neighborhood of 1500.

Only recently have a substantial number of films been in release. The experience of the next year will therefore be most interesting as regards absorption of the films into the educational procedure.

Already, however, several influences not fully anticipated have been attributed to the films. The large extent of industrial interest and use has been surprising. To student audiences, a variety of personalities, each a leader in his subject and with an individual style, has been reported as refreshing and instructive, in some cases perhaps inspirational. A wide variety of examples, graphically depicted, and extending beyond what is possible with words alone in a lecture course, does indeed open the student mind to the scope of the subject. Because film, with its double impact of sight and sound, can effect wonders of compression, topics that might be diffused through weeks of a lecture course may be brought into close juxtaposition, and thereby synthesized or contrasted. Even the simplest demonstrations in fluid mechanics convey the inherent complexity of fluid motions; without explicit exhortation, therefore,

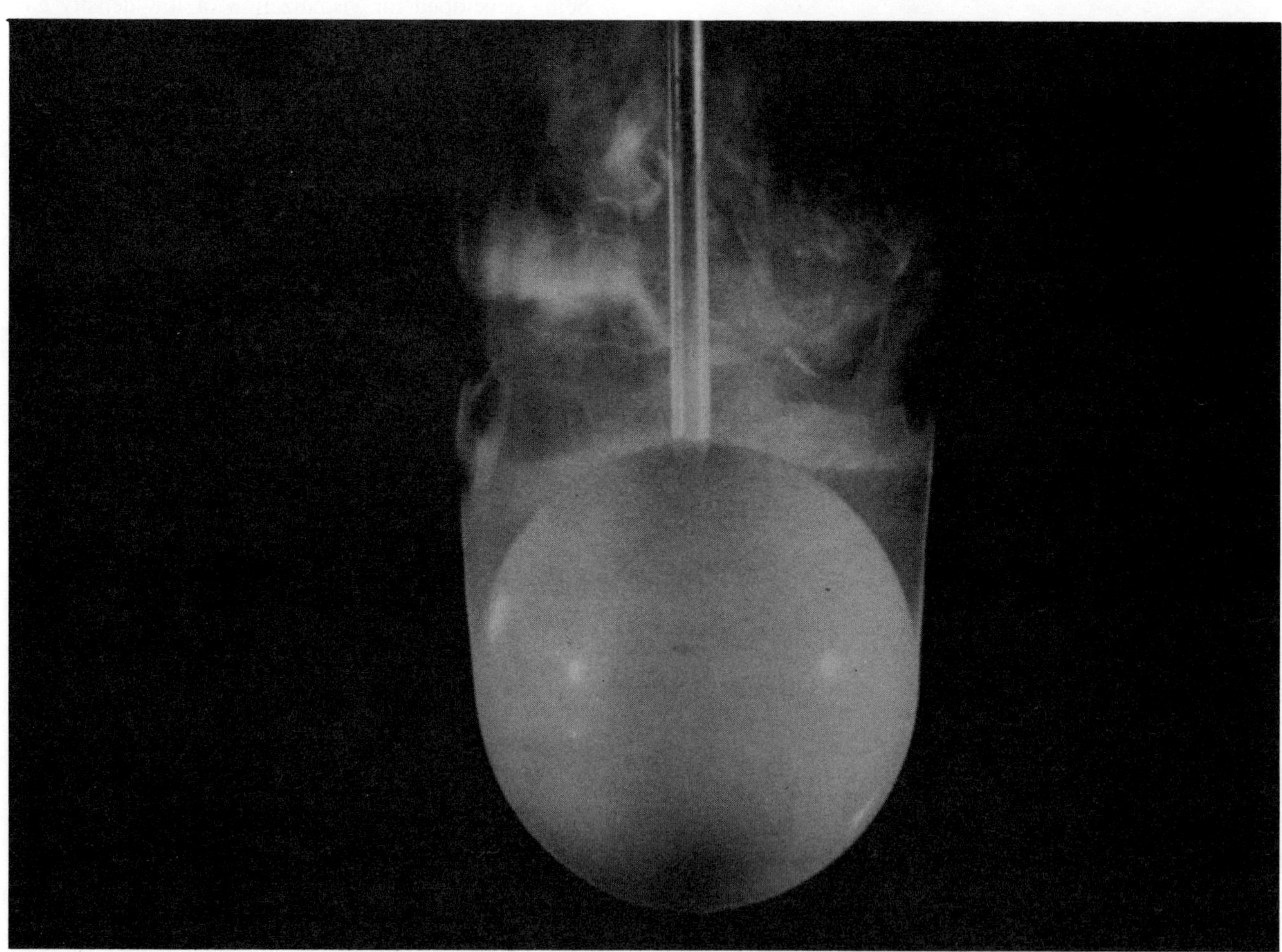

Separated flow past a sphere is visualized by titanium tetrachloride smoke issuing from a droplet at nose.

Fig. 14. From "Fluid Dynamics of Drag" (A. H. Shapiro)

the point comes through clearly: fluid motions are often so unforeseeable that without suggestive and critical experiments we could not develop a meaningful theory. This realization, brought home forcefully, seems to arouse in students interest in the experimental side of the subject.

How Should Film Be Used?

If educational films are indeed to be used in the university, we must face the question: *how* should they be used? Most lecturers seem to think automatically of showing film as part of the lecture. This makes good sense for the four-minute interpolation of the cartridge loop. But a half-hour film with sound would seem as inappropriate in a lecture as would reciting from a book for half an hour. It is better, we know, to send the student to the library to read the book. Would it not also be better to send the student to the library to see the film? After all, the book and the film both represent ways of permanently recording information, using mechanical means of replication.

The trouble, of course, is that while the technology of books is relatively simple and is perfected, the technology of film use is relatively complicated, comparatively expensive, and by no means perfected.

But new developments are sure to come soon. Al-

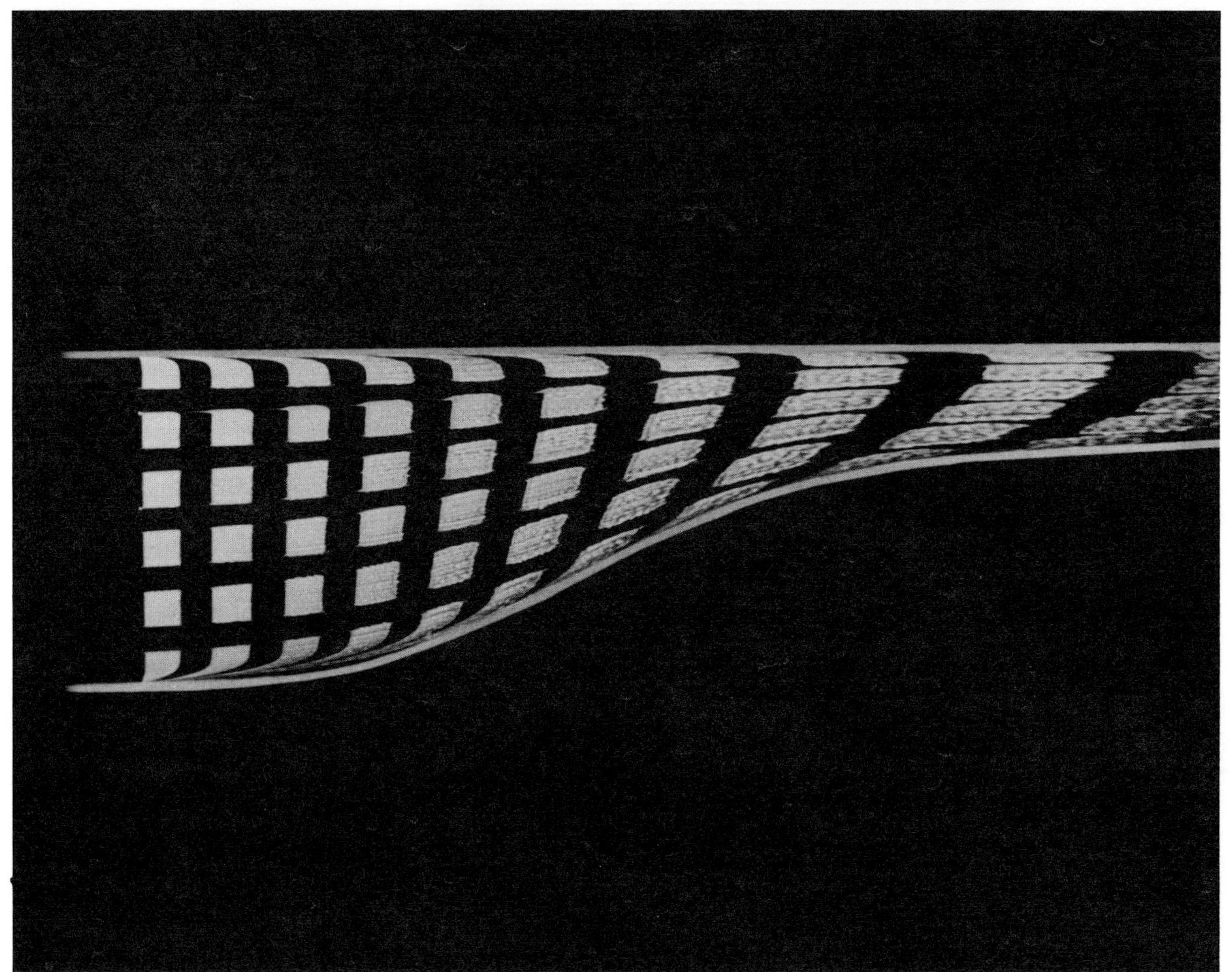

Water flows from left to right in a two-dimensional contraction. Hydrogen bubbles are electrolysed at a wire stretched across the channel at the left. The wire has sections alternately insulated and uninsulated, and the current is pulsed. The sequence of square fluid elements marked by bubbles shows streamlines, transverse fluid lines, integrated displacement, local velocities and fluid deformations.

Fig. 15. From "Flow Visualization" (S. J. Kline)

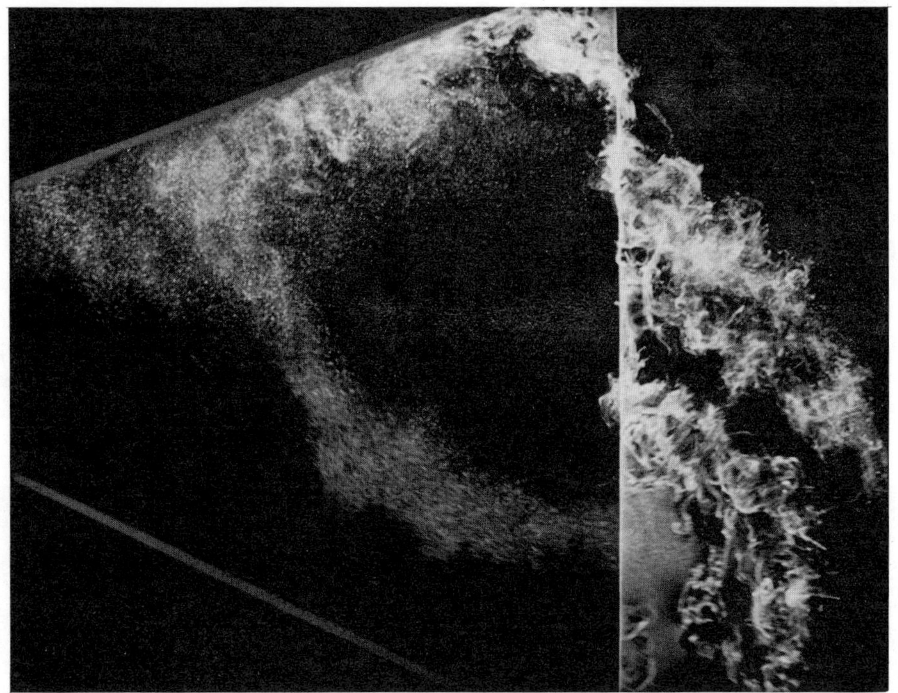

The flow separates at one wall because of the excessive angles of divergence.

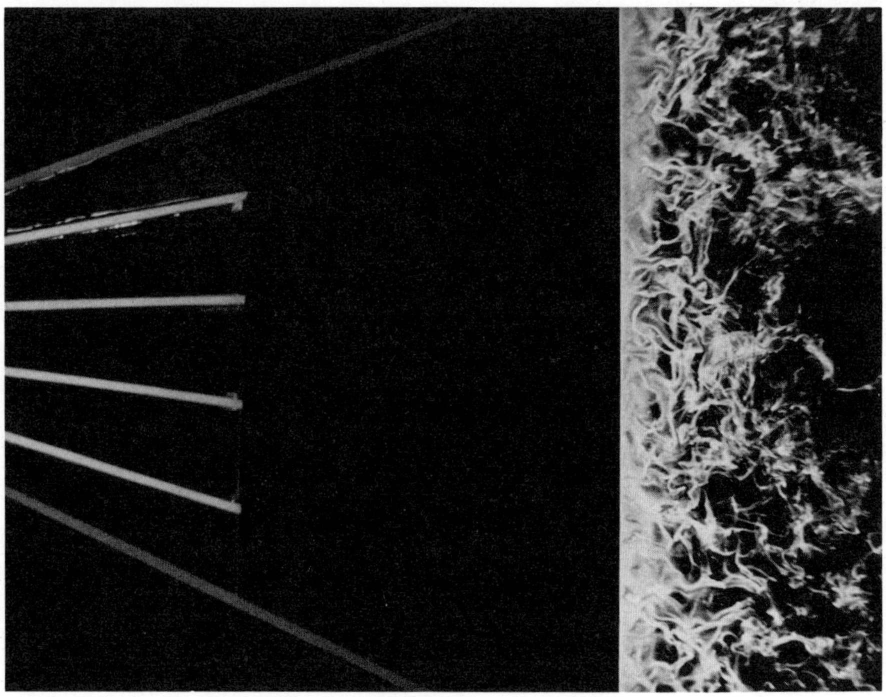

The flow separation is eliminated by short vanes of appropriate design.
Water flows from left to right in a two-dimensional wide-angle diffuser. Hydrogen bubbles electrolysed at a wire show the flow.

Fig. 16. From "Flow Visualization" (S. J. Kline)

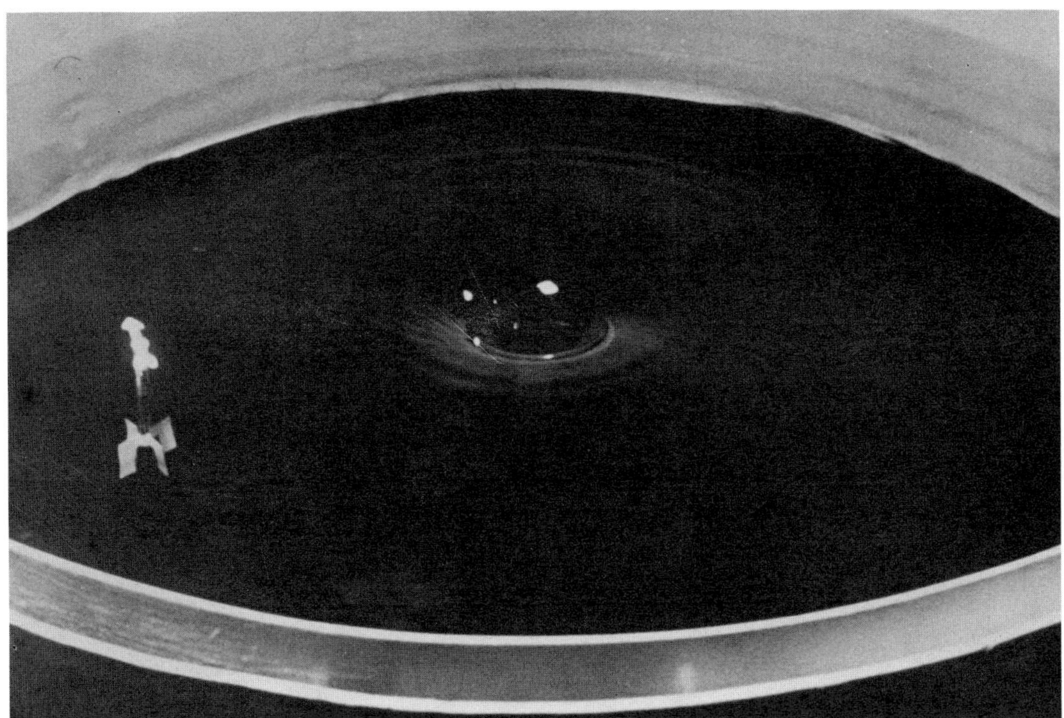

A potential sink-vortex flow—the vorticity meter, containing four crossed vanes in the water and an indicating arrow above the water surface, moves in circles in pure translation, thus illustrating the irrotational character of the flow.

Fig. 17. From "Vorticity" (A. H. Shapiro)

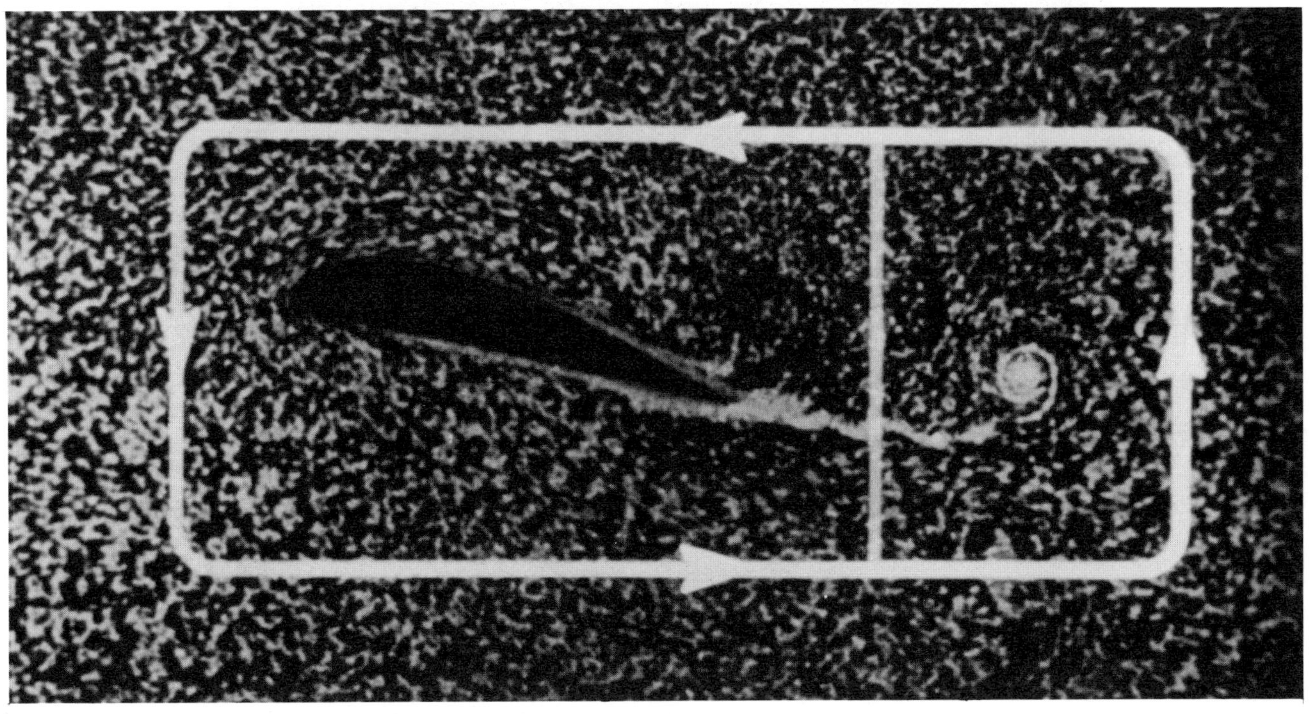

An aerofoil started in impulsive motion sheds a starting vortex. (The overlay is to illustrate various circuits for which the circulation is reckoned.)

Fig. 18. From "Vorticity" (A. H. Shapiro)—this scene was adapted from a film by L. Prandtl

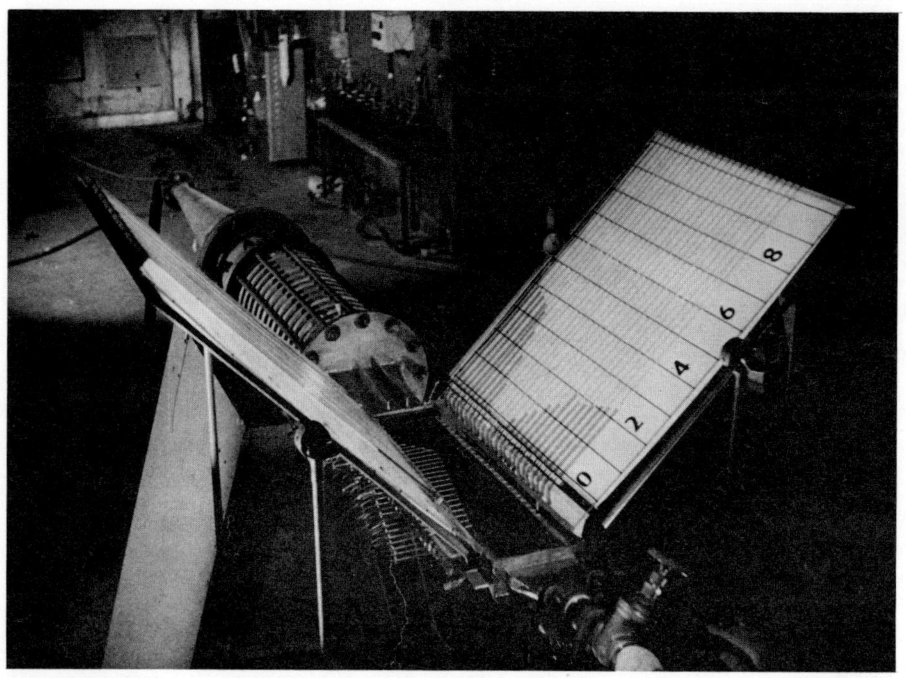

(1) General view, showing inclined manometer boards. Flow enters channel at upper left.

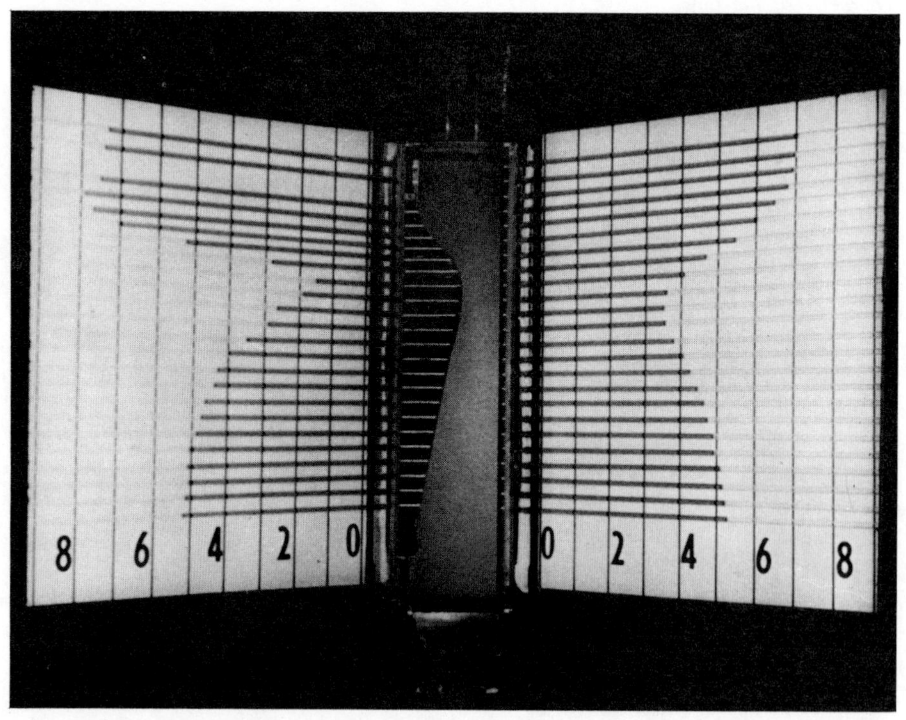

(1) View from above, showing pressure distributions on straight and curved walls.

Flow through a two-dimensional venturi with one straight wall.

Fig. 19. From "Pressure Fields and Fluid Acceleration" (A. H. Shapiro)

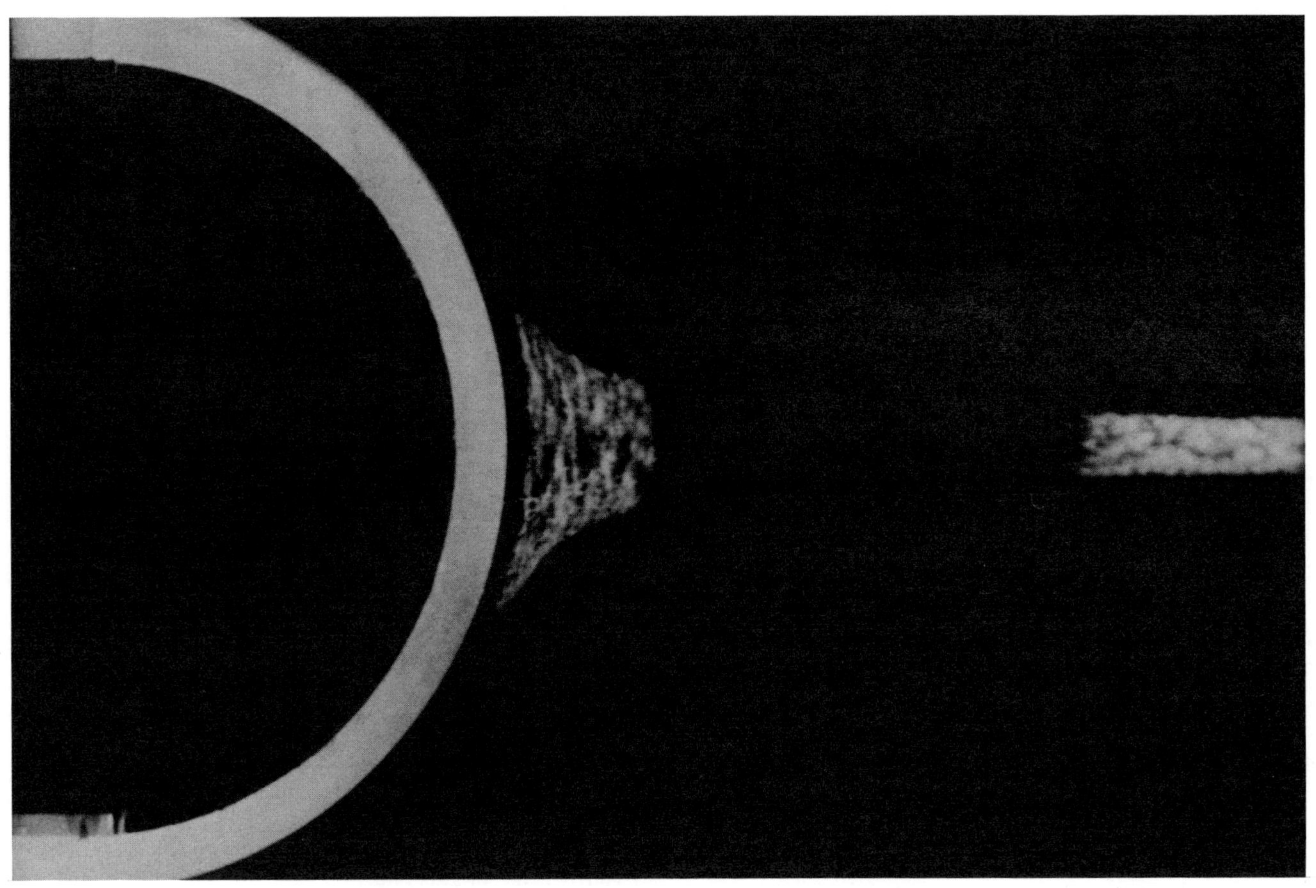

Hydrogen bubble patches approaching a stagnation point.

Fig. 20. From "Pressure Fields and Fluid Acceleration" (A. H. Shapiro)

ready the Technicolor Cartridge Projector has made the four-minute silent cartridge loop almost as convenient to use as a book. With library use in mind the N.C.F.M.F. provides for each cartridge loop a sturdy box with the usual information on the spine, so that it may be set like a book on the library shelf. On the inside covers of the box is printed explanatory written matter relating to the loop. At several universities in the U.S.A., the loop cartridges with a projector are made available at the library, to be looked at either in a screening cubicle or with a special sound-proofed screening box.

At least one commercial company in the U.S.A. has started pilot production of a projector handling sound films loaded in cartridges. The cartridge holds from 20 minutes to 30 minutes of film. The sound may be heard either from a loudspeaker or through earphones, and the image appears on a built-in screen. It is easy to imagine rows of projectors such as these on library tables, with students sitting before them, each studying a different film.

Today it is no novelty to see in libraries facilities for listening to gramophone records which may be borrowed from the lending desk. Let us hope that as educational films become available in quantity, the technology of projection equipment will make possible similar library facilities for film, and that libraries will be forward-looking enough to plan ahead for this eventuality. Then the lecturer will be able to assign to his students, for outside study, not only readings in texts and problems for exercise, but also films to be seen.

THE SEMICONDUCTOR ELECTRONICS EDUCATION COMMITTEE

by Campbell L. Searle

1. *The Nature of the Problem*

Prior to 1960, very few colleges had adequate courses at the undergraduate level in semiconductor electronics. In many schools, the entire subject of transistors was taught in two or three weeks chiselled out of a course in vacuum tube electronics. The reason for this inadequate treatment was directly connected with the rapid growth of the transistor in the '50's: within ten years of its invention in 1948, the transistor had assumed a dominant position in many areas of electronics research. In a field which has such a phenomenal growth rate as this, it is exceedingly difficult for university professors to keep abreast of the developments, let alone to have time to synthesize the material into a form suitable for teaching to undergraduates.

2. *The Committee*

In the fall of 1960, a group of us at M.I.T., after studying the difficulties of teaching semiconductor electronics, concluded first that the problem was national in scope: almost all engineering schools in the country were having the same difficulty teaching this material. Second, we concluded that to solve this problem we would have to appeal for broad technical support, because it was clear that a tremendous breadth of technical knowledge would be required in order to produce uniform, high-quality teaching materials. It was essential to obtain strong support both from other universities and from industrial organizations active in the field. Industrial representation on the committee was particularly important because only industrial members could provide information on present practice and future trends in semiconductor circuit and device design.

To this end, in February 1961 we formed the Semiconductor Electronics Education Committee (SEEC), and subsequently obtained support from the Ford Foundation and the National Science Foundation, and began working under the aegis of Educational Services Incorporated. It is of course impossible to list all the people who contributed in some way to the SEEC. However those listed in Table 1 have either been active in the Committee since its inception or have made major contributions since then.

Table 1

From Universities

California, Berkeley: D. O. Pederson
Imperial College, London: A. R. Boothroyd
Iowa State: H. L. Ablin*
M.I.T.: R. B. Adler, P. E. Gray, A. L. McWhorter, C. L. Searle, A. C. Smith, R. D. Thornton, J. R. Zacharias, H. J. Zimmermann (Research Laboratory of Electronics), J. N. Harris (Lincoln Laboratory)
Minnesota: E. R. Chenette
New Mexico: W. W. Grannemann
Polytechnic Institute of Brooklyn: E. J. Angelo, Jr.
Stanford: J. F. Gibbons, J. G. Linvill
U.C.L.A.: J. Willis

From Industries

Bell Telephone Laboratories: J. M. Early, A. N. Holden, V. R. Saari
Fairchild Semiconductor: V. R. Grinich
IBM: D. DeWitt
RCA: J. Hilibrand, E. O. Johnson, J. I. Pankove
Transistron: B. Dale**, H. G. Rudenberg†
Westinghouse Research Laboratories: A. I. Bennett, H. C. Lin, R. L. Longini‡

*Now at the University of Nebraska, Department of Electrical Engineering
**Now at Sylvania Corporation
†Now at A. D. Little, Inc.
‡Now at Carnegie Institute of Technology, Department of Electrical Engineering

3. *Basic Philosophy*

In the course of many meetings during the fall of 1960

Professor Searle is Chairman of the Semiconductor Electronics Education Committee. He is a professor of electrical engineering at the Massachusetts Institute of Technology.

and the spring of 1961, a quite specific philosophy evolved.

(1) The course was to be specifically designed for use at the third year college level, although we recognized that parts of the material would also be suitable for fourth year or graduate level, as well as for in-plant training in industry.

(2) It was definitely not to be a first course in electronics. We assumed therefore that the students would have already completed courses in linear circuit theory and introductory electronics.

(3) The course was to be taught concurrently with an existing third-year course in quantum mechanics.

(4) It was clear that the course could not possibly cover all semiconductor devices, without degenerating into a survey presentation, so we decided to concentrate on the transistor as a representative semiconductor device. The physics presentation therefore was to be just sufficient to make the student feel comfortable with those properties of semiconductors which bear directly on transistor performance.

It was agreed, however, that a "sufficient" presentation of transistor physics would involve much more than a two-lecture broad-brush treatment. The transistor is fundamentally a more complicated device than the vacuum tube in that its performance in a circuit is more dependent on ambient temperature, dc voltage and dc current. Thus in dealing with the transistor we are forced to develop models that are not only convenient to work with from the point of view of circuit analysis, but also at the same time are closely related to the physical processes going on inside the transistor. Only in this will the parameters in the models be a relatively simple and predictable function of voltage, current and temperature.

Other factors also reinforce this conclusion about teaching semiconductor physics. To describe the behavior of transistor switching circuits, it is essential to have a fundamental understanding of the physics of the device, because no simple circuit model has yet been devised which adequately describes transistor switching behavior. Also, the advent of integrated circuits has in effect blurred the dividing line between the device and the circuit in such a way that it is essential for circuit designers to have quite specific knowledge concerning the problems of semiconductor device design.

These decisions lead us to some fairly definite conclusions about the format. To cover the broad range of topics, a combination of the text material, laboratory experiments, and films (that is, similar to the PSSC) would be required. To meet the varying needs of different schools, we decided to publish the material as a series of paperbacks rather than one or two large hardbound books. This format was also well suited for industrial use and well suited for multiple authorship, (the latter being essential in order to obtain uniform high quality of coverage over a broad range of topics).

4. *How the Project was Carried Out*

Most of the writing of text material took place in the course of three workshops, during the summers of 1961, 1962 and 1963 at the Wayland High School, Wayland, Massachusetts. Professors Adler, Thornton, Gray and myself worked approximately three months full time during each of these summers, while various other members of the Committee joined the workshops for periods ranging from three to six weeks. Full-scale "feedback meetings" of the Committee were held twice a year to make overall policy decisions, and discuss and evaluate teaching trials taking place at various schools and industrial organizations. Including time spent during each academic year (September through June), approximately ten man–years of effort have been invested in this program from February, 1961 to June, 1965.

4.(*a*) *Texts*

The list of SEEC text books, together with a brief description of the contents of each is given on page 200. Much of the text material has passed through two preliminary editions, SEEC Notes I and SEEC Notes II. In fact, substantial amounts of the material in Volumes 1 and 2 appeared in a "pre-preliminary edition" in 1961, and was taught during the spring term of 1962 to a group of thirty M.I.T. seniors.

First preliminary editions (SEEC Notes I) of the first five books were prepared in 1962, and used for trial teaching at twelve universities. Feedback meetings were then held in February and July of 1963 to evaluate these trials. On the basis of these evaluations, the Second Preliminary Editions (SEEC Notes II) of Books 1, 2, 3, 5, and 6 were prepared during the summer and fall of 1963 (Book 5 of SEEC Notes I was organized into two books: Book 5 of SEEC Notes II dealt only with multistage linear circuits and Book

6 of SEEC Notes II contained the material on digital circuits). In addition, a seventh book appeared, which contained a wide variety of circuits for use in laboratory experiments. This book is discussed in more detail in Section 4(b) below. All of these books were again used in trial teaching during the academic year 1963-64, this time at fifteen academic institutions and three industrial organizations. The following institutions in the academic and industrial communities used one or more of the preliminary editions:

BELL TELEPHONE LABORATORIES, INC.
BRADLEY UNIVERSITY
UNIVERSITY OF CALIFORNIA, BERKELEY
CARNEGIE INSTITUTE OF TECHNOLOGY
CASE INSTITUTE OF TECHNOLOGY
GEORGIA INSTITUTE OF TECHNOLOGY
IMPERIAL COLLEGE
IBM CORPORATION
IOWA STATE UNIVERSITY
MASSACHUSETTS INSTITUTE OF TECHNOLOGY
UNIVERSITY OF MICHIGAN
UNIVERSITY OF MINNESOTA
NEW YORK UNIVERSITY
NORTHEASTERN UNIVERSITY
POLYTECHNIC INSTITUTE OF BROOKLYN
PURDUE UNIVERSITY
RCA SEMICONDUCTOR AND MATERIALS DIVISION
UNIVERSITY OF RHODE ISLAND

On the basis of these teaching trials, final manuscript copy was prepared for Volumes 1, 2 and 3 during the spring and summer of 1964. These three books are now available from John Wiley and Sons, both in paperback and hardbound form. Sales figures so far have been encouraging, amounting to approximately 800 copies per month for each book. During the fall of 1964 and spring of 1965, final manuscripts have been prepared for Volumes 4, 5, 6 and 7.

4.(b) Laboratory

During the 1962 summer workshop, a major breakthrough was made by Brian Dale and David DeWitt in the preparation of undergraduate laboratory materials in the area of semiconductor physics. Specifically, six experiments were prepared on such topics as resistivity, Hall Effect, drift mobility, etc., which could be performed using commercially available germanium bars and non-toxic chemicals. Thus the experiments are safe enough to be performed without special facilities. Detailed write-ups of each of these experiments are now included in the Appendix at the end of Volume I.

The Committee felt that the circuits laboratory material to accompany this course should not present detailed laboratory write-ups. Most schools had adequate instrumentation to perform transistor circuits labs, and required only some guidance in the selection of appropriate circuits. To this end, therefore, the Committee has prepared a seventh book in the series, entitled "Handbook of Basic Transistor Circuits and Measurements," which presents a large number of simple circuits to be used as "raw material" for laboratory experiments. Some indications of the types of transistors (high speed or low speed, germanium or silicon) are indicated on the circuit diagrams. All circuits in the book have been built and tested by students in the course of the last two summer workshops.

4.(c) Films

Three 16 mm. sound films have been prepared by the Committee. These films are listed in Table 2 below. Pending arrangements for commercial distribution, the films are available for purchase or rental directly from Educational Services Incorporated, 37 Galen Street, Watertown, Massachusetts. The first two films are designed to be shown in connection with Volume 1, and the third film is tied closely to the material in Volume 2. Footnotes at appropriate points in the text indicate approximate places where the films can be shown.

Table 2

MINORITY CARRIERS IN SEMICONDUCTORS, by Richard Haynes, Bell Telephone Laboratories, Incorporated, and William Shockley, Shockley Laboratories, Clevite, Incorporated. (16 mm. sound, black and white)

GAP ENERGY AND RECOMBINATION LIGHT IN GERMANIUM, by Jacques I. Pankove, RCA Laboratories, Incorporated, and Richard B. Adler, Massachusetts Institute of Technology. (16 mm. sound, black and white)

TRANSISTOR STRUCTURE AND TECHNOLOGY, by James M. Early, Bell Telephone Laboratories Incorporated, and Richard D. Thornton, Massachusetts Institute of Technology. (16 mm. sound, color)

SEEC Text Books

Volume 1

Introduction to Semiconductor Physics

By R. B. ADLER, Massachusetts Institute of Technology; A. C. SMITH, Massachusetts Institute of Technology; and R. L. LONGINI, Carnegie Institute of Technology.

CONTENTS

THE VALENCE BOND MODEL OF A SEMICONDUCTOR
THE ENERGY-BAND MODEL OF A SEMICONDUCTOR
THE EQUILIBRIUM DISTRIBUTION OF ELECTRONS IN THE BANDS
NONEQUILIBRIUM TRANSPORT OF CHARGE CARRIERS
APPENDIX: LABORATORY EXPERIMENTS

Volume 2

Physical Electronics and Circuit Models of Transistors

By P. E. GRAY, Massachusetts Institute of Technology; D.

DEWITT, IBM Corporation; A. R. BOOTHROYD, Queen's University, Belfast; and J. F. GIBBONS, Stanford University.

CONTENTS

Semiconductor Junction Devices. Physical Operation of pn-Junction Diodes. The dc Behavior of pn-Junction Diodes. Other Effects in pn-Junction Diodes. Dynamic Behavior of pn-Junction Diodes. Lumped Models for Junction Diodes. Structure and Operation of Transistors. Small-Signal Transistor Models. The Ebers-Moll Model for Transistor Volt-Ampere Characteristics. Transistor Models for Dynamic Switching. Appendixes.

Volume 3

Elementary Circuit Properties of Transistors

By C. L. SEARLE, Massachusetts Institute of Technology; A. R. BOOTHROYD; E. J. ANGELO, JR., Polytechnic Institute of Brooklyn; P. E. GRAY; and D. O. PEDERSON, University of California, Berkeley.

CONTENTS

Transistor Physical Electronics and Circuit Models. Circuit Models for Transistor Volt-Ampere Characteristics. Parameter Determination and Circuit Properties of Hybrid-π Model. Dependence of Small-Signal Model Parameters on Operating Conditions. Transistor Bias Circuits: Analysis and Design. Frequency Response and Step Response Calculations. Common-Base and Common-Collector Configuration: Models and Properties. Tuned Amplifiers. Dynamic Behavior of Transistor Switches.

Volume 4

Characteristics and Limitations of Transistors

By R. D. THORNTON, Massachusetts Institute of Technology; D. DEWITT; E. R. CHENETTE, University of Minnesota; and P. E. GRAY.

CONTENTS

Transistor Performance at Extremes of Current and Voltage. Temperature and Power Limitations. Transistor Speed Limitations. Noise.

Volume 5

Multistage Transistor Circuits

By R. D. THORNTON; C. L. SEARLE; D. O. PEDERSON; R. B. ADLER, Massachusetts Institute of Technology; and E. J. ANGELO, JR.

CONTENTS

Gain and Bandwidth Calculations. Amplifier Calculations Using a π Model. Feedback Amplifier Concepts. Stability of Feedback Amplifiers. Broadband Video Amplifiers. DC Amplifiers. Tuned Multistage Amplifiers. Interrelations between Frequency Domain, Time Domain, and Circuit Parameters.

Volume 6

Digital Transistor Circuits

By J. N. HARRIS, Lincoln Laboratory, Massachusetts Institute of Technology, and P. E. GRAY.

CONTENTS

Transistors as Switches, Nonregenerative Switching Circuits, Regenerative Switching Circuits, Boolean Algebra, Circuit Realizations of Boolean Functions, Direct-Coupled Transistor Logic, Current-Mode Logic. Appendices: Binary Numbering Systems, Basic Digital Operations, Digital System Problems.

Volume 7

Handbook of Basic Transistor Circuits and Measurements

By R. D. THORNTON; J. G. LINVILL, Stanford University; E. R. CHENETTE; H. L. ABLIN, University of Nebraska; J. N. HARRIS; A. R. BOOTHROYD, and J. WILLIS, University of California, Los Angeles.

CONTENTS

Basic amplifier configurations and biasing. Regenerative switching circuits. Oscillators. Simple applications. Design examples. Use of the transistor curve tracer. Measurements of transient switching parameters of transistors. Transistor noise measurement.

IX
THE SCIENCE TEACHING CENTER AT THE MASSACHUSETTS INSTITUTE OF TECHNOLOGY

THE SCIENCE TEACHING CENTER AT THE MASSACHUSETTS INSTITUTE OF TECHNOLOGY

by Robert I. Hulsizer, Jr.

and

Malcolm K. Smith

AT PRESENT the Science Teaching Center is concentrating its efforts on the improvement of science education in the institutions of higher learning. As an outgrowth of this activity, we hope that the educational process and problems of education in all areas of learning over a wide range of student maturity will become better understood. Gaining a university education in science has always been a difficult task, often possible only for highly gifted students. The rapid growth in the complexity of science, and the rapid rate at which science is becoming an integral part of our culture make it particularly important to improve science education. Not only is it difficult for the gifted student to gain an education in modern science, but there are increasing numbers of people not so gifted for whom such an education is essential. Better methods for teaching science to people with a wide variety of talents and perceptive aptitudes must be developed, and means must be provided to enable teachers of less than ideal ability and training to work with the large number of students.

Specifically, the first area that requires attention is the development of clear presentations which are more coherent and more accurate than most previous texts. In a former era, when the student body was limited to those who were determined to become scientists, terseness of presentation, highly formal style, and even errors could be tolerated: the students were expected to master their field with a minimum of detailed explanation or assistance. There were, in fact, schools of scientific education dedicated to the idea that the only things one should give a student were a series of clues and the conclusions. A worthy student was expected to work from these clues; and the fewer the clues he needed, the prouder he could be of having mastered the material.

Another school of presentation was quite common, particularly in the introductory college courses. It favored a textbook that was a compendium of knowledge devoid of much attempt to convey understanding of the relationships between phenomena and devoid of much effort to develop independent creative ability in the students. The student was expected to learn a mass of information about a field without much genuine understanding; it was assumed that he would gain understanding in advanced courses, or in graduate work. This approach required great dedication of a student since he was expected to devote years of study to a field before he could hope to understand it. Our experience to date has shown that students who gain understanding as they study learn much more of the field than students who are forced simply to learn without insight or understanding.

A serious attempt is being made at the Institute's Science Teaching Center, and elsewhere, to bring to bear on the creation of introductory materials the keenest and clearest insights of those who are working at the frontiers of knowledge. It is a common phenomenon that leading scientists often have extremely simple ways of thinking about their fields, stemming from deep understanding of their material. Experience gained from high school science curriculum development activities, as well as in the current Science Teaching Center work,

---

Dr. Hulsizer is the Director of the Science Teaching Center; Mr. Smith is its Executive Officer.

demonstrates the substantial gains which can result from a well-organized team effort applied to the development of educational materials and apparatus. Good scientists attempting to make a point clear can do it, whether or not they had a simple, clear point of view when they started. This is why continued application of talent and cooperative activities are important.

The second area of interest is the development of a variety of learning aids and a variety of approaches to any particular subject. The Center has experimented with the use of filmed demonstrations, filmed lectures, corridor exhibits and experiments, lecture demonstrations, laboratory experiments (some of them in kit form for students to use on their own) and a variety of other materials. In addition, the Center has been experimenting with the use of computer-generated displays for representing complicated molecular structures, complicated mathematical functions, and three-dimensional figures, and to calculate relationships which cannot be studied easily by other computational techniques. It is well known that students learn by taking advantage of a wide variety of aptitudes; some learn by mathematical arguments, others by geometrical visualization, and still others by word-pictures or actual experience. The goal of the Center is to develop means for appealing to all of these avenues of perception.

Another area of interest to the Center is the possibility of improving instruction, as well as serving a wider variety of student needs, by integrating the traditional scientific disciplines in at least the introductory courses. The collaboration required to develop such courses should sharpen the appreciation of the authors for the inter-relationships among the sciences that are already known or are becoming known through recent advances. For example, many newer chemistry courses deal in great measure with problems traditionally considered to be physics; the chemists on the other hand often understand thermodynamics and can illustrate it much more clearly than particle physicists, for whom this is an alien subject. One important outcome of this collaboration between scientists in the different disciplines could be a single physical science course that would be suitable for prospective elementary and secondary school teachers.

Still another area of concern is the need facing science faculties, and educators generally, to gain a clear understanding of the learning process. Such insight could lead to major improvements in teaching methods and educational practices. A scientist not only does research in his area of interest—he also develops new techniques of research; a teacher should not only teach, but also should continually be experimenting, studying and developing new techniques of teaching.

The fifth area of interest concerns experimentation with the use of computers as aids to teaching and learning.

The Center also wants to attempt to understand what psychological factors students bring to school. The psychiatric clinic at M.I.T. has been studying for a number of years certain factors in the personalities of entering students and the correlation between these factors and the behavioral patterns and academic success of the students at the Institute. The other side of the same coin is the influence of the educational environment on the students, both in the development of attitudes towards education and professional training and in the deeper impact that the environment has on the personality development of the students. It is hoped that such a study will indicate steps by which the college environment can be made more conducive to learning and to the development of effective citizens as well as productive scientists.

Finally, the Center is interested in the impact of current pressures in our society on the educational system and the means by which the educational system can cope with these pressures and changes. The growing affluence of the community, the increased number of students, the growing need for a scientific education to qualify one for employment in a technological society, competition for admission to select colleges and graduate schools all act to perturb the educational system. The roles of education, testing and selection need to be identified, separated, and protected from overwhelming each other. It is felt that a great deal needs to be learned about testing as an educational tool as well as a tool for diagnosis and for selection. The personality factors that lead to productive activities are still difficult, if not impossible, to identify, and measures of "true" learning are still hard to come by. The Center feels that there is much to be learned about the different roles of the institutions of higher learning and how the different roles can each be preserved.

In the past the activities of the Center mainly involved the development of a new introductory course in physics: this included the creation of text material, the development of improved apparatus for demonstrations and experiments, and a number of films for college and university audiences. The experimental apparatus (as mentioned earlier) included a number of lecture demonstrations, and corridor demonstrations and experiments which have received wide use by the student body. Both the text material and some of the experimental apparatus have been used in other universities on a trial basis. The new physics course is discussed by Professor A. P. French in the following article.

While this development was taking place in physics, the Educational Policy Committee of the Institute recommended a number of major reforms, one of which was to encourage the development of teaching laboratories in which students carried out individual work requiring planning, analysis, and development of experiments. One of these project laboratories has been taught by the Physics Department for three semesters and two different project laboratories have been developed and taught in the Biology Department. The Science Teaching Center is cooperating with the respective departments in the development of these methods and the necessary experimental facilities.

The Chemistry Department, while not yet at the point of offering a project laboratory, has been working with the Science Teaching Center in a substantial review of its introductory courses and has been experimenting with various modifications of the laboratory and of the course organization.

Several specific projects in chemistry and biology have been initiated at the Center that involve the use of the time-shared console facilities of the M.I.T. Computation Center and of Project MAC (Multiple-Access Computers). The need to introduce students to the active role that computers are playing in the design and research activities of scientists and engineers is imperative, and these projects offer interesting possibilities for this kind of training and education.

Recently a set of computer programs has been written which allows the construction, display and analysis of macromolecules using a digital computer and an oscilloscope display. With this computer-controlled display and real-time rotations of the projections of a molecule, it is possible for an observer to obtain a true three-dimensional visualization of the molecule. The first program written in this project calculated the coordinates of the atoms in a protein, using as the input variables only those angles about which rotation is possible. All other rotation angles and chemical bond lengths were entered as rigid constraints in the program. Molecules commonly studied in biology have as many as 1,500 atoms and it is not practical to construct mechanical models of such molecules or to calculate the energies of different configurations of the atoms without the use of a high speed computer. The combination of a high speed computer and a display which the computer can generate showing, by rotation, the three-dimensional structures of a molecule offers a powerful tool for teaching molecular chemistry and molecular biology to students or for demonstrating such structures and making films showing such structures.

A group of physicists will gather in the summer of 1966 to develop a unit for a programmed learning experiment in connection with the introductory course in physics at M.I.T. Various combinations of programmed text and computer-aided teaching-machine material will be developed. During the winter of 1966-1967, this material will be used in the freshman course at M.I.T. on a large enough group of students to obtain some appreciation for problems of using the material and, if possible, a measure of the success of such material relative to more conventional methods of presenting it.

In addition to experiments on the use of computer-generated displays and on computer-aided programmed learning, techniques for generating films with the computer display will be developed. Many of the displays that can be generated on a cathode ray tube by a computer would be invaluable for lecturers, or for student use on films. The development will involve preparation of utility display programs and development of the hardware for making high quality films.

The Department of Psychology at M.I.T. and the Science Teaching Center are planning to conduct a series of seminars on subjects of mutual interest to the Center and the Department. The emphasis of the seminars will be on the developments in the field of learning and perception and their relevance to the practice of teaching at colleges and universities.

The Science Teaching Center is an inter-departmental center in the School of Science at M.I.T. The Director reports to the Dean of Science and sits with the heads of various science departments on the Science Council. Participation in the program of the Science Teaching Center and use of its facilities are open to any member of the faculty of the Institute, and there is a great deal of formal and informal participation in the work of the Center by faculty members of the different departments.

The Center cooperates with other schools and colleges nationally through trial use of its material, exchange of faculty through visits to the Center by faculty members from other schools, and by participation in workshops and other cooperative activities.

In essence, the M.I.T. Science Teaching Center aims to provide an environment where experienced teachers and outstanding research scientists and engineers drawn from a variety of departments and disciplines can work together to improve undergraduate education. The Center aims to be a training ground for persons interested in carrying on such work not only at M.I.T. but also in other academic institutions and in industrial organizations interested in participating in this rapidly expanding activity.

A NEW INTRODUCTORY PHYSICS COURSE AT THE MASSACHUSETTS INSTITUTE OF TECHNOLOGY

by A. P. French

DESPITE the air of definiteness that may be implied by the title of my talk, the remarks that I shall offer you this morning are in the nature of a progress report. I should like to tell you something about the results, and the future plans, arising out of the work that has been going on at the Science Teaching Center at M.I.T. over the past few years. One of our chief aims has been to take a fresh look at introductory physics at the college and university level. Our work at M.I.T. is of course by no means the only effort of this kind; there has been a surge of interest, in various places in this country, in the whole question of what should be present in the general course in physics, and how it should be presented. Before I get down to the specifics of our course at M.I.T., it might be worthwhile to spend a few moments considering the problem in general.

The task of any basic course in physics should presumably be to give an accurate and balanced picture of what the physical world is like. That is a tall order, to be sure, but I think there has been a growing conviction that the typical elementary course presented during the freshman and sophomore years falls lamentably short of this goal. One might suppose that it should be almost axiomatic that a physics course worth its name, even at the elementary level, should contain the really important notions that underlie our description and understanding of the world. As far as physics is concerned, there are two outstanding ideas that the twentieth century has contributed and which should surely be introduced at an early stage in any general course in physics. These are relativity on the one hand and quantum physics on the other. Both of them are so deeply imbedded in our understanding of nature, and our ability to describe it, that they should occupy a central position in any physics course. The world is not a classical Newtonian structure to which relativity and quantum behavior are added as an afterthought or as a reward to students for perseverance after a year or two of grind. Yet, until recently, that is the kind of footing on which relativity and quantum theory have been presented to students at the beginning levels in colleges and universities. Many of you no doubt have made the acquaintance of the lectures, now coming out in book form, that Richard Feynman gave at Caltech during 1961-63. In the preface to his lectures he observes that students coming out of high school "have heard a lot about how interesting and exciting physics is — the theory of relativity, quantum mechanics, and other modern ideas." He goes on: "By the end of our previous course, many would be discouraged because there were really very few grand, new and modern ideas presented to them. They were made to study inclined planes, electrostatics, and so forth, and after two years it was quite stultifying."

Of course one may sympathize with these opinions, and yet still have doubts about what should be the content of a beginning course at the university level. After all, so long as we do not probe too deeply, classical physics provides a wonderful description of much of our physical experience. Newtonian mechanics provides a thoroughly accurate account of any motion that we can see with our eyes. It is obviously

---

This article is the text of a talk given by Professor French to an Advanced Placement Conference at Case Institute, in Cleveland, Ohio, on June 25, 1964. The new physics course will be taught during this academic year 1964-1965 at Washington University, St. Louis, Missouri, and at San Diego State College, as well as at M. I. T. The Science Teaching Center was organized at M. I. T. in 1960 for the purpose of making innovations in science teaching at the college and university level.

Copyright © 1964 by the Science Teaching Center at the Massachusetts Institute of Technology

relevant to our description of nature, and we know that students need a lot of practice in using it before they are adept with it. But in limiting ourselves to a description of the physical world in these terms, we are preventing ourselves — and our students — from probing into many of the questions that ought to be of supreme interest, because we are condemning ourselves to an acceptance of gross matter as we happen to find it. Why is glass transparent? Why is sulfur yellow? Why is mercury a liquid? Why don't atoms collapse under the attraction of their positive and negative charges? I am not suggesting that a freshman course in physics can give satisfactory answers to all of these, but I do think we are cheating the student if we do not put him on the road to quantum mechanics and the atomic description of matter.

In these last remarks I have indicated one of the key features of the approach to physics that we have been developing at M.I.T. It is what we have chosen to call "the particulate view." We start from the assumption that a workable, meaningful description of the physical world can be made in terms of particles and their behavior. The question immediately arises — "What is a particle?" Ultimately, perhaps, only the fundamental particles — electrons, nucleons, and so forth — may qualify, but that, from our standpoint, is too restrictive. The dynamics of a star in a galaxy, or of a planet in the solar system, is as much the dynamics of a particle as is the motion of an electron in a cathode ray tube. (You might even say that it is more so, because wave-mechanical properties can be safely neglected.) Once we have developed a familiarity with the individual particles and their behavior as described by classical or quantum mechanics (whichever may be the more appropriate) we shall be ready to consider the motions and properties of aggregates of particles and of matter in bulk. One of the advantages that we see as coming out of this kind of approach is a breaking down, at least in part, of the customary barriers and compartments into which the subject of physics is conventionally divided. We have a splendid chance in fact to show how physics enables us to put together facts and ideas that might have seemed separate at one time, and to relate the microscopic and the macroscopic aspects of nature. Thus to take an obvious example, one of the triumphs of this century in astrophysics has been the emergence of a rather full understanding of how something as large as a star works through the operation of reactions occurring on the nuclear scale. To establish a connection between the largest and the smallest in this way is certainly one of the really exciting things in the whole world of intellectual experience, and there is no reason at all why this sort of thing shouldn't start right at the beginning of a college course. Moreover, by opening the student's eyes to such relationships one can continually impress on him that the scale of distance of the universe that he lives in has markings over a colossal range — from 10^{-15} meters to 10^9 light years — and that to narrow down one's attention to familiar terrestrial objects — from grains of sand (10^{-3} meters) to mountains (10^3 meters) — involves a drastic limitation of our field of interest, however convenient that may be in everyday life. But I have said quite enough about generalities; let me now turn to some of the details of the course as we have been teaching it to M.I.T. undergraduates.

Our course actually begins with the Millikan experiment. This has several advantages. It leads us at once to a fundamental granularity in nature, it provides us with a universal atomic constant, and it paves the way for a simple discussion of dynamical problems involving charged particles. We then turn at once to electrons. After presenting some of the evidence that electrons are constituents of all kinds of matter, we discuss the motions of electrons of low energies in electric fields. This gives us the chance to develop or review a certain amount of kinematics and Newtonian dynamics for motion in one and two dimensions. Moreover, we want to lose no time in introducing electronic devices as detectors for various other types of particles and processes. A student does not need to understand all the niceties of surface phenomena or gas discharges in order to appreciate the use of electron multipliers or Geiger counters as detectors.

Next we turn to atoms and molecules. Again the purpose is twofold. We want to give the students a feeling for the reality of atoms — particles with masses and sizes that can be measured in ways that he can readily understand. But we can also push our review of dynamics a little further; we can point to the evidence that individual atoms, just like baseballs, carry momentum and fall under gravity. Next we say something about ions and mass spectrometry. The student learns something about the measurement of atomic masses, but he also makes the acquaintance of the velocity-dependent magnetic force. Thus, by a few examples of genuine physical importance, he is introduced to several different types of forces and the motions that they produce. I should emphasize that this is not a part of our formal development of dynamics; it makes use of no more than a student might reasonably be expected to have learned in high school.

Our account of atomic particles ends with a brief discussion of nuclei. We consider these as particles having mass, electric charge, certain characteristic numbers of neutrons and protons, and certain rather well-defined sizes. It is not at all our intention at this stage to give a detailed descriptive account of atomic and nuclear physics; nor do we want to bring in the new fundamental particles that are the concern of high-energy physics. We do want to say something to indicate the scale and the structure of the atomic world, and we want to give the student a feeling for how one can learn about such matters by making suitable observations. Indeed, we have consciously taken as our text what Newton wrote in his preface to the *Principia:* ". . . for the whole burden of philosophy seems to consist in this — from the phenomena of motions to investigate the forces of nature, and then from these forces to demonstrate the other phenomena."

At this point we have thought it appropriate to insert a chapter called "Randomness." Here, we develop, explicitly and in some detail, the consequences of having a system made up of a finite number of particles. After introducing some of the elementary ideas of probability, we consider various examples of fluctuation phenomena — radioactive counting, Brownian motion, etc.

We now return to particles, but of a distinctive kind — photons. After presenting some of the evidence that photons are particles that can be counted, we demonstrate that this goes hand-in-hand with wave behavior. In order to talk usefully about the interference properties of photons, we must say something about waves and the interference of waves in general. We need not, however, call upon anything beyond the usual double-source interference problems. With the help of actual experiments (films) we can show how the maxima of the interference patterns are correlated with maxima of the probability for a photon to arrive at a given point on the detector. Thus the essentially statistical nature of atomic phenomena makes its appearance in this course. Having introduced the wave-particle duality for photons, we then point to the existence of this same duality for the particles — electrons, atoms, etc. — whose purely particulate nature we had accepted up to this point.

The remainder of this first part of the course consists of a rather brief survey of the larger types of particles, from molecules up to stars. The chief purpose of this is to introduce the scale of magnitudes involved, although the operation of different kinds of forces for different sizes of particles — nuclear forces for nuclei, electric forces for almost everything else, gravitational forces for very large objects — is something to be brought out at this stage.

Let me reiterate at this point that everything that I have described so far falls within one-third of the first semester of the course. If the purpose were to fill the student with detailed information about the particles in question, the time would be totally inadequate. However, as I have pointed out, this is not at all the purpose of the exercise. It is, if you like, almost an impressionistic approach. But it is far from being purely descriptive. The student begins to learn to tackle quantitative problems in dynamics, as well as handling order-of-magnitude calculations and approximations. And of course, as always, the consideration of randomness and probability calls for clear and logical thinking.

I have chosen to describe this first part of the course in rather considerable detail, despite its brevity, because it does much to define the spirit in which we have approached the whole program, and also because it is in many respects the most unconventional part of the enterprise.

In Part II of the course, which as we have taught it occupies the rest of the first semester, we turn to the classical mechanics of particles. We have sought to lay particular emphasis on the conservation laws for momentum and energy, and to solve problems with the help of these concepts, rather than through the direct use of $F = ma$. Free use is made of potential energy diagrams as a basis for analyzing motions of constant total mechanical energy. We develop the parabolic expansion of a potential about its minimum, and treat such problems as the vibration of an atom in a one-dimensional lattice. From one-dimensional problems we turn to two-dimensional problems and central forces. Again we make free use of the potential diagram, in this case with the centrifugal potential included. In these terms we treat the Kepler problem and Rutherford scattering. We limit ourselves throughout to what are effectively point particles; there is no discussion of rigid bodies. We do introduce angular momentum as an important conserved property for motion of a particle under a central force. Our study of one-dimensional motions in a potential, of course, includes the linear harmonic oscillator. We solve this in the first instance from the equation for conservation of energy, and we also discuss Newton's law as a differential equation applying to this problem. This and other dynamical problems show how one can begin developing a solution by numerical methods in cases where the exact analytic solution may be unknown to the student (or perhaps to anyone else).

In this discussion of dynamics, we are looking ahead to some of those features that will reappear in relativity and quantum mechanics. Emphasis on energy methods is one example of this. Two other examples are: the use of transformations between different frames of reference (pointing toward relativity) and an introduction to perturbation methods in simple dynamical problems with an eye on their future possible use in quantum mechanics.

Part III of our course — the first half of the second semester—is devoted to the subject of special relativity. Today, of course, we have access to a wealth of experimental information that did not exist in 1905 when Einstein made his theory. By pointing to some of this evidence — to the existence of a limiting speed for energetic electrons, the dynamical properties of photons, and the large time-dilation effects exhibited by mesons — the need for a non-Newtonian dynamics is made quite clear, but for the systematic development of relativistic mechanics we return to Einstein's postulates and their consequences. We discuss a number of applications of relativistic kinematics and relativistic dynamics including the calculation of threshold energies for the creation of particles in nuclear collisions. We take the formal analysis as far as the transformations of energy, momentum and force.

I think there are several good reasons for introducing relativity at this stage, even though we have not yet done with our development of classical mechanics. First, relativity is necessary to provide a correct description of the dynamics of a particle, for in working with electrons we quickly discover that Newtonian mechanics is not enough. Second, the great principles of special relativity — the equivalence of inertial frames and the relativity of simultaneity — are basic tenets of a physicist's creed. Third (perhaps a meretricious reason) the students love it, and if you say the word "relativity" you can be sure of their rapt attention. Fourth, although the ideas are grand and important, the mathematics is easy.

Next we come to Part IV — oscillations and waves. Our discussion of the harmonic oscillator in Part II of the course does not go beyond an analysis of the sinusoidal vibration of an undamped particle under a linear restoring force. Now we take up all the problems associated with forcing, resonance, and dissipative effects. The detailed shape of the response curve of a resonant system, the relation between line width and decay time, and the analysis of energy and power input for a forced oscillator, are all considered in some detail. The analysis is tied primarily to a mechanical system, but the appearance of resonance in all sorts of other physical systems is illustrated. This subject clearly requires the free use of differential equations. Most of our students have not yet had any significant contact with differential equations in mathematics. However, at this stage they have had at least one and one-half semesters' experience with calculus, and are able to recognize reasonable forms of solutions, and verify them by substitution.

Our next step — in keeping with our description of complicated systems as made up of individual particles — is to consider the problem of coupled oscillators. We begin with a system of two oscillators, which we solve for its normal modes, and show how any arbitrary motion of the system can be described in terms of superposition of these normal modes. Once again we are deliberately introducing ideas and approaches that are purely classical, but which will be of value when quantum mechanics is discussed.

We proceed next to the normal modes of a many-particle coupled system, and finally to a continuous medium as represented by a string. (Though, as we point out, not even a string is really continuous, and under sufficient enlargement would appear as a system of coupled particles with spacings of a few angstroms.)

Our emphasis now shifts to progressive waves. We point out how a normal mode of a stretched string, for example, can be described as a superposition of waves traveling in opposite directions, and in this way we are able to relate the wave velocity to what we have already learned about the coupled oscillations. By referring back to the coupled oscillations with a finite number of particles, we can introduce here the distinction between phase and group velocities. The remainder of this part of the course is devoted to mechanical waves in two and three dimensions. And thus ends the first year of our course.

At this point my account ceases to be a progress report and enters its planning phase. The second year of our course has not yet been formally taught to students, and many of its details remain to be sorted out. The broad picture, at least of our intentions, is however clear. The first semester of the second year will be devoted to electromagnetism. We shall expect to follow a fairly well-beaten path for the first half of this semester, assembling the facts of electrostatics, magnetostatics, and electric and magnetic induction. This will bring us to a statement of Maxwell's equations. Immediately following this (or perhaps interwoven with it, as appropriate) will be an exposition of electromagnetism from the viewpoint of relativity. In essence, what is done here is to start with Coulomb's law and the relativistic transformations, and analyze the interactions between point charges in various states of motion. Such a treatment brings out in all its glory the interconnection between electric and magnetic fields, and highlights the essentially relativistic charac-

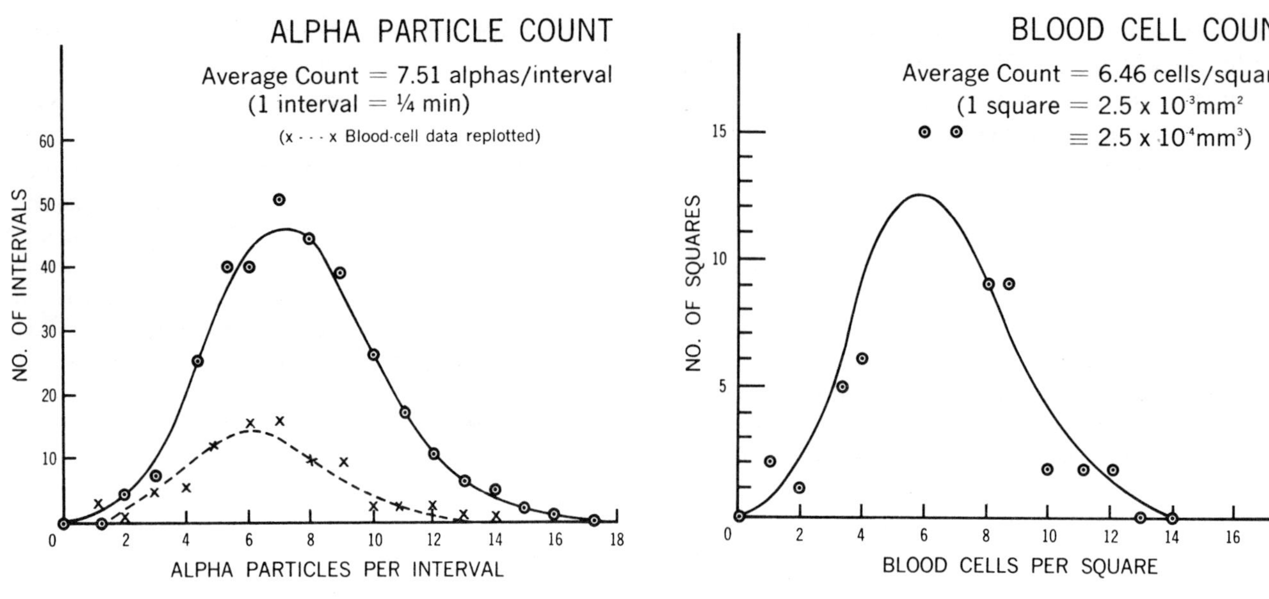
ALPHA PARTICLE COUNT
Average Count = 7.51 alphas/interval
(1 interval = ¼ min)
(x - - - x Blood-cell data replotted)
NO. OF INTERVALS
ALPHA PARTICLES PER INTERVAL
BLOOD CELL COUNT
Average Count = 6.46 cells/square
(1 square = 2.5 x 10⁻³mm²
≡ 2.5 x 10⁻⁴mm³)
NO. OF SQUARES
BLOOD CELLS PER SQUARE

FIGURE 1

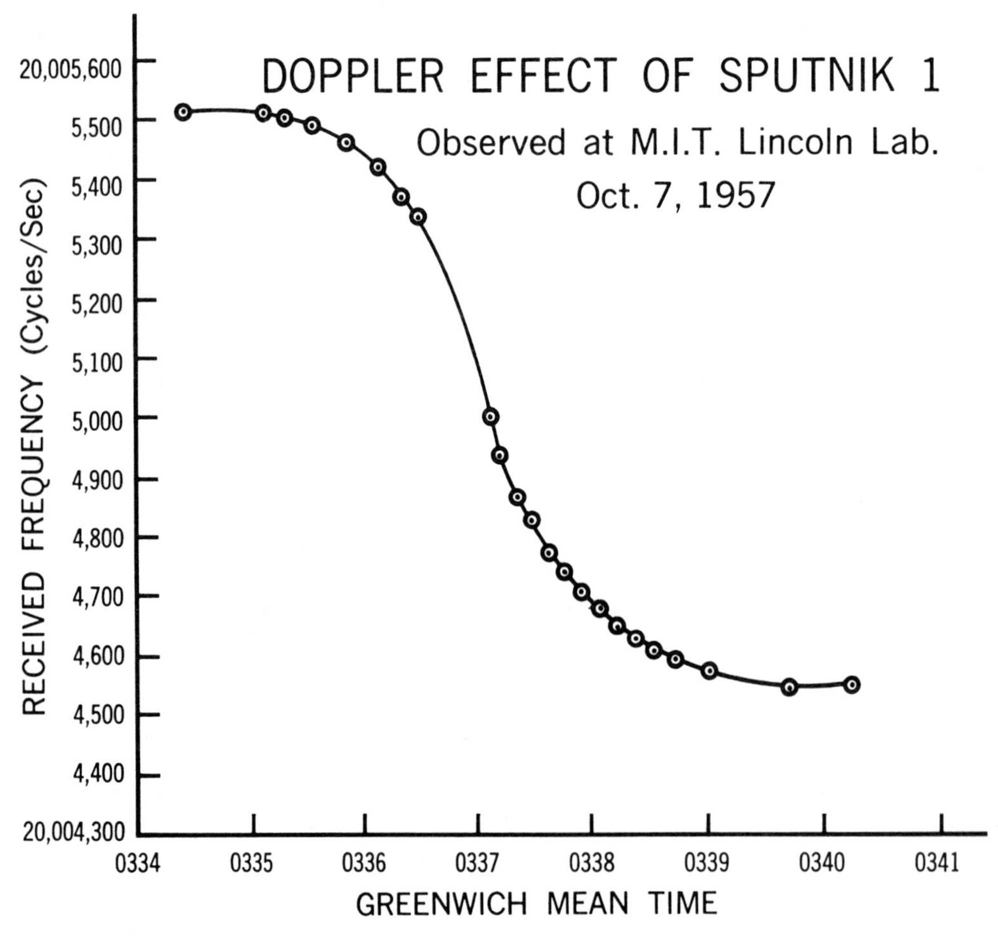
DOPPLER EFFECT OF SPUTNIK 1
Observed at M.I.T. Lincoln Lab.
Oct. 7, 1957
RECEIVED FREQUENCY (Cycles/Sec)
20,005,600
5,500
5,400
5,300
5,200
5,100
5,000
4,900
4,800
4,700
4,600
4,500
4,400
20,004,300
0334
0335
0336
0337
0338
0339
0340
0341
GREENWICH MEAN TIME

FIGURE 2

ter of electromagnetic theory (a feature that Einstein himself, of course, took as a starting point in 1905).

In the remainder of this third semester of our course, we shall go as far as we can in the discussion of electromagnetic radiation. Clearly our selection of topics here must be very limited, and we expect to restrict ourselves to plane-wave solutions of Maxwell's equations. Our main discussion of wave optics must, however, come here, and it would be highly desirable to analyze with some care the main features of interference and diffraction phenomena for microwaves and light.

The fourth semester of our course is reserved for an introduction to quantum physics. A presentation of the ideas of quantum mechanics in an elementary yet satisfactory way, during the students' sophomore year, presents a real challenge. Regular discussions of this problem were held throughout the Spring semester at M.I.T. this year, and two experimental seminars for sophomores were conducted so as to try out some possible approaches. No final decisions have been reached, but there is a balance of opinion in favor of beginning with the selection of discrete states of atoms in magnetic fields, rather than with the more usual elementary approach via de Broglie waves. The Schrödinger equation and its solutions will of course come along later, when its status and content can be better appreciated. Some discussion of systems containing identical particles is also regarded as being of the highest importance.

If time permits (which is pretty unlikely) we should like to end our two-year sequence with some discussions of the properties of bulk matter, on the basis of its being composed of huge numbers of particles. One of the points to be emphasized here would be that the statistical averages for such numbers of particles lead to collective properties such as pressure, temperature, elasticity, etc. It is here, if at all, that we shall be concerned with any kind of presentation of the ideas of thermodynamics. Traditionally, of course, heat and thermodynamics would come hard on the heels of the mechanics during the first year of our course. We have deliberately turned away from this possibility, feeling that the continuum approach to thermodynamics might be appropriately taught (and often, perhaps, better taught) in departments of chemical or mechanical engineering or chemistry.

This, then, is the structure of our course as we envisage it at present, although it remains to be seen how much material we can in fact get through during the second year. I could perhaps end here, but I don't propose to do so. A course is much more than just a syllabus, and I should like to say enough to convey something of the flavor that we have tried to give to our course, as well as sharing with you some of our ideas about the teaching of physics.

I myself feel very strongly that elementary physics teaching — and indeed undergraduate instruction generally — is altogether too much the slave of the textbook. And textbook instruction has acquired a life and character of its own. Physics as it is presented on the pages of many textbooks often bears surprisingly little resemblance to physics as it is actually practiced. What I mean by this, chiefly, is that the material is sterilized, abbreviated and codified so that one loses all sense of the actual process of discovery — the real experiments, the false starts, the inspired guesses, and all that goes into a living, developing science. A certain amount of streamlining is of course necessary and desirable, or the beginning student would be hopelessly lost. But one of the most valuable things we can do is to put the student in touch with the raw material of the subject — real data and original papers — so that it is not a desiccated scholastic discipline, but a human activity in which he is involved at first hand. In developing our material at the Science Teaching Center, we have tried hard to instill this approach. Let me give you a couple of examples of our "documentation" of our text material. My first example comes from our discussion of randomness. In Figure 1 you will see two graphs, both constructed from original data. One of them shows the result of a blood count: the distribution of blood cells on the identical squares of a hemacytometer slide. The other shows the results of an experiment by Rutherford, a study of the numbers of alpha particles arriving in equal intervals from a very weak radioactive source. The same laws of random distributions apply to both, and the student can make his own analyses of the data. He is not just learning the theory of random distributions, he is put in touch with the research laboratory. My second example concerns the Doppler effect. In Figure 2 you see a graph, taken from the research literature, which shows the received frequency of the radio signal emitted by the first Sputnik as it passed over the M.I.T. Lincoln Laboratory a few days after it was launched. From these data the student can draw his own conclusions about the altitude, as well as the speed, of the satellite. And we are trying to introduce such examples at various appropriate points throughout our text material. In the same spirit we have given frequent references to original papers that the student may profitably refer to. Every freshman can read and understand the first few pages of Einstein's first paper on relativity. When he has done so, he has not only learned what are the postulates of special relativity, but he has also learned that Einstein's mind is not totally remote from his own. By proceeding along these lines the text can, I believe, be what it ought to be, namely a channel of communication between the student and the science, rather than being what it so often is—a barrier between the two.

This leads me to some still more general observations, with which I shall conclude my talk. The notion that a course in science is the study of a single textbook is very deeply imbedded in the educational system. I am far from alone in believing that this is a narrow and wrong point of view. The student cannot be blamed if he gets the idea that there is a well-defined and limited set of facts and principles to be learned, and that the textbook is the source of them. We need to break down this monolithic structure and diversify the student's experience. This means that he should read from many sources, and not from just one textbook, that he should do meaningful and relevant experiments in laboratory, and that his acquaintance with real phenomena should be enriched with the help of demonstrations and films. Every conscientious teacher knows this, and does his best to put it into practice. But the monolithic textbook, between hard covers, remains like a millstone around one's neck, making freedom of movement almost impossible. We at the Science Teaching Center at M.I.T. do not want to add one more millstone to the stockpile. And what we have in mind is that, instead of just another monolithic text, we should present the various parts of our course as a set of separate monographs. We would aim to produce more of them than could ever be covered in a two-year course anywhere. And then it would be open to the individual teacher to make his selection from the list, according to his own ideas and local circumstances. In this way, I hope, we could get away from anything in the nature of orthodoxy and settled traditions (new style). In other words, what I have tried to describe to you is *an* introductory course in physics, which will not, I hope, be ossified into *the* introductory course at M.I.T. or anywhere else.

X
EDUCATIONAL ASSISTANCE OVERSEAS

SCIENTIFIC AND ENGINEERING EDUCATION IN NEWLY DEVELOPING COUNTRIES

by Jerrold R. Zacharias

In August of 1960, I was invited to speak at an "International Conference on Science in the Advancement of New States," at the Weizmann Institute in Rehovoth, Israel. The program of the Conference included numerous subjects (energy sources, nuclear and solar; agriculture; soil and water conservation; desalination and rain making; public health; economics; education) and brought under discussion many of the problems which face the emerging states. Several hundred people, from all six continents, attended, many of them distinguished in some field of science, technology, government or administration.

Since the participants lived and took meals together in the Weizmann Institute Guest House, it was possible to become reasonably well-acquainted, during the two weeks of the Conference, with the other participants, and there were among us many able and interesting men. As the Conference proceeded, it became clear, however, that one man stood out above all the others, the Reverend Solomon B. Caulker of Sierra Leone. He was an African of tribal origin, educated in the United States at the University of Chicago and at the Union Theological Seminary in New York. At the time of the Conference, he was Vice-Principal of Fourah Bay College, Freetown, Sierra Leone. Although he was not an official speaker on the program, he was called upon several times to express himself on subjects under discussion. I am offering, in the following pages, examples of these impromptu remarks, transcribed from tape recordings of the Conference.

The first three or four talks of the Conference were concerned with science in the modern world and dwelt at length on nuclear power and nuclear reactors. On this subject, Reverend Caulker made the following comment:

"I have listened with intense interest to the discussion, and I do want to make one or two statements. (As representing one of the new countries, new nations, I think I have already made it clear in one of the previous sessions that I am here almost under false pretenses because I am not really going to be a new nation until next year, but you can grant me the few months before that time that we become a new nation.) . . . Having reached a point where we are no longer under foreign political domination, where we no longer open our mouths in wonder at the power of Western soldiers, imperialism of any sort you like, having passed that stage, we must now be careful not to be dominated intellectually by being presented with such highfalutin problems of nuclear physics and so on, that we leave the countries of this kind completely discouraged and feeling we can never achieve anything at all. I say this because the problems we face immediately in many of our countries in West Africa are problems that are from the ground up. I agree 100% with what Professor Zacharias has said because, when I came to this Conference, I came enthusiastically, believing that here I could receive some inspiration, so that in any way in which I am able, [I could] influence policy at home. I can do it because I come from a country, ladies and gentlemen, in which first of all, while it is of great interest to talk about nuclear physics and fusion and all these things, and we do read about them and follow what is happening in the world, it is even of greater interest to know how to save so many of our babies,

Jerrold R. Zacharias is Institute Professor at the Massachusetts Institute of Technology and Vice President of Educational Services Incorporated. This article was prepared as a paper for the M.I.T. Centennial Conference on Science and Engineering Education held in April, 1961.

for in Sierra Leone 8 out of every 10 babies who are born die before they are one year old. This is a very real question and has nothing, for the moment, to do with the building of nuclear reactors. It's a question of saving children who are born and poorly taken care of, are undernourished. I'd like to know from this Conference what suggestions it has along that line. We cannot believe that Nature, God, call it what you like, loves English children, or American children, or Israeli children any more than African children. Surely, if it has been done somewhere else, it *can* be done. This is a genuine problem of health of the children of Africa in these new nations. For this problem, in my own thinking, interesting as nuclear fission is, it is a bit too far removed at the moment.

"Now the next problem also is one of just the ordinary maintenance of health. The standard of living in West Africa, by and large, the average life expectancy age, by and large, is in the low 30's as you know, compared to many of these advanced countries where the average age has gone to 60 or near 70. Most of our people die of leprosy, malaria, under-nourishment of all kinds, eating just one kind of food. The need for detailed study of the kind of food that is good, the amount of calories needed for people—these are real problems that we face today. And this Conference would be going a great way if it opened to us the doors to say: 'You can have *life* as we've had it, in terms of good food and good health.' So that, interesting as nuclear fission is (and I'm not saying here that we shouldn't listen to something about it), from the point of view of the pressing peril of the moment, this is the real thing."

Caulker distinguished between the problems which the Africans can and will solve for themselves and the much greater problems which require help from the outside.

"You see, new nations face two types of problems. One of these types of problems is of little interest to this Conference, and there is not very much you can do to help us. The first problem is what one might call the problem of obedience. That is the problem of transferring the respect from the colonial powers to respect for our own people. It is very easy to accept what an English district commissioner says, what an English governor says, what an English provincial commissioner says. In fact, we have an interesting situation, if I may digress one minute, Mr. Chairman. Recently the Prime Minister of our country was traveling in the interior and arrived in a town where there is a rest house, which all these years has always been used by the district commissioner or the provincial commissioner or the governor or English people, British people. . . . The Prime Minister, it was announced, was arriving and arrangements were made for him to go and stay in the rest house. But as soon as word got around that a very junior district commissioner was arriving soon, the parliament chief got all panicky and went to the Prime Minister and said, 'I'm sorry, sir, but the district commissioner is coming and you'll have to go and stay somewhere else, because he'll have to take the rest house.' In other words, there is that problem of obedience, respect for the new African authority, the new African government. But as I say, this isn't a problem in which you can help me very much. It's one we shall solve.

"But the problem in which you can help us is in moving from where we are to the next stage of development, economic and social. This involves the problem of teaching in our schools. Professor Zacharias has mentioned something I said to him about our problem of the teaching of science. It's very easy for you, very many of you, who have been raised in the Western outlook, in Western philosophy of history and so on, to take this for granted. But in our own thinking, first of all, one of the most difficult problems of the African people in these under-developed states is to even understand that there is any relationship physically between cause and effect. This is a primary problem: whether typhoid is caused by drinking dirty water or whether it is caused by someone who has bewitched you; whether your babies are dying because you are not feeding them properly, or whether they die because someone who hates you has put sickness on them. It can take years, if you're not careful, even generations, just to combat that single point of view, and instill what might be called philosophy of a world-wide view of history and of cause and effect. Now you see, as important as nuclear fission and all these things are, it is even more important to let these people realize, in these new states, that there is a direct relationship between the kind of water you drink and the kind of health you have, between the kind of food you eat and the kind of health you have, and your resistance to disease. Is there any hope? This question is of far more importance to me, and I am hoping that towards the end of the Conference, I can go back home and say that there is a possibility that these things do change."

He believed that scientific training and instruction from the Western world is essential to the healthy growth and development of the new African states and, thereby, to the maintenance of the peace and equilibrium of the whole world.

"Now I've already implied, I think, that the whole question of help, of science, in the new states is not a question of science as a disembodied spirit, moving by itself, and going into Africa. It's a question of *men* of science men of good will through training, helping the African people to develop. This means our schools. The teaching of science is far removed from many of our schools today. We need scientists, men who can come in and teach these very simple things I've been talking about here, and this takes training. This kind of training can be done either at home at a very low level, or, as for many of us who have had the opportunity, by going abroad and coming back with new insights and training. But this is an urgent matter. If I may say this, Mr. Chairman, without being visionary, I think it should be of tremendous interest to everybody here, not only at this Conference, but throughout the Western world, that a great balance in power in the interests of peace and equilibrium in our world is going to be found in the attitude that African people develop as they grow up, as they move into nationhood. Therefore, one might almost say even if not for the love of the African, but in the interest of world peace, everyone ought to take an interest in helping this great continent in raising its health, raising its economic development so that it can continue to exercise a wholesome influence on the deliberations of nations. We need tools with which our young people can be freed from their hopeless and fatalistic attitude towards life, to the point where they can believe that they can combat the problems that face them, the diseases that face them, and they can be victorious over them."

He gave examples of how help was already being given by other nations:

"If I may just mention one thing that happened in the last few days as the kind of help I mean: we need a great many teachers of all types, especially in the scientific side, and we have been having a lot of young British people coming over. But the problem always is a problem of how to pay them an inducement allowance; one doesn't blame people for not wanting to leave their homes and come into the tropics and so on. In the last two weeks came the electrifying announcement from the British Government that, from now on, for all British people coming into the colonies to help, even after independence, except for their basic salary (which we shall pay), all their allowances, including inducement allowances, will be paid by the British Government. This is one of the greatest helps that has ever come to us. We can now have more people coming to help because we can now afford to take care of them without having to worry about the inducement allowances, which do become a great item.

"There has been some talk here about agriculture. Certainly our economy is fundamentally one of agriculture, and I wholeheartedly agree that something must be done in agricultural research. At the moment we have fifteen Sierra Leonians here in Israel, who have generously been awarded scholarships by the Israeli Government to come here and study practical methods of agriculture. They arrived here two weeks ago and will be here for nine months. I have no doubt that when these fifteen young men return to Sierra Leone there will be a little revolution in terms of simple agriculture in our village life. This is the kind of thing, this is science helping Sierra Leone through Israel. This is science helping Sierra Leone through the offer that the British Government has made, and science can help Sierra Leone or any of these under-developed countries through this exchange of people, through teaching and so on."

He explained that the new African states' most serious and urgent problems are more fundamental than most Westerners can grasp. They are concerned with life and death, and the very first rudiments of education.

"Now in the development of technology, we want people who can come and look at our soil, look at our forestry, look at our plants, and help us get rid of diseases that destroy our plants, and stop soil erosion in areas where rainfall is so heavy that much of the topsoil is washed away. Now you see then, Mr. Chairman, what our policy here in brief is: that we, as new nations, are not against talking about high sounding aspects of technology. We are establishing schools of engineering, faculties of applied science in our own colleges, and we believe that we can move slowly. But there is what one might call a holy impatience in us that too many of our people are living sub-normal lives, both in health and all other aspects, as I have already mentioned in terms of children who are dying, and we believe quite firmly that if any help can come to us, it will be most significant if it is in this area of health, in this area of better food, in this area of beginning—and believe me—at a very preliminary level of teaching science to our schools, to our children.

"Again, let me conclude by saying that the problem

is far more primary than many of you would realize. It is a problem, first of all, of attacking a people's world view, a philosophy of history, if you like, and changing their point of view. A people whose counting does not go beyond the ten fingers, in many of the tribes; a people to whom exact measurements are absolutely of no meaning whatsoever, where there's only long and short. . . . Surely, this Conference has a great deal to offer us in terms of this basic need, which I believe firmly can only be met by a knowledge of science used in a very broad sense. In the meantime, we will grow up in our universities, in research, very slowly, but we do not and cannot afford to use the resources we have at the moment for the prestigious projects: merely to say then, because we are a new nation, we must have a nuclear reactor; because we are a new nation, we must have this and this. Because we are a new nation, we want peace and equilibrium. We want health for our children. Thank you very much, Mr. Chairman."

In answer to the suggestion, made by one speaker, that Africans who go abroad for training are often tempted to remain abroad, Caulker said the following:

"The question has been raised of people not returning home because they have greater offers abroad. Now, I think you're going to find out that increasingly as these countries develop, this is going to change. There were some very basic psychological and sociological reasons why this was so. In the colonial days, no matter how trained a native was, he always had to work under a foreigner. In other words, the foreigner was superior. Often your training was superior to the foreigner's, but by the very fact that you were a native, you had to work under him. This created some very tense situations in these countries; and therefore some men, not because they did not love their country but on principle, refused to accept that kind of relationship. Now, that situation is changing. In my own country we started a program of Africanization some years ago in which everyone who is to be trained, who goes abroad to be trained, is followed very carefully. He is trained for something quite specific, and a foreigner is employed on the basis of contract, so we know when the contract is to be completed; we know when the young man or young woman is to be coming home, and these positions are open for them. And I say here, anyone who is skeptical can check the records of Sierra Leone, but most of our people now who are trained abroad are ready and willing to come home, even when they are offered far greater inducements abroad, because they know they have their freedom when they come back home to head important projects in which they can work, in which they can take a share in the development of their own country. So this problem no longer exists, because even the foreigner now realizes that he comes not to be the boss, but to work. He is no longer coming to work *over* the African; he is coming to work *with* the African; and this has changed the whole atmosphere, the whole attitude, and you are going to find out that increasingly young men and young women who are trained abroad are going to come home. I can assure you of this. Therefore there should be no fear here about the training abroad. I may say this because all along I have noticed in this Conference, there is a certain degree of skepticism as to people going abroad.

"Now, let me say this, Mr. Chairman, ladies and gentlemen, that it is a mistake for this Conference to begin on the assumption that new states and the people of new states are not human beings exactly as people of the more developed states. They are. They love; they hate; they quarrel. (We call it *palava* at home.) They have ambitions just like anybody, and they are conniving just like anybody else. And therefore because one man decides to stay in the United Kingdom or in America or somewhere else and make money does not mean that all the others are going to behave in the same way. And if you cannot generalize in this respect for Britishers, or for Americans, or for Israelis, it is unfair to the new states to generalize in that respect."

He hoped that Africa would never become isolated from the rest of the world, that it would be possible for Africans to receive training in many parts of the world and that people from everywhere would always come to work in Africa.

"Now, let me come then to the whole question of training. I have already said from this platform that training is the key in the development of these new states. Training on all fronts, training at home and training abroad. I, for one, have said this from public platforms in my own country many times: I would hate to see the time ever to come when my own university —and as I have reminded you before, it is the oldest university south of the Sahara Desert, barring none, a college 150 years old with a long tradition of a high standard of education, affiliated with the University of Durham in the United Kingdom; but even though we are moving into independence as a new state, I hope I never live to see the day when we shall have an all-

African staff. One of the essential characteristics of a university is the crossing of minds of all people throughout the world. And I hope the day will come when we shall not only have Britishers, but we shall have Israelis, we shall have French, we shall have Germans, we shall have anyone who has something to contribute in the way of research. We want a free atmosphere to move back and forth in our university; we want no parochialism of any kind to stultify our thinking and make us lower our perspectives. We shall want to look to the world as a university. And therefore training at home in our universities, whether it is in the sciences or other aspects of our training, will always be training in which we will share cooperatively with people of all the world. In this respect, I want to say here that we advertise for staff in all the papers of the world to be able to reach them; and this year we are employing a classicist from Ceylon, we are employing a librarian from some other country, and we actually go out of our way because we want to bring into Sierra Leone an international staff. And therefore training at that level can become a real contribution, as countries who see our advertisements are able to come and share with us. And that is training at the local level. But training at the local level, as I insist, must go side by side with training abroad. There are certain facilities for training that for the longest time to come will not be available in Africa. Certain specialized forms of training will be available abroad, and we do want some of our young people who have distinguished themselves, having taken their first degree at home, to be able to go abroad and to specialize so that they can come back —not only for the contribution they themselves can make to the country, but for the inspiration they can become to the young people, to assure them that there are no limits to the boundaries of knowledge when opportunities are given. Therefore, this training abroad must be a very serious one.

"This means, of course, that universities abroad must open their doors. I would like to see some of our finest students in science coming to the Weizmann Institute with a program clearly laid out that they can follow. I would like to see some of our students going to other countries where the opportunities are made available."

Caulker's plea was that help be given to the Africans, not in order to quiet or subdue them, but because they need and want it and are ready for it.

"Now, let me say this as I conclude, Mr. Chairman. What we do not like, and here I must speak for Sierra Leone of course, is the feeling that our problems are of no interest, that our needs are of no urgency to the greater powers of the world, until we begin to misbehave ourselves—and then there's a rush. You must not wait until we start killing white people before you rush in with scholarships. You must come in while our need is there, while we can accept you in friendship, and not hang over us a bale of dollars and saying, 'If you are good boys, you can have this money.' As long as that attitude prevails, you will find that, no matter how much money is poured into these countries, the net result will always be resentment. But when it comes with the genuine thought that we are a part of the world, that our training will contribute to the peace of the world, we know that we have a contribution to make; and therefore, in a larger sense we are Israelis, in a larger sense we are Americans, in a larger sense we are British. Thank you very much, Mr. Chairman."

This was his closing speech:

"Mr. Chairman, ladies and gentlemen. If I went home and were asked whether I expressed thanks for this Conference on behalf of Sierra Leone and I said no—well, I would never be forgiven, because, while there are many weaknesses in our country, ungratefulness or ingratitude is not one of them.

"I came to this Conference not really knowing at first whether there was any contribution Sierra Leone would make or how much I should be able to learn to take home, but I want to state here, Mr. Chairman, ladies and gentlemen, that these days we have spent here in Israel have become such great days in my life that I am quite sure I will never be the same person again when I return home. And I hope that the infection which I will take from here will spread very rapidly among the people of Sierra Leone. We have been entertained royally everywhere. The Weizmann Institute where some of us have stayed has opened its doors to us, and I think that I can say quite honestly from the bottom of my heart that there has been nothing left undone that could have been done. And so I want first to say on behalf of my delegation, of which I happen to be the only member, that I am very grateful to have been here. At the same time I would like to say to you, Mr. Eban, Mr. Chairman, that a cynic has defined gratitude as a lively sense of more favours to come, and so I say this to you as a hint that more Sierra Leonians may have the opportunity that I have had. Now it is not easy, ladies and gentlemen, to assess a Conference of this kind. We have listened here to many learned people, men of great talent and ability, who have given of their time to come here and to open our eyes. From these people we have seen many of the problems of the new states, and I think for myself it is true to say we have seen them for the first time as they are, in their proper perspective. Not only that. I have also come to the conclusion that, great as these problems are, we shall not, because of all we have seen and heard, allow ourselves to be stampeded into reckless attempts of all sorts. These programs do require planning, concentration of thought, a great deal of energy, men of goodwill from all over the world coming together. As I see the problems, they have varied. To some people it is a problem of over-population; to other people it is a problem of under-population. To some people it is a problem of a shortage of water; to some other people it is a problem of too much water and nowhere to put it. To some people it is the problem of improving their educational program. To some others of us it is the problem of making an entirely new beginning to set forth for the first time a liberating kind of education that would bring abundant life to the people. But to all of us, whether it has been an over-population or under-population, to all of us has come a realization that science, through ever-changing and growing insight, can liberate human kind and help us all stand up with pride and believe that we are members of the human race. This has come to me with such an impact, Mr. Chairman, that I feel moved to say to you that, if nothing else can be done for Africa in the next twenty years, you can very well afford to rest. You've done a great deal in these ten days. From this Conference, therefore, I want to go home with a grateful heart, for, when I came here ten days ago, Mr. Chairman, it was night, it was dark, one couldn't see very far ahead of one. One was lonely. When I leave here on Sunday, it will be light not only physically but metaphorically, for somehow, because of the dedication of the scientists who have come here to share with us their will, their insight, their research, I no longer go home feeling that we are isolated in our problems. For I believe now that, not only are we interested in our problems, we are in a community of men of goodwill all over the world who are bringing to bear their fine minds and abilities to help us solve these problems. Therefore we no longer stand alone, but we belong to a great program. I say to you, Mr. Eban, to all of you, that when the new day dawns, as I see it dawning beyond the horizon, I begin to see the rays of the sunlight and all the world awake to greet that dawn. The Rehovoth Conference gives me the message for the people of Sierra Leone and we, too, shall be standing beside you to greet that dawn. Thank you from the bottom of my heart, Israel, for the stimulating environment in which you have made this Conference to meet. Thank you, the Weizmann Institute, for your generosity and the ease of atmosphere in which you have made us feel that we are not strangers. God bless you all. I shall certainly come back to Israel."

Afterword

What I learned from the Rehovoth Conference and, most especially from Caulker, triggered a wish to bring together a group of experts of all kinds to study the possibility of educating tropical Africans, children and adults alike, of guiding them away from their old ways of thinking toward a more rational appreciation of cause and effect. This study, in which Caulker was to have been the bridge between his world and ours, will take place here in Cambridge this summer. But it will take place without Caulker, who died in an airplane crash in Dakar, on August 30, 1960, on his way home from the Conference.

THE USE OF PSSC IN OTHER COUNTRIES

by Uri Haber-Schaim

WHILE work on the preliminary edition of the PSSC course was still in progress, inquiries and requests for materials started coming in from many countries. Some people had only vague ideas as to what was going on, but the magnitude of the project sounded intriguing. As the work progressed, the foreign interest became more specific; and by the summer of 1959 several teachers and science supervisors from other countries attended PSSC summer institutes alongside their American colleagues. The summer of 1960 saw another group of visitors from other countries. Their expenses in this country were covered by the National Science Foundation, and their travel was arranged through three regional organizations: the Organization for Economic Cooperation and Development, the Pan American Union, and the Asia Foundation.

At that time it became evident that in several countries the interest in PSSC had grown to such an extent that they were planning to use the PSSC course in some schools on an experimental basis. The expense of bringing a large number of teachers across the Atlantic would have been considerable. Moreover, these teachers would have attended institutes which were aimed at the American teacher and his environment, leaving them the entire task of "transposing" the course to their own situations. Finally, considering the language barrier which exists in many cases, it was realized that in order to proceed further, PSSC instructors would have to go abroad and teach the course on a local or regional basis. Although individual teachers from other countries still participate in American summer institutes, the bulk of the international participation has moved abroad. Table I lists the full-fledged PSSC courses held abroad to date. They each lasted between 4 and 6 weeks, giving the participants the opportunity to study the course in detail and to become familiar with the full range of learning aids: the text, laboratory, films, tests, teacher's guide, and supplementary reading.

The first few institutes abroad were at least partially staffed by experienced PSSC physicists from this country. It is indeed a source of great pleasure to note that several institutes have recently been staffed entirely by local personnel.

Teacher training courses are not the only medium by which the PSSC course has been brought to the attention of colleagues abroad. The Physical Science Study Committee has received numerous invitations for the presentation of its ideas at various seminars and conferences. These are listed in Table II. Naturally it is extremely hard to convey the spirit of the PSSC course in a presentation of a few hours or even a few days. Nevertheless in several cases the participation in a short course has created interest in further study of PSSC materials.

Today the PSSC course is used in several countries on an experimental basis. These are: Sweden, Norway, Italy, Israel, Brazil, Uruguay, Chile, Canada, and New Zealand. It is used on a private basis in many other countries. Although school systems differ from country to country, it is interesting to note the similarity of the problems in teaching physics. We reprint here the prefaces from the Japanese and the Swedish editions of our material, and excerpts from the "PSSC Newsletter" from New Zealand and Brazil. These excerpts could just as well have been taken from area meetings of American PSSC teachers. A comparison of the standard texts currently in use around the world may offer an explanation for the reception that PSSC receives; these texts are quite similar, and have, therefore, the same weaknesses that many American texts have. Since physics has become a universal science, it is easy to understand why "PSSC movements" should start in countries with different backgrounds and school systems.

A Translation of the Introduction to Swedish Edition, PSSC Text

The new physics course created by the Physical Science Study Committee has aroused a justified interest in Sweden as well as in many other lands. In 1960, a representative of the Royal Administration for Vocational Training received a stipend from OECD and the National Science Foundation in order to take part in an American study course for physics teachers in "PSSC

Dr. Haber-Schaim is the Director of the Physical Science Study Committee.

physics." One of the results of his visit was that in the beginning of 1961 the Royal Administration for Vocational Training invited Dr. Uri Haber-Schaim, one of the leaders of the PSSC, to present the course before physics teachers in Sweden.

In the summer of 1961, OECD arranged a four-week international seminar in Cambridge, England, where the PSSC course was described and discussed in detail. Because of the interest in the course already generated by Dr. Haber-Schaim's visit, a Swedish delegation was sent to the seminar. On their recommendation, the Royal School Administration and the Administration of Vocational Training decided, in the autumn of 1962, to begin a trial program in certain higher public and technical secondary schools, with a physics course based on the PSSC. For this purpose, the administrations appointed a joint work group in which a number of physicists with teaching experience discussed how to adapt the PSSC course for use in Swedish schools.

When Norway showed interest in a similar program, the two countries established cooperation, primarily regarding the translation and preparation of the course. Cooperation was also established with the Physical Science Study Committee in Watertown, Massachusetts, which is engaged in further development of the course, and which has supplied us with new material as it has come out.

The PSSC course is based upon a unified combination of a textbook, problems, homework, labs, films, and related reading material. For adaptation to our school system, as stated previously, the course has been specially prepared and expanded. The preliminary edition, which follows, should not, however, be looked upon as a finished product. The aim of the trial program is to discover, through practical experience, wherein the course should be further modified to be of greatest possible benefit to our schools.

It should be mentioned that a certain amount of caution had to be exercised in the preparation so as not to lose the characteristic quality and value of the original course, which is primarily what the trial program is intended to examine. Among other things, there are some relatively elementary sections (mostly in part I) which might be more suitable for an elementary school course than for a gymnasium. The teacher is free to skip these parts or to use them in summary fashion as a review of earlier physics courses. On the other hand, it might be necessary for technical gymnasiums to supplement certain sections, particularly those on electricity.

The role of the teacher in the trial program is somewhat unusual. Because of the detailed text, which has been arranged so that students can easily — and, it is hoped, with interest — read new sections themselves, less time will be devoted to the preparation of homework. Instead, more importance will be given to discussion of what students have read, or subjects suggested by situations in the course's "discussion problems." Obviously, the teacher shall decide when demonstrations should be made.

It is the hope of the committee that this course and related trial program will lead to an increased interest in physics among students as well as to a greater knowledge of physical relations and a greater capacity for independent work in physics.

MATS HULTIN
Chairman of the Joint Work Group of the School and Vocational Training Administrations

A Translation of the Preface to Japanese Edition, PSSC Laboratory Guide

The preface to the original edition of "Laboratory Guide for Physics" tells why and how the book was published. In this preface the translators would like to show as far as possible the extent to which the aim of the PSSC physics course is realized in the laboratory guidebook.

At a PSSC Seminar in Tokyo in September 1961, Dr. Haber-Schaim and Dr. Youtz of the Physical Science Study Committee emphasized that the distinctive character of PSSC physics could not be grasped from its textbook alone, and that the course consisted of the textbook, proper selection of experimental materials for students, programs of demonstration experiments in the classroom, movies of experiments that are difficult to demonstrate in the class, a guidebook for teachers, and selected supplementary reading for students. Among all these, they said, the experiments to be done by students are the most important.

As the textbook of PSSC physics is written much more carefully and matters are explained in much greater detail than in Japanese textbooks, the class can be planned so that each student may read the text carefully, and thus time ordinarily spent on explanations can be given to experiments. Therefore students can confirm their understanding of the text by the work in the laboratory.

Topics of experiments and their order are very carefully planned according to the system described above. However important we consider the teaching of physics, there is a limit to the time available, and the selection of topics and their order is a vital point. As a matter of fact, this problem has been discussed among Japanese scholars with reference to scientific education. We must admit that there is a remarkable difference between the selection of topics of PSSC physics and that of our own.

For instance, the experiments designed to show the relationship between the motion of a mass and the force acting on it, or more basic experiments to measure time, distance, mass, etc., have a great prominence in this guidebook. And we have never seen any Japanese textbooks which treat the relation between gravitational mass and inertial mass in as complete detail as the PSSC textbook. In the experiment to investigate the behavior of an accelerated mass, it is suggested that the force should be applied by hand through rubber strands and the effect of gravity minimized. When Dr. Haber-Schaim demonstrated this experiment in the Tokyo seminar, he emphasized that it was important and necessary to apply a force by hand through rubber strands, admitting, however, that it might be difficult to apply a constant force by such a method. We were deeply impressed by such a consistent point of view, which is characteristic of PSSC physics.

With respect to friction, it is merely shown that the kinetic energy of a coin sliding on a sheet of paper changes into some other form, leading up to the conservation of momentum in case of a collision of atoms. This is quite different from the general principle of Japanese textbooks. Here the principle of PSSC physics is that there should be many other fundamental experiments on kinematics in physics at the high school level, instead of going further into the problems of friction. It is because of the same principle that there is no experiment on the moment or buoyancy force. In fact, there is strong emphasis on understanding the relationship between the motion of a mass and the acting force, or the conception of the field of force, through students' experiments, instead of going further into the electrical or magnetic theory.

Another characteristic of PSSC physics is its treatment of units of measure. It is made clear in both the PSSC textbook and the laboratory guide that the units of length, time, and mass may be chosen only for convenience and that the principle of physics is independent of its unit system. For example, in the experiment on the motion of mass, students can confirm that the period vibration which can be measured by the dots on paper made by a pendulum is constant, and after that they may use this period as a unit of time so that they may organize the data and find the relationship between travel distance and time, or that between velocity and time.

Such a system of experiments, according to PSSC, gives students an understanding of the meaning of units commonly used, such as second, meter, kilogram, etc. For example, the experiment on the natural temperature scale, simple as it is, is thought out very carefully and completely to give students an understanding of the physical meaning of temperature, or its definition. The same system is used in the case of units in the experiments on light, electricity, and magnetism.

Such a system has another advantage in that it can reduce the necessary expense of experimental apparatus for students. In Japan we can buy very cheap graduated glass cylinders and measuring tapes which may only have relatively constant and consistent spacing in their units; on the other hand, the officially approved ones are rather expensive. We also know that a laboratory-type oscilloscope is too expensive for ordinary school use. Yet experiments for students become meaningless unless all students are able to do them. To make it most effective, the number of students in a group should be

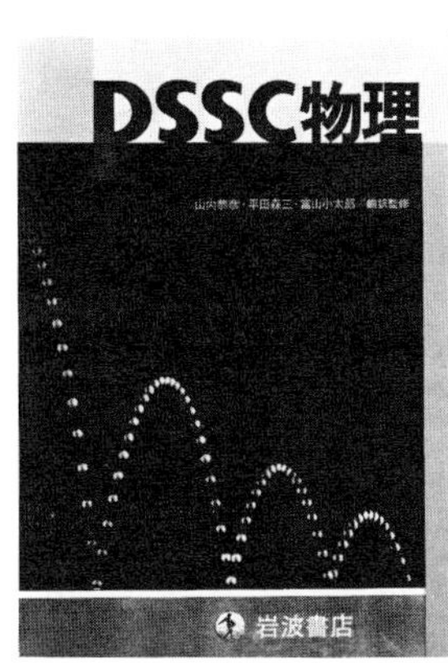

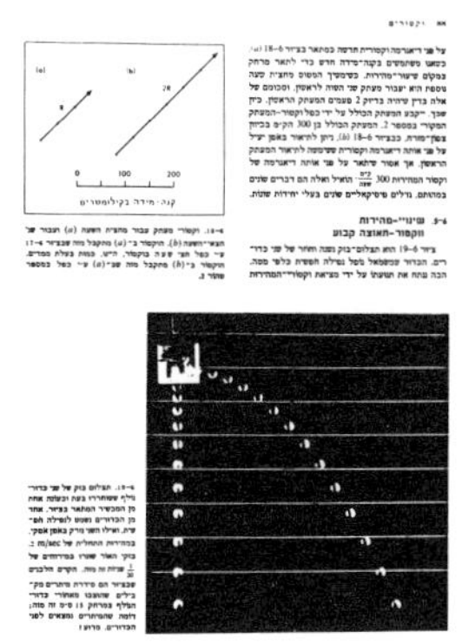

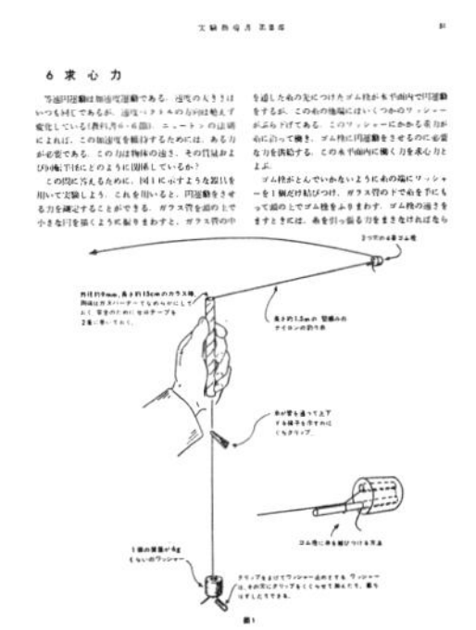

two or three — at most, four. In other words, the number of pieces of apparatus which should be prepared for an experiment is one-third or one-fourth of the number of students in the class. It is significant that even in the United States much effort was devoted to making the experimental apparatus cheaper, and that almost all of the materials in this guidebook are simple adaptations of mass-produced common articles.

All of the apparatus in the guidebook is also very simple. There is no expensive apparatus like the so-called "Dr. So-and-so's apparatus" with which we are so familiar. However, we should say that this fact is not due only to the economical reason mentioned above. It is also based on the fact that simple apparatus and conditions are much more effective in making an experiment understood than precise but complicated ones. This fact is emphasized in the original preface of this guidebook; however, we must add that it is not so easy to design such simple but effective apparatus. This remarkable achievement was the result of cooperation by the top-level scholars of many universities and high school teachers after several years of actual tests. A piece of apparatus which may seem perfectly simple is the fruit of careful study from many points of view.

This simplicity of experimental apparatus for students makes it easy for a teacher to buy necessary materials at stores and to assemble it as shown in this guidebook. Some teachers, however, may not have time for this. Therefore, PSSC has interested commercial manufacturers in producing and selling the necessary apparatus in kit form. In these kits even the most common articles such as paper clips, rubber strands, cotton thread, and razor blades are included if they are necessary to the experiments. Each kit enables a group of from two to four students to do an experiment.

There may be people who have negative reactions to PSSC physics, especially to its principle and selection of topics. However, we have to consider and decide which is the best way to improve the present educational situation in Japan. With respect to the apparatus for experiments it is desirable to find a way to supply such experimental apparatus at a low cost. We should not place all the burden on the eagerness of high school teachers.

This guidebook is translated by Junzo Iwaoka and Masao Kojima under the supervision of Uamaura, Hirata, and Tomiyama.

Representing the Translators
TAKAHIKO YAMANOUCHI
MORISO HIRATA
KOTARO TOMIYAMA

Some Excerpts from Foreign PSSC Newsletters

Brazil

IBECC AND PSSC

Instituto Brasileiro de Educacao, Ciencia e Cultura program was formally proposed in 1952, and began in 1954. Among other basic assumptions of this program we stressed especially: a) improvement in science education must start in the secondary schools; b) one cannot expect to improve science education without using top scientists as leaders in establishing what and how to teach; and c) science education cannot be properly done without an emphasis on scientific experiments, using simple equipment and avoiding the fancy chrome plate instruments leading to cook-book directions.

On visiting Educational Services Incorporated, after an exchange of letters, we were able to find how much in common our programs and aims were, and how impossible it would be for Brazil to make a comparable effort by itself. We have followed up the progress of PSSC materials and books from the initial multigraphed copies. Preliminary preparation of the ground work introducing some of its experiments, as well as some general discussion with physicists and physics teachers, took place during 1959 and 1960. In 1961 IBECC published the first foreign translation of the laboratory guide, and started to make some of the equipment. One of IBECC's staff members attended a PSSC Summer Institute during that year.

FIRST SUMMER INSTITUTE

With the sponsorship of the Pan American Union, financial assistance of the Ford Foundation, and the technical advice of the National Science Foundation, in January 1962, the First Summer Institute was held in Sao Paulo, as a joint effort of Educational Services Incorporated and IBECC.

The staff for this Institute was: Dr. Uri Haber-Schaim, from ESI, and Dr. Aaron Lemonick, from the Department of Physics of Princeton University, as lecturers; Dr. Dario Moreno, from the University of Chile, as assistant lecturer; Dr. Elliot Coen, from the University of Costa Rica, and Philip Rosete, from Tampa, Florida, as laboratory lecturers; and Rachel Gevertz, from IBECC, as laboratory lecturer and general director assistant.

Participants came from Brazil (19), Argentina (3), Chile (4), Colombia (5), Costa Rica (1), Nicaragua (1), Panama (1), Paraguay (4), Peru (1), and Uruguay (3).

The course took six weeks, with five full days a week, including lectures, group discussions, laboratory sessions, films, and examinations.

At the end of the course a few days were devoted to a round table discussion of the value of PSSC, its applicability in Latin America, the problems involved, and follow up ideas.

MULTIPLICATION FACTOR

As one of the results of the First Summer Institute, some good teachers were selected to constitute the staff for other Institutes. This summer, as a result, it was possible to run an Institute in Brazil with IBECC's staff trained in the First Institute as well as to provide members for the staff of the Institutes run simultaneously in Costa Rica and Uruguay. Both the directors and the lecturers in Brazil and Uruguay were Latin Americans present at the First Summer Institute.

SECOND SUMMER INSTITUTE

This was held in Rio de Janeiro under the sponsorship of IBECC with financial assistance from the Ford Foundation and the Brazilian Ministry of Education. It took place at the Institute of Physics of the Catholic University of Rio de Janeiro.

The Institute was directed by Dr. Pierre H. Lucie, and with the following instructors: Antonio de Sousa Teixeira, Jr., from the Faculty of Sciences, University of Sao Paulo; Helio Pinto Guedes, from the Institute of Physics of the Catholic University of Rio de Janeiro; Rodolpho Caniato, from the University of Campinas; and Rachel Gevertz, from IBECC. This team was entirely responsible for the teaching.

In addition to the teaching staff, Dr. Philip Morrison, from Cornell University, and Dr. Uri Haber-Schaim also participated.

As an experiment, IBECC invited Dr. Newton Braga from the University of Ceara, Dr. Ramiro Porto Alegre Muniz from the University of Brazilia, and Dr. Waldez B. daCunha from the University of Bahia as visiting teachers to become acquainted with this new course, and eventually to start preparing to become directors for successive Institutes.

Thirty-eight Brazilian participants came from ten states.

PSSC Books and Films

We cannot expect to introduce PSSC in Brazil unless we have the full materials available, including textbook, equipment, laboratory guide, teacher's resource books, films, tests, and even the supplementary literature (paperback books).

During 1963 we are making a concentrated effort to make available the textbook and part of the series of pocket books. This translation program is being carried out with the Ford Foundation's and the Ministry of Education's (Emergency Plan under Prof. Darcy Ribeiro) financial assistance. The textbook is going to be printed this year by the University of Brazilia Press. A multigraphed edition is already available, and was used during the Second Summer Institute, as well as by some experimental classes. About ten of the pocket books will be ready for publication during the year, and will be printed by IBECC and the University Press of Sao Paulo.

The translation of the teacher's resource books is progressing, too.

Films are being translated, and during the year we expect to make available part of the set, using the facilities of Federal Audio-Visual Services, and/or the Regional Center of Educational Research's Audio-Visual Aids Service in Sao Paulo (CRPE-Michigan University project).

PSSC Equipment

The actual PSSC teaching after the First Institute was very limited, due to lack of books in Portuguese, but the major difficulty was laboratory equipment. Without laboratory equipment, none of the teachers decided to use PSSC, as such.

During 1962 IBECC has concentrated on preparations for the production of the full line of equipment, and is able today to supply almost all the items, locally made, excluding the slinky and pocket-type radiation dosimeter. This production has necessitated the making of a great number of tools.

It must be pointed out that the participants in the Second Summer Institute have received some equipment to start PSSC during 1963.

PSSC Activities in 1962

In 1962, the use of the PSSC course was very restricted for obvious reasons.

Several participants in the First Summer Institute conducted limited trials, and IBECC has provided equipment and films on loan. A full PSSC course was used for physics students, under Dr. Pierre H. Lucie at the Institute of Physics of the Catholic University of Rio de Janeiro. IBECC has provided equipment and films on loan.

A small in-service Institute was conducted by Rachel Gevertz and some participants of the First Summer Institute.

PSSC Activities in 1963

Besides the program for printing the textbook, at least 10 pocket books, and the translation of some of the films during the year, several other activities will be conducted:

(a) Many of the participants will use PSSC programs. IBECC will provide, in some cases, equipment on loan and multigraphed reprints of the textbook.

(b) The Department of Physics of the Faculty of Sciences of the University of Sao Paulo has engaged Antonio de Souza Teixeira, Jr., as instructor of "didactic equipment for teaching physics," and from 1964 on he will prepare all future physics teachers who will be graduated by the University of Sao Paulo to teach PSSC.

(c) The translation of the teacher's resource books will continue, eventually with special additional information for Brazil.

(d) Dr. Pierre H. Lucie was engaged by IBECC and, as a member of its staff, was sent to Boston to stay a year at ESI, working on the "Advanced Topics."

New Zealand

The first training course, lasting four weeks, will be held during the August vacation and the first week of the third term. About thirty New Zealand teachers will be taken through the PSSC work in preparation for teaching it next year. Mr. Roberts, who is now back in New Zealand, will be course chairman.

PSSC physics has roused great interest in Victoria, and a physics study committee there has recommended its introduction in the schools. Three physics teachers are being sent to our August course. Their training will provide the authorities with the nucleus of a team for future in-service training work.

We are looking forward to having the group with us as their presence will add greatly to the value and interest of the course.

H. W. Sayers
Chairman, Physics Study Committee

PSSC NEWSLETTER NO. 3

Last week the Auckland members met with Mr. Roberts and had a very full discussion on the work of the course. That a new point of view emerged is seen from the following extracts from the minutes of the meeting:

> *"Generally teachers feel that none of Part III should be omitted."*
>
> *"Some feel that Part III should be done in full, and Part IV be treated in VIA."*
>
> *"It was felt that reasonable coverage for 1962 would be Chapters 1 to 29, but omitting Chapter 26."*

I have again discussed the matters of coverage and examinations with Dr. Ross, and he agrees that it is not possible at this stage to reconcile the two viewpoints. This is, after all, an experimental year, and the more approaches tried, the better.

PSSC NEWSLETTER NO. 4

This finds us with Easter upon us. The cricket tests are over, small boys are playing marbles, and goal posts are going up on the football fields. The PSSC old hands are waltzing through Part I but most of those who are doing it for the first time are feeling the need for starting the course in Form V. Experience does help but there seems little doubt that PSSC work prior to Form VI would be an advantage and there is now a sufficient body of experience to make this practicable. In fact, it is no exaggeration to say that the spirit of PSSC has permeated almost all of our science teaching in New Zealand, so that the ideas of inquiry, readiness, and the humanism of science are very much in evidence.

• • • •

Equipment is being sent to schools as it arrives from the manufacturers and can be assembled into sets. The task of calling tenders, checking the materials, and assembling it into kits has been one that we would not like to tackle too often, although we would undoubtedly gain from our experience with this first exercise. Altogether, more than 40,000 items were in-

volved, and the Department's Stores Division is to be congratulated on the magnificent job it has done in organizing the complicated work of supply and dispatch. Its task has not been made easier by the inability of some of the manufacturers to meet their deadlines. Usually its difficulties have been with some small but vital part, leaving a series of kit-sets almost completed but not quite ready for sending to schools.

Fortunately, most of the difficulties have now been ironed out, and it is hoped that the work of the schools has not suffered too much from the late arrival of certain items.

Next year these delays will not occur as full school sets of equipment are now being assembled in advance.

New Zealand Representative at Educational Services Incorporated: *Mr. John Coulter of Pakuranga College (formerly Putaruru High School) left a few weeks ago on the express invitation of Professor Uri Haber-Schaim to take part in the development of the Junior program. John has our best wishes for a successful and profitable stay in Massachusetts. After hearing of Don Nelson's and Ted Mead's year in New England John is under no illusions about its being a holiday.*

PSSC physics as a prerequisite for Technicians' Courses in Polytechnics: *Doubt has been expressed by two teachers as to the suitability of PSSC for this work, which is definitely technological in nature. If I remember correctly, Frank Stevens answered this at last year's evaluation course. He feels that PSSC is very suitable because of the greater understanding it brings to students.*

• • • •

It was suggested at the evaluation course held last year that a section of the Newsletter should be devoted to teaching hints. The idea was that when a teacher discovered some valuable approach to the text, the use of the apparatus, the solution of problems, etc., he should make his brain child available through the Newsletter to other PSSC teachers. Any ideas you have will be welcome and will assist other teachers. Please let me have them while they are fresh in your mind. In fact, any contributions of interest to others will be welcomed for publication.

PSSC NEWSLETTER NO. 5

Although the schemes submitted by individuals vary quite a bit in detail, there are already one or two common threads of agreement. For instance, it seems clear that quite an amount of physics with a PSSC flavour can be taught below Sixth Form level. Again it is fairly evident that, whatever syllabus is finally decided upon, an alternative course will be required for the less able pupils. Courses would not only need to lead naturally into Sixth Form physics, but also provide for termination at the end of three years. Also, it appears that the suitability for Trade Certification and other allied courses of the physics taught must be given further consideration. The writing committee cannot hope to provide at the December conference much more than a basis for a trial scheme in 1964. This is in conformity with the recommendation No. 7 on page 14 of the 1962 Evaluation Report.

• • • •

Some of you may not be aware that a PSSC in-service course is being held at Christ's College for three weeks commencing 19 August. Some 40 teachers, mainly from independent schools, are expected to attend. Talks will be given by departmental and University representatives, but the lectures and demonstrations will be in the hands of teachers who have been through previous PSSC courses at Lopdell House. We wish them a very successful period together.

• • • •

We have had a visit recently from Mr. F. Reid, Assistant Director of Education for Fiji. About the same time we had an enquiry from the headmaster of a post-primary school in Fiji. It appears that there is a live interest in the PSSC work over there. Mr. Reid has gone back loaded with information, and we should be hearing further from them.

• • • •

The PSSC course is going according to plan so far. I made up a timetable for the whole year, taking into account as much as possible extraneous activities that might interfere with it. It has worked out very satisfactorily so far.

A pity we had to miss out on the slinky experiments. I have been using rubber tubing and showed the film on waves, so the pupils have not missed too much. At the moment we are "rippling." The Ecko lamps supplied for the light source are practically useless, particularly so in the refraction experiments, where the outline of the glass plate does not even show. I have been using 6V - 24 Watt lamps (from ray-boxes) instead, with good results.

I have marked all the individual kit-sets alphabetically and, where possible, even the parts in the set. The larger kits, supplied for two groups of two each, such as the ripple tanks, trolley-sets etc., I have marked AB, CD and so on. Even the dry cells, screwdrivers, clamps, etc. are marked accordingly. Two students are assigned to each group for the year and so far I have not come across snatching and interchanging of parts; moreover, the equipment is kept tidy and is looked after very well. Where there are spares, such as rubber bands, coated straws, etc., I have put them in boxes in my own safekeeping. Parkinson's Law or a modification thereof seems to work here: as many items are used as are supplied!

To help the students with their experimental write-up, I have them mark paragraphs containing related questions alphabetically in their lab guide. Their results are labelled accordingly. I find that the students are less liable to overlook or ignore certain questions altogether, and the tidiness of their books has much improved since I introduced this system.

The Fifth Form is now used to the system of objective tests. It takes time to compose these tests; my questions are by no means original, but they serve their purpose. Incidentally, they also provide a useful check upon the work of other teachers in Form V physics. Parts of Chapter 3, Chapters 5, 6, 11, 12, 13, 14 I have introduced so far in the Fifth Form without any undue difficulty. Parts of Chapter 27 and of 31 are on the program. I am looking forward to John Mills' proposed textbook for third and fourth forms, it sounds most encouraging.

• • • •

While in Australia last month attending the 12th Conference of the Australian Science Teachers' Association, I met Dick Gardiner again and spoke over the phone with Graham Miller. Both sent their regards to Kiwi PSSC'ers. Jackie Lang had just left for the U.S.A. Victoria is almost ready to adopt their own version of PSSC on a two-year basis. I had a long talk with Dr. MacDonnell of Monash University, who is chairman of the PSSC committee in Victoria. Dick showed me over his fine physics department at Melbourne Church of England Grammar School.

The big event in New South Wales is the publication of their massive new science book which will be the standard text for science at the Form I to V or VI stage for many years to come. It was "unveiled" during the opening address at the Conference by Mr. R. W. Stanhope of Sydney Teachers' College. The writing committee has done a wonderful job on this £40,000 project. Many barrels of midnight oil were burned with Professor Messell trimming the wick and keeping the forced draught going. It is bold; it is modern; it assumes that boys and girls at school can handle things we have been inclined to think were too hard, and that they will work hard if they think it is worth while and are challenged. It is being distributed to all New South Wales schools but is not yet available for purchase.

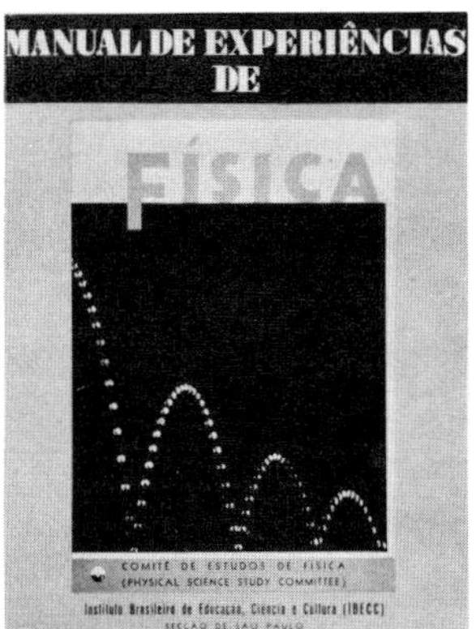

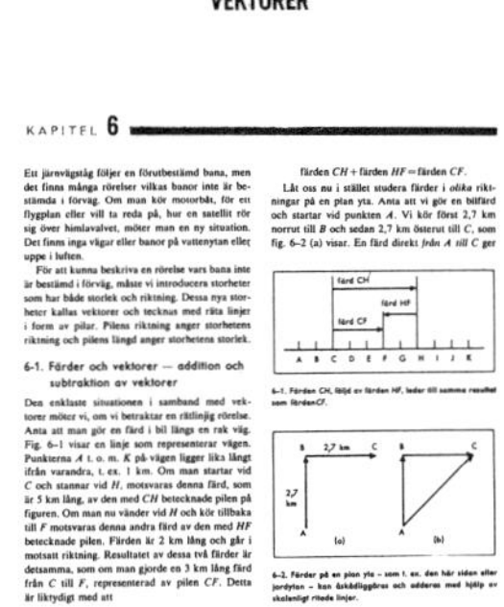

VEKTORER

KAPITEL 6

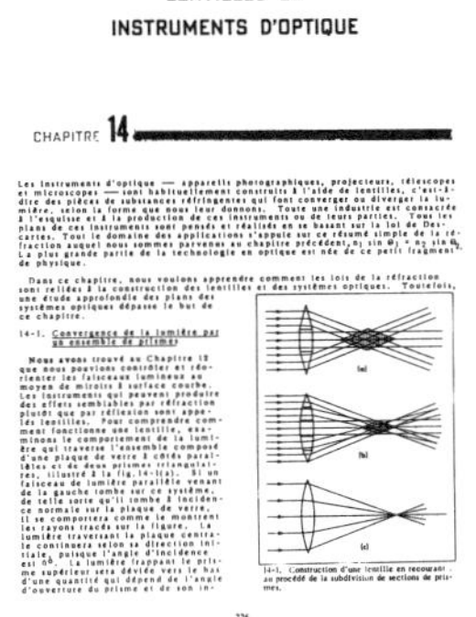

LENTILLES ET INSTRUMENTS D'OPTIQUE

CHAPITRE 14

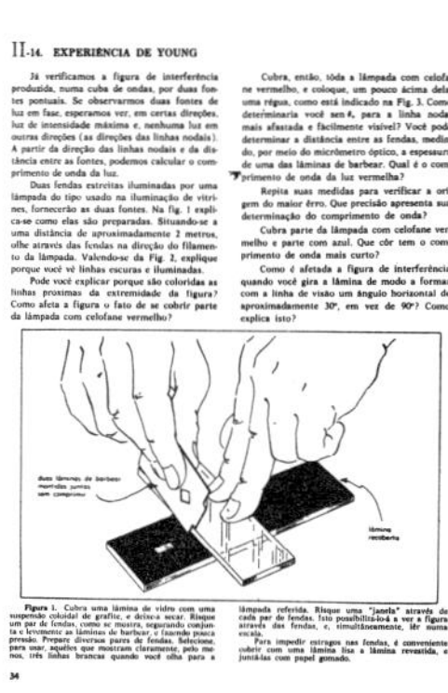

The Full Report of the PSSC Institute at the University College of Rhodesia and Nyasaland

PHYSICS IN THE SECONDARY SCHOOL AND UNIVERSITY

A Course provided by the Department of Physics in conjunction with the Institute of Education 2nd September to 12th September, 1963

I. INTRODUCTION

The starting point of this course is the interest of the University College in the work of the schools, the concern of Departments of the College, school teachers, and education officers to review their curricula and methods in the light of new developments and needs, and the wish to use the facilities of the University College to work out new approaches in the teaching of physics. The plan of the course originated from a visit to the College by Professor J. R. Zacharias, Professor of Physics at the Massachusetts Institute of Technology, and by Professor L. J. Lewis, Head of the Department of Education in Tropical Areas, University of London Institute of Education. At a meeting with Professor E. L. Yates in the Department of Physics the work of the Physical Science Study Committee — and the development of its program through the African Education Study organization of Educational Services Incorporated — was considered for its relevance to physics teaching in Rhodesia, and as an opportunity for local discussion and experiment. The Department of Physics was already in touch with such developments in the United States, and Mr. P. G. S. Gilbert, Department of Education, had spent some months there studying in science curricula workshops.

It was decided to set up a small Planning Committee composed of representatives of the University College Departments of Physics and Education, of the Institute of Education, of the schools and the inspectorate, to prepare the way for a residential course for teachers. This committee assembled the essential literature and examined it, initiated some experiments in parts of the PSSC course in schools, and over a period of six months planned the program and made the necessary contacts with Educational Services Incorporated, with local Ministries of Education, and with teachers of physics.

II. PRELIMINARY CONFERENCES AND THE AIMS OF THE COURSE

The Planning Committee of fifteen members was drawn from the University College, the schools—both European and non-European, from Northern and Southern Rhodesia — and from the inspectorate. Working papers were presented by Professor Yates (Department of Physics) on physics in the University College, and by Mr. Gilbert (Department of Education) on the work of the Physical Science Study Committee, and on the content and methodology of PSSC. Mr. Gilbert also provided extracts from the Teachers' Resource Book and Guide, and from the Students' Laboratory Guide. Dr. A. Brock (Department of Physics) contributed an analysis of the PSSC approach to Newton's Law of Motion, and Mr. A. P. Knottenbelt (Fletcher High School) a report on the Conference on Science in General Education, held at Pius XII College, Roma, Basutoland. Developments in science curriculum study in Britain also came under review.

The preliminary conferences were also concerned with formulating the requirements of a reconstituted school physics course against the background of the local examination syllabuses.

The general objectives were: to arrive at a statement of principles and practice which would take into account the urgent attention which must be given in developing countries to the fundamental sciences in order that they can ensure the necessary supply of competent technicians; to consider the methods by which school pupils might acquire sound methods of learning; to prepare students who were to go on to university studies so that they had a clear understanding of fundamental principles.

The Planning Committee agreed that an intensive study of PSSC would at least offer very valuable experience from which to approach such objectives. It was anticipated that the PSSC course would not fit existing syllabuses, that its adoption would entail radical changes in teaching and in examinations, and that there would have to be a re-teaching of the teachers themselves.

The aims of the course were therefore to learn by lectures and practical experience of the PSSC approach to physics teaching, to work through the texts and to try out the experimental laboratory methods, and to consider the implications and the practicability of adapting the PSSC course to the work of the schools in Rhodesia.

Six of the teachers on the Planning Committee offered

to experiment with one part of PSSC on one of their classes, so that some experience of its operation might be conveyed to the members of the course itself.

III. ARRANGEMENTS FOR THE COURSE

1. Membership

Invitations to attend the course were sent through the Ministries of Education and also direct to the schools, and emphasized that the course was open to all teachers of physics in secondary schools whether or not they were specialists. As a result seventy-six teachers, and eight others from the University College, the inspectorate and elsewhere, attended the course: to plenary sessions visitors also came from the Ministries of Education. The teachers were from Northern and Southern Rhodesia, from state and from private schools; most of the European, Asian and African secondary schools which have a physics course were represented. Of the eighty-four members, twenty-seven were in residence at Carr-Saunders Hall throughout the course. On the first evening guests were invited to dinner, with the members, and included the Principal of the University College, Dr. Walter Adams, and Mrs. Adams.

2. The Lecturers

The Planning Committee had always in mind the necessity of securing as lecturers teachers who were experienced in the operation of the PSSC course in the United States. In the event, the organizers were immensely fortunate that two outstanding teachers were able to come. They were:

PROFESSOR BYRON YOUTZ, *Professor of Physics at Reed College, Portland, Oregon.*

Professor Youtz, before going to Reed, taught physics at the American University of Beirut, Lebanon. He has been associated with PSSC since 1958, and is a member of its Steering Committee. He has worked in various phases of the project, including Advanced Topics and Films, and has taught PSSC in a number of summer programs, including one in Tokyo.

MR. DONALD A. SCHAEFER, *physics teacher at Bettendorf (Iowa) Senior High School.*

Mr. Schaefer has used the PSSC course in his own school since 1958, has been a staff member at several summer institute programs for high school teachers, and is at present one of the experimental group for Advanced Topics materials now being produced.

3. Assistance from the United States

The two lecturers were able to come as a result of the efforts and generosity of a number of people and organizations, of Professor Zacharias in the first instance, and of:

Mr. Stephen White, Program Director of the African Education Program, and Assistant to the President of Educational Services Incorporated;

Mr. Stephen H. Stackpole, Executive Associate of the Commonwealth Program of the Carnegie Corporation of New York which provided a grant of $5,800 to Educational Services Incorporated for the travel expenses of the lecturers and for some of their equipment.

Extraordinary efforts were also made by the lecturers themselves to ensure that a sufficiency of equipment arrived in time; it became necessary to arrange air transport for the final consignment.

4. A Combined Operation

Within the University College the resources of the Institute of Education, the Department of Education, and the Department of Physics were combined. Professor Yates had recently been organizer and chairman of the Leverhulme Conference on Physics in the University — a conference which drew to the University College university teachers of physics from many parts of Africa and from overseas. He now acted as chairman of the present course and arranged that all physics lecture rooms, laboratories, workshops, and technical staff should be made available. Much of the materials needed by the members was made before and during the course in the physics workshops by the technical staff, and Professor Yates also arranged that a supply of the necessary text books and other literature was ready before the course began.

The Northern Rhodesia Ministry of Education defrayed the expenses of its own teachers, and the Federal Ministry met part of the residential fees and travel expenses for those who came from European and Asian schools. A feature of the membership was the inclusion of physics teachers from training colleges and technical colleges as well as from schools. A direct interest in the outcome of the course was expressed by Audio Visual Services of the Federal Ministry of Education, two of whose senior officers attended some of the sessions. A link was also made with the Nairobi Science Teaching Centre through the attendance of its Director, Mr. T. D. Benjamin.

The opportunity was taken to make contact with professional science associations, and a dinner was arranged for the members by the Association for Science Education in Central Africa at which the guest of honor was Dr. Warren Brown, Cultural Affairs Officer of the United States Information Services. Dr. Brown gave an address on Science Fairs.

5. Books and Exhibitions

An important service to the members was provided by the assembling of science books and exhibitions and directories of equipment. In the Reading Room of the new extension to the Physics Department a full set was displayed of the Science Study Series published to date (32 volumes). These books were brought by the American lecturers, and at the end of the course were given to the developing Science Education Centre of the Department of Education. In addition, the United States Information Services made available some seventy science books covering a wide range of topics. These also, at the end of the course, were given to the University College.

The Book Centre — a Salisbury bookseller — arranged an extensive exhibition of physics and mathematics books appropriate to the various teaching levels of these subjects. This firm was able to acquire forty-five copies of the PSSC text and laboratory guide for sale on the first morning of the course. All these were sold and orders were placed for many more, and for the Teacher's Guide. Educational Supply Company (Pvt.), Ltd. exhibited several items of PSSC equipment — British version — supplied by Philip Harris and Company of Birmingham.

The local branch of Baird and Tatlock Ltd. exhibited a representative selection of their scientific apparatus, backed by regular attendance of members of their staff. The interest of the members of the course was sufficient to warrant an approach by this firm to Macalaster Scientific Corporation, Cambridge, Massachusetts — approved suppliers of PSSC apparatus in the United States — seeking their representation in Central Africa. This arrangement has been made, and as a result an essential service is now available for teachers in the Rhodesias.

In one laboratory a permanent display of demonstrations suitable for use in school physics courses was arranged by the chief laboratory steward, Mr. J. H. Houston. Mr. Houston's long and extensive experience of physics teaching at school and college level was apparent in this series of fascinating and effective demonstrations.

6. Study Groups and Steering Committee

With so large a course membership, and in order that there should be an effective working structure, it was decided to organize discussion through eight study groups, the leaders of each to form a Steering Committee which would act as a central planning body and also report the results of discussions to plenary conferences. In the second week, when the discussions were largely to be on the implications of PSSC for Rhodesian schools, the study groups were combined into four.

The groups were so arranged that varieties of experience were represented in each: experience of work in state and private schools, European, Asian and African schools. The Steering Committee, at the outset, was of great value in redesigning the provisional program so as to take account of the requests of the lecturers, and at the halfway stage, in amending the program for the second week in the light of findings of the first.

IV. THE WORK OF THE COURSE

1. Lectures

In Appendix I will be seen an outline of the timetable. The first seven days were devoted entirely to an examination of the PSSC course. It is to be noted that the lecturers were accustomed to courses with half as many members, and of six weeks' duration. That they unquestionably succeeded in covering the essentials effectively and that the members fully carried out their assignments of practical and theoretical work, is a measure of their own brilliance in exposition and of the sustained industry of their students.

2. Laboratory Work and Apparatus

Since the essential character of the PSSC course largely lies in the apparatus and its use, it was important to provide first-hand experience of it, however formidable the task with over eighty people. In the event, all spent over seven hours in the laboratories, and most made time for additional, individual, practical work.

The apparatus, specially designed, is startlingly simple; the reaction to it varied at first from outright scorn to fascination and delight. As the course proceeded initial doubt tended to fall away, and there was an appreciation of its appropriateness and efficiency which may be instanced as follows:

(i) A student can better concentrate on what he is doing and record observations if he is uncluttered by elaborate technical devices and mystifying "black boxes."

(ii) A young student the more readily accepts that physics is not a remote mystique, its disciples living in a world apart, using a jargon of their own, and studying phenomena unrelated to life, when the apparatus of physics includes familiar objects such as coffee tins, elastic bands, toy motors, springs, electric bell timers, trolley carts, cigarette boxes filled with sand, batteries, cheese boxes, drinking straws, razor blades, and clothes pegs. The films are consistent with this use of "real" objects and situations. The performers are well-known American physicists working naturally in their own laboratories.

(iii) The apparatus is cheap. In the U.S.A. the required twenty-seven kits of apparatus for a class can be purchased for approximately £270. Demands on storage space are light, and a school with only basic workshop facilities can reproduce most of the apparatus without difficulty.

3. Study Groups and Steering Committee

The division of the members into study groups permitted day-to-day discussion of the work and of the problems met by individuals. The group leaders who also formed the Steering Committee, effectively crystallised views and difficulties and made possible a coherent set of resolutions in the final plenary session. During the first week these discussions concentrated upon the PSSC course itself. Examples of matter discussed were: the time in the school curriculum to be allocated to each chapter of the course; adaptation of the course to pupils of moderate ability; the under-emphasis in PSSC of the technological aspects of physics; the question of the importance of inducing accuracy; MKS units; the relevance of pupils' background in physics before entering PSSC; student laboratory records.

In the second week the study groups approached the question of the implications of PSSC for schools in Rhodesia, and other matters of local concern. Examples of questions put to the groups were:

(i) Bearing in mind that we are considering the teaching of physics at the secondary school level, are we satisfied that the PSSC objectives are basically sound?

(ii) Assuming a favourable reply to the previous question, how far do our present school physics courses accord with such objectives? In what regard are they lacking?

(iii) If there is an expression of general dissatisfaction with our present courses, does the PSSC course, as far as you are able to judge, fulfill the major aims it sets out to achieve?

(iv) If PSSC is introduced locally, what modification of language, style, content and teaching methods might be necessary to fit it to our school situation?

(v) Appropriate examination techniques are vital to the success or otherwise of a school course. How far is it satisfactory to think in terms of special syllabuses, remembering that the present examiners overseas will set the questions? Would the establishment of a local examining authority be advantageous?

(vi) What are the needs with regard to
(a) teacher training?
(b) in-service courses?
(c) supply of apparatus?

(vii) On what lines should further experimentation with and study of PSSC be pursued?

V. THE OUTCOME OF THE COURSE

Resolutions adopted by the final Plenary Conference held on 12th September, 1963

(i) The Conference is unanimous in its opinion that the PSSC course forms the basis of the new thinking in physics teaching, and strongly urges that the PSSC course should be introduced as widely and as soon as possible.

(ii) To facilitate the implementation of the foregoing resolution, a Working Committee is appointed to keep under consideration the following:
(a) The appropriate use of PSSC in the secondary schools; lines of adaptation. (The Conference accepts as fundamental that it will be necessary to fit existing courses to PSSC, and not PSSC to existing courses.)

(b) *At whatever level the PSSC is introduced there must be a suitable course preparatory to it. The Committee should advise on the "pre-PSSC" course when it becomes available and/or on any alternative course.*

(c) *What extensions of PSSC are necessary and at what stages.*

(d) *Co-ordination and co-operation with chemistry, mathematics and biology curricula and methods.*

(e) *The desirability of appointing ad hoc committees whether on an area or subject basis.*

(iii) *Texts: the Conference considers that texts of PSSC should be published in convenient parts.*

(iv) *Examination syllabuses: urgent consideration should be given to means of providing appropriate examinations which would be recognised by relevant examining boards.*

(v) *Films: it is a minimum requirement that one complete set of PSSC films together with four or more copies of each of a number of selected films should be housed at convenient centres such as the Audio-Visual and Television Centres.*

(vi) *Continuing contact should be maintained with Educational Services Incorporated.*

(vii) *Further courses and conferences: the conference stresses that it is a necessary condition of the implementation of the scheme that:*

(a) *A number of teachers should be given the opportunity of attending PSSC courses in the United States, and should then undertake the organization and teaching of local courses.*

(b) *A systematic scheme of in-service courses should be organized and that UCRN be asked to co-operate in this.*

(c) *Means should be found for defraying teachers' and other expenses in the organization of the above.*

(viii) *The Conference expressed its sincere appreciation to Educational Services Incorporated, to the Carnegie Corporation of New York, to the visiting lecturers (Professor Youtz and Mr. Schaefer), to the academic staff (Professor Yates, Professor Milton and Mr. Gilbert) and the administrative staff (in particular to Mrs. Miller-Cranko) of UCRN for their most important contributions to the success of the course.*

(ix) Constitution and composition of the Working Committee

(a) *At the conclusion of the Conference the following persons were elected to serve on the Working Committee:*

A. R. Brimble	*Munali Secondary School, Lusaka*
J. D. Campbell	*Inspector of Schools, Federal Ministry*
T. T. Chagonda	*Goromonzi School*
Dr. A. J. Cooper	*St. Stephen's College, Balla Balla*
R. E. D. Cowper	*Milton High School, Bulawayo*
P. F. de Bruijn	*Prince Edward School, Salisbury*
A. W. Dock	*Luanshya High School*
P. G. S. Gilbert	*Education Department, UCRN*
Sr. Mary-Benita Goller	*Empandeni Institution, Plumtree*
S. C. Johnson	*The Teachers' College, Bulawayo*
A. P. Knottenbelt	*Fletcher High School, Gwelo*
D. M. Luckin	*Gilbert Rennie School, Lusaka*
G. S. Morgan	*Prince Edward School, Salisbury*
Mrs. D. E. Sibson	*Townsend School, Bulawayo*
A. H. Siemers	*Inspector of Schools, Federal Ministry*
Prof. E. L. Yates	*Professor of Physics, UCRN*
R. J. Yon	*Morgan High School, Salisbury*

It was agreed that the Ministries of Education (the Federal Ministry, the Southern Rhodesia Ministry and the Northern Rhodesia Ministry) should be invited to nominate representatives to serve on the Working Committee.

(b) *Secretary/Convenor: Mr. P. G. S. Gilbert (UCRN) was appointed.*

(c) *The Working Committee was empowered to set up sub-committees to consider individual topics, and to co-opt additional members to serve on it.*

VI. CONTINUANCE AND EXTENSION OF STUDY

The interest and enthusiasm of the members, especially in the PSSC course itself, was not only occasioned by the experience of learning which they had gained at the hands of two remarkable teachers. There was throughout a conviction that fundamental changes were due in the present curricula and methods of physics teaching, and that the PSSC approach was likely to provide a sound basis to this end. If there was any doubt as to its appropriateness to local conditions, there was none on the necessity of working out alternatives to present practice. But the general wish was for a continuation of the study of PSSC and the working out of means for introducing it in the schools.

The organization of such a continuing study and experiment will necessitate the development of a program in which university, schools, and Ministries of Education co-operate. Resources will have to be found to build up a Science Education Centre, to provide materials, equipment, and films, to meet the expenses of lecturers, research workers, and teachers. The fact that there is an equal interest, and a similar opportunity, to explore curriculum development in other sciences, and that at the University College of Rhodesia and Nyasaland there is the necessary combination of teaching skill, suitable accommodation, and organization, might be regarded as a justification for widening the scope of the studies which this Course has begun.

VII. ACKNOWLEDGEMENTS

That the course depended for its success primarily on the excellence and generosity of the two lecturers, Professor Youtz and Mr. Schaefer, will be apparent. To Educational Services Incorporated and to the Carnegie Corporation we owe not only the resources and forethought which furnished the teaching, but also the apparatus which made the teaching possible. This equipment was, at the conclusion of the course, given to the University College. It has already been used by graduates training to be teachers, under the direction of tutors who were members of the course, and has been on loan to teachers in Northern and Southern Rhodesia. Acknowledgements are also due to the United States Information Services, to the Book Centre, the Educational Supply Company, and to the local branch of Baird and Tatlock Ltd., for various contributions to the course.

The technical staff of the University College Department of Physics made it possible for all members to have adequate materials to work upon. The enterprise and skill especially of Mr. J. H. Houston, Chief Laboratory Steward, was called upon throughout the course. Ripple tanks, stroboscopes, inertial balances, refraction particle sets, and trolley carts, were made, as they were required, to supplement the equipment provided by Educational Services Incorporated.

Finally, it is appropriate to emphasize that the course was jointly sponsored and organized by three departments of the University College: the Department of Physics, the Department of Education, and the Institute of Education. To Professor E. L. Yates, the chairman, and Head of the Department of Physics in which the course was held, a particular debt of thanks is to be acknowledged.

ALAN MILTON
Professor of Education
and
Director of the Institute of Education
University College of Rhodesia and Nyasaland

October, 1963.

APPENDIX I.

PHYSICS IN THE SECONDARY SCHOOL AND UNIVERSITY

PROGRAM

MONDAY — 2nd September

a.m.	*10:00-11:30*	*Steering Committee*
	12:00-12:45	*Opening of the Course*
p.m.	*2:15- 3:15*	*History and over-view of PSSC course*
	3:45- 5:00	*Chapters 2, 3, 4. Homework: Experiment 1-4*
	5:00- 5:30	*Discussion groups*

TUESDAY — 3rd September

a.m.	*8:30-10:15*	*Chapter 5. Film: "Straight Line Kinematics" Chapter 6*
	10:45-12:30	*Chapters 7, 8, 9; Chapters 11, 12, 13*
p.m	*2:00- 4:30*	*Groups rotate through 3 laboratory experiments: Exp. I-1, I-5, I-8*
	4:30- 5:00	*Discussion groups*
	8:00	*Steering Committee*

WEDNESDAY — 4th September

a.m.	*8:30-10:00*	*Chapters 15, 16*
	10:30-12:30	*Groups 1-4 Laboratory (Ripple Tanks)* *Groups 5-8 Problems*
p.m.	*2:00- 4:15*	*Groups 5-8 Laboratory (Ripple Tanks)* *Groups 1-4 Problems*
	4:15- 5:00	*Discussion groups*
	8:15-10:00	*Films: "Scaling," "Introduction to Optics," "Pressure of Light"*

THURSDAY — 5th September

a.m.	*8:30-10:15*	*Chapters 19, 20, 21*
	10:45-12:30	*Chapters 23, 24, 25*
p.m.	*2:00- 4:15*	*Groups 5-8 Laboratory (Exp. III-2, III-3, III-11)* *Groups 1-4 Problems*
	4:15- 4:45	*Film: "Frames of Reference"*
	4:45- 5:15	*Discussion groups*

FRIDAY — 6th September

a.m.	*8:30-10:45*	*Groups 5-8 Problems* *Groups 1-4 Laboratory (Exp. III-2, III-3, III-11)*
	10:45-12:30	*Chapters 27, 28* *Films: "Coulomb's Law," "Millikan Experiment"*
p.m.	*2:00- 3:15*	*Chapters 29, 30*
	3:45- 5:00	*Chapter 31*
	8:15-10:00	*Films: "Crystals," "Projectile Motion," "Mass of Electron," "Angular Momentum" (optional)*

SATURDAY — 7th September

a.m.	*8:30-12:30*	*Chapters 32, 33*

MONDAY — 9th September

a.m.	*8:30- 9:30*	*Completion of PSSC*
	9:45-10:15	*Pre-PSSC*
	10:45-11:45	*Advanced Topics*
	12:00-12:30	*Films*
p.m.	*2:00- 3:15*	*Plenary — Testing and Summary*
	3:45- 4:45	*Groups (3): How to introduce PSSC*
	4:45- 5:30	*Steering Committee*
	8:15	*Films*

TUESDAY — 10th September

a.m.	*8:30- 9:00*	*Plenary — Report from groups*
	9:00-10:15	*Study groups — as for Monday*
	10:45-12:00	*Laboratory work OR Advanced Topics detail*
	12:00-12:30	*Films*
p.m.	*2:00- 3:15*	*Groups continued*
	3:45- 5:30	*Laboratory work OR Films*
	8:15	*Lecture: Dr. D. I. Gough. "Palaeomagnetism, Polar Wander and Continental Drift"*

WEDNESDAY — 11th September

a.m.	*8:30-10:15*	*Plenary — Reports from groups*
	10:45-11:45	*Groups continued*
	11:45-12:30	*Steering Committee OR Films*
p.m.	*2:00- 5:00*	*Laboratory work*
	7:00 for 7:30	*ASECA Dinner — Kentucky Hotel*

THURSDAY — 12th September

a.m.	*8:30-10:15*	*Plenary — Framing of resolutions*
	10:45-12:00	*Plenary — Appointment of continuation Working Committee*
p.m.		*Course disperses*

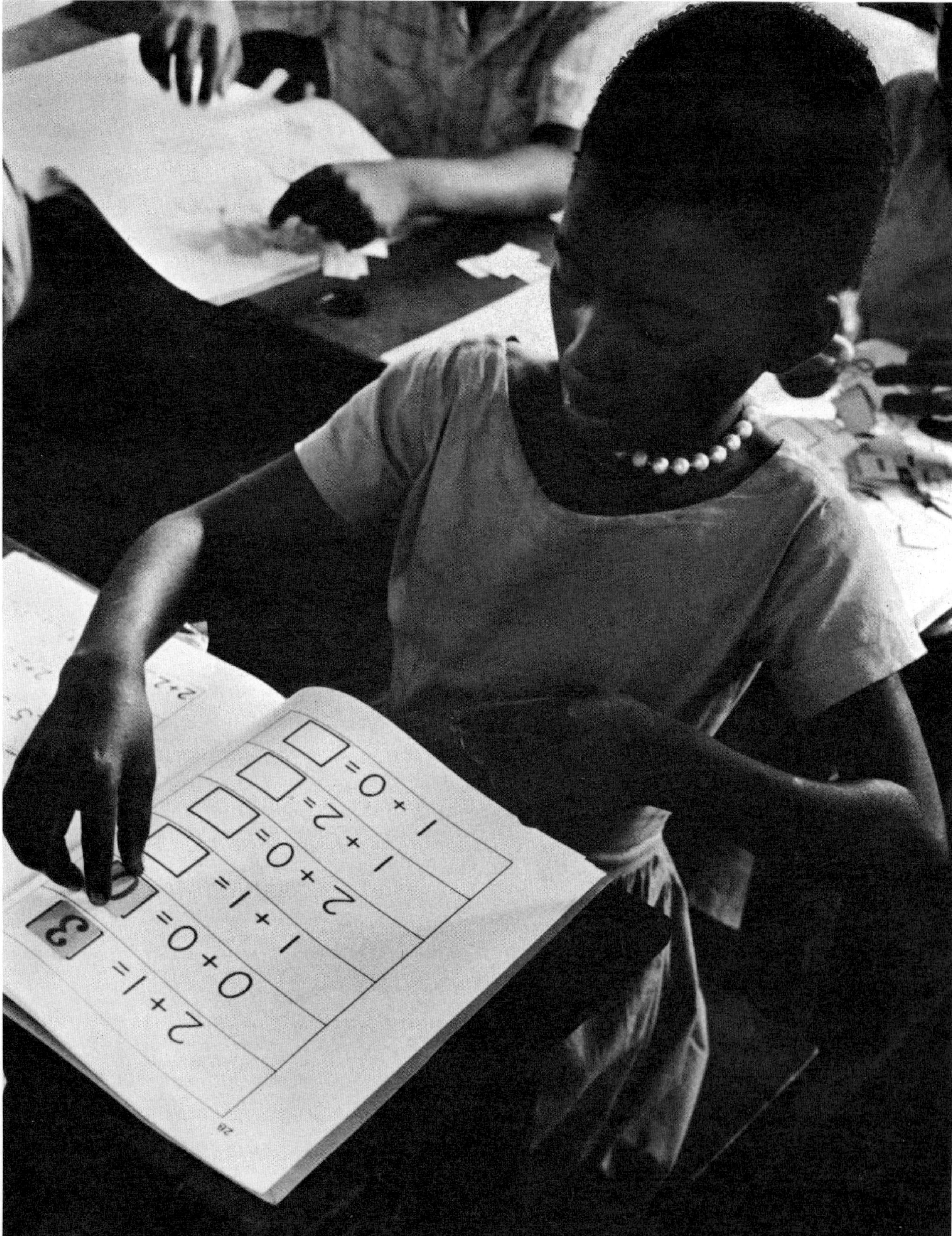
2 + 1 =
0 + 0 =
3
1 + 1 =
2 + 0 =
1 + 2 =
1 + 0 =
28

THE AFRICAN EDUCATION PROGRAM

Activities in Mathematics and Science

by W. T. Martin and J. L. Aldrich

THE African Education Program, a cooperative program among scientists, mathematicians, school teachers and educators from Africa, the United Kingdom and the United States of America, seeks to bring to Africa some of the newer and more effective methods of preparing improved school curricula in mathematics and the sciences based on the American experience in school reform over the past decade. The Program intends to apply the methods of curriculum development in conjunction with African scholars and teachers for the purpose of developing new course materials indigenous to African needs and relevant to African aspirations.

The idea for an African Education Program was inspired by an African, the late Reverend Solomon B. Caulker, Vice-Principal of Fourah Bay College in Freetown, Sierra Leone, at the International Conference on Science in the Advancement of New States, held at Rehovoth, Israel, in 1960. The Rev. Dr. Caulker urged the delegates to the Conference—among them Dr. Jerold R. Zacharias, Vice President for Academic Affairs of Educational Services Incorporated and a professor of physics at the Massachusetts Institute of Technology—to concern themselves more with the dissemination of basic scientific knowledge in the new states than with sophisticated research and technology. During the conference the Rev. Dr. Caulker and Dr. Zacharias discussed the possibility of applying the methods used in the development of the new Physical Science Study Committee's high school physics course (now being taught to approximately fifty per cent of all high school students studying physics in the United States) to the development of improved curricula for students in African schools.

The Rev. Dr. Caulker was killed when his plane crashed on the way home from the conference. Dr. Zacharias returned to the United States determined to pursue Dr. Caulker's suggestions; he and the other officers of Educational Services Incorporated, including Dr. James R. Killian, Jr., the Chairman of the Board of Educational Services Incorporated and the Chairman of the Corporation of the Massachusetts Institute of Technology, and Mr. Stephen White, former Assistant to the President of Educational Services Incorporated, decided that a meeting should be held to study the feasibility of initiating an educational program in Africa whose purpose would be to implement some of the aims set forth by the Rev. Dr. Caulker.

During the summer of 1961, a six-week meeting was held at Dedham, Massachusetts, at which a group of forty-eight scholars, teachers and educators, representing many disciplines, formally brought into being the African Education Program. This meeting—which came to be known as the Endicott House Conference—established a plan of action for effecting educational innovations in African schools. Fifteen Africans participated in the Endicott House Conference; they came from Ghana, Nigeria, Sierra Leone and Uganda. Representatives from the United Kingdom, including Professor L. John Lewis of the University of London, England, helped to plan, as well as participated in the conference. The participants decided that the curriculum reforms would be made in mathematics and science, language and social studies, and in the education of in-service and pre-service teachers. It was also recognized

---

Since 1947, Professor Martin has been head of the Department of Mathematics at the Massachusetts Institute of Technology. He is the Chairman of the African Mathematics Program Steering Committee and is also Chairman of ESI's Mathematics Curriculum Study. This summer he will be in Africa, participating in the African Mathematics Program's fourth summer workshop, at Mombasa, Kenya. He is co-chairman of the workshop with Mr. John O. Oyelese, a lecturer in mathematics at the University of Ibadan, Nigeria. Mr. Aldrich is a deputy director of Educational Services Incorporated and the Administrator of the African Education Program.

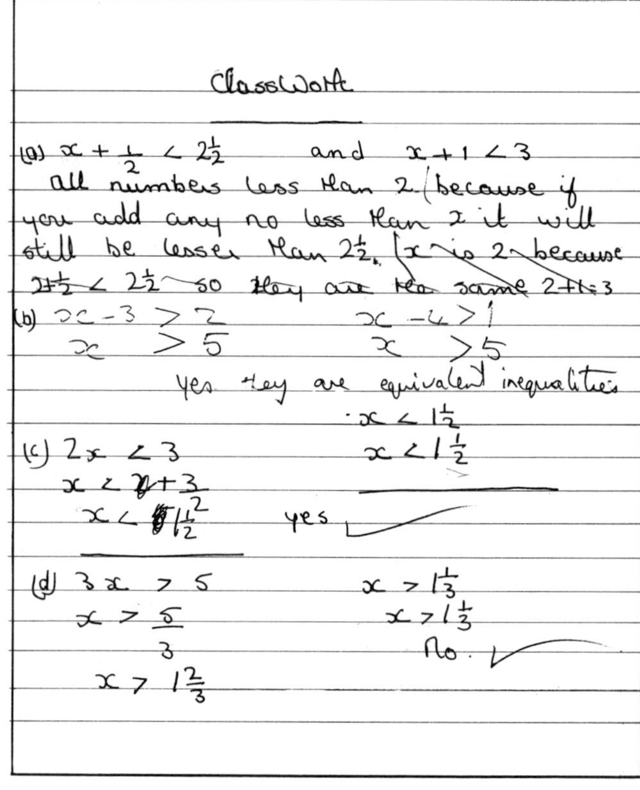

Exercises done by students in Form I, corresponding roughly to seventh-grade students in United States schools. They are working on problems from the African Mathematics Series.

that it would be desirable to create in Africa, after certain courses had been prepared for testing in African schools, an African Institute to conduct further educational research and development.

The African Mathematics Program, the first part of the African Education Program to begin work, has accomplished much since its inception four years ago. The mathematics materials, produced at three successive summer workshops held at Entebbe, Uganda, are part of the development of a sequence of mathematics textbooks that are designed to present in a systematic and logical manner, exciting to both students and teachers, some of the fundamental mathematical ideas and skills essential in a modern, technologically-based society.

The mathematics materials are being used in schools or teachers' colleges in ten African nations: Ethiopia, Ghana, Kenya, Liberia, Malawi, Nigeria, Sierra Leone, Tanzania, Uganda and Zambia. Twenty-three textbooks have been published and ten more are now being printed; these include pupils' textbooks and teachers' guides for the first three years of primary education and the first three years of secondary education. Approximately ninety-four thousand textbooks have thus far been sent to Africa and are being used in approximately four hundred schools in the countries named.

The textbooks are listed below:

Entebbe Mathematics Series

PRIMARY I
Revised Preliminary Edition
Pupil Book: Two volumes
Teachers' Guide: Two volumes
PRIMARY II
Preliminary Edition
Pupil Book: Two volumes
Teachers' Guide: Two volumes
PRIMARY III
Preliminary Edition
Pupil Book: Two volumes
Teachers' Guide: Two volumes
Entebbe Mathematics Teachers' Handbook, Primary I-III, Preliminary Edition
SECONDARY I
Preliminary Edition
Student Text: Three volumes
Teachers' Guide: Three volumes
SECONDARY II
Preliminary Edition
Student Text: Three volumes

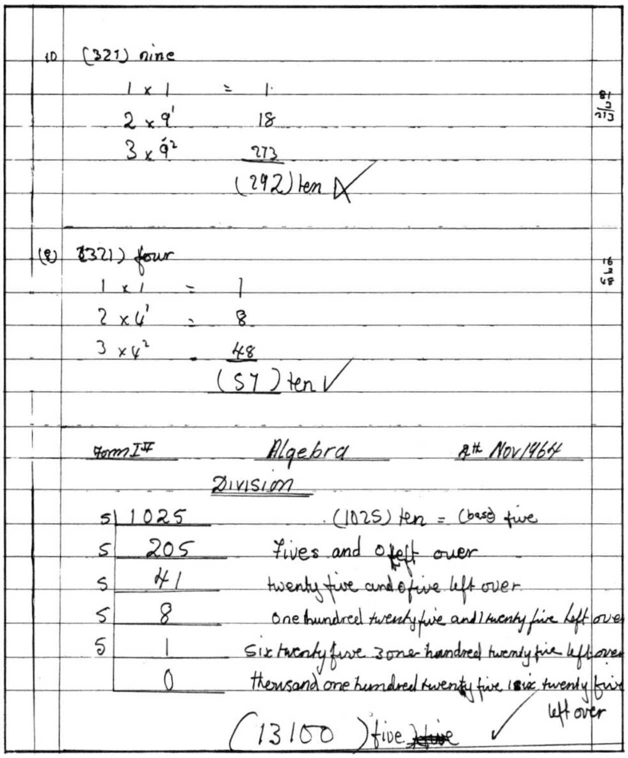

Change of base.

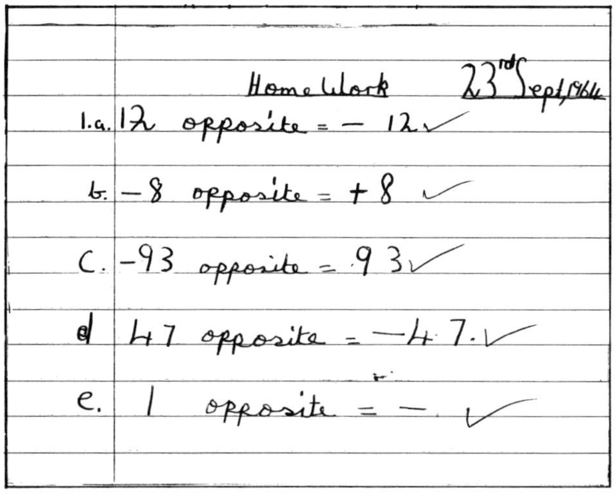

Numerical opposites.

Teachers' Guide: Three volumes

SECONDARY III
Preliminary Edition
Student Text: Algebra—One volume
Geometry—One volume
Teachers' Guide: Algebra—One volume
Geometry—One volume

BASIC CONCEPTS OF MATHEMATICS
An Introductory Text for Teachers
Preliminary Edition
Volume 1—*Structure of Arithmetic*—Chapters 1-21
Volume 2—*Structure of Arithmetic*—Chapters 22-46
Volume 3—*Foundations of Geometry*—Chapters 47-57

The Entebbe Workshops have been attended by an average of sixty participants each year: thirty-seven Americans (mainly professors of mathematics from such universities as the University of California at Berkeley, University of Washington, Williams College, Columbia University, Brooklyn College, California Institute of Technology, Northern Illinois University, the Massachusetts Institute of Technology, University of North Carolina, Stanford University, Lehigh University, and Franklin and Marshall College); three British (including one from the Cambridge Examinations Syndicate); twenty-three expatriates from the United States and the United Kingdom with long teaching experience in the African schools; and fifty-four African mathematicians and educators (from many parts of English-speaking Africa and from as far south as Northern Rhodesia, representing such schools as Milton Margai Training College, Sierra Leone; the University of Ibadan, Western Nigeria; the Secondary Technical School, Zanzibar; the University of Ghana; the Uhuru Street School, Dar-es-Salaam, Tanganyika; the Federal Emergency Science School, Lagos, Nigeria; Cuttington College, Liberia; University of Liberia; Makerere College School, Kampala, Uganda; University College, Haile Selassie I University, Addis Ababa, Ethiopia; Alliance High School, Kikuyu, Kenya; and the Achimoto School, Accra, Ghana). Representatives from various African Ministries of Education and education officers of the United States Agency for International Development have also participated in these workshops.

In 1965, the African Mathematics Workshop will be held at Mombasa, Kenya, for six weeks beginning July 5, 1965.

class work 27-x-64
(Base five)
① 142 − 23 = 114 ② 210 − 2 = 203 ③ 100 − 40 = 10
④ 412 − 34 = 323 ⑤ 402 − 13 = 334
(Base 12)
⑥ 24 − 13 = 11 ⑦ 12 − 3 = 11 ⑧ 10 − 4 = 8
⑨ 20 − 12 = 10 ⑩ 216 − 27 = 111

Subtraction to base 5.

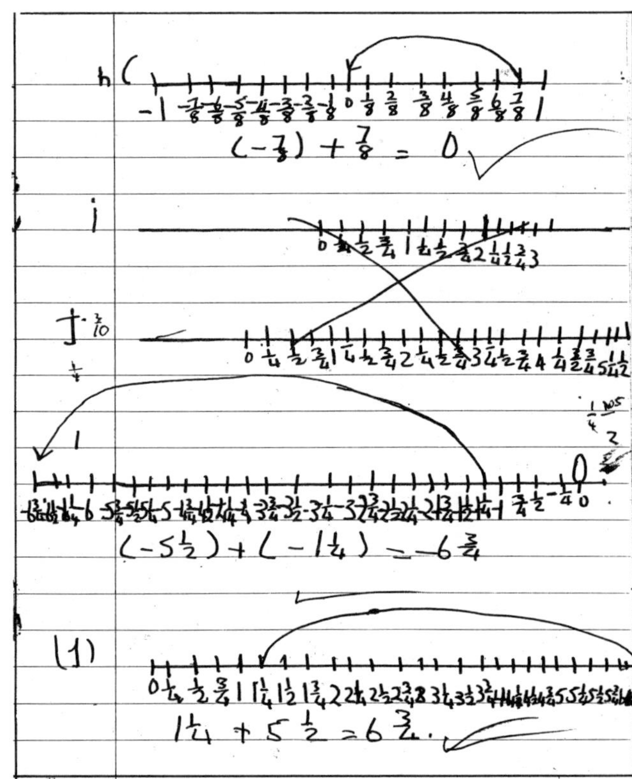

Using the number line for subtraction.

The African Mathematics Program is now operating in four areas:

1. The Program prepares and publishes teaching materials in mathematics for use in the schools, teacher-training institutions and for in-service training.
2. The Program supplies those materials for experimental testing in the schools and teacher-training institutions.
3. The Program trains teachers who will conduct the experimental use of the materials.
4. The Program trains the faculty of the teacher-training institutions.

To date fourteen teacher education institutes have been held with the sponsorship or assistance of Educational Services Incorporated. They have met for sessions of ten days to three weeks. Over five hundred African teachers and tutors have attended these institutes, which have been staffed by visiting American professors and African educators from African universities and local Ministries of Education, as well as by expatriates teaching in Africa. The task of educating large numbers of teachers in Africa is by no means dissimilar from the task in the United States. In this area especially, the full complement of teaching and learning aids, including films to educate teachers in content and method for real classroom situations, will be necessary. Innovation and experimentation along these lines are proceeding well in the United States and suggest ways of meeting the problem of educating large numbers of teachers in Africa.

Although the mathematics program was the first to get under way and has accomplished the most so far, the African Education Program has planned from the start to include development in other fields of education as well, most particularly in science. Perhaps the main reason that mathematics came first lies in the nature of the subject itself; mathematics is the easiest (and yet the most subtle) form of study to transport into the classroom. With chalk and paper and pencil, it is possible to bring into the classroom a vast body of complex models for making conjectures, verifying guesses, and developing insight and new ways of looking at and describing one's knowledge of the world. With insights obtained through the study of mathematics, it is possible to make more effective use of materials that are representative of the world of science. Then, too, the innovations in mathematics instruction in the United States made by several groups, including the School Mathematics Study Group, the University of Illinois Arithmetic Program, the University of Illinois Committee on School Mathematics, the Syracuse University-Webster College Madison Project, and the Stanford Arithmetic Project had reached a comparatively advanced stage of development, and the experience gathered from these efforts could most readily be applied to the African situation.

Since the mathematics program was begun in Africa, much has been accomplished in the United States to develop new ways of teaching science to young children, not only by the Elementary Science Study at Educational Services Incorporated but also by other curriculum reform groups. Consequently, with the urging of African participants from the Endicott House Conference and with the concurrent development of new approaches to science teaching in the United States, the African Science Program is ready to move forward. Over the past several years, Africans have come to the United States to observe the development of new course materials at the Elementary Science Study's headquarters in Watertown, Massachusetts, and what has resulted is that not only have the Africans been observers but that they also have participated in the development of new materials, from the initial stages through periods of trial teaching in the classroom. There have also been several preliminary meetings to propose guidelines for the program; one was held last summer in Rome, attended by Africans, Americans, and representatives from the United Kingdom. Since then, planning for this activity has continued apace, and last February a meeting was held in Kano, in Northern Nigeria, to discuss science education in Africa and to make recommendations for implementing a broad program in science education.

The African Elementary Science Conference was held in Kano through the co-operation and assistance of the Northern Nigeria Ministry of Education. Approximately half of the sixty-two participants at the conference represented ten African States (Basutoland, Ghana, Kenya, Liberia, Malawi, Nigeria, Rhodesia, Sierra Leone, Tanzania, Uganda). The other representatives came largely from the United States, with several additional representatives from the United Kingdom and one from Jamaica.

The conference took the form of presentations, classroom drawings and discussions. The presentations were begun by Dr. A. Babs Fafunwa, Dean, Faculty of Education, University of Nigeria, Nsukka, Eastern Nigeria, and Mr. John Gitau, Chief Inspector of Schools, Ministry of Education, Nairobi, Kenya. They described the work being done in beginning science centers in Nsukka and in Nairobi. There were presentations by Mr. E. R. Wastnedge, Organizer for Junior Science for the Nuffield Foundation, London, England, and Mr. Leonard Sealey of the Education Department of the Leicestershire Education Committee in England and by Dr. Philip Morrison, Professor of Physics at the Massachusetts Institute of Technology. Mr. Wastnedge and Mr. Sealey talked about school experiments in England and Dr. Morrison discussed basic educational philosophy. There were additional presentations by other participants.

The participants were also able to attend demonstration classes based on the work of M. B. R. Savage, a former ESS staff member, who had been working in Africa for the past ten months. For several weeks previous to the Kano conference, Mr. Savage had been working with teachers from four Kano Primary Schools (Kwalli Primary School, Gita Makama Primary School, Magwam Primary School and the Girls Provincial Primary School), instructing these teachers in the use of units prepared by the Elementary Science Study, and adapted at Nsukka for Africa, in particular *Batteries and Bulbs* and *Pendulums*. Then, for the benefit of the participants at the conference, these primary school teachers gave demonstration classes with local children whom they had not taught before.

After three days of presentations and demonstration classes the participants divided into six groups: one representing the five parts of Nigeria; one for the countries of East Africa; one for Ghana; one for Sierra Leone and Liberia; one for Zambia, Rhodesia, Malawi, and the High Commission territories; and finally a group composed of the U.S. and U.K. members. Following these meetings the participants assembled in one group with substantive and administrative recommendations. They agreed that the two beginning science centers already in existence in Nairobi, Kenya, and Nsukka, Nigeria, should be increased in size as soon as possible; in addition, that smaller science centers should be started in many parts of Africa and should be encouraged to increase in size and scope.

The participants agreed that a summer workshop should be held this summer at Entebbe, Uganda, to be directed by Dr. Jack S. Goldstein, Professor of Physics at Brandeis University. The workshop in science will begin on July 5, 1965, and will continue for six weeks.

Selected representatives of the primary schools, teacher training institutes and university science departments from each of the Tropical African countries will attend this workshop. The workshop has three objectives: to develop primary school science units, to exchange information about primary school science activities from the countries represented, and to develop a corps of people from each country who would be equipped to staff school science resource centers in each of the countries.

The African Education Program transcends regional and national boundaries, as well as scholastic and academic ones, and it has, with the support of the United States Agency for International Development (AID), the Ford Foundation, and the Louis and Pauline Cowan Foundation, brought men of good will and achievement together to work on major problems of common concern. A participant in the African Education Program, Dr. O. Ukeje, of the Harden College of Education of the University of Nigeria, at Nsukka, best expressed this spirit of accomplishment and cooperation when he wrote after the first Entebbe Workshop: ". . . the Entebbe Mathematics Workshop is not only a project to make available new concepts and new methods in mathematics to African countries, but also it is to me an experiment in international cooperation, and a successful one at that. Here we have for the first time American professors and teachers of mathematics, British officials, professors and teachers of mathematics, African government officials, lecturers and teachers of mathematics—people from different nationalities, cultures and backgrounds working together harmoniously for the good of Africa and progress of mankind. To me, and I am sure, to most participants, particularly the African participants, the participation in this experiment has been an invaluable experience. I have personally learned a good deal both in mathematics and in group cooperation; and I am sure others have done the same. It is indeed an experience which I think every participant will always remember and appreciate. Those who have made this experience possible can very well feel sure that they have made a remarkable contribution not only to the development of Africans and Africa but also to the fostering of the brotherhood of man."

THE INDIAN INSTITUTE OF TECHNOLOGY AT KANPUR

by Norman C. Dahl

THE pattern of education evolving at the IIT/Kanpur, now in its fourth year of operation, is strongly reflective of the lines along which American engineering and scientific institutions are developing—with strong science, humanities and social science activities interacting with parallel engineering programs—but it is not identical since it also must be clearly reflective of India's cultural traditions and its educational needs. The primary engineering educational need is for engineering graduates who will be *problem recognizing* and *problem solving,* men who will recognize India's problems and will have the confidence, inclination and training to do something about them. It is the aim of the IIT/Kanpur to have academic and research standards of recognized international quality, not for the international recognition but rather because only at this level of quality can it play its assigned role in the development of India. The problems facing India require no less engineering, scientific and social insight for their solution than do some of the problems facing more advanced countries; the academic and research program of the IIT/Kanpur is being built upon this premise.

At present there are five-year undergraduate degree programs in aeronautical, chemical, civil, electrical, mechanical and metallurgical engineering. Research and graduate study is being carried on in these engineering fields as well as in chemistry, mathematics and physics and in those areas of social science and humanities where there are qualified faculty. The undergraduate programs consist of a three-year common core followed by two years of concentration in one field of engineering. There is a strong emphasis on experimental investigation and on the technical arts needed to carry out such work. However, in India the students' experience and the general environmental background are different from those of American students, and there is still much to learn about how to make effective this vital part of the educational program. Humanities and social science occupy about one-seventh of the undergraduate curriculum. The quality of the students and Indian faculty is such that the courses are taught at levels comparable to those in the Consortium institutions.

Although good progress has been made on developing the undergraduate program, a major effort must be sustained over the next few years, by Indian as well as American faculty, to provide continuing emphasis on the solution of undergraduate education problems. The first class of students is graduating this year, and the experience gained so far has already pointed the way toward improvements in various aspects of the undergraduate program. The process of evaluating the present program and evolving improvements will be a valuable learning process for the entire faculty. Sound traditions need to be established in laboratory instruction, in lecture demonstrations and in the use of visual and other teaching aids. Experience in these critical areas is gained slowly. Initiative can be dissipated because progress may be slow, and rewards are often hard to see. All this means that a continuing effort must be concentrated in these areas.

Beginning this academic year, 1964-1965, graduate instruction has been offered in all departments. Several departments now have master's programs with a number of students enrolled, and some have doctoral candidates. There will be an increasing emphasis on graduate study and research and the American faculty will work with their Indian colleagues to make the graduate work pertinent and productive. Equipment that has been installed or is on order makes the research opportunities at Kanpur far above the average in India and good in many areas by American standards.

In reviewing what has been accomplished these past

Norman C. Dahl is a professor of mechanical engineering at the Massachusetts Institute of Technology. He was the first Program Leader in Kanpur and is now the Institute's representative to the Steering Committee of the Kanpur Indo-American Program.

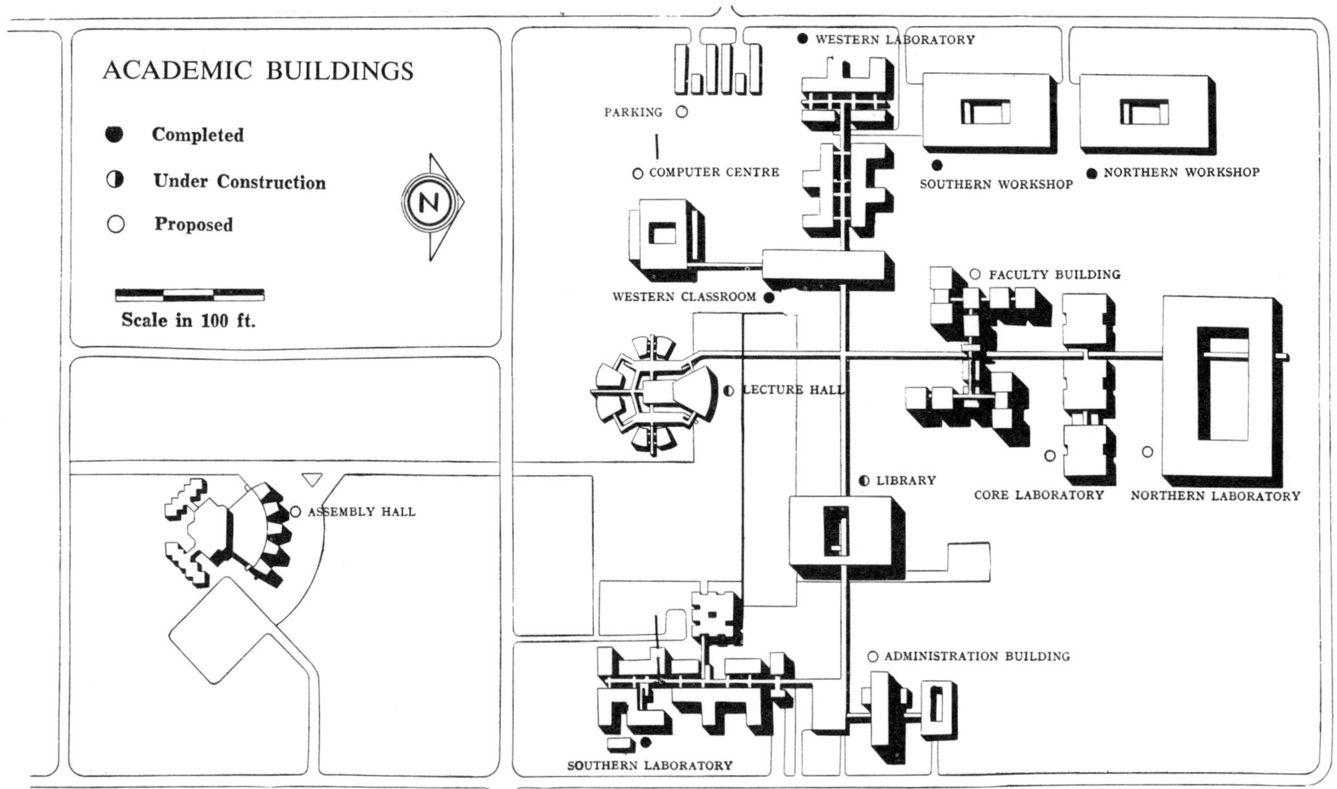

The Indian Institute of Technology/Kanpur

three years, it is clear that the most significant event has been the increase of the Indian faculty, which during this period has increased from about thirty faculty members to well over one hundred. From the results of the past three years it now is clear that it will be possible to attract to the Institute the two hundred and fifty highly qualified Indian faculty members who will be required to make it the institution of excellence which is the aim of all concerned. This is a great satisfaction since the assembling of a first-rate faculty is the cornerstone on which all else rests. Throughout the period of organization of the Program and, indeed, throughout the first year and a half of the Program's operation this had to be taken as an article of faith rather than of fact.

The most significant reason that the IIT/Kanpur is attracting first-rate faculty is that the Director of the Institute, Dr. P. K. Kelkar, is providing leadership for the development at Kanpur of an academic, research and faculty structure which is attractive to Indians who have known and experienced this type of academic structure outside of India. Many of the ideas of academic and faculty organization being worked into the Kanpur scheme are new to Indian education, and their introduction gives heart to many of the younger generation of Indian scholars who are eager to participate in needed reforms of Indian university education. This certainly is one of the major reasons why the Institute has been able to attract so many good men back to India on rupee salaries roughly numerically equal to their dollar salaries in the United States and, in several cases, at a faculty grade equivalent to the grade the man had in a ranking American university. The recruitment of a high percentage of the new faculty from abroad is a source of satisfaction since it has added vitally needed, competent manpower to the Indian educational scene. The Program has been of assistance in the recruitment of new faculty both directly and indirectly, the latter in the sense that the presence of the Program faculty makes more possible the development of the new structure at the Institute and the availability of equipment makes more possible the type of laboratory and research work needed to support this structure and the faculty in their scholarly activities.

The student enrollment also has increased steadily, now standing at about eight hundred undergraduates and one hundred graduate students; plans call for sixteen hundred undergraduates and four hundred graduate students. Undergraduates are admitted on the basis of a national competitive examination which is common for all five of the IIT's.

The campus is located on a twelve-hundred acre tract of land in the village of Kalyanpur, which is about six miles outside of Kanpur. Kanpur is three hundred miles southeast of New Delhi on the Ganges River. The Institute will be wholly residential and eventually will constitute a community of five or six thousand people. About one-third of the planned building has been completed. A second third has been authorized and much of it let out for bid. The Program has on site an architectural planning consultant who works intimately with the faculty and with the Indian architects in interpreting the faculty's educational and research needs in architectural terms. While progress on campus development has been good and there is promise that the campus will be an attractive environment, those now living on the campus must contend with the usual problems of a community being created *de novo* as well as some problems peculiar to the local situation.

The laboratories are becoming working units with the arrival of equipment, both from the United States and from within India. Equipment from the United States is ordered on the initiative of Indian faculty but with the advice and collaboration of Program faculty. One of the major items is an IBM 1620 computer with auxiliary equipment including magnetic tape units. The Program has had top flight computer faculty in residence at Kanpur, and as a result Kanpur has become the most active computer center in India, with much of the initiative now resting in Indian faculty hands. Engineers and scientists throughout India are making use of the institution's computation center. Because of this rapid development the IBM World Trade Corporation has offered to sell to the IIT/Kanpur an IBM 7044 system for rupee payment, without a dollar foreign exchange requirement, and with an educational discount. With the advent of an IBM 7044 system, the first units of which should arrive this year, IIT/Kanpur will become more of a center for Indian engineering and scientific research and for research on some of the large systems problems that face the Planning Commission and other government ministries.

The Program and the IIT/Kanpur have collaborated in two unique ways in connection with books and library resources. In the first instance, textbooks not available in India have been purchased in the United States by the Program and sold to the students at subsidized prices roughly equivalent to what the cost would be if the books were reprinted in India under an existing joint U.S.-Indian government-subsidized book publishing program. Books which are found suitable for textbook use in Kanpur will be recommended for reprinting under this publishing program. Important benefits of this availability of textbooks have been a decrease in class contact hours and a corresponding increase in self study and homework problems with, it is hoped, a concomitant increase in initiative and self reliance on the part of the students. The second example has been the direct assistance of the Purdue Library in building up the library collection at Kanpur. This assistance has several aspects. When Purdue buys a new book in a field in which Kanpur is working, a second copy is bought at the same time and subsequently catalogued and sent to Kanpur. Purdue also has been active in searching for and purchasing retrospective journal collections. These and a vigorous program of acquisition in Kanpur have built the collection from about fifteen thousand to fifty thousand volumes in the past three years.

In the process of the collaboration the Program has found itself in many activities which it had not anticipated. One example was the work of some of the wives of Program faculty together with Indian faculty and staff on a project which resulted in the establishment on the campus last summer of a school for the children of all campus residents. Another was the planning and, as it turned out, the supervision of the construction of an airfield on the campus. This is used in the flight testing program, which is an important part of the aeronautical engineering program in line with the IIT/Kanpur aim to produce graduates who are oriented towards *problem recognizing* and *problem solving*. Numerous other examples of unanticipated but important activities could be cited; these have made clear the message, if we have forgotten it, that education is in its largest sense an experimental activity.

Much remains to be done at Kanpur but the Institute can be said to be fairly started with excellent prospects for the future. The Program takes great satisfaction in what has developed at Kanpur, and one aspect of that pride results from the fact that along with other major participants in the activity—the Indian faculty and administration, the Government of India, the United States government—the Program has found it possible to make a significant contribution in a complex cross-cultural situation where progress often is difficult and sometimes impossible. In addition to the progress at Kanpur the institutions in the Consortium can point with pride to the fact that there has been real collaboration among them. Of the approximately fifty American faculty who have been or are now resident in Kanpur, no one of the nine institutions has produced fewer than four or more than seven.

It is planned that the Program will continue for about ten years, until 1972, at which time it is hoped that the IIT/Kanpur will be self-sustaining as well as a significant factor in Indian education and national development.

Undergraduate Program

The three-year core curriculum of the Institute is intended to impart a general education in mathematics, physics and chemistry, humanities and social sciences, engineering sciences and technical arts such as graphics, measurements, engineering design and manufacturing processes, workshop skills and computation technology. This creates a strong base which will enable the student to undertake effectively the professional areas of his choice with a high degree of awareness of the interplay between the various branches of technology, science and other aspects of human endeavour.

The Core Curriculum at IIT/Kanpur

First Year

General Chemistry
General English I, II
Mathematics I, II
General Physics I, II
Technical Arts I, II

Second Year

Mathematics III, IV
General Physics III
Mechanics of Solids
Physical Chemistry
Thermodynamics
Technical Arts III, IV
Introduction to Psychology
Introduction to Logic

Third Year

Organic Chemistry
Mathematics V
Modern Physics
Theory and Design of Structures
Mechanics of Fluids
Electrical Science I, II
System Dynamics
Rate Processes
Nature and Properties of Materials
Analog and Digital Computation
Man, Society and Culture

Departments of Engineering Course Offerings

Undergraduate specialization in fourth and fifth years

Aeronautical

Engineering Analysis
Aeronautical Engineering I
Flight Vehicle Dynamics, Performance and Control
Aerodynamics
Aeronautical Structures I, II
Experimental Methods

Chemical

Introduction to Chemical Engineering
Transfer Processes I, II
Thermodynamics
Chemical Rate Processes
Chemical Engineering Analysis
Process Dynamics
Chemical Technology
Chemical Engineering Laboratory
Combined Operations
Chemical Engineering Operations
Chemical Engineering Kinetics
Chemical Engineering Design I, II
Process Development
Electrochemical Engineering
Molecular Theory of Matter
Principles of Combustion

Civil

Applied Fluid Mechanics
Hydrology and Hydraulic Engineering
Structural Mechanics
Structural Analysis and Models Laboratory
Reinforced Concrete
Soil Mechanics
Geotechnical Sciences
Engineering Materials
Sanitary Engineering I, II
Surveying I, II
Concrete Technology and Transportation Laboratory
Structural Design
Structural Dynamics
Foundation Engineering
Transportation Engineering I, II
Construction Planning and Management

Electrical

Network Theory
Linear Systems
Networks and Fields Laboratory

Electric and Magnetic Properties of Materials
Advanced Electronics
Statistical Methods
Electromechanical Energy Conversion I, II
Electromagnetic Theory
Network Synthesis
Pulse Techniques
Communication Systems
Communication System Practice
Electromechanical Energy Conversion
Power System Analysis
Power System Practice
Nuclear Power Engineering
Application of E. M. Theory
Control Systems
Power and Control Devices
Analog and Digital Computer Technology

Mechanical

Machine Elements I, II
Instrumentation and Control
Gas Dynamics and Combustion
Principles of Energy Conversion I, II
Heat Transfer
Engineering Materials
Manufacturing Production
Materials Handling
Advanced Mechanics of Solids
Hydraulic Turbines and Pumps M. E. System
Power Systems I, II
Engineering Design I, II
Experimental Analysis I, II

Metallurgical

Principles of Material Separation
Fuels and Refractories
Metallurgical Thermodynamics
Introduction to Process Metallurgy
Electrochemistry and Corrosion
X-ray Crystallography
Introduction to Physical Metallurgy
Kinetics and Ternary Systems
Plastic Deformation of Metals
Engineering Metallurgy
Extractive Metallurgy (Ferrous)
Extractive Metallurgy (Non-Ferrous)
Metallurgical Process Design
Physics of Solids
Heat Treatment of Alloys
Alloy Steels
Deformation Processing
Introduction to Ceramics

XI
LEARNING BY TEACHING

"The children were also very inventive when it came to naming the parts of the bulbs and batteries. Among the names for the terminals of the battery were: terminal, top and bottom, bump, right and left, the blue and silver ends. Among the many names I heard for the parts of the bulb several were very intriguing. One small boy called the silver terminal the 'beginning' while he also called the gold terminal the 'end.' Therefore the electricity had to go from the beginning to the end. Finally, there was one perceptive boy who refused to call them anything except contacts because, he maintained, there was no difference, anyway, so why try to remember which was which?"

—Thomas Seitz
PSSC Student
Shaker Heights High School
Shaker Heights, Ohio

LEARNING BY TEACHING

by Jerrold R. Zacharias

TALKING ABOUT EDUCATION is so difficult. One has the feeling that everything has already been said, that all of the questions have been asked, that somewhere somehow in our vast and various educational establishment, all the answers are to be found. Perhaps. But I have always liked James Thurber's maxim, "It is better to know some of the questions than all of the answers." And I think it is still better to know some experiments to try. An experiment, of course, is a form of question.

Today, I want to press for bringing the colleges and the schools closer together. I want to press for the increased involvement of students with the education of other students—a well-known behavior pattern that I shall call "learning by teaching." And I want to propose some experiments.

All of us have had the experience of learning something by doing it. This is the method of choice, the most powerful method of all. But all of us, I think, have also had the experience of learning something by teaching it to someone else, or helping someone else to learn it. This also is a powerful method in education.

Speaking for myself, I have learned some things by doing them. I learned something about experimental physics only by working in a laboratory. No scientific paper or textbook ever refers to the false starts, the mistakes in design, the mishaps, the short views that really characterize experimental science. They record only the happy hours. But I have learned other things by teaching.

Sir Charles Snow wants every intellectual to understand the second law of thermodynamics. Perhaps he is asking too much; so many physicists, myself included, find that they understand thermodynamics only because they taught it to someone else, or maybe only *after* they taught it to someone else. (*Post hoc* is frequently confused with *propter hoc.*) But the second law of thermodynamics, among other things, serves as a theoretical basis for understanding why no one can construct a perpetual motion machine that runs itself in an organized way. Yet if we look at smoke with a microscope, we see that the small particles are indeed in a state of perpetual motion. As a child I wanted to know why the power company of my small town could not see its easy path to wealth by connecting an electric motor to the power lines and letting it drive the generator to feed the power lines. Was it just impractical, or was there something fundamentally wrong? Perhaps this subject seems too abstruse, too complicated to be what I call manageable in early teaching. Yet every time one of us tries to teach it we find new insight, new learning, because, in the process of teaching, you have wallowed in all of the right reasons, all of the wrong reasons, all of the data, all of the implications, all of the various ways of saying, doing, thinking which are provoked by that blessed student who won't just take it without argument, or without demanding some different point of view, or by driving the assumptions back and back to more fundamentals.

What is true for university professors is also true for school teachers. A teacher will himself learn a bit of mathematics if he really tries to answer his pupils when they ask him, say, "Why is minus two times minus three equal to plus six?" Remember it is not enough merely to reply, "Because minus times minus is always plus, and no more foolish questions please." (To be sure, that is the way I learned it—by being hit over the head.)

I have never tried teaching this piece of mathematics to a classroom of children, but some of my friends have. There are various ways a teacher might begin. You could start by interpreting negative numbers as debts. You owe each of two people three dollars, and you know that plus two times minus three equals minus six; therefore, you owe six dollars. But what in the world

---

Dr. Zacharias is an Institute Professor at the Massachusetts Institute of Technology and ESI's Director for Academic Affairs. This article is the text of a talk he gave at the White House Conference on Education last year.

do you mean by negative debts? Or you could pose a problem involving the multiplication of negative numbers in which you already have an answer from another route. You know that plus two times minus three equals minus six; you know that your three equals, say, five minus two. Now, what mathematical assumptions must you make, or invent, so that in the interests of consistency, you get $-2\ (5-2) = -10 + 4 = -6$? If these ways do not work completely, or even if they do, try geometric interpretations, physical interpretations like a beam balance with two weights three units away on one side and a pull up of three weights pulling up on the other side. I claim that after you have taught all these ways, you will really know why minus times minus equals plus as you never in your life knew it before, and you also know what the word "equals" means.

Let me propose an experiment involving teaching the phenomena and theories of light, a piece of science which is easily managed. Light is all around us. We live by it; we admire its manifestations. Even the word "vision" implies our reaction. But frequently we ignore the beauty of *understanding* it. You may say that you have heard that light is a form of wave-motion —oh, yes, electromagnetic waves, whatever they are— and let it go at that.

I would like to begin a college (freshman, sophomore, junior, or senior) course in light by having the members of the class start by teaching light to children, preferably those golden, glowing ten-year olds. We can see an object, not by having something move from the eye to the object but by having something go from the object to the eye. (This was not obvious to the ancients, nor is it now to some cartoonists.) But what goes from the object to the eye? How does it go? In straight lines? *Sometimes.* And when? Can we see how light travels by using shadows, mirrors, reflections of all sorts—diffuse reflections from leaves, reflections from smoke? Why are some clouds black? Is the moon white, black, or gray? Can a child find out for himself by asking the moon—not a teacher or a book?

Some of my colleagues have prepared a simple, pictorial teacher's guide showing how to use sunlight and the shadows in the sunlight, how to use small light sources indoors. Outdoors in the sunlight if I cast a shadow on the sidewalk with my hand, does the size of the shadow change as I move my hand away or toward the ground? Does the character of the shadow change? Now try some experiments indoors with a small source of light, using your hand to cast some shadows on the wall and ask the same questions. Why? How?

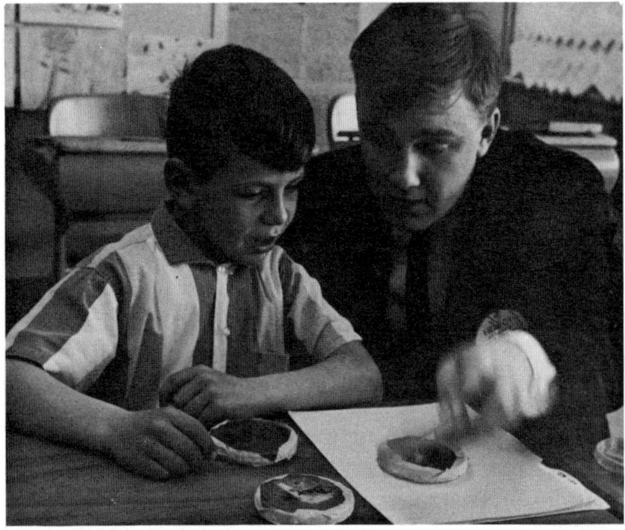

In this way, the ten-year olds and the eighteen-year olds will not just be learning facts. They will be learning how to learn, how to see, and observe, how to reason, *and* they will be learning something about the properties of light. Presently theory begins. Is light carried by particles? waves?

And now a course in optics is off to a sound start. The college student understands the fundamentals and wants to learn more. Who knows, he may end up *not* fearing science, or learning, or searching, or even (to use a vulgar verb) researching. I believe that fear is the enemy of action and of love and, therefore, of progress. Fear, I believe, is a contagious disease, and if young teachers—and young mothers—are fearful of intellectuality of any sort, that fear can be caught by the child.

Although the particular course that I just described is not now being tried, it is nonetheless similar to courses going on in several colleges. I shall not name the colleges or people, for fear of omitting many.

There is a second virtue in this use of students as teachers. So far I have been talking about a student learning a subject by teaching that subject, but the student-as-teacher, of course, is also learning how to teach. And he is learning this by the most powerful of all methods, learning by doing. At present, a prospective teacher, if he studies science, is likely to begin it in the early years of his college career, while his practice teaching comes later on. I believe that the two programs could be combined to make one whole, with advantages to both programs.

Notice that the subject, as I have described it, is not only initially manageable for the children and for their student teachers, but is also open-ended—open-ended in a variety of directions, for a variety of students and their teachers. And my example of an initially manageable, interesting piece of subject matter, which is open-ended, is not unique. Others can be found in many fields—mathematics, science, social science, literature, art, music, cooking, breakfast—anywhere.

In describing this experiment, I am not just referring to college students who expect to become teachers, but to any college student—students who expect to become scientists, who expect to go into business, who expect to become artists, who do not yet have much of an idea what they will do when they are graduated. My guess is that such an effort would result not only in an immediate improvement in the education of the ten-year olds and eighteen-year olds involved, but also in the recruiting of a new group of enthusiastic teachers —perhaps for a lifetime, perhaps only for a short period, but that is all right, too. And the alumni of the course, no matter what they do as adults, will have a better understanding of the valuable and tough job that is teaching, and the valuable and tough job that is school administration.

The fact is, I do not know what the limits are to this general pattern of bringing together youngsters in such a way that we are not quite sure which group constitutes the learners and which group the teachers. High school students can teach elementary school students. College seniors can teach college freshmen. Graduate students can teach in college as a matter of course. How these things are best done are all matters for experiment.

Teaching is somehow required of almost everyone, certainly of mothers and fathers. Of late, several psychologists have discovered the wonderful age of learning in the years 3 to 6. Presently they will discover the age from 0 to 3, and there will be a lot of talk about infant schools, infant learning, and infant teaching. And who is going to do this teaching? Mothers for sure; fathers too, I hope. Not all of these will have attended colleges. So I think we should apply the system of learning by teaching to the high school students as teachers.

And why stop here? We can also get some mileage out of students being the same age as their pupils. This is especially valuable in communication arts of speaking, listening, reading, and writing. We need a bold plan to promote pen pals, typing pals, and tape pals who will write to each other, to help each other, to correct each other.

There are two tortures which Dante could not even imagine. One I know personally; it is the screening of other people's poor educational movies. One I have only heard about; it is to read, understand, change, consult about, and evaluate one hundred student essays per week. No teacher should have to do that. One hundred students can each do one or two pieces. This is not the blind leading the halt; it is the buddy system. It works in space: why not here?

I have talked about learning by teaching, but not a word about good, old-fashioned learning by being taught. Well, that is pretty much the established pattern we now have, sometimes done well, sometimes done poorly. Certainly, I am not arguing for some new over-all educational pattern to replace an existing pattern. What is needed is a great increase in the kinds of teaching offered in the schools, coupled with the opportunity for teachers, parents, and students to choose among those offerings. I believe that learning by teaching is a much neglected educational practice, which would be eagerly sought by a good proportion of the school population, both students and teachers, if it were available. One must not lose sight of the administrative problems that would arise as they inevitably do in making changes in a system. Simple calculations show that you can get more for less money if the students are part of the teaching system. But this could be the subject of another speech.

The venture in learning by teaching need not start from scratch. In the teaching of science, for example, a certain portion of the new efforts in curriculum reform would be useful. (I dare not mention the names of particular sets of instructional materials or the persons developing them. But let me describe the general characteristics of some of the new materials for elementary school.)

Instead of attempting to develop a complete curriculum, or even a complete course, some of the new programs are developing self-contained units of four to six weeks' duration, usable at various levels of sophistication. The teachers and the schools can then use them singly or in combination in ways that best fit into their own program. The units include inexpensive but elegant (I should say inexpensive because elegant) laboratory equipment which pupils can use at their desks or at home; work-sheets and teaching guides; and optional learning aids including films, film loops, and supplementary reading.

The units are built around phenomena that children can investigate in their own way, not around the terminology and disciplines of science already codified. The student interrogates nature directly, but the teacher helps by giving him hints on how to ask questions. The units open up to the intellectual, spiritual and practical heavens; no student, no teacher need be thwarted by the unit's having an end.

Curriculum reform in science and mathematics has been the result of a new collaboration between research scientists and mathematicians, and people in the schools. What I am urging now is the greatly increased involvement of college teachers, and college students too, not just in curriculum reform but in such new programs as learning by teaching. The experiments will require the cooperation not only of the colleges, but also of the schools. Both institutions will have to look afresh at their established procedures. Much as I stress the importance of reform in instructional materials, much can be done through experiments in administrative practices and through reallocation of present resources.

Unfortunately, my examples are all drawn from science. But I believe that comparable efforts are possible in every field. And just as the work in science and mathematics has involved research scientists and mathematicians, so the work in other fields — in history, music, visual arts, writing, and so on—must involve historians, musicians, artists, and writers.

Let me conclude by trying to restate what I am saying in the form of a proposal. It is easy enough for anyone to point to an alternate way of teaching this, that, or the other. It is another thing to be sure that we have come to a statistically valid conclusion—valid in terms of children's capabilities, teachers' willingness, and school systems' interest. When, as a professional physicist, I try an experiment in my laboratory, my molecules come cheap and by the billions. In education the molecules of the system are children, teachers, teachers of teachers, teachers of teachers of teachers, principal-teachers, principal-administrators, and so on. Several percent of each of these populations must be involved in an innovation before we can say that the innovation is valid.

Through the foresight of the Congress, the Office of Education, the National Science Foundation, the Executive Office of the President, and particularly of the President himself, in formulating and enacting the new education legislation, it is now possible to try innovations in education which are on a scale large enough to show statistical validity.

My proposal is that a fair number of universities and colleges—the academic as well as education faculties—high schools and elementary schools work together to devise experiments in learning by teaching. We need a large variety of attempts. Naturally some of these should be in science and mathematics. But we also need experiments in social studies, in the arts, in vocational education—in any field in which someone finds the inspiration that provides the courage to try something new.

LEARNING BY TEACHING: A PILOT PROGRAM

by Stefan Machlup

LAST JUNE I was sitting in a cafeteria at M.I.T. having lunch with Ervin Hoffart of ESI, when we were unexpectedly joined by Jerrold Zacharias. Before the conversation had got very far, Professor Zacharias seemed to have an idea: "What's the best way to learn something?" Machlup: "You teach it." JZ (evidently satisfied with the answer): "For the first time in the history of education, we now have in existence a bunch of materials for teaching science to elementary school children that can be used by teachers who are themselves not sophisticated about science." Then he said something about the right kind of attitude being necessary—scepticism, humility, willingness to believe your own observations rather than the printed word, the experimental approach — and added, "And we also have a pool of several tens of thousands of potential teachers who have been trained with this 'right' kind of attitude toward science." I flinched; then it took: "You mean the kids taking PSSC physics!"

Well, the idea that school kids—high-school juniors and seniors—could go and actually *teach* little children physics, and do it as a way of learning the physics themselves—that idea got me very excited. Somehow I got Professor Zacharias to phone his secretary to say he'd be delayed for 45 minutes and to come up and talk off the cuff about the Elementary Science Study. I liked a unit he called "Batteries and Bulbs," where the kids start with a flashlight battery, a miniature bulb, and 8 inches of copper wire. Later in the summer, I had the opportunity to teach this unit to five 12-year-old volunteers for an hour a day on four successive days. I had never taught "little" kids before, and those four sessions were among the most thrilling experiences of my life. Actually, *they* were teaching *me* about electricity. They did the talking, and they burned out some bulbs, and they warmed up some batteries. At the end of that week I thought about those same bright-eyed kids only six years from now, having to sit through (say) my Freshman Physics lectures, instead of continuing to putter and ask their own questions and formulate their own conclusions—and it seemed somehow wrong.

In November we had our local Area Meeting of PSSC teachers here in Cleveland. By this time I knew that Professor Zacharias hadn't just dreamed up that scheme right there at the lunch table. In fact, in July he proposed it at a White House Conference! I had discussed the difficulties with a few of the high school physics teachers: You could only do it where a grade school was within walking distance of the high school, where there was an enterprising and interested elementary school teacher, and where the physics teacher and the elementary teacher together could talk both their principals into it. The PSSC students would have to do it entirely on a volunteer basis; the scheduling program seemed insurmountable. Well, at the Meeting we equipped everybody with battery, bulb, and wire, and I gave the after-lunch lecture on "the symmetries of nature": You could turn the battery around, and the bulb will still light. What else could you turn around? Could you change a positive into a negative charge? Right into left? (At this point we imagined ourselves equipped with magnetic compasses.) North pole into south pole? This brought up the non-conservation of parity, and I ended with the possibility of CP-violation, so I couldn't be accused of having talked only 5th-grade science. And then I told them about Zacharias' scheme.

By a marvellous stroke of luck, Erv Hoffart, who is in charge of the PSSC Area Meetings program, was also present, and catalyzed some of the immediate reactions. A number of people did a lot of work and planning between November and February: teachers, principals, PSSC students, and (of course) Erv Hoffart.

Dr. Machlup is a professor of physics at Western Reserve University. He has been associated with the PSSC program from the start and has served as principal lecturer in PSSC teacher training programs in this country and in New Zealand and Western Nigeria.

Here are some excerpts from letters:

November 24, 1965

Dear Mr. Hoffart:

Pursuant to the plot you and Dr. Machlup outlined to the PSSC group in Cleveland earlier this month, we have enlisted some conspirators here in Shaker. The would-be cell has the following members:

Mrs. Beth Becka, a young, enthusiastic teacher at Onaway Elementary School, with a class of 24 third-graders;

Mrs. Pearl Kuhels, Coordinator of Elementary Science Education for the Shaker Heights school system, who is already acquainted with ESS materials and eager to try some of the units at various grade levels;

Mr. Wayne French and myself, PSSC teachers at Shaker Heights High, who will undertake to choose and train some of our students to work with Mrs. Becka's class;

The principals at the high school and the elementary school, whose respective blessings we have secured. . . .

What we would like to do is try the Batteries and Bulbs unit with the third-graders beginning late in January. Thus we would need copies of the Teachers Guide as soon as possible. We plan to present the unit to the PSSCers first, just as they might in turn present it to the third-graders. Since they haven't got to Vol. IV yet, some of the ideas will be fresh and new to them too. I don't know yet how many we will try to train, but at least four as a starter. If the pilot goes well, we might like to repeat it with other grades and units. . . .

Subversively yours,
JEAN H. BRATTIN
(Mrs. William J.)

December 13, 1965

Dear Mr. Machlup:

I finally received a tentative OK from our superintendent to do the "Batteries and Bulbs". . . .

Sincerely yours,
G. R. GLASGOW
(Boardman High School,
Youngstown, Ohio)

December 17, 1965

Dear Mrs. Brattin:

. . . we are sending you copies of the Teachers Guide for the elementary school science unit "Batteries and Bulbs." Two copies of the first of three parts are enclosed; the remainder will be along as soon as it can be retyped. . . .

Sincerely,
ERVIN H. HOFFART
(E.S.I.)

January 4, 1966

Dear Mr. Hoffart:

. . . I am starting to train the PSSCers immediately so they can go into action about January 31. If you have any suggestions on an inexpensive source of batteries and bulbs for a class of 24 third-graders, we need to know quickly to get them in time.

You seem to have hit on a very potent idea when you thought of involving PSSC students. Let me tell you what happened when I asked for volunteers for the teaching project. I did a very soft sell, stressing the qualifications needed and the large amount of time they would have to give up both for training and teaching. If a dozen had indicated an interest I would have been surprised and pleased. I got 43 — all anxiously pestering me to be chosen . . . Of course we may all fall flat on our faces, but it won't be for lack of interest.

Thank you for sending the box full of [ESS] kits. I am gradually working my way through them; enjoying and learning from every one. I wonder what high school students would be like if they had all been brought up with experiences like these. . . .

Sincerely,
JEAN H. BRATTIN

January 11, 1966

Dear Erv,

. . . Report on the Laurel School: Two very good senior girls (Susan and Ann, to me) intend to start using "Gases and Airs" with five fourth-graders each. Spent a lovely 45-minute "free period" with them burning candles over water. They will be very well supervised . . . by Mrs. Marte Arnold, who is the Junior High School science teacher (with some influence in the lower school). She was shocked when I suggested that the children might not learn anything you could test. So was Ann. Susan was not. I think she really understood. I also got the headmaster and the head of the lower school to burn candles . . . Thought this was quite a *coup,* especially since our three water levels scattered wildly. They did not seem to mind my refusal to explain the non-reproducibility of the results, and thought the fourth-graders would enjoy splashing . . .

Report on Shaker High: Spent close to an hour with six of Mrs. Brattin's PSSC students and Batteries and Bulbs. Most of them lit up immediately; all of them tried nonsense as soon as I said, "Are there any other ways . . .". When we started messing around with "other materials" there was no stopping them. . . . Again and again I am impressed with the importance of having just the right equipment. Example: The modeling clay was old and brittle, no use at all. The six kids (five B & one G) will each have four third-graders, probably three times a week for three or four weeks, with two grownups in the room . . .

Sincerely,
STEFAN

January 11, 1966

Dear Mr. Hoffart:

. . . Please don't bother about the batteries; we can get them locally and hope to scrounge our bulbs from G.E.'s local Lamp Division. However, Professor Machlup says you might be able to supply us with unlacquered wire, which is hard to find, and tell us or send us just the right variety of rubber band for that battery holder. Our Fahnstock clips are too big, but we discovered that cut in half they are great to mount on the lamp sockets—much better than whole ones . . .

Sincerely yours,
JEAN H. BRATTIN

P.S. Dear Dr. Machlup:

Today they discovered that any odd number of batteries in any combination would light the bulb, and invented a brightness scale to tell how many were contributing. Oh, the excitement and joy of it all! I wasn't even in the room and had absolutely no role in the monumental discovery. They thought the bulbs might turn out the same way, but have now decided that they are two-way streets, even though batteries are sort of one way.

January 20, 1966

Dear Erv,

Well, three Zach-inspired programs (PSSC kids teaching little ones with ESS materials) are now under way. Mrs. Brattin has sent me a carbon of her two-page letter to you. My visit to Laurel School, which I described to you last week, netted the enclosed four-page thank-you note. You are probably getting reports from Mr. Malburg (Hawken School) independently; I am receiving them verbally. They have forty elementary school kids involved, with six PSSCers plus three well-versed adults all in the room. I am reminded of the series of jokes whose punch lines are "that I gotta see!".

Sincerely,
STEFAN

February 14, 1966

Dear Erv,

. . . The program at Hawken is now in its fourth week and I have some feedback. Mr. Malburg's principal comment was that he thought he had not prepared the PSSCers sufficiently and that more orientation sessions might have been useful. A couple of the boys seemed to be slightly frustrated and a little unsure of themselves, but the fourth-graders are having a ball. One quotation, "This is much better than regular teachers" . . .

Sincerely,
STEFAN

February 7, 1966

Dear Mr. Hoffart:

My "teachers" have just returned from their first class this morning and I guess I've never seen seniors so excited! I told them to make notes of all their unusual experiences so we could send them to you.

The worst problem is one of supply. I ordered 100 batteries 3 weeks ago but only picked up 50 Saturday. Also, #48 and #41 bulbs are very hard to locate . . .

Sincerely,
G. RICHARD GLASGOW

February 14, 1966

Dear Mr. Hoffart:

. . . I think I cleaned out the total supply of #48 bulbs in Youngstown! I got 10 at about 3 electronics suppliers and the last one had 135 in cartons—so old he gave me the whole lot for $10.00 . . .

The scheduling of students to teach the 6th-graders also took a little time . . . We try to meet 15 minutes before class each day . . . They are all having a grand time teaching, but they all get back late for the next class and the office is giving me trouble because of this. (I'm not complaining—this is just part of the report!) . . .

The school we are working with is only across the street from our parking lot, so all of them walk over and walk back. The school itself has been very helpful . . .

Sincerely,
G. RICHARD GLASGOW

February 17, 1966

Dear Erv,

I visited Mr. Malburg with his 40 fourth-graders, all lighting bulbs in the school cafeteria. Each lunch table is taught by one 11th-grade PSSCer. I walked around, introduced myself to the boys, both little ones and big ones, and witnessed a few amusing inventions. Example: One boy invented a switching circuit which involved shorting out one bulb of a series connection. He noticed that the other bulb got brighter. The discussion he had about this with the 11th-grader was not something you would put in a physics textbook, but I thought it was very instructive. I happened to pick the day when most of the boys were developing switching circuits—series, parallel, and various combinations. The 11th-graders had designed some fancy "prediction sheets," but the 4th-graders were much more imaginative—and elaborate. My visit at Hawken was organized by the educational psychologist who consults for the school. He stood around, and didn't seem to get excited by all the kids inventing things: "If he can't verbalize it, he hasn't really learned it." And you know, Erv, I really think he believes that! . . .

Sincerely,
STEFAN

March 3, 1966

Dear Professor Machlup:

. . . Just starting Circuits and Magnets next Monday . . . Our superintendent seems to want us to go on, even though we thought it would be two weeks, and the principal of Stadium Drive Elementary School is very impressed.

Sincerely,
G. RICHARD GLASGOW

March 15, 1966

Dear Erv,

. . . Some lessons from the local pilot programs:

The ratio of one PSSCer to five or six elementary students seems about right. At Hawken, each PSSCer had his own six kids. At Shaker, they began by circulating around the room; later each PSSCer adopted a table of four. Incidentally, the five PSSCers from Shaker were selected for their promise as pedagogues rather than as physicists. They were really wonderful with the third-graders—gentle, understanding, knew all the kids' names. (One was the captain of the H. S. Football team!) At Hawken, I heard one fourth-grader referring to his fifteen-year-old teacher as "you old meanie." I investigated and found out it was not a discipline problem. The little kid was just bursting with curiosity, and the PSSCer was responding to his questions with questions, rather than answers. Evidently the technique worked, since the fourth-grader was next seen busily connecting wires to bulb holders . . .

I had urged the teachers to keep their pilot program short, no longer than three weeks. Shaker did this, and the twelfth-graders, but especially the third-graders, were very sad when it ended. Hawken went on for six weeks (twice a week) and the fourth-graders were sorry to see it end. I have a feeling it was a bit long for the PSSCers. Similar indications come from Mr. Glasgow in Youngstown.

It is obviously too much work for any teacher to order the supplies locally. Batteries, OK, but the rest of the equipment should come in a kit. The standard kit for a class of 24 might well contain about a hundred bulbs; also supplies for the junk box.

I have a feeling the David Hawkins article, "Messing About in Science" (*Science and Children,* Vol. II, No. 5, February 1965; reprinted in the *ESI Quarterly Report,* Summer-Fall 1965), might be compulsory reading for every science teacher. Would there be any chance of obtaining 75 reprints to distribute at the March 26th Area Meeting here?

Sincerely,
STEFAN

March 16, 1966

P.S.

This will slay you. It seems the other 3rd-grade class at Onaway School in Shaker put pressure on its teacher: They wanted Batteries and Bulbs too. So Mrs. Becka organized a corps of her initiated third-graders to go over and teach their contemporaries in the other homeroom. How's that for chain reaction?

MORE ABOUT LEARNING BY TEACHING

by Ervin H. Hoffart

THE UNIQUE AND FLEXIBLE structure of the PSSC area meetings* encourages a variety of topics for discussions and presentations. At a number of meetings during the past six months, workshops (one to two hours) have been conducted using science materials prepared for use in elementary school classrooms. The rationale behind this unusual approach is the recognition that PSSC physics teachers are concerned about the quality of science instruction at all levels and many of them are in a strong position to do something about it in their schools. There are numerous obvious ways that they might put to use their knowledge of elementary science curriculum materials. Perhaps the least obvious way is suggested in the article by Professor Jerrold R. Zacharias. An interesting account of the consequences of one of the workshops is found in the article by Professor Stefan Machlup who is responsible for stimulating the experimental programs in the Cleveland area.

I conducted an experimental program during the 1965 spring term in which first year college students taught sixth grade students using elementary school science materials. The overwhelming success of this program led to the trials by PSSC teachers and students during the current year.

Briefly the experimental program provides opportunities for PSSC physics students to teach elementary school students using the new science course materials. The PSSC teacher is responsible for briefing the PSSC students in advance and conducting follow-up discussions.

The following selections from some of the reports by participating teachers and students tell an interesting story:

"Because of the natural enthusiasm and vitality of the high school students, this material was alive and fascinating to the elementary students.

"The teachers involved were cooperative and enthusiastic about the program. The elementary pupils' reactions were favorable in every instance. To be more specific (and I quote) they found the program interesting, exciting, and fun; they learned something, liked working together, liked finding answers by experimenting, and it was good to be successful. Our high school students gained in two ways; one, they reviewed a great deal about circuitry, and two, they had an exposure to teaching, which could lead to their consideration of a teaching career. We found the program to be very rewarding for all concerned and we have high hopes for the future.

"Several of the elementary principals in this district have asked that they be included in a similar program next year. I have discussed this with my administrators and they have reacted favorably to a more comprehensive program for next year."

J. RONALD TELLER
Chairman, Science Department
Maine Township High School South
Park Ridge, Illinois

"The PSSC students performed surprisingly well in their new roles. They proved to be quite critical of themselves, capable of finding solutions to their problems, and willing to reorganize teaching methods. They worked well together as a team with an easy flow between large and small group instruction."

GEORGE SMITH
Physics Teacher
South Hadley High School
South Hadley, Massachusetts

*The PSSC area meetings grew out of the feedback program associated with the early development of the PSSC course materials and was established as a going concern in 1960. At present there are 60 area meeting centers, each with a chairman (a high school physics teacher or university physicist) who organizes two meetings a year and invites PSSC teachers and others who are interested. The area meetings provide a forum for the exchange of ideas pertinent to physics and physics teaching through open discussions, lectures by physicists, and prepared papers.

Mr. Hoffart is the Director of ESI's Area Meeting Program.

"The principal (grade school, Mr. Al Taylor) has had nothing but glowing praise the whole time. He stated that of all things the grade students do—most of which doesn't seem very important (outside of regular classes)—this seems head and shoulders above all else. He once said that if they could teach their social studies by this method, we would teach the year's work in about two or three weeks."

G. RICHARD GLASGOW
Physics Teacher
Boardman High School
Youngstown, Ohio

"One of the most exciting things to observe was the fact that many of the more quiet children became accustomed to talking more, and became more outgoing. This was a big delight to me, to their parents, and, I'm sure, to them. The children absolutely loved having Senior High students—they associated closely with them and had a great deal of respect for them. At the end of the program, after the seniors stopped coming, the children hated to return their equipment. We continued using it one more week, but after that had to share with other third grades."

BETH BECKA
Teacher
Third Grade
Onaway School
Shaker Heights, Ohio

"What the children discovered on their own not only was easier for them to understand, but was to them most convincing. Personally, I feel that another excellent way to learn is to teach others. I got carried away when I discovered something myself in the process of teaching. I was opening a battery for a group of children to find out why a battery was so essential. But what's important here is that by this method of teaching, I was learning and teaching at the same time. If we said something, they would refuse to believe it. I thought that this attitude was excellent, because if they would not believe something all they were told to do was to try it. I remember planning to teach my group in the next session about the use of two wires, but when I arrived they wanted to still work on the idea of more than one battery with one wire. When teaching, we should not avoid them, but should rather work with them and their needs."

DENNIS KLEIN
PSSC Student
Shaker Heights High School
Shaker Heights, Ohio

"As for my personal reactions toward the experiment, I can honestly say that it was one of the highlights of my high school studies. Beside the considerable amount of basic knowledge I acquired, I also achieved a completely changed outlook on teaching and the educational process. Never before this experiment had I realized the great amount of planning and psychology that a teacher must have to teach a class, especially one this young; not to mention the amount of patience needed."

ROGER FAULB
PSSC Student
Shaker Heights High School

"Teaching really tests the teacher's understanding of a topic. I found myself looking up in a chemistry book to see exactly how a flashlight battery works and was surprised to see all the misconceptions I had."

RANDY HUGHES
PSSC Student
Shaker Heights High School

"The difference in speeds with which the students caught on was amazing. After giving one boy his battery, one piece of wire, and bulb, I turned to pick up another piece of wire and by the time I looked back he already had his battery lighting his bulb. A few days later this same boy constructed a rather complex circuit from one of the prediction sheets. When I asked him if it would work he explained in a sort of condescending tone that 'the resistance of the tungsten filament inside the bulb' was much greater that of 'the zinc and copper wires I'm using.' Since we had so carefully avoided using these words I was completely taken aback.

The children were also very inventive when it came to naming the parts of the bulbs and batteries. Among the names for the terminals of the battery were: terminal, top and bottom, bump, right and left, the blue and silver ends. Among the many names I heard for the parts of the bulb several were very intriguing. One small boy called the silver terminal the 'beginning' while he also called the gold terminal the 'end.' Therefore the electricity had to go from the beginning to the end. Finally, there was one perceptive boy who refused to call them anything except contacts because, he maintained, there was no difference, anyway, so why try to remember which was which?"

THOMAS SEITZ
PSSC Student
Shaker Heights High School
Shaker Heights, Ohio

XII
PERSPECTIVES ON CURRICULUM REFORM

INTUITIVE AND ANALYTIC THINKING

by Jerome S. Bruner

MUCH HAS BEEN SAID about the importance of a student's intuitive, in contrast to his formal, understanding of the subjects he encounters. The emphasis in much of school learning and student examining is upon explicit formulations, upon the ability of the student to reproduce verbal or numerical formulae. It is not clear, in the absence of research, whether this emphasis is inimical to the later development of good intuitive understanding—indeed, it is even unclear what constitutes intuitive understanding. Yet we can distinguish between inarticulate genius and articulate idiocy—the first represented by the student who, by his operations and conclusions, reveals a deep grasp of a subject but not much ability to "say how it goes," in contrast to the student who is full of seemingly appropriate words but has no matching ability to use the ideas for which the words presumably stand. A careful examination of the nature of intuitive thinking might be of great aid to those charged with curriculum construction and teaching.

Mathematicians, physicists, biologists, and others stress the value of intuitive thinking in their respective areas. In mathematics, for example, intuition is used with two rather different meanings. On the one hand, an individual is said to think intuitively when, having worked for a long time on a problem, he rather suddenly achieves the solution, one for which he has yet to provide a formal proof. On the other hand, an individual is said to be a good intuitive mathematician if, when others come to him with questions, he can make quickly very good guesses whether something is so, or which of several approaches to a problem will prove fruitful.

The development of effectiveness in intuitive thinking is an objective of many of the most highly regarded teachers in mathematics and science. The point has been repeatedly made that in the high school plane geometry is typically taught with excessive emphasis upon techniques, formal proofs, and the like, that much more attention needs to be given to the development of students who have a good intuitive feel for geometry, students who are skillful in discovering proofs, not just in checking the validity of or remembering proofs with which they have been presented. There has been very little done, for example, on the use of diagrams as geometrical experiments as in Hilbert and Cohn's *Geometry and the Imagination,* in which visual proof substitutes for formal proof where possible. Similarly, in physics, Newtonian mechanics is typically taught deductively and analytically. In the judgment of many physicists, at least, there is too little attention to the development of intuitive understanding. Indeed, some have suggested that improving the use of intuitive thinking by teachers is as much a problem as improving its use by students.

Yet, as one member of the Conference put it, it is wrong to look at intuition as "all à la mode and no pie." The good intuiter may have been born with something special, but his effectiveness rests upon a solid knowledge of the subject, a familiarity that gives intuition something to work with. Certainly there are some experiments on learning that indicate the importance of a high degree of mastery of materials in order to operate effectively with them intuitively.

Jerome S. Bruner is a professor of psychology at Harvard University and the Director of Harvard's Center for Cognitive Studies. He also directs the Elementary Division of ESI's Social Studies Curriculum Program.
This article is a chapter from Dr. Bruner's book, The Process of Education, an account of the Woods Hole Conference of 1959, at which some 35 scientists and other scholars and educators discussed how education in science might be improved in primary and secondary schools. The meeting was called by the National Academy of Sciences; Dr. Bruner was the Chairman of the Conference. Among the participants at the Conference were the late Francis L. Friedman, professor of physics at the Massachusetts Institute of Technology, and Dr. Jerrold R. Zacharias, Institute Professor at M.I.T. and Director for Academic Affairs at ESI. This article is reprinted with the kind permission of the publisher, Harvard University Press, and of the President and Fellows of Harvard College.

Those concerned with the improvement of curricula in physics and mathematics particularly have often cited as one of their important aims the use of procedures that will contribute to the improvement of intuitive thinking. In their attempts to design such procedures, there has been a question of the kind of systematic psychological knowledge that would be of help. Unfortunately, little systematic knowledge is available about the nature of intuitive thinking or the variables that influence it. What seems most appropriate at this point, therefore, is an attempt to outline the kinds of research which, if even only partially carried out, would begin to provide information useful to those concerned with the improvement of particular courses or, more generally, of the curriculum as a whole. What kinds of questions do we need the answers to?

Questions about the nature of intuitive thinking seem to center upon two large issues: what intuitive thinking is, and what affects it.

One can say many more concrete things about analytic thinking than about intuitive thinking. Analytic thinking characteristically proceeds a step at a time. Steps are explicit and usually can be adequately reported by the thinker to another individual. Such thinking proceeds with relatively full awareness of the information and operations involved. It may involve careful and deductive reasoning, often using mathematics or logic and an explicit plan of attack. Or it may involve a step-by-step process of induction and experiment, utilizing principles of research design and statistical analysis.

In contrast to analytic thinking, intuitive thinking characteristically does not advance in careful, well-defined steps. Indeed, it tends to involve maneuvers based seemingly on an implicit perception of the total problem. The thinker arrives at an answer, which may be right or wrong, with little if any awareness of the process by which he reached it. He rarely can provide an adequate account of how he obtained his answer, and he may be unaware of just what aspects of the problem situation he was responding to. Usually intuitive thinking rests on familiarity with the domain of knowledge involved and with its structure, which makes it possible for the thinker to leap about, skipping steps and employing short cuts in a manner that requires a later rechecking of conclusions by more analytic means, whether deductive or inductive.

The complementary nature of intuitive and analytic thinking should, we think, be recognized. Through intuitive thinking the individual may often arrive at solutions to problems which he would not achieve at all, or at best more slowly, through analytic thinking. Once achieved by intuitive methods, they should if possible be checked by analytic methods, while at the same time being respected as worthy hypotheses for such checking. Indeed, the intuitive thinker may even invent or discover problems that the analyst would not. But it may be the analyst who gives these problems the proper formalism. Unfortunately, the formalism of school learning has somehow devalued intuition. It is the very strong conviction of men who have been designing curricula, in mathematics and the sciences particularly, over the last several years that much more work is needed to discover how we may develop the intuitive gifts of our students from the earliest grades onwards. For, as we have seen, it may be of the first importance to establish an intuitive understanding of materials before we expose our students to more traditional and formal methods of deduction and proof.

As to the nature of intuitive thinking, what is it? It is quite clear that it is not easy either to recognize a particular problem-solving episode as intuitive or, indeed, to identify intuitive ability as such. Precise definition in terms of observable behavior is not readily within our reach at the present time. Obviously, research on the topic cannot be delayed until such a time as a pure and unambiguous definition of intuitive thinking is possible, along with precise techniques for identifying intuition when it occurs. Such refinement is the goal of research, not its starting place. It suffices as a start to ask whether we are able to identify certain problem-solving episodes as more intuitive than others. Or, alternatively, we may ask if we can learn to agree in classifying a person's style or preferred mode of working as characteristically more analytic or inductive, on the one hand, or more intuitive, and, indeed, if we can find some way to classify tasks as ones that require each of those styles of attack. It is certainly clear that it is important not to confuse intuitive and other kinds of thinking with such evaluative notions as effectiveness and ineffectiveness: the analytic, the inductive, and the intuitive can be either. Nor should we distinguish them in terms of whether they produce novel or familiar outcomes, for again this is not the important distinction.

For a working definition of intuition, we do well to begin with Webster: "immediate apprehension or cognition." "Immediate" in this context is contrasted with "mediated"—apprehension or cognition that depends on the intervention of formal methods of analysis and proof. Intuition implies the act of grasping the meaning, significance, or structure of a problem or situation without explicit reliance on the analytic apparatus of one's craft. The rightness or wrongness of an intuition is finally decided not by intuition itself but by the usual methods of proof. It is the intuitive mode, however, that yields hypotheses quickly, that hits on combinations of ideas before their worth is known. In the end, intuition by itself yields a tentative ordering of a body of knowledge that, while it may generate a feeling that the ordering of facts is self-evident, aids principally by giving us a basis for moving ahead in our testing of reality.

Obviously, some intuitive leaps are "good" and some are "bad" in terms of how they turn out. Some men are good intuiters, others should be warned off. What the underlying heuristic of the good intuiter is, is not known but is eminently worthy of study. And what is involved in transforming explicit techniques into implicit ones that can be used almost automatically is a subject that is also full of conjecture. Unquestionably, experience and familiarity with a subject help—but the help is only for some. Those of us who teach graduate students making their first assault on a frontier of knowledge are often struck by our immediate reactions to their ideas, sensing that they are good or impossible or trivial before ever we know why we think so. Often we turn out to be right; sometimes we are victims of too much familiarity with past efforts. In either case, the intuition may be weeks or months ahead of the demonstration of our wisdom or foolhardiness. At the University of Buffalo there is a collection of successive drafts of poems written by leading contemporary poets. One is struck in examining them by the immediate sense one gets of the rightness of a revision a poet has made—but it is often difficult or impossible to say why the revision is better than the original, difficult for the reader and the poet alike.

It is certainly clear that procedures or instruments are needed to characterize and measure intuitive thinking, and that the development of such instruments should be pursued vigorously. We cannot foresee at this stage what the research tools will be in this field. Can one rely, for example, upon the subject's willingness to talk as he works, to reveal the nature of the alternatives he is considering, whether he is proceeding by intuitive leaps or by a step-by-step analysis or by empirical induction? Or will smaller-scale experimental approaches be suitable? Can group measurement procedures involving pencil and paper tests be used to provide a measure? All of these deserve a try.

What variables seem to affect intuitive thinking? There must surely be predisposing factors that are correlated with individual differences in the use of intuition, factors, even, that will predispose a person to think intuitively in one area and not in another. With respect to such factors, we can only raise a series of conjectures. Is the development of intuitive thinking in students more likely if their teachers think intuitively? Perhaps simple imitation is involved, or perhaps more complex process of identification. It seems unlikely that a student would develop or have confidence in his intuitive methods of thinking if he never saw them used effectively by his elders. The teacher who is willing to guess at answers to questions asked by the class and then subject his guesses to critical analysis may be more apt to build those habits into his students than would a teacher who analyzes everything for the class in advance. Does the providing of varied experience in a particular field increase effectiveness in intuitive thinking in that field? Individuals who have extensive familiarity with a subject appear more often to leap intuitively into a decision or to a solution of a problem—one which later proves to be appropriate. The specialist in internal medicine, for example, may, upon seeing a patient for the first time, ask a few questions, examine the patient briefly, and then make an accurate diagnosis. The risk, of course, is that his method may lead to some big errors as well—bigger than those that result from the more painstaking, step-by-step analysis used by the young intern diagnosing the same case. Perhaps under these circumstances intuition consists in using a limited set of cues, because the thinker knows what things are structurally related to what other things. This is not to say that "clinical" prediction is better or worse than actuarial prediction, only that it is different and that both are useful.

In this connection we may ask whether, in teaching, emphasis upon the structure or connectedness of knowledge increases facility in intuitive thinking. Those concerned with the improvement of the teaching of mathematics often emphasize the importance of developing in the student an understanding of the structure or order of mathematics. The same is true for physics. Implicit in this emphasis, it appears, is the belief that such understanding of structure enables the student, among other things, to increase his effectiveness in dealing intuitively with problems.

What is the effect on intuitive thinking of teaching various so-called heuristic procedures? A heuristic procedure, as we have noted, is in essence a nonrigorous method of achieving solutions of problems. While heuristic procedure often leads to solution, it offers no guarantee of doing so. An algorithm, on the other hand, is a procedure for solving a problem which, if followed accurately, guarantees that in a finite number of steps you will find a solution to the problem if the problem has a solution. Heuristic procedures are often available when no algorithmic procedures are known; this is one of their advantages. Moreover, even when an algorithm is available, heuristic procedures are often much faster. Will the teaching of certain heuristic procedures facilitate intuitive thinking? For example, should students be taught explicitly, "When you cannot see how to proceed with the problem, try to think of a simpler problem that is similar to it; then use the method for solving the simpler problem as a plan for solving the more complicated problem"? Or should the student be led to learn such a technique without actually verbalizing it to himself in that way? It is possible, of course, that the ancient proverb about the caterpillar who could not walk when he tried to say how he did it may apply here. The student who becomes obsessively aware of the heuristic rules he uses to make his intuitive leaps may reduce the process to an analytic one. On the other hand, it is difficult to believe that general heuristic rules—the use of analogy, the appeal to symmetry, the examination of limiting conditions, the visualization of the solution — when they have been used frequently will be anything but a support to intuitive thinking.

Should students be encouraged to guess, in the interest of learning eventually how to make intelligent conjectures? Possibly there are certain kinds of situations where guessing is desirable and where it may facilitate the development of intuitive thinking to some reasonable degree. There may, indeed, be a kind of guessing that requires careful cultivation. Yet, in many classes in school, guessing is heavily penalized and is associated somehow with laziness. Certainly one would not like to educate students to do nothing but guess, for guessing should always be followed up by as much verification and confirmation as necessary; but too stringent a penalty on guessing may restrain thinking of any sort and keep it plodding rather than permitting it to make occasional leaps. May it not be better for students to guess than to be struck dumb when they cannot immediately give the right answer? It is plain that a student should be given some training in recognizing the plausibility of guesses. Very often we are forced, in science and in life generally, to act on the basis of incomplete knowledge; we are forced to guess. According to statistical decision theory, actions based on inadequate data must take account of both probability and costs. What we should teach students to recognize, probably, is when the cost of not guessing is too high, as well as when guessing itself is too costly. We tend to do the latter much better than the former. Should we give our students practice not only in making educated guesses but also in recognizing the characteristics of plausible guesses provided by others — knowing that an answer at least is of the right order of magnitude, or that it is possible rather than impossible? It is our feeling that perhaps a student would be given considerable advantage in his thinking, generally, if he learned that there were alternatives that could be chosen that lay somewhere between truth and complete silence. But let us not confuse ourselves by failing to recognize that there are two kinds of self-confidence—one a trait of personality, and another that comes from knowledge of a subject. It is no particular credit to the educator to help build the first without building the second. The objective of education is not the production of self-confident fools.

Yet it seems likely that effective intuitive thinking is fostered by the development of self-confidence and courage in the student. A person who thinks intuitively may often achieve correct solutions, but he may also be proved wrong when he checks or when others check on him. Such thinking, therefore, requires a willingness to make honest mistakes in the effort to solve problems. One who is insecure, who lacks confidence in himself, may be unwilling to run such risks.

Observations suggest that in business, as the novelty or importance of situations requiring decision increases, the tendency to think analytically also increases. Perhaps when the student sees the consequences of error as too grave and the consequences of success as too chancy, he will freeze into analytic procedures even though they may not be appropriate. On these grounds, one may wonder whether the present system of rewards and punishments as seen by pupils in school actually tends to inhibit the use of intuitive thinking. The assignment of grades in school typically emphasizes the acquisition of factual knowledge, primarily because that is what is most easily evaluated; moreover, it tends to emphasize the correct answer, since it is the correct answer on the straightforward examination that can be graded as "correct." It appears to us important that some research be undertaken to learn what would happen to the development of intuitive thinking if different bases for grading were employed.

Finally, what can be said about the conditions in which intuitive thinking is likely to be particularly effective? In which subjects will mastery be most aided by intuitive procedures followed by checking? Many kinds of problems will be best approached by some combination of intuitive and other procedures, so it is also important to know whether or not both can be developed within the same course by the same teaching methods. This suggests that we examine the mode of effective operation of intuition in different kinds of fields. One hears the most explicit talk about intuition in those fields where the formal apparatus of deduction and induction is most highly developed—in mathematics and physics. The use of the word "intuition" by mathematicians and physicists may reflect their sense of confidence in the power and rigor of their disciplines. Others, however, may use intuition as much or more. Surely the historian, to take but one example, leans heavily upon intuitive procedures in pursuing his subject, for he must select what is relevant. He does not attempt to learn or record everything about a period; he limits himself to finding or learning predictively fruitful facts which, when combined, permit him to make intelligent guesses about what else went on. A comparison of intuitive thinking in different fields of knowledge would, we feel, be highly useful.

We have already noted in passing the intuitive confidence required of the poet and the literary critic in practicing their crafts: the need to proceed in the absence of specific and agreed-upon criteria for the choice of an image or the formulation of a critique. It is difficult for a teacher, a textbook, a demonstration film, to make explicit provision for the cultivation of courage in taste. As likely as not, courageous taste rests upon confidence in one's intuitions about what is moving, what is beautiful, what is tawdry. In a culture such as ours, where there is so much pressure toward uniformity of taste in our mass media of communication, so much fear of idiosyncratic style, indeed a certain suspicion of the idea of style altogether, it becomes the more important to nurture confident intuition in the realm of literature and the arts. Yet one finds a virtual vacuum of research on this topic in educational literature.

The warm praise that scientists lavish on those of their colleagues who earn the label "intuitive" is major evidence that intuition is a valuable commodity in science and one we should endeavor to foster in our students. The case for intuition in the arts and social studies is just as strong. But the pedagogic problems in fostering such a gift are severe and should not be overlooked in our eagerness to take the problem into the laboratory. For one thing, the intuitive method, as we have noted, often produces the wrong answer. It requires a sensitive teacher to distinguish an intuitive mistake—an interestingly wrong leap—from a stupid or ignorant mistake, and it requires a teacher who can give approval and correction simultaneously to the intuitive student. To know a subject so thoroughly that he can go easily beyond the textbook is a great deal to ask of a high school teacher. Indeed, it must happen occasionally that a student is not only more intelligent than his teacher but better informed, and develops intuitive ways of approaching problems that he cannot explain and that the teacher is simply unable to follow or re-create for himself. It is impossible for the teacher properly to reward or correct such students, and it may very well be that it is precisely our more gifted students who suffer such unrewarded effort. So along with any program for developing methods of cultivating and measuring the occurrence of intuitive thinking, there must go some practical consideration of the classroom problems and the limitations on our capacity for encouraging such skills in our students. This, too, is research that should be given all possible support.

These practical difficulties should not discourage psychologists and teachers from making an attack on the problem. Once we have obtained answers to various of the questions raised in this chapter, we shall be in a much better position to recommend procedures for overcoming some of the difficulties.

RESEARCH SCHOLARS AND CURRICULUM DEVELOPMENT

by Jerrold R. Zacharias

YOUR Executive Secretary has asked me to discuss a particular aspect of our recent efforts involving the schools. The question, specifically, is why are scientists willing to spend large parts of their short lives outside their lovely ivory towers, trying to help the schools to help themselves. Surely it might be, but is not, only an excess of missionary zeal. Nor is it that science itself is getting too difficult or too precious, though sometimes we have our moments of depression, when we believe that science is moving away from the concerns of people. Of course, it is not. No, in our ivory towers it is still true that a molecule may not talk but it never talks back; moreover, its feelings are never hurt, and it never does one thing because you ask it to do another. Ask a molecule a sensible question, and you will get a sensible answer.

I think that I can give a reasonable account of the motivation of the scientists in their return to school, which in a way, they never left. But I would like also to try to understand why many professional research scientists have become involved with the schools, while, for the most part, professional humanists have not. In neither instance am I referring to those who are primarily teachers. Just as I am referring to people who are research scientists who also teach, so also am I referring to literary artists who may also teach.

First of all I do not think it is right to separate the worlds of the humanists and the scientists. Contrary to stereotype, scientists do not live isolated from human realities. Literature, music, the arts, the world of politics, the pressures of finance—hand, head, heart, and eye—are theirs too. Sometimes the work of a scientist looks to outsiders as if it were devoid of beauty and of deep human involvement. In the laboratory itself one can ask why, in the growth of a snowflake, do the molecules go to the deficient sides instead of to the more available, easier, larger parts to make them still larger, still easier to find. No, a snowflake enjoys a balanced growth and is all the more appealing for it. Lovely questions and we love them. And we can ask tougher, to me more exciting, questions such as why, since all matter is interpenetrative, and anything can be in the space where anything else is, does my fist not go through the table when I pound it? Or, how can we make all of the complexity we see around us out of a few dozen atomic species? How can the complexity I think of as me be carried in code and transmitted through the small compass of a sperm and an ovum? Questions as lovely as a late Beethoven Quartet, if less demanding.

We scientists are amateurs in the schools, and the intellectual and spiritual values of science which are part of our love are part of what we want to share. Obviously, your concerns are different from ours. But the fundamental problems of education, we share. And what is education? In the opening lines of *Hard Times*[1], Charles Dickens wrote this of education:

> " *'Now, what I want is, Facts. Teach these boys and girls nothing but Facts. Facts alone are wanted in life. Plant nothing else, and root out everything else. You can only form the minds of reasoning animals upon Facts: nothing else will ever be of any service to them. This is the principle on which I bring up my own children, and this is the principle on which I bring up these children. Stick to Facts, sir!'*

1. Dickens, Charles, *Hard Times*, pp. 1-2, Chapman and Hall, London.

This article is adapted from an address given by Professor Zacharias at the General English Meeting of the Seventy-Ninth Annual Meeting of the Modern Language Association in New York City on December 29, 1964. Professor Zacharias is the Director for Academic Affairs of Educational Services Incorporated and a professor of physics at the Massachusetts Institute of Technology.

"The speaker and the schoolmaster, and the third grown person present, all backed a little, and swept with their eyes the inclined plane of little vessels then and there arranged in order, ready to have imperial gallons of facts poured into them until they were full to the brim."

A caricature, perhaps, but that is how education looked to some of us, too. And it still does to most people. The quiz kid is the caricature of that type of schooling.

No, education must be different from that. I think it is learning how to communicate with each other, how to reason, to examine evidence, to create. But most especially, it is loving all of this in the learning. Then learning and doing become indistinguishable. Mr. Justice Holmes knew that learning and doing are not only indistinguishable but are also what keeps a man all his life "twisting the tail of the cosmos."

It was largely a matter of social conscience, I believe, that motivated us to school work. As scientists, we seek evidence before we try to create order, or orderliness, and we do not expect, nor even hope for, complete proof. Earlier, I referred to a law of physics which I believe, that all of the complexity of our universe is carried by a few dozen atomic species. I only wish there were enough time to give you the evidence for my belief; after giving evidence and more evidence, I would still have to admit that my belief is gray, and that conclusions are rarely black and white. We live in world of necessarily partial proof, built on evidence which, although plentiful, is always limited in scope, amount, and style. Nevertheless, uncompleted as our theories may be, they all enjoy, in a sense, the benefits of due process of law. Dogmatism cannot enter, and unsupported demagoguery has a tough time with us. A Hitler or a McCarthy could not survive in a society which demands evidence which can be subjected to examination, to reexamination, to doubt, to question, to cross-examination. It may be this lesson that gives us a missionary zeal.

Let me now change my line of argument to a seemingly irrelevant topic. While I was working in military technology, some years ago, people used to ask me why the Soviets succeeded with large missiles so much earlier than we in the West. My reply was simple: the Russians, by reason of their geography, needed missiles of short range, which they were capable of making at the time. Next, they were ready for slightly larger ones, and so on, until they were able to make a gigantic missile booster (the one with which they keep a jaunty lead in the space-race). On the other hand, by reason of *our* geography, we had need only for missiles of long range. We were forced to start big, so big that we almost couldn't start. Not until we made an initial effort of tremendous boldness, did we get our missiles working. "Easy does it" is a fine motto if the hurdles are not too high at the start. A man's reach should exceed his grasp, but not by too much.

Is this the sort of difficulty that the humanists face? Are your hurdles too high? Is the material with which you deal too sophisticated? Unashamedly, the scientists are willing to study only the simplest problems. When a problem is too difficult for us, we put it off for a decade, a century, or a millenium. But the problems of the humanists cannot be deferred. You are perforce dealing with men, their interactions, their morals, their emotions. Who knows better than you the range of men's complexities?

Now, in teaching, you have additional troubles. Let me quote from a collection of essays by E. M. Forster called *Two Cheers for Democracy*[2]. In the piece entitled "The Raison d'Etre of Criticism in the Arts," he says:

"For now our trouble starts. We can readily agree that criticism has educational and cultural value; the artist helps to civilise the community, builds up standards, forms theories, stimulates, dissects, encourages the individual to enjoy the world into which he has been born; and on its destructive side criticism exposes fraud and pretentiousness and checks conceit. These are substantial achievements. But I would like if I could to establish its raison d'être *on a higher basis than that of public utility. I would like to discover some spiritual parity between it and the objects it criticises, and this is going to be difficult. The difficulty has been variously expressed. One writer—Mr. F. L. Lucas—has called criticism a charming parasite; another—Chekhov—complains it is a gadfly which hinders the oxen from ploughing; a third—the eighteenth century philosopher Lord Kames —compares it to an imp which distracts critics from their objective and incites them to criticise each other. My own trouble is not so much that it is a parasite, a gadfly, or an imp, but that there is a basic difference between the critical and creative states of mind, and to the consideration of that difference I would now invite your attention.*

"What about the creative state? In it a man is taken out of himself. He lets down as it were a bucket into his subconscious, and draws up something

2. Forster, E. M., *Two Cheers for Democracy*, pp. 113-114, Harcourt, Brace & Co., New York, 1951.

which is normally beyond his reach. He mixes this thing with his normal experiences, and out of the mixture he makes a work of art. It may be a good work of art or a bad one—we are not here examining the question of quality—but whether it is good or bad it will have been compounded in this unusual way, and he will wonder afterwards how he did it. Such seems to be the creative process. It may employ much technical ingenuity and worldly knowledge, it may profit by critical standards, but mixed up with it is this stuff from the bucket, this subconscious stuff, which is not procurable on demand. And when the process is over, when the picture or symphony or lyric or novel (or whatever it is) is complete, the artist looking back on it, will wonder how on earth he did it. And indeed he did not do it on earth."

We, the scientists, take stuff from the bucket. When we let down our scientific buckets, we come up with some lovely stuff which we, as children, wanted, and which children today still seem to enjoy. Lovely pieces, crystal clear, that only come to the surface with dipping. And we think that we can help the children dip, until our children out-dip us. Can you, too, dip in your buckets and help the children dip? I think you can. But you can't know until you try.

I should perhaps be required to give an example of dipping, in order to exhibit a piece of the science we love. Unfortunately, here I can use only words; with the pupils I could use things. One problem set before ten-year-olds is: how does a mealworm find its meal? The children go to work with mealworms and bran on a large board. They tilt the board, illuminate the mealworm in various ways, heat it, cool it, twist it, turn it until they drop. The answer comes out, the mealworm gets to its meal by a random process, but when he is there, he knows he is there. This, of course, raises another question: "How *does* he know that he is under bran?" No easy scientific study. No trivial result. There are lessons to be learned, other tries to make—other worlds, other ways. Of course, as a professional scientist, I am envious of David Webster who thought up this mealworm exercise and found the ways to make it play[3]. He dipped, and up came a beauty.

You have such beauties. Here is one, from *Huckleberry Finn.* I will introduce it with a passage from Lionel Trilling's essay[4].

And if Huck and Jim on the raft do indeed make a community of saints, it is because they do not have an ounce of pride between them. Yet this is not perfectly true, for the one disagreement they ever have is over a matter of pride. It is on the occasion when Jim and Huck have been separated by the fog. Jim has mourned Huck as dead, and then, exhausted, has fallen asleep. When he awakes and finds that Huck has returned, he is overjoyed; but Huck convinces him that he has only dreamed the incident, that there has been no fog, no separation, no chase, no reunion, and then allows him to make an elaborate 'interpretation' of the dream he now believes he has had. Then the joke is sprung, and in the growing light of the dawn Huck points to the debris of leaves on the raft and the broken oar.

" Jim looked at the trash, and then looked at me, and back at the trash again. He had got the dream so strong in his head that he couldn't seem to shake it loose and get the facts back into its place again right away. But when he did get the thing straightened around he looked at me steady without ever smiling, and says:

" 'What do dey stan' for? I'se gwyne to tell you. When I got all wore out wid work, en wid de callin' for you, en went to sleep, my heart wuz mos' broke bekase you wuz los'. En I didn' k'yer no mo' what became er me en de raf'. En when I wake up en fine you back agin, all safe en soun', de tears come, en I could a got down on my knees en kiss yo' foot, I's so thankful. En all you wuz thinkin' 'bout wuz how you could make a fool uv ole Jim wid a lie. Dat truck dah is trash; *en trash is what people is dat puts dirt on de head er dey fren's en makes 'em ashamed.'*

"Then he got up slow and walked to the wigwam, and went in there without saying anything but that. "

It may seem to you that a study by children of the behavior of mealworms is remote from a study by children of a passage from *Huckleberry Finn.* The mealworm experiments may take six weeks of school work, but the children are captured by the problems, which are just the kind of problems that capture the scientists. It is never the teacher who has the answers to the students' questions. Nature, with the mealworm as spokesman, reveals the answers only when asked properly. It is the inventing of the questions and proposing ways for nature to answer that capture the pupils' interest and love. They are doing and learning and loving it. I believe

3. Educational Services Incorporated Elementary Science Study, *Behavior of Mealworms* (Teacher's Guide), Houghton Mifflin Company, Boston, 1964.

4. Clemens, S. L. (Mark Twain), *The Adventures of Huckleberry Finn,* introd. by Lionel Trilling, pp. xii-xiii, Holt, Rinehart and Winston, New York, 1964.

that you might use a piece like the one from Huck Finn that I quoted to capture a child's sustained interest. But I would never know until I tried. The doing of that is the work of humanists. I believe that your involvement in some such exercise might need to be as time consuming as ours. Many, many children and many teachers must be involved before you can feel confident that the topic or sequence of topics that you choose to try will survive. You must be careful not to be entrapped by the public stereotype of learning. For science, the public belief is that there are laws of science that the student must learn. He must be able to state them and to work with them. I believe that the children will learn the laws, at least the ones that we think we know, if they come to them from specific experience with specific events and observations. I believe, at least I am willing to bet, that this statement holds for literature and its languages. So when I plead with you to go to the schools, I mean that you go not with commas or spelling but with clear ideas and with love, patience, and the willingness to let the children carry the day, their way.

THE NEW CURRICULA AND THE EDUCATIONAL CLIMATE

by B. Alden Thresher

THE new curricula that are now crowding in upon the educational scene are part of a new educational and social climate of opinion made up of a number of interacting ideas. To appreciate these, we need a century or so of perspective. We know our schools are not nearly good enough, but in our discouragement at how little has been done compared with what needs to be done, it is easy to forget how much better schools are now than they used to be. So let us first take a retrospective look, then consider the scene as it is today.

An informal study of the boyhood of eminent scientists (prior to age 21) and limited to published material, turned up over 1,000 names for which some bits and fragments of biography could be found. In 68 of these something was said about the subject's schooling. Only 28 had anything favorable to say of it, while 40 felt that their schooling was bad in some respect—sometimes in all respects. This, remember, was "little science" in Derek Price's meaning of the term. These men are almost all now dead; otherwise little published biographical material would be available. The list reaches back over the last three centuries and is heavily weighted with the great names of science, because it is these who have been most studied and written about. "Little science" was carried on by giants. So the list antedates the contemporary era of "big science" in which it can be said that ninety per cent of all scientists who ever lived are now alive.

The list begins with Linnaeus, the Swedish naturalist, born in 1707, and ends with Casimir Funk, the Polish biochemist, born in 1884. So we have a sample of schools covering more than two centuries, mostly European, but with a few in the United States. It was not simply that in these schools little attention was paid to nature as a system. It was too soon for that, and the idea had to grow. It was rather that in so many instances whatever the schools taught was ill taught; great literature, to say nothing of arithmetic, history and geography, fared as badly as the natural sciences. Linnaeus said of the lower grammar school which he entered in 1717: "Here brutal teachers, to give the children a taste for scholarship, used an equally brutal method that made their hair stand on end." Or one might cite St. Katherine's school in Braunschweig, which Hans Christian Gauss entered at age 7: "Herr Buttner, whip in hand, would go back and forth among about 200 pupils . . . The school had the cut and style of the middle ages."

Nineteenth century Britain could show many horror exhibits on how not to run a school. I will cite only one from Sir Oliver Lodge's autobiography. He wrote of the Newport Grammar School in Shropshire, which he entered in 1859 at age eight:

> My school days were undoubtedly the most miserable part of my life. . . . The school was a large one with a master at one end and one in the middle . . . we had to be in our places before the bell stopped on pain of being summoned up to the headmaster and receiving a blow on the head from his walking stick. The one large room called the school was extraordinarily dirty. . . . There was a large stove in the middle of the room, but the founder had laid it down that it was not to be lighted till the 5th of November, and sometimes October was uncommonly cold.
>
> I remember my first morning in school. I was given a copy of the Eton Latin Grammar, every word in Latin, and told to learn the first page. I hadn't the least idea what it was about. There was a lot of small print and then some bigger print, with N.G.D.A.V.A. in a column with variations on the word *musa* after

Copyright 1964 B. Alden Thresher

Mr. B. Alden Thresher is Professor Emeritus of Economics and Director of Admissions Emeritus at the Massachusetts Institute of Technology. He received his undergraduate degree from M.I.T. and did his graduate work at Harvard.

On opposite page: Dr. Frank Oppenheimer of the University of Colorado and a consultant to the Elementary Science Study conducts an experiment in light and optics.

> them. Having at that time a wonderful memory, and being quite accustomed to learn by heart, I was depressed to find that the task was hopeless. I sat over it all morning and gradually dissolved into tears. . . . The only one of my textbooks in which I took the smallest interest was the geography book, not the part of the geography which we had to pore over, but the first introductory chapter dealing with the shape of the earth, the phases of the moon, latitude and longitude, and some inkling of the solar system. This chapter aroused my keen interest, though officially we were supposed to skip it. Geography and history were, however, very subordinate subjects, only dealt with twice a week. The bulk of the attention was given to Latin grammar.

Lodge then gives a detailed exposition of the technique of caning and flogging, with practical pointers on how to mitigate the pain inflicted by this brutality. Such accounts explain the characteristic statements made by more than one man of that era that whatever they accomplished in the world was in spite of their schooling, not because of it. Such passages illustrate how easy it is for any curriculum, indeed any system of education, to become fossilized. The great illumination of the Revival of Learning which had spread the glories of classical literature and philosophy over Europe had, by the mid-nineteenth century, run to seed in a sterile grammatical discipline. It was a rigid, pedantic approach to learning, ignoring literary and historical values; even as linguistics, it was ignorant and primitive.

So much for perspective. Let us look now at some of the educational thought that forms the contemporary climate of opinion. We can distinguish a series of seminal ideas, some well rooted, some barely beginning to dawn on the public consciousness.

First, an advance is now evident in public appreciation of the key importance of education. What used to be thought of as a fringe benefit, a minor, routine function of local government, along with roads, water supply and sewers, is at last coming to be seen in the most central position of all, and as the foundation on which our polity, our economy and our culture actually rest. In a society pressing hard against the limits of its educated manpower, education is the key objective. We have still far to go, but the mountain of public apathy is beginning to stir.

Second — and perhaps this is the most important idea of the last decade — is the discovery that we have a great deal more of potential and undeveloped talent than we had ever suspected. This idea has been long in evolving, since it runs counter to most earlier thought. Our inheritance from the feudal age, only slowly modified even during the Industrial Revolution, was the stereotype of a vast, illiterate population, the "lower orders," the "swinish multitude," or in the Marxian era, "the masses." Over against this, in the medieval tradition, had been a small ruling class, itself for the most part little educated, but fitfully influenced by clerks, priests and scholars. Out of this milieu came, for example, the social ideas of 18th century military organization exemplified by the armies of Frederick the Great, with the caste of "officers and gentlemen" separated by a great gulf from the rank and file. The influence of this tradition persisted even in the United States, with its relatively open society. Although a steadily increasing fraction of the population was going on to higher education, the conventional belief was that only a narrow limited group was either able to cope with college or interested in it. Secondary education at the turn of this century was largely focussed upon the needs of this minority. Even as late as the mid-twentieth century the conventional technique of college recruiting was to make a circuit of private schools and of the high schools in the prosperous suburbs to skim off the "cream" of youngsters conditioned by a complex of home and community circumstances to value and seek higher education. We have remained unconsciously under the spell of inherited social concepts with access to education tied closely to social class.

Third, ideas have been evolving about how to salvage human ability. Beginning about 1950, the concept of a "talent search" gained currency: one must look for the promising candidates; since they are so few, we cannot afford to lose any. This was a step forward as compared with the lazy assumption that true talent will overcome all obstacles — an assumption based on no evidence except the observation that here and there, at long intervals, some youngsters actually did overcome all obstacles. But the talent search idea was at best a haphazard, passive approach to a major problem. Implicit in it was the assumption that the only real talent was that fraction which had survived all early blight to become visible in the later stages of a high school course, ready and eager for college. The popular remedy in this era was scholarships: simply ring the bell and offer money. Any young person who did not immediately respond, come forward and compete was clearly not seriously interested, and hence not really "college material."

A few people, teachers, guidance counselors, social workers, perceived the fallacy in this. They sensed that much ability was being pinched off at very early stages by a combination of poverty, poor schooling and a socio-psychological climate that imposed on the child a low level of aspiration. We speak of these children as culturally deprived. So they are, in one sense. It might be more accurate to regard them as molded and conditioned by an urban culture so powerful in its impact as largely to blank out the more subtle, complex, and differentiated signals that the school is designed to transmit. One has to learn to want an education.

We now know through carefully planned experimental studies extending over a period of years that even in the most unpromising environments, such as "slum" schools in the large cities, a substantial proportion of children can be salvaged, encouraged to develop their full abilities and urged on to solid achievement. The average performance of a junior high school group in such a basic measure as reading skill can be raised by a matter of two years. These things were actually done in the New York City Demonstration Guidance Project, at a moderate increase in per pupil cost. They were accomplished by a combination of enriched teaching, intensive counseling, and a curriculum supplemented by many outside experiences of an educational nature which took students for the first time outside the circle of their poverty-imposed ghetto.

All this required a dedicated staff and a determined effort to reach into the home in order to enlist parents' interest and cooperation. The key to these results lays in raising the student's level of aspiration. Instead of perceiving himself as alienated, as a marginal member of society, always struggling and always on the fringe, he could for the first time picture himself as getting an education. He began to realize that doors could open to him, and he would have a chance to fulfill his potentialities. It is now an established fact that good education, at least within wide limits, is a purchasable commodity. If we want better education and are willing to tax ourselves, we can have it. This realization, within the last decade, is a landmark in education and sociology.

Fourth, our philosophy of educational selection is changing. A century ago Francis Galton advocated what he called "eugenics" — selective breeding from the ablest human strains. He had demonstrated to his own satisfaction, but by a line of reasoning that we should now regard as very dubious, that gifted people are very scarce indeed. Ergo, we should raise more of them from the few, identifiable gifted strains. Little troubled by such problems as how to agree on who was gifted or how this quality could be measured, or what to do about the propagation of the non-gifted, Galton confidently launched his crusade. From today's perspective we see that crusade not so much as mistaken, but rather as superfluous. We know now that we are by no means utilizing the talent we have, but are wasting much of it. It is useless to increase the wheat crop if rats and mildew ruin half of it; it is better to conserve what we already have. Today we stress the development of every child to his full potential, realizing that much depends on what happens in the home. As each generation of parents becomes better-educated, the influence of the home sector improves; this impact is already being felt.

Selection, of course, will always be necessary. Some youngsters will always be brighter than others. Our mistake has lain, not in exercising selection, but in carrying it out by negative and destructive means. Traditional methods of selection for the European universities, for example, have identified and trained an elite of high capability, but at a cruel cost. "Human scrap piles" at every stage of selection cast a blight of failure and frustration upon thousands of able students, whose real need was simply redirection and encouragement. The key idea should be classification rather than selection, and always on a tentative basis. Any decision about a child's educational future is rebuttable by later evidence, and no decision need be irrevocable.

We know little as yet about the dimensions of human ability or the dynamics of human personality. Ability is not measurable on any single numerical scale despite our glib habit of talking about the "top tenth" of a class. Blind, wholesale rejection is a great deal simpler and easier administratively than skillful nurture and salvage on a painstaking, individual basis. It is all very well to educate an elite of leaders—this will always be a prime necessity—but an ignorant or poorly-educated populace cannot respond even to the most enlightened leadership. Leadership is not a soliloquy, but a dialogue; the rank and file must understand what the leaders are talking about in order to respond intelligently. This is obvious in the context of an industrial society; automation must promote the worker beyond his present skills or disqualify him. Education for intelligent political response is more subtle and will take longer.

We can no longer be satisfied just to look for talent, but must actively nurture and develop it by maintaining an environment in which it can come to fruition. We look back on 19th century schools as often stupid and brutal; we do better now, in spots. But the over-all impact of most urban environments on most children is not of a kind to develop talent. This is not a new discovery. The novelty lies in the realization that something can be done about it. These degenerative processes are partly reversible. Many youngsters whom we dismiss as uneducable are very educable indeed if we will take the necessary trouble. This includes spending a great deal of money, but more than money is required to do the job.

The human race, for thousands of years, has ignorantly passed by most of the natural resources that lay around it; we lacked the knowledge and the techniques to use them. We picked up only what we could devour, wear, or fashion into crude artifacts. Most of the resources of the environment were unsuspected and untouched. When it comes to recognizing and using human abilities, we are in much the same case as the frontiersman with his fowling piece. All unconscious, he passes by the uranium ores in the cliffs, the penicillin in the soil, the petrochemicals under his feet.

Clues to the nature of electricity and magnetism existed for thouands of years before Faraday. Clues to the nature and potential of human ability are now beginning to be teased out from the complicated confusion of human relationships and motives. We can expect a great deal to come of all this if we continue to work patiently at it—if we learn to educe from the child some increased part of the potential which he carries with him. Parents and teachers attuned to these things have sensed these potentialities and elicited them. But this has been a sporadic process, seldom organized, extended, multiplied, or controlled. Now we have enough demonstrable evidence from new, experimental projects to hold out some hope of harnessing the sporadic intuitions that have hitherto guided education only in its most fortunate moments.

Fifth, today's new educational projects speak so directly to the child's innate urge to learn, that they provide in themselves a powerful influence to salvage and develop talent that would otherwise be lost. One example is the remarkable work of O. K. Moore in putting children aged from 2 to 5 years in a "responsive environment," including an electric typewriter that pronounces each letter as it writes it. The child learns a cluster of related skills — writing, reading, listening and speaking in much the same unconscious way in which children have always learned to talk. All this is done without pressure, at the child's own pace, utilizing only the child's growing delight in getting the hang of something that he quickly discovers to be an interrelated system of symbols, behavior and meaning. He can manipulate it; it responds and is related to his interests and concerns. This, like Educational Services Incorporated's Elementary Science Study, is an "autotelic" activity — in Moore's phrase — one that is its own end and reward, bringing pleasure in and of itself. All this, of course, is the farthest removed from the 17th century opinion that "all children are little vipers, and must be stirred up dreadfully to fear God" — or from the characteristic 19th century view that it makes no difference what a boy studies so long as he dislikes it.

Of course, there is always a disciplinary side to education as to any other human activity, but the inherent pleasure of teaching and learning somehow keeps breaking through if given half a chance. A happy illustration of this is the quite spontaneous and informal summer school started a few years ago by M.I.T. undergraduates for such high school students as might be interested (there were 900 last summer). No one gets paid; no one gets any credit, but these young people have discovered for themselves that both teaching and learning are immense fun. There are clearly other elements in this besides "discovery," and Philip Morrison has rightly warned against using this as a too-easy catchword. Some complex of puzzlement, curiosity, exploration, observation, trial-and-error, reasoning and conviction seems to be involved in these processes; the main point is that they are self-rewarding and habit-forming.

Sixth, and last, back of a number of advances in the educational thought of our times lies one central intuition: that all education is a seamless web, all of a piece from cradle to grave, the stages into which it is customarily divided being due partly to historical accident and partly to administrative convenience; and the earlier stages are the most crucial.

Margaret Mead long ago demonstrated the important determinative effect on any culture of the methods used in the management of small children. She has likewise pointed out the reciprocal principle: that no element in a culture is truly grasped, internalized, appreciated and incorporated as a living component of that culture *unless it is taught to children.* Hitherto, science for the most part has *not* been taught to children. It has been introduced to late adolescents unprepared for any intuitive grasp of its values, methods or significance, and so has often been rejected even by youngsters in whom it might have flourished, given an adequate introduction. It is essential to start young. The spiral of more mature, detailed and sophisticated attention can then return repeatedly to extend and deepen knowledge. Therefore, projects like the Elementary Science Study are far more basic in their significance to our entire culture than is generally realized. A generation exposed to early influences of this kind should have in the end better judgments about many public questions involving science.

Miss Mead's doctrine establishes and defines the *need* for projects like the Elementary Science Study. To *supply* the need is to give effect to Jerome Bruner's central thesis that any subject can be taught in some intellectually satisfying way to children of any age. This fundamental insight clears the way for a much earlier introduction of the *meaning* of a subject — almost any subject — at some appropriate level. All this is in marked contrast to the earlier emphasis on rote learning aimed at giving the child an armamentarium of tools. Both tools and understanding of course go together, but we have stressed tools. We have made too little use of children's penetrating insight into values and motives. Children, being much smarter than we realize, intelligently balk at learning many of the things thrown at them. They have an innate resistance to learning anything that they sense as insincere, artificial or merely conventional. They "see through" adults very fast, especially their parents and teachers. They throw up their defenses against cant and hyprocrisy, as well as against useless drudgery.

The view that education is all of a piece has an interesting corollary. The most important and lasting effect of the new curricular efforts in the long run may turn out to be a facilitating, continuous self-renewal in educational methods and goals. The PSSC, the SMSG and the others that have followed them were brought about by the growing isolation of the high school teacher from the productive scholars in their respective fields. Mathematics, physics, and other branches of learning had been moving forward, their outlook entirely transformed in the space of a generation or two. Nobody bothered to tell teachers about all this; little of the changed outlook came through to them, and almost none trickled through to the student. The problem was to get the ablest people in the field — those at the cutting edge of new research — to direct their full and sustained attention to formulating the subject in the optimum manner for the beginner. This proved to be much more difficult than anyone had expected. It is reassuring that the current solutions are not regarded as final. There is less danger that these subjects will soon again assume a fixed or classic shape, formalized and rigid. The participants show a reassuring reluctance to admit that they have found a final, or perfect solution. This self-renewing attitude of continuous experiment, innovation and change offers great hope.

As we look back over the last century in education in the United States, we can see, with benefit of hindsight, some ways in which we went wrong. The colleges and universities failed to recognize their most urgent obligation, and in so doing muffed their greatest opportunity, namely the education of teachers for the explosively expanding system of public education. Consequently it became necessary to establish a separate structure — first the normal schools, then the teachers colleges — to meet this massive social demand. These *ad hoc* institutions were largely cut off from the scholarly traditions and standards of the universities.

There were several reasons for this: the college curriculum in the old line institutions was only partly relevant to a surging, expanding society needing to cope simultaneously with massive immigration, westward expansion and the growth of industry, transport and trade. Partly it was an arrogant disregard of these parvenue schools. Most of all, it was that scholars found themselves too entranced with their own fascinating concerns to be bothered with spreading the word about what they were up to. It was pleasant to work with a little group of disciples already conditioned to absorb one's own values and to reflect one's own enthusiasms. It was not merely that undergraduate teaching was something looked upon as a bore. The most serious effect in the end was that the shaping and direction of elementary and secondary education in a manner to reflect the evolution of new knowledge and new thought was almost wholly neglected. The academic world was very much like the father so immersed in his business that he gives no time to his children for whose benefit the business is ostensibly conducted.

It was the remarkable achievement of Zacharias, Friedman, and their associates to bring about a widespread reversal of this attitude. They were guided by the central educational (and social) intuition that learning of any kind must not only be continuously added to, updated and revised. It must, even more fundamentally, be reshaped, recreated and newly summarized in the changing perspective of new discovery. No discipline so fully enforces and facilitates this process of summary and reformulation as that of conveying the gist of the subject to beginners, preferably children.

The true significance of physics (or mathematics, biology or history) lies, in the last analysis, in the fact that they are human activities; they speak to the human condition. Unless children, at an early age, begin to sense what all this is about, what the disciplines are that constrain it, and what the values are that make it enticing, science (or history or whatever) will remain an unassimilated lump in the body politic. These projects, in their wider meaning, are more than just an effort to convey knowledge downward from the source; that image is much too condescending. Rather, the discipline of constantly re-evaluating and restating the essence of a subject, sloughing off nonessentials, seeking the core at the center, discovering analogues elsewhere — all this is of the first importance. To do this requires constant feedback from the teacher at the front line.

It was a matter of necessary practical tactics for the PSSC to start first with a high school unit of physics. To get this done for six million dollars was a bargain. But in the long view, though, all levels are important; the earliest are the most vital. The potentialities concealed within the elementary science project and similar experiments are so great that in the end the work on the high school curriculum may well appear to have been only a trial run for what may turn out to be a thoroughgoing reconstruction of education.

EVALUATING NEW SCIENCE MATERIALS: Thoughts on Methods and Goals

by G. C. Quarton, M.D.

THE evaluation of such social action as education is controversial. On the one hand, there are those who argue that no action of this type should be continued unless it can be proven to be effective. On the other hand, there are those who believe that evaluation is both destructive of the effort being evaluated and impossible to carry out effectively, in any case, due to the complex interactions of the factors involved. It is likely that both of these views represent extremes, but it is not particularly useful to say that the truth lies somewhere in between unless fairly precise statements can be made concerning the types of evaluation that are effective and those that are not. Some of the assumptions underlying these two positions are not factual but are based on strong opinions assigning priorities to important human goals. Those who wish to have evaluation of a social action program early in its development usually assume that a rather restricted goal of the program is the only relevant goal. For instance, it is assumed that efforts to teach mathematics to third grade children have as their only goal an increase in the mathematical skills of this particular group of children. Those who oppose "evaluation" often see the teaching of mathematics as a vehicle for accomplishing a wide range of objectives which include increasing mathematical skills but which also include developing logical thinking, changing motivation and interest patterns, and so forth. Such individuals often think that premature evaluation may interfere with the achievement of long range goals.

I shall assume that the most important justification for evaluation is to provide prompt, simple, and realistic feedback to the people planning the science units so that they can benefit from their own successes and failures in future revisions of an evolving curriculum. The trick is to keep such simple feedback from getting lost either in methodological complexities or in political manipulation. A secondary but still important use for evaluation is to provide a factual base for arguments that something believed to be worth doing is in fact doing what it is supposed to do.

Methodological Considerations

If it is agreed that the primary purpose of an evaluation of teaching methods is to provide simple feedback of information on success or failure to those developing the curriculum so that they can try to improve their own efforts, then methodology loses some of its awe-inspiring character. A real beginning can be made by a clear separation of the goals of evaluation from those of curriculum development and by recognizing that evaluation is a means to an end. We are then likely to interpret evaluation broadly to include a number of activities: the day-to-day observation of results by those carrying out the teaching program; the more systematic observation of results by independent and perhaps less biased observers; intuitive evaluations by those with unique training or unique opportunities for spotting special aspects of the program; systematic experimental studies with controls; and so forth. Each of these approaches may play a useful role in an evolving curriculum which is modified by a process of successive approximations, but each must also be judged with practical common sense, since each of these approaches in some way complements the others.

Dr. Quarton is Program Director of the Neurosciences Research Program at the Massachusetts Institute of Technology and an Associate in Psychiatry at the Massachusetts General Hospital, Harvard Medical School. He is a member of the Steering Committee of ESI's African Education Program.

The Task of Clarifying Evaluation Goals

Just what is being evaluated is not always clear. In some sense it is possible to evaluate almost any type of human activity, but in designing a specific evaluation program, there are obvious advantages in being clear. In this discussion, we are talking about the evaluation of specific teaching methods that are in some way bound to specific subject matter. It is convenient to call these "units." We are not evaluating students, teachers, school systems, our success in recruiting good teachers, or our success in developing motivation in teachers.

The Task of Clarifying Curriculum Development Goals

Our great scientists may be highly intelligent, and they may have a great mass of factual knowledge at their command, but what makes them successful is that they have by successive steps learned to solve problems posed by nature. They can transfer problem-solving techniques from one area to another.

It does not seem to be too difficult to find out whether students have acquired scientific "facts." It is much more difficult to determine whether students have developed new problem-solving skills as a result of a series of teaching exercises. It is even more difficult to know whether students can carry over problem-solving methods from one task to another. We need to develop evaluation methods that are concerned with this aspect of learning. If people believe they are interested in teaching effective scientific problem-solving, yet try to evaluate their results by finding out if students have acquired facts clearly, they are unsure what their curriculum development goals are. They not only don't get an answer to the question they believe they are interested in, they also shift the perception of the goal in the minds of everyone concerned.

Conflicts Between Evaluation Goals and Curriculum Development Goals

An evaluation process may provide useful information and yet interfere in some way with the realization of broad teaching objectives. For instance, an evaluation program can antagonize the teachers or the students and in this way spoil the very program it is designed to assist. Evaluation often takes time that could be spent in other ways; it often requires a somewhat compulsive attitude toward record keeping which is not compatible with a spirit of enthusiasm or with moment-to-moment flexibility in exploiting chance occurrences in the classroom. Because it is easier to evaluate simple skills like memorization of facts than the more complex skills of inductive reasoning, evaluation programs sometimes work subtly to lead the teacher to prefer those teaching strategies that lead to easily measurable results, even if these are less important in the long run than those that are difficult or impossible to measure. Evaluation programs often employ outside teachers and observers. Such individuals, even if they are friendly and are motivated to assist the teacher, may inhibit the processes of teaching and learning. These examples are not listed to discourage evaluating methods of teaching. They are mentioned to emphasize that since such conflicts can occur, it is important for those planning or carrying out evaluation to be aware of this fact and to act to minimize the conflict whenever possible, and to be aware that evaluation goals are really subordinate to the teaching goals.

The Problem of Experimental Design

An evaluation of the effectiveness of a teaching unit is really an experiment of considerable complexity, if we wish to know at some level of confidence how far we can safely generalize from our conclusions. It is useful to examine an analogy, the evaluation of the effectiveness of drugs in treatment of disease. Since drugs are given to complex human beings, a large number of individual differences may influence the outcome, namely, age, sex, inherited differences, previous learning, personality differences, attitude, and many others. Each of these really represents an alternative explanation for results we attribute to our drug treatment. The real point of experimental design, in my opinion, is to select the most plausible alternative explanations that might account for our treatment effect and then design studies in which these factors are held constant, are varied systematically, or are investigated to determine that they behave in a random fashion. Among the most difficult factors to "control" in drug studies are those attitudes in both subjects and investigators that can be lumped under the heading of suggestibility. Drug studies must be designed to evaluate this type of factor. We have a similar problem in evaluating the effectiveness of teaching methods, with the additional difficulty that one additional group of persons can be suggestible—the teachers. All of this suggests that if teaching experiments are to be designed so carefully that we can be very sure which component of the total situation is contributing the major component of the alleged treatment effect, we must be very thorough indeed in planning an elaborate design.

A very similar line of reasoning can be followed in discussing the possible confusion of treatment effects and changes that are due to the selection of participating subjects. Very sophisticated sampling methods are needed to ensure that our alleged treatment effects are not due to some unknown characteristic of our sample of subjects.

In teaching, even our treatment variables represent a set of factors rather than one discrete input. If our students appear to be benefiting from the workbook being used, they may, in fact, be benefiting much more from longer periods of study.

Experimenters who are quite sophisticated in the use of experimental designs are good judges of the applicability of different methods. There is some danger that those who are not so experienced will not know when to use an elaborate design. They may also feel they are doing the correct thing just because they are using "controls," even though the logic of the experiment is not at all clear. Such inexperienced individuals might get more usable information from a thoughtful observation of the phenomenon they are investigating, even if the observers are biased. At least they wouldn't be fooling themselves as much as they would be if they over-interpreted an experiment that was poorly thought out.

The Use of Statistical Models

Much of what has been said about experimental design is relevant to the problem of the selection of statistics. It is often the case that inexperienced people are comforted by the use of a statistical formula when they have not clearly identified the variables that provide the numbers that are fed into the formula.

In experiments studying human behavior we may guess that a large number of factors account for the variance. It might seem logical, then, to set up very large designs, using, let us say, a multifactorial analysis of variance as a statistical treatment. Such studies are often not useful on purely technical statistical grounds. The assumptions about the characteristics of population distributions are often not met. Furthermore the interactions of the factors are often based on nonlinear relationships among the variables.

Problems of Personnel Selection and Training

Experiments on rats can be carried out by a few well-trained technicians. Studies on human beings require the same or greater training, but it turns out that many more people are often involved as experimenters and many additional skills are needed. Human beings must be treated like human beings. This requires that some of the members of the experimental team be sensitive to human needs and skillful in arranging for compliance to simple requests. They must, however, also meet the requirements for careful experimental design and careful uniform reporting of observations. These skills are not easy to find in the same individuals. As a result, teams are often set up. This adds still another requirement—an effective team leader. There can now be the difficulty that the team may be bigger than the group of people being studied or that at least such a large team will be a distracting influence. A major quality that is required in investigators of human behavior is the willingness to be found wrong. It requires a great deal of sophistication to be comfortable while ones's favorite hypothesis is torn to shreds by a systematic team.

Establishing a Climate for Effective Evaluation

Research always goes on in a larger social setting. Studies of rats can be done out of sight of most people in a laboratory, so that they often do not need much evidence of real social approval to be possible. Studies of human behavior cannot be hidden and should not be hidden. As a result, any good investigation of human behavior must occur in a social setting that is congenial. It is often very difficult to know what the reaction to a study will be until it has begun. Pilot studies are often required to find out whether certain types of investigation are feasible.

Summary Statement on Methodology of Evaluation

The evaluation of a teaching method can be considered as a scientific experiment requiring the most sophisticated techniques of design and statistics, highly trained teams of investigators, and a receptive social setting. If these requirements are not met, the result may be at best meaningless and at worst destructive. Systematic investigation should not be abandoned when it is difficult, but it should not be begun if it is impossible. Instead of beginning an investigation that cannot be effective, it might be reasonable to substitute a strategy of developing the capacity to investigate; but this effort should be kept in scale. The evaluating tail should not wag the teaching dog.

XIII
DISTRIBUTORS AND APPROXIMATE PRICES OF ESI CURRICULUM MATERIALS

SCHOOL CURRICULUM PROJECTS

UNIVERSITY CURRICULUM PROJECTS

STUDIO OPERATIONS

The publishers of *Curriculum Improvement and Innovation: a Partnership of Students, School Teachers and Research Scholars,* Robert Bentley, Inc., are making special kits available that comprise the apparatus and materials for performing all the experiments discussed in Section II, SCIENCE IN THE ELEMENTARY SCHOOL (Elementary Science Study, ESS), Section III, SCIENCE IN THE JUNIOR HIGH SCHOOL (the Introductory Physical Science Program, IPS), and Section IV, PHYSICS IN THE HIGH SCHOOL (the Physical Science Study Committee, PSSC). Kits normally include the book, *Curriculum Improvement and Innovation,* but the apparatus and materials can be purchased separately by those who already have the book.

Kit #1.

(a) Apparatus and materials for the 2 ESS experiments (from the Elementary Science Study text, *Kitchen Physics).*

(b) Apparatus and materials for the 8 IPS experiments (from the Introductory Physical Science text, *Introductory Physical Science).*

(c) Apparatus for the 1 PSSC experiment (from the Physical Science Study Committee text, *Physics).*

(d) 1 copy of *Curriculum Improvement and Innovation: a Partnership of Students, School Teachers and Research Scholars.*

Price: $40.30 (Kit #1)

Kit #2.

(a) Apparatus and materials for the 2 ESS experiments (from the Elementary Science Study text, *Kitchen Physics).*

(b) 1 copy of *Curriculum Improvement and Innovation: a Partnership of Students, School Teachers and Research Scholars.*

Price: $16.00 (Kit #2)

Kit #3.

(a) Apparatus and materials for the 8 IPS experiments (from the Introductory Physical Science text, *Introductory Physical Science).*

(b) 1 copy of *Curriculum Improvement and Innovation: a Partnership of Students, School Teachers and Research Scholars.*

Price: $26.65 (Kit #3)

Kit #4.

(a) Apparatus for the 1 PSSC experiment (from the Physical Science Study Committee text, *Physics).*

(b) 1 copy of *Curriculum Improvement and Innovation: a Partnership of Students, School Teachers and Research Scholars.*

Price: $13.75 (Kit #4)

Kit #5.

(a) Apparatus and materials for the 2 ESS experiments (from the Elementary Science Study text, *Kitchen Physics).*

(b) Apparatus and materials for the 8 IPS experiments (from the Introductory Physical Science text, *Introductory Physical Science).*

(c) Apparatus for the 1 PSSC experiment (from the Physical Science Study Committee text, *Physics).*

Price: $32.25 (Kit #5)

Kit #6.

Apparatus and materials for the 2 ESS experiments (from the Elementary Science Study text, *Kitchen Physics).*

Price: $7.95 (Kit #6)

Kit #7.

Apparatus and materials for the 8 IPS experiments (from the Introductory Physical Science text, *Introductory Physical Science).*

Price: $18.60 (Kit #7)

Kit #8.

Apparatus for the 1 PSSC experiment (from the Physical Science Study Committee text, *Physics).*

Price: $5.70 (Kit #8)

Curriculum Improvement and Innovation: a Partnership of Students, School Teachers and Research Scholars, edited by W. T. Martin and Dan C. Pinck is available at $8.95.

The above kits are distributed exclusively by Robert Bentley, Inc. Kits should be ordered by number. Orders should be sent direct to Robert Bentley, Inc., 872 Massachusetts Ave., Cambridge, Massachusetts 02139. (Foreign orders for kits should also be sent directly to Robert Bentley, Inc.)

DISTRIBUTORS AND APPROXIMATE PRICES OF ESI CURRICULUM MATERIALS

ESI's projects in curriculum development have as their object the creation of new course materials; their eventual production in quantity and distribution to schools and universities is done by various publishers and equipment manufacturers by arrangement with ESI.

The preparation of new trial materials and the publication or manufacture of materials at a more advanced stage are continuing processes. There are often many possible arrangements for obtaining materials from a distributor in the form most suited to a teacher's needs. The list which follows of ESI materials which are available in quantity, with their distributors and their approximate prices, should be consulted with all of the above qualifications in mind. Those wishing to obtain materials from a particular project should write to that project or to the distributor of its materials for fully up-to-date and complete information on how to obtain the materials of interest. Prices are, of course, subject to change.

Descriptive brochures, catalogs, or leaflets are often available from ESI projects and the distributors. Some of these brochures are also listed below.

All correspondence sent to an ESI project should be addressed as follows:

(Name of the project)
Educational Services Incorporated
55 Chapel Street
Newton, Massachusetts 02158

Introduction

Curriculum Improvement and Innovation

Robert Bentley, Inc., the publisher of *Curriculum Improvement and Innovation: A Partnership of Students, School Teachers and Research Scholars,* is making special kits available that comprise the apparatus and materials for performing all the experiments discussed in Section II, SCIENCE IN THE ELEMENTARY SCHOOL (Elementary Science Study, ESS), Section III, SCIENCE IN THE JUNIOR HIGH SCHOOL (the Introductory Physical Science Program, IPS), and Section IV, PHYSICS IN THE HIGH SCHOOL (the Physical Science Study Committee, PSSC). Kits normally include the book, *Curriculum Improvement and Innovation,* but the apparatus and materials can be purchased separately by those who already have the book.

Kit #1: (a) Apparatus and materials for the 2 ESS experiments (from the Elementary Science Study text, *Kitchen Physics*); (b) Apparatus and materials for the 8 IPS experiments (from the Introductory Physical Science text, *Introductory Physical Science*); (c) Apparatus for the 1 PSSC experiment (from the Physical Science Study Committee text, *Physics*); (d) 1 copy of *Curriculum Improvement and Innovation: A Partnership of Students, School Teachers and Research Scholars.* $40.30

Kit #2: (a) Apparatus and materials for the 2 ESS experiments (from the Elementary Science Study text, *Kitchen Physics*); (b) 1 copy of *Curriculum Improvement and Innovation: A Partnership of Students, School Teachers and Research Scholars.* $16.00

Kit #3: (a) Apparatus and materials for the 8 IPS experiments (from the Introductory Physical Science text, *Introductory Physical Science*); (b) 1 copy of *Curriculum Improvement and Innovation: A Partnership of Students, School Teachers and Research Scholars.* $26.65

Kit #4: (a) Apparatus for the 1 PSSC experiment (from the Physical Science Study Committee text, *Physics*); (b) 1 copy of *Curriculum Improvement and Innovation: A Partnership of Students, School Teachers and Research Scholars.* $13.75

Kit #5: (a) Apparatus and materials for the 2 ESS experiments (from the Elementary Science Study text, *Kitchen Physics*); (b) Apparatus and materials for the 8 IPS experiments (from the Introductory Physical Science text, *Introductory Physical Science*); (c) Apparatus for the 1 PSSC experiment (from the Physical Science Study Committee text, *Physics*). $32.25

Kit #6: Apparatus and materials for the 2 ESS experiments (from the Elementary Science Study text, *Kitchen Physics*). $7.95

Kit #7: Apparatus and materials for the 8 IPS experiments (from the Introductory Physical Science text, *Introductory Physical Science*). $18.60

Kit #8: Apparatus for the 1 PSSC experiment (from the Physical Science Study Committee text, *Physics*). $5.70

Curriculum Improvement and Innovation: A Partnership of Students, School Teachers and Research Scholars, edited by W. T. Martin and Dan C. Pinck, is available at $8.95.

The above kits are distributed exclusively by Robert Bentley, Inc. Kits should be ordered by number. Orders should be sent direct to Robert Bentley, Inc., 872 Massachusetts Avenue, Cambridge, Massachusetts 02139. (Foreign orders for kits should also be sent directly to Robert Bentley, Inc.)

School Curriculum Projects

Elementary Science Study

Except as noted, the materials listed below are obtainable from the Elementary Science Study. Beginning in September 1966, items marked with asterisks (*) will be available in unlimited commercial distribution from the Webster Division of the McGraw-Hill Book Company, Manchester, Missouri 63011. These items, again with exceptions noted, are available in limited quantities from the Elementary Science Study for use in the summer of 1966.

Some of the units listed are accompanied by films or film loops. The latter are 8-mm films in cartridges for use with a Technicolor projector. They are 3 to 4 minutes in length and are all in color except for the Bones loops (hence the price difference).

Price Each

Attribute Games and Problems (Classification and sorting exercises with logical games)

Teacher's Guide	$ 2.00
Set of materials including "A" Blocks, Color Cubes, People Pieces, Problem Cards	5.00

Batteries and Bulbs (Introductory circuit theory)

Teacher's Guides: Book 1 — CIRCUITS I	2.00
Book 2 — CIRCUITS AND MAGNETS	1.00
Book 3 — CIRCUITS II	1.00
Classroom Kit (for 30 Students)	83.00

**Behavior of Mealworms* (Behavior patterns of a simple organism)

Teacher's Guide	1.29

Bones (Structure and function of skeletons)

Teacher's Guide	2.00
Student Booklet: HOW TO MAKE A CHICKEN SKELETON	.75
Student Booklet: BONE PICTURE BOOK	1.00
In quantities of 20 or more:	
HOW TO MAKE A CHICKEN SKELETON	.50
BONE PICTURE BOOK	.75
Film loops (probable availability date Sept. 1, 1966)	
ES-32 X-Ray Motion Pictures, HEAD AND NECK	4.50
ES-33 X-Ray Motion Pictures, SHOULDER	4.50
ES-34 X-Ray Motion Pictures, KNEE AND ELBOW	4.50
ES-35 X-Ray Motion Pictures, HAND	4.50
ES-36 X-Ray Motion Pictures, FOOT	4.50

**Gases and "Airs"* (Properties of the active fraction of air)

Teacher's Guide	1.95
Teacher's Kit	45.00
2-Student Kit	5.25
16 Worksheets (10 Student sets)	2.70
Film: GASES AND "AIRS" IN THE CLASSROOM (16mm, sound, black and white, 32 min.; for teachers) (rental 6.00 per use)	126.00
Film loops:	
ES-1 CANDLE BURNING TECHNIQUES:	6.00
ES-2 CANDLE BURNING I	6.00
ES-3 CANDLE BURNING II	6.00
ES-4 THE MOUSE AND THE CANDLE	6.00

**Growing Seeds* (Seeds, non-seeds, and a self-graphing process)

Teacher's Guide (currently not available until fall 1966 in commercial edition)	.72
Teacher's Kit (not available until fall 1966)	12.00
Film loops:	
ES-7 BEAN SPROUTS	6.00
ES-6 PLANT GROWTH-GRAPHING	6.00

Ice Cubes (Quantitative observation of melting rates, change of state, temperature vs. heat)

Teacher's Guide	.75

Inspection Carton (To be discontinued after the summer of 1966; contains sample materials from *Behavior of Mealworms, Gases and "Airs," Growing Seeds, Kitchen Physics,* and *Small Things*) 20.00

**Kitchen Physics* (Some properties of liquids)

Teacher's Guide	1.35
Teacher's Kit (currently not available until fall 1966 in commercial edition)	7.50
10-Student Kit (not available until fall 1966)	18.00
7 Worksheets (10-student sets) (not available until fall 1966)	2.10
Film loops:	
ES-5 BEADING OF A WATER COLUMN	6.00
ES-27 WATER RISE IN BLOTTER STRIPS: GRADED WIDTHS (currently not available until fall 1966 in commercial edition)	6.00
ES-28 WATER RISE IN BLOTTER STRIPS: EXPOSED AND ENCLOSED (not available until fall 1966)	6.00

Light and Shadows (Geometric optics for the primary grades)

Teacher's Guide	.50

Melting Ice Cubes (Heat transfer and change of state)

Teacher's Guide	1.50

Microgardening (Growth and nutrition of molds)

Teacher's Guide	2.50
MICROGARDENING COOKBOOK	1.00
ILLUSTRATED HANDBOOK OF SOME COMMON MOLDS	3.00
Classroom Kit (For 30 students) (not available in present edition)	145.00
Film loops:	
ES-21 ALTERNARIA	6.00
ES-22 RHIZOPUS	6.00
ES-23 FUSARIUM	6.00
ES-24 PENICILLIUM	6.00
ES-25 TRICHODERMA GROWTH RINGS	6.00
ES-26 ROTTING PEAR	6.00
ES-20 MUSHROOM GROWTH AND REACTION	6.00

Mirror Cards (Reflection and symmetry)

Teacher's Guide	.50
Mirror Cards with mirrors	5.50

Mystery Powders (Properties of common substances)

Teacher's Guide	.50

Peas and Particles (Counting and estimation of large numbers)

Teacher's Guide	1.00
Classroom packet of pictures and Guide	2.00

Pendulums (Factors influencing single and coupled pendulums)

Teacher's Guide	1.50

**Small Things* (Introduction to the use of the microscope)

Teacher's Guide (Currently not available until fall 1966 in commercial edition)	2.07
Teacher's Kit (not available until fall 1966)	12.00
5-Student Kit	15.00
12 Worksheets (5-Student sets)	3.45
Set of 20 Photos (1 per class) (not available until fall 1966)	2.25
Student Booklet: THE FAITHFUL EYE OF ROBERT HOOKE	.25
Film: PARAMECIUM, EUGLENA AND AMOEBA (16mm, sound, color, 15 min.) (rental 6.00 per use)	129.00
Film loops:	
ES- 8 PARAMECIUM	6.00
ES- 9 EUGLENA	6.00
ES-10 AMOEBA	6.00
ES-11 BUDDING OF YEAST CELLS	6.00
ES-12 BLEPHARISMA	6.00
ES-13 STENTOR	6.00
ES-14 ROTIFER	6.00
ES-15 VORTICELLA	6.00
ES-16 VOLVOX	6.00
ES-17 STYLONYCHIA	6.00
ES-29 COMPARATIVE SIZES OF MICROSCOPIC ANIMALS	6.00

Also available:

Film: FROG DEVELOPMENT—FERTILIZATION TO HATCHING (silent, 16mm, 16 minutes, color) (rental 6.00 per use)	120.00
Technicolor projector (for 8mm cartridge loops) (rental 10.00 per month; can be applied to purchase price)	72.50

Descriptive Literature: The Elementary Science Study issues the ESS NEWSLETTER and occasional other descriptive material.

Introductory Physical Science Program

Distributors

Written materials and laboratory apparatus: Educational Book Division, Prentice-Hall, Inc., Englewood Cliffs, New Jersey.
Laboratory apparatus only: Macalaster Scientific Corporation, 60 Arsenal Street, Watertown, Massachusetts 02172.

Materials and Approximate Prices

Textbook, INTRODUCTORY PHYSICAL SCIENCE, Preliminary Edition	$1.40
Teacher's Guide	3.50
Achievement Tests, Chapters I-IX (package for 10 students)	9.00

Laboratory Apparatus: Cost varies according to the standard laboratory supplies a school already has on hand. The special IPS-designed apparatus for a class of 24 costs under $400.00; this price does not include the necessary standard laboratory equipment and chemicals. Distributors' catalogs describe various assortments of IPS equipment and of standard equipment and supplies needed in the course, and these catalogs should be studied to make a selection suited to the needs of the particular class.

Descriptive Literature: A brochure, INTRODUCTORY PHYSICAL SCIENCE: A PROGRESS REPORT, is available from the IPS Program.

Physical Science Study Committee

Distributors

Text, Laboratory Guide, and Teacher's Guide: D. C. Heath and Company, 285 Columbus Avenue, Boston, Massachusetts.

Student Achievement Tests: Cooperative Test Division, Educational Testing Service, Princeton, New Jersey.

Laboratory Apparatus: Macalaster Scientific Corporation, 60 Arsenal Street, Watertown, Massachusetts; The Welch Scientific Company, 7300 N. Linder Avenue, Skokie, Illinois, 60076; and Science Electronics Division, General Electronics Labs, Inc., 1085 Commonwealth Avenue, Boston, Massachusetts.

Films and Teacher's Guides to the films: Modern Learning Aids, 1212 Avenue of the Americas, New York, N. Y. 10036.

Science Study Series: Doubleday Anchor Books, Garden City, L. I., New York.

Materials and Approximate Prices

Text, PHYSICS, Second Edition	
Hardcover	$ 6.12
Paperback, Vol. 1	2.44
Vol. 2	2.28
Vol. 3	2.44
Vol. 4	2.28
First Edition, Hardcover	5.80
Laboratory Guide, Second Edition	1.60
First Edition	1.52
Teacher's Resource Book and Guide	
Second Edition (4 Vols.) Complete set	10.00
(Separate Vols. 3.00 each)	
First Edition (4 Vols. and Supplement)	15.00

Student Achievement Tests: Various selections are available. A set of ten tests for a single student costs $2.00; three different sets are available. Twenty answer sheets cost $1.00, and sets of scoring stencils are obtainable for all three editions of tests, at $1.50 to $2.50. Two of the test editions include handbooks for teachers at $2.00 each. Specimen sets of tests can be purchased for $2.00.

Laboratory Apparatus: Even more than in the case of IPS apparatus, distributors' catalogs offer a wide choice of assortments, depending on the individual needs of the school or class. To start from scratch, buying basic laboratory supplies and all materials needed for a class of 24 to begin using the PSSC course, costs about $3,300.00; to buy a sample set of special PSSC-designed equipment, including a text, laboratory guide, and teacher's guide, from Macalaster, costs about $230.00.

Films: A descriptive leaflet on the PSSC films is available from Modern Learning Aids. The films are listed below with purchases prices; they can also be rented for three days at $6.00 each or eight days at $12.00 each. A set of teacher's guides to the films is available for $2.00 (free of charge with purchase of a film or rental of six or more films). An asterisk (*) denotes new films released in 1966.

TIME AND CLOCKS	$150.00
LONG TIME INTERVALS	120.00
SHORT TIME INTERVALS	120.00
MEASURING LARGE DISTANCES	150.00
MEASURING SHORT DISTANCES	120.00
CHANGE OF SCALE	120.00
STRAIGHT LINE KINEMATICS	150.00
VECTORS (rental only)	
VECTOR KINEMATICS	90.00
ELEMENTS, COMPOUNDS AND MIXTURES (color)	260.00
DEFINITE AND MULTIPLE PROPORTIONS	150.00
*THE MASS OF ATOMS (Parts I and II)	250.00
CRYSTALS	
(black & white)	135.00
(color)	190.00
BEHAVIOR OF GASES	90.00
RANDOM EVENTS	150.00
MEASUREMENT	120.00
INTRODUCTION TO OPTICS (color)	180.00
PRESSURE OF LIGHT	120.00
SPEED OF LIGHT	120.00
SIMPLE WAVES	150.00
SOUND WAVES IN AIR	150.00
FORCES	120.00
INERTIA	150.00
INERTIAL MASS	120.00
A MILLION TO ONE (purchase only)	30.00
FREE FALL AND PROJECTILE MOTION	150.00
DEFLECTING FORCES	150.00
PERIODIC MOTION	150.00
FRAMES OF REFERENCE	150.00
ELLIPTIC ORBITS	90.00
UNIVERSAL GRAVITATION	$150.00
COLLISIONS OF HARD SPHERES	120.00
ELASTIC COLLISIONS AND STORED ENERGY	150.00
ENERGY AND WORK	150.00
MECHANICAL ENERGY AND THERMAL ENERGY	120.00
*MOVING WITH THE CENTER OF MASS	150.00
CONSERVATION OF ENERGY	150.00
COULOMB'S LAW	150.00
ELECTRIC FIELDS	120.00
ELECTRIC LINES OF FORCE	40.00
MILLIKAN EXPERIMENT	150.00
COULOMB FORCE CONSTANT	150.00
COUNTING ELECTRICAL CHARGES IN MOTION	120.00
ELEMENTARY CHARGES AND TRANSFER OF KINETIC ENERGY	150.00
EMF	120.00
ELECTRICAL POTENTIAL ENERGY AND POTENTIAL DIFFERENCE (Parts I & II)	300.00
A MAGNET LABORATORY	120.00
ELECTRONS IN A UNIFORM MAGNETIC FIELD	60.00
MASS OF THE ELECTRON	90.00
ELECTROMAGNETIC WAVES	150.00
THE RUTHERFORD ATOM	150.00
PHOTONS	90.00
INTERFERENCE OF PHOTONS	90.00
PHOTOELECTRIC EFFECT (color)	220.00
MATTER WAVES	150.00
THE FRANCK-HERTZ EXPERIMENT	150.00

Science Study Series: These paperback volumes and their prices are listed below. The books priced at $1.25 and $1.45 are available to schools at $.85 and $1.10 respectively, when ordered by mail from the publisher.

THE NEUTRON STORY: Exploring the Nature of Matter Donald J. Hughes	$1.25
MAGNETS: The Education of a Physicist, Francis Bitter	1.25
SOAP BUBBLES AND THE FORCES WHICH MOLD THEM (reprint) C. V. Boys	1.25
ECHOES OF BATS AND MEN: Seeing with Sound Waves Donald R. Griffin	1.25
HOW OLD IS THE EARTH?: New Answers to an Ancient Riddle Patrick M. Hurley	1.25
CRYSTALS AND CRYSTAL GROWING: Order in Nature Alan Holden and Phylis Singer	1.45
THE PHYSICS OF TELEVISION: Vision Beyond Sight Donald G. Fink and David M. Lutyens	1.25
WAVES AND THE EAR: What We Hear and How W. A. van Bergeijk, J. R. Pierce and E. E. David, Jr.	1.45
THE BIRTH OF A NEW PHYSICS: From Copernicus to Newton I. Bernard Cohen	1.25
HORNS, STRINGS AND HARMONY: The Science of Enjoyable Sounds Arthur H. Benade	1.45
THE RESTLESS ATOM: The Awakening of Nuclear Physics Alfred Romer	1.25
MICHELSON AND THE SPEED OF LIGHT: Biography of a Scientist Bernard Jaffe	1.25
THE UNIVERSE AT LARGE: Views of Cosmology, Hermann Bondi	1.25
PASTEUR AND MODERN SCIENCE, Rene Dubos	1.25
THE WATERSHED: A Biography of Johannes Kepler, Arthur Koestler	1.45
ACCELERATORS: Machines of Nuclear Physics Robert R. Wilson and Raphael Littauer	1.45
WATER: Mirror of Science, Kenneth S. Davis & John Arthur Day	1.25
THE NATURE OF VIOLENT STORMS: Physics and the Weather Louis J. Battan	1.25
NEAR ZERO: The Physics of Low Temperature, D. K. C. MacDonald	1.25
SHAPE AND FLOW: Fluid Dynamics of Drag, Ascher H. Shapiro	1.25
GRAVITY: Classic and Modern Views, George Gamow	1.25
LIFE IN THE UNIVERSE: A Scientific Discussion Michael W. Ovenden	1.25
RADAR OBSERVES THE WEATHER: New Understanding of Cloud Physics Louis J. Battan	1.25
NERVES AND MUSCLES: An Introduction to Biophysics Robert Galambos	1.25
THE ORIGIN OF RADAR: An Epic of Modern Technology Robert Morris Page	1.25
HEAT ENGINES: Thermodynamics in Theory and Practice John F. Sandfort	1.45
COUNT RUMFORD: Physicist Extraordinary, Sanborn C. Brown	1.25
CLOUD PHYSICS AND CLOUD SEEDING: Introduction to Applied Meteorology, Louis J. Battan	1.25
LADY LUCK: The Theory of Probability, Warren Weaver	1.45
KNOWLEDGE AND WONDER: The Natural World as Man Knows It Victor F. Weisskopf	1.45
MATHEMATICAL ASPECTS OF PHYSICS: An Introduction, Francis Bitter	1.25
FARADAY, MAXWELL AND KELVIN, D. K. C. MacDonald	1.25
WAVES AND BEACHES: The Dynamics of the Ocean Surface Willard Bascom	1.45
RUTHERFORD AND THE NATURE OF THE ATOM: E. N. da C. Andrade	1.25
RELATIVITY AND COMMON SENSE: A New Approach to Einstein Hermann Bondi	1.25

BIRD MIGRATION: The Biology and Physics of Orientation Behavior Donald R. Griffin	1.25
ELECTRONS AND WAVES: An Introduction to the Science of Electronics and Communications, John R. Pierce	1.25
PERPETUAL MOTION: Electrons and Atoms in Crystals Alec T. Stewart	1.25
SOUND WAVES AND LIGHT WAVES: The Fundamentals of Wave Motion Winston E. Kock	1.25
A SHORT HISTORY OF CHEMISTRY: An Introduction to the Ideas and Concepts of Chemistry, Isaac Asimov	1.45
SIR ISAAC NEWTON: His Life and Work (reprint) E. N. da C. Andrade	1.25
COMPUTERS AND THE HUMAN MIND: Artificial Intelligence Donald G. Fink	1.45
THIRTY YEARS THAT SHOOK PHYSICS (1900-1930): The Story of Quantum Theory, George Gamow	1.45
QUANTUM ELECTRONICS: The Fundamentals of Transistors and Lasers, John R. Pierce	1.25
The SCIENCE STUDY SERIES CLASSROOM REFERENCE SHELF 71 books (a complete set of the Series plus multiple copies of selected titles) in a permanent box, with a guide, "Using the Science Study Series."	62.50

Descriptive Literature on the PSSC: A short brochure, A NEW PHYSICS PROGRAM FOR SECONDARY SCHOOLS, is available from the PSSC. Also, the distributors of PSSC laboratory apparatus issue detailed catalogs, and Modern Learning Aids puts out a descriptive leaflet on the PSSC films.

Social Studies Curriculum Program

Social Studies materials are in developmental stages and, except for several films, none are yet available commercially. All inquiries should be addressed to the Social Studies Curriculum Program.

Films: These are available for purchase, and usually for loan also, from the Film Librarian, Educational Services Incorporated.

NETSILIK ESKIMOS FISHING AT THE STONE WEIR (2 parts)	$400.00
CORN AND THE ORIGINS OF SETTLED LIFE IN MESO-AMERICA	275.00
LAND AND WATER IN IRAQ	90.00
ARCHAEOLOGY IN MESOPOTAMIA	110.00
THE EARLIEST WRITING	75.00

Descriptive Literature: Occasional Papers, research reports on the work of this program, are available from the Social Studies Curriculum Program. The first three Occasional Papers are now out of print; the following are available:

No. 4, MAN AND POLITICS, by Franklin K. Patterson
No. 5, MYTH AND ART AS TEACHING MATERIALS, by Elli Maranda
No. 6, THE EMERGENCE OF THE AMERICAN, by Edmund S. Morgan
No. 7, GAMES FOR LEARNING, by Clark C. Abt

There is a charge for bulk orders of Occasional Papers but not for single copies.

For more general information, A SHORT HISTORY OF THE SOCIAL STUDIES PROGRAM and THE SOCIAL STUDIES CURRICULUM PROGRAM: SPRING REPORT 1966 can be obtained from this group.

University of Illinois Arithmetic Project

All materials are obtainable from the Project; single copies are free of charge. The following booklets and articles are available:

NUMBER LINE SAMPLE (1958)
PROBABILITY (reprint, 1959)
DO SOMETHING ABOUT ESTIMATION (1960)
TEACHING CREATIVITY IN MATHEMATICS (reprint from the *Arithmetic Teacher,* 1961)
MANEUVERS ON LATTICES, An Example of "Intermediate Invention" (1962)
ARITHMETIC WITH FRAMES (1962, revised)
WELL-ADJUSTED TRAPEZOIDS, from *Updating Mathematics* (1962)
NUMBER LINES FOR THE ORBITING ATOMIC TEACHER (reprint from *Grade Teacher Magazine,* 1962)
WAYS TO FIND HOW MANY (1965, revision of SHIRTSLEEVE MATHEMATICS, 1962)

Pre-College Program for Students From Low-Income Families

A brochure is available from the Pre-College Program, describing its activities. Inquiries about units in English and Mathematics should be addressed to the Program; as of May 1966 all units are in mimeographed form and availability is limited.

Mathematics Curriculum Study

GOALS FOR SCHOOL MATHEMATICS is obtainable for $1.00 from Houghton Mifflin Company, 2 Park Street, Boston, Massachusetts. THE CAMBRIDGE CONFERENCE ON SCHOOL MATHEMATICS: A REPORT, and also the following mimeographed reports and unit guidelines, are available free of charge from the Mathematics Curriculum Study:

A PROPOSED SYLLABUS FOR THE 7TH GRADE
ELEMENTARY MODERN MATHEMATICS FROM THE ADVANCED STANDPOINT
PROPOSED PROGRAM FOR THE 10TH GRADE
ORDER STRUCTURE IN ELEMENTARY MATHEMATICS
A PROBLEM
UNITS
PROBABILITY
NOTES ON DESIRABLE RESPONSES AT END OF SIXTH YEAR
STREAM OF IDEAS ON CHECKS, APPROXIMATIONS, AND ORDER OF MAGNITUDE CALCULATIONS
COMPLEX NUMBERS LEADING TO TRIGONOMETRY
USE OF NEGATIVE DIGITS IN ARITHMETIC
USE OF SHIFT THEOREM IN DIFFERENTIAL EQUATIONS
TOPOLOGY IN 10TH GRADE AND AFTER
SMSG AND THE "GIFTED" CHILD
WHAT HIGH SCHOOL JUNIORS AND SENIORS DON'T KNOW
THE USE OF UNITS
EXPLORATION
THE EXPONENTIAL FUNCTION
A PROPOSED COURSE IN 9TH GRADE GEOMETRY
MULTIPLICATION OF NEGATIVE NUMBERS
KINDERGARTEN
MORSE SCHOOL — 1ST GRADE (Inequalities Unit)
MORSE SCHOOL — 2ND GRADE (Multiplication)
MORSE SCHOOL — 3RD GRADE (Chip Trading)
MORSE SCHOOL — 3RD & 6TH GRADES (Graphs and Their Application)
MORSE SCHOOL — 3RD GRADE (Vector Geometry)
MORSE SCHOOL — 7TH GRADE (Slopes & Limits)
MORSE SCHOOL — SLOPES & LIMITS (Lessons & Commentary)
REPORT OF ACTIVITIES IN CAMBRIDGE DURING JULY AND AUGUST 1964 UNDER CCSM
EXPERIMENTAL TEACHING
PALO ALTO — SECOND GRADE (Geometry, Logic and Matrices)
STANFORD — EIGHTH GRADE (Geometry through Symmetry)
PROGRESS REPORTS ON ESTABROOK PROJECT, by Earle Lomon, covering March 1964 through June 1965
DEMONSTRATION OF MIRROR CARDS TO ESTABROOK TEACHERS; INFORMAL GEOMETRY FOR YOUNG CHILDREN: SYMMETRY MOTIONS FOR ELEMENTARY SCHOOL (Parts I and II)
ELEMENTARY NUMBER THEORY (Hosmer School, 6th grade, 1964/65)
REPORT OF SMSG/CCSM CONFERENCE IN MARCH 1965
COLLECTED REPORTS OF CCSM WRITING CONFERENCE, SUMMER 1965 (21 reports and guidelines on geometry, functions, and applications)

African Education Program

The Entebbe Mathematics Series is available for distribution in Africa, without charge. Inquiries about it should be addressed to the African Mathematics Program.

Primary Materials

PRIMARY ONE:
Revised Preliminary Edition
Pupil Book: One Volume
Teachers' Guide: Two Volumes

PRIMARY TWO:
Preliminary Edition
Pupil Book: Two Volumes
Teachers' Guide: Two Volumes

PRIMARY THREE:
Preliminary Edition
Pupil Book: Two Volumes
Teachers' Guide: Two Volumes

PRIMARY FOUR:
Preliminary Edition
Pupil Book: One Volume
Teachers' Guide: One Volume

PRIMARY FIVE:
Preliminary Edition (to be written at 1966 Workshop)

ENTEBBE MATHEMATICS TEACHERS' HANDBOOK, PRIMARY I-III, Preliminary Edition

Secondary Materials

Five Year Course

SECONDARY ONE:
Preliminary Edition
Student Text: One Volume
Teachers' Guide: Three Volumes

SECONDARY TWO:
Preliminary Edition
Student Text: Three Volumes
Teachers' Guide: Three Volumes

SECONDARY THREE:
Preliminary Edition
Student Text:
ALGEBRA: One Volume
GEOMETRY: One Volume
Teachers' Guide:
ALGEBRA: One Volume
GEOMETRY: One Volume

Four Year Course

SECONDARY C ONE:
Preliminary Edition
Student Text:
ALGEBRA: One Volume
GEOMETRY: One Volume
Teachers' Guide:
ALGEBRA: One Volume
GEOMETRY: One Volume

SECONDARY C TWO:
Preliminary Edition (to be written at 1966 Workshop)

SECONDARY C THREE:
Preliminary Edition (to be written at 1966 Workshop)

SECONDARY FOUR:
Preliminary Edition
Student Text:
ALGEBRA: One Volume
GEOMETRY: One Volume
Teachers' Guide:
ALGEBRA: One Volume
GEOMETRY: One Volume
(Secondary Four is at the press)

SECONDARY FIVE:
Preliminary Edition (to be written at 1966 Workshop)

Teacher Training Materials
BASIC CONCEPTS OF MATHEMATICS, Preliminary Edition: An introductory Text for Teachers:
Volume I STRUCTURE OF ARITHMETIC — Chapters 1-21
Volume II STRUCTURE OF ARITHMETIC — Chapters 22-46
Volume III FOUNDATIONS OF GEOMETRY — Chapters 47-57
Volume IV MEASUREMENT, FUNCTIONS AND PROBABILITY — Chapters 58-68
(Volume IV is at the press)

Descriptive Literature: A REPORT OF AN AFRICAN EDUCATION PROGRAM is obtainable from this project, describing its activities.

University Curriculum Projects

College Physics Committee

Distributors
Written materials: McGraw-Hill Book Company, 330 West 42nd Street, New York, New York 10036.

Laboratory Apparatus: Hickok Teaching Systems, 545 Technology Square, Cambridge, Massachusetts; Heath Company, Benton Harbor, Michigan; and Science Electronics Division, General Electronics Labs, Inc., 1085 Commonwealth Avenue, Boston, Massachusetts.

Materials and Approximate Prices
Texts:

Vol. 1, MECHANICS, by Charles Kittel, Malvin A. Ruderman and Walter D. Knight	$5.50
Vol. 2, ELECTRICITY AND MAGNETISM, by Edward M. Purcell	5.50
LABORATORY PHYSICS, Parts A, B, and C-D each	2.25

More texts are in preparation.
Laboratory Apparatus: Five commonly available electronic instruments constitute the basic equipment for two students to do the laboratory work for the course. They can be obtained from the above distributors and elsewhere. These instruments vary hugely in price; a set of instruments suitable for the course, plus the extra equipment for Part A, can be obtained for about $900. Additional equipment to cover Part B costs about $300 and the additional equipment for Part C costs about $200.

Materials and Approximate Prices
Texts: The price of each of these is $2.65 in paperback and $4.50 in hardcover.
Volume I, INTRODUCTION TO SEMICONDUCTOR PHYSICS, by R. B. Adlei (M.I.T.), A. C. Smith (M.I.T.), and R. L. Longini (Carnegie Institute of Technology)
Volume II, PHYSICAL ELECTRONICS AND CIRCUIT MODELS OF TRANSISTORS, by P. E. Gray (M.I.T.), D. DeWitt (I.B.M.), A. R. Bootnroyd (Queens University, Belfast), and J. F. Gibbons (Stanford University)
Volume III, ELEMENTARY CIRCUIT PROPERTIES OF TRANSISTORS, by C. L. Searle (M.I.T), A. R. Boothroyd (Queens University, Belfast), E. J. Angelo, Jr. (Polytechnic Institute of Brooklyn), P. E. Gray (M.I.T.), and D. O. Pederson (University of California, Berkeley)
Volume V, MULTISTAGE TRANSISTOR CIRCUITS, by R. D. Thornton (M.I.T.), C. L. Searle (M.I.T.), D. O. Pederson (University of California, Berkeley), R. B. Adler (M.I.T.), and E. J. Angelo, Jr. (Polytechnic Institute of Brooklyn)
The three remaining books in this series are scheduled for publication before September 1966.

Semiconductor Electronics Education Committee

Distributors
Texts: John Wiley & Sons, 605 Third Avenue, New York, New York.
Films: Film Librarian, Educational Services Incorporated.

Films: The two films completed to date, MINORITY CARRIERS IN SEMICONDUCTORS and GAP ENERGY AND RECOMBINATION LIGHT IN GERMANIUM cost, respectively, $125.00 and $140.00. They can also be borrowed from the Film Librarian at ESI.

Studio Operations

College Physics Film Program

Distributors
Regular 16-mm films and experimental films: Film Librarian, Educational Services Incorporated.

Short silent film demonstrations:
Canadian Laboratory Supplies Ltd., 80 Jutland Rd., Toronto 18, Ontario, Canada
The Ealing Corporation, 225 Massachusetts Avenue, Cambridge, Massachusetts
Macalaster Scientific Corporation, 60 Arsenal Street, Watertown, Massachusetts
Science Electronics Division, General Electronics Labs, Inc., 1085 Commonwealth Avenue, Boston, Massachusetts
Modern Learning Aids, 3 East 54th Street, New York, New York 10022
The McGraw-Hill Book Company (for complete set only), 330 West 42nd Street, New York, New York

Films and Approximate Prices
(* denotes films released during the past year)

16-mm sound films (approximately one-half hour, black and white, except as noted):

*POSITRON-ELECTRON ANNIHILATION	$125.00
THE SIZE OF ATOMS FROM AN ATOMIC BEAM EXPERIMENT	125.00
ANGULAR MOMENTUM, A Vector Quantity	125.00
THE ULTIMATE SPEED, An Exploration with High Energy Electrons	140.00
TIME DILATION, An Experiment with *Mu*-mesons	140.00
MOMENTUM OF ELECTRONS (color, 10 min.)	75.00
Ripple Tank Wave Phenomena Series:	
I REFLECTION AND REFRACTION (17 min.)	75.00
II INTERFERENCE AND DIFFRACTION (19 min.)	75.00
III BARRIER PENETRATION (8 min.)	35.00
IV BRAGG REFLECTION (10 min.)	35.00
V DOPPLER EFFECT AND SHOCK WAVES (8 min.)	35.00
Electron Emission Film Series:	
* PHOTO EMISSION OF ELECTRONS (4 min.)	20.00
FIELD EMISSION OF ELECTRONS (4 min.)	20.00
THERMIONIC EMISSION OF ELECTRONS (color, 6 min.)	40.00
SOLDER GLASS TECHNIQUE (color, 20 min.)	150.00
Experimental Films:	
QUANTUM MECHANICAL HARMONIC OSCILLATOR (computer-animated film, silent, 4 min.)	15.00
FORCE, MASS AND MOTION (computer-animated film, prepared by Bell Telephone Laboratories; available for loan from ESI)	— —
Excerpts from PSSC Films:	
From FORCES: Cavendish Experiment (8 min.)	25.00
From FRAMES OF REFERENCE:	
I. Linear Accelerated Frames (7 min.)	25.00
II. Rotating Frames (6 min.)	25.00
From PHOTOELECTRIC EFFECT:	
Qualitative Demonstrations (color, 9 min.)	60.00

Arrangements can usually be made to borrow the above films from the ESI Film Librarian for short periods free of charge.

Short Silent Film Demonstrations: These vary in length from 2 to 4 minutes. Depending on the distributor, the price of these in an 8-mm cartridge format (available from all distributors) ranges from $6.25-$8.50 each, except for the three color loops in the Coupled Oscillator Series which range in price from $8.50-$12.00 each. In addition, Macalaster, Modern Learning Aids and Science Electronics offer each film in an 8-mm reel for $4.50-$4.75 (Coupled Oscillator films $6.75-$7.00) and a 16-mm reel for $10.50-$10.75 (Coupled Oscillator films $18.75-$19.00).

Coupled Oscillator Series: (color)
CO-1 ENERGY TRANSFER
CO-2 OTHER OSCILLATORS
CO-3 NORMAL MODES

Ripple Tank Wave Phenomena Series: (b & w)
RT-1 REFLECTION OF STRAIGHT WAVES FROM STRAIGHT BARRIERS
RT-2 REFLECTION OF CIRCULAR WAVES FROM VARIOUS BARRIERS
RT-3 REFLECTION OF WAVES FROM CONCAVE BARRIERS
RT-4 REFRACTION OF WAVES
RT-7 BARRIER PENETRATION BY WAVES
RT-8 BRAGG REFLECTION OF WAVES
RT-9 DOPPLER EFFECT
RT-10 FORMATION OF SHOCK WAVES
RT-11 SUPERPOSITION OF PULSES
RT-12 INTERFERENCE OF WAVES
RT-13 THE EFFECT OF PHASE DIFFERENCES BETWEEN SOURCES
RT-14 SINGLE SLIT DIFFRACTION OF WAVES
RT-15 MULTIPLE SLIT DIFFRACTION OF WAVES
RT-16 DIFFRACTION AND SCATTERING OF WAVES AROUND OBSTACLES

Vector Kinematics Series: (b & w)
VK-1 THE VELOCITY VECTOR
VK-2 VELOCITY IN CIRCULAR AND SIMPLE HARMONIC MOTION
VK-3 THE ACCELERATION VECTOR
VK-4 VELOCITY AND ACCELERATION IN CIRCULAR MOTION
VK-5 VELOCITY AND ACCELERATION IN SIMPLE HARMONIC MOTION
VK-6 VELOCITY AND ACCELERATION IN FREE FALL

Other Films:
SF-1 SOAP FILM OSCILLATIONS

Feynman Lectures: This series of films was made by the British Broadcasting Company in cooperation with Cornell University. Educational Services Incorporated is the United States distributor for the series; write to the Film Librarian at ESI.

The set of seven lectures, including a printed transcript costs $975.00; single lectures cost $175.00. The rental charge for the entire series is $90.00; a single lecture can be rented for $15.00. The rental period is 5 days per lecture. All of these films are 16-mm, black and white and about 50 minutes to an hour in length.

THE LAW OF GRAVITATION, AN EXAMPLE OF PHYSICAL LAW
THE RELATION OF MATHEMATICS TO PHYSICS
THE GREAT CONSERVATION PRINCIPLES
SYMMETRY IN PHYSICAL LAW
THE DISTINCTION OF PAST AND FUTURE
PROBABILITY AND UNCERTAINTY — THE QUANTUM MECHANICAL VIEW OF NATURE
SEEKING NEW LAWS

Descriptive Literature: A descriptive brochure on the longer films in this program and an information sheet on the Feynman lectures are available from the ESI Film Librarian; descriptive catalogs on the short silent demonstrations can be obtained from their distributors.

National Committee for Fluid Mechanics Films

All films are distributed by Encyclopaedia Britannica Films, 1150 Wilmette Avenue, Wilmette, Illinois 60091.

16-mm Sound Films: These are listed below with purchase prices. They can also be obtained for preview or rented. Films are black and white except as noted.

THE FLUID DYNAMICS OF DRAG (in four parts, totalling 118½ min.)	$475.00
VORTICITY (in two parts, 44 min.)	170.00
FLOW VISUALIZATION (31 min.)	115.00
PRESSURE FIELDS AND FLUID ACCELERATION (30 min.)	115.00
DEFORMATION OF CONTINUOUS MEDIA (38 min.)	145.00
SURFACE TENSION IN FLUID MECHANICS (color, 29 min.)	225.00
WAVES IN FLUIDS (33 min.)	125.00
SECONDARY FLOW (30 min.)	115.00
RHEOLOGICAL BEHAVIOR OF FLUIDS (22 min.)	85.00
BOUNDARY LAYER CONTROL (25 min.)	95.00

8-mm Cartridge Loops: The purchase price of each of these is $9.50. The films are also available on 8-mm reels for the same price, and on 16-mm reels at $9.50 for black and white and $12.00 for color. Loops are black and white except as noted.

FM-1 SOME REGIMES OF BOUNDARY LAYER TRANSITION
FM-2 STRUCTURE OF THE TURBULENT BOUNDARY LAYER
FM-3 SHEAR DEFORMATION OF VISCOUS FLUIDS
FM-4 SEPARATED FLOWS (Part I)
FM-5 SEPARATED FLOWS (Part II)
FM-6 BOUNDARY LAYER FORMATION
FM-7 PROPAGATING STALL IN CASCADES
FM-8 THE OCCURRENCE OF TURBULENCE
FM-10 GENERATION OF CIRCULATION AND LIFT FOR AN AIRFOIL
FM-11 THE MAGNUS EFFECT
FM-12 FLOW SEPARATION AND VORTEX SHEDDING
FM-13 THE BATHTUB VORTEX
FM-14a VISUALIZATION OF VORTICITY WITH VORTICITY METER (Part I)
FM-14b VISUALIZATION OF VORTICITY WITH VORTICITY METER (Part II)
FM-15 INCOMPRESSIBLE FLOW THROUGH AREA CONTRACTIONS AND EXPANSIONS
FM-16 FLOW FROM A RESERVOIR TO A DUCT
FM-23 TOLLMIEN-SCHLICHTING WAVES
FM-24 WING-TIP VORTEX
FM-26 TORNADOES IN THE LABORATORY AND IN NATURE
FM-28 TRANSONIC FLOW PAST A SYMMETRICAL AIRFOIL (color)
FM-29 OCCURRENCE OF SUPERSONIC ZONES ON AIRFOILS IN SUBSONIC FLOW
FM-30 SHOCK-BOUNDARY LAYER INTERACTION ON TRANSONIC AIRFOIL
FM-31 INSTABILITIES IN CIRCULAR COUETTE FLOW
FM-32 TURBULENT FLOW BETWEEN CONCENTRIC ROTATING CYLINDERS
FM-33 STAGNATION PRESSURE
FM-35 RADIAL FLOW BETWEEN PARALLEL DISKS
FM-36 VENTURI PASSAGE
FM-37 STREAMLINE CURVATURE AND NORMAL PRESSURE GRADIENT
FM-38 STREAMWISE PRESSURE GRADIENT IN INVISCID FLOW
FM-44 ELASTOID-INERTIA OSCILLATIONS IN ROTATING FLUID CYLINDER
FM-45 VELOCITIES NEAR AN AIRFOIL
FM-46 CURRENT-INDUCED INSTABILITY OF A MERCURY JET
FM-47 PATHLINES, STREAKLINES, STREAMLINES, AND TIMELINES IN STEADY FLOW
FM-48 PATHLINES, STREAKLINES, STREAMLINES, AND TIMELINES IN UNSTEADY FLOW
FM-49 FLOW REGIMES IN SUBSONIC DIFFUSERS
FM-51 SIMPLE SUPERSONIC INLET
FM-65 WIDE-ANGLE DIFFUSER WITH SUCTION
FM-67 FLOW THROUGH RIGHT-ANGLE BENDS
FM-68 FLOW THROUGH PORTED CHAMBERS
FM-69 FLOW THROUGH TEE-ELBOW
FM-70 THE SINK VORTEX
FM-72 EXAMPLES OF SURFACE TENSION (color)
FM-73 SURFACE TENSION AND CONTACT ANGLES (color)
FM-74 FORMATION OF BUBBLES (color)
FM-75 SURFACE TENSION AND CURVED SURFACES (color)
FM-76 BREAKUP OF LIQUIDS INTO DROPS (color)
FM-77 MOTIONS CAUSED BY COMPOSITION GRADIENTS ALONG LIQUID SURFACES (color)
FM-78 MOTIONS CAUSED BY ELECTRICAL AND CHEMICAL EFFECTS ON LIQUID SURFACES (color)
FM-79 MOTIONS CAUSED BY TEMPERATURE GRADIENTS ALONG LIQUID SURFACES (color)

Descriptive Literature: The National Committee for Fluid Mechanics Films issues a NEWSLETTER describing 16-mm films and new loops. Descriptive notes on all of the film loops are available from Encyclopaedia Britannica Films.

American Meteorological Society Film Program

Address inquiries to the American Meteorological Society, 45 Beacon Street, Boston, Massachusetts.

LIBRARY
JUNIOR COLLEGE DISTRICT
ST. LOUIS, MO.

INVENTORY 74

JAN 28 '77

INVENTORY 1983